Artists Handbooks

Directory of Exhibition Spaces

4th edition

edited by
Janet Ross

PUBLICATIONS

AN Publications

By giving access to information, advice and debate, AN Publications aims to:

- **empower artists individually and collectively to strengthen their professional position**
- **raise awareness of the diversity of visual arts practice and encourage an equality of opportunity**
- **stimulate good working practices throughout the visual arts.**

Credits

Editor
Janet Ross

Cover illustration
Eilis O'Baoill, detail from *Momento,* 1994

Design & layout
Neil Southern & Richard Padwick

Grant aid
Arts Council of England

Printer
Mayfair Printers, Print House, Commercial Road, Sunderland SR2 8NP

ISBN
Fourth edition 0 907730 27 2

AN Publications is an imprint of Artic Producers Publishing Co Ltd
PO Box 23, Sunderland SR4 6DG, tel: 0191 567 3589

Contents

Introducing the directory

When we first published the *Directory of Exhibition Spaces* in 1985, we had no idea how important a book it would become to the visual arts profession, who'd previously had to rely on idiosyncratic listings and on the dubious veracity of 'the grapevine' to keep abreast of developments in the gallery world.

The *Directory of Exhibition Spaces* changed all that. By describing all kinds of galleries and exhibition spaces, however large or small and however traditional or unusual their setting, this was a book which in one fell-swoop opened our eyes to the complete range and scope of contemporary galleries and exhibition spaces. And what's more, it didn't just look at 'London' and 'the regions' but acknowledged that galleries are run all over the UK. New editions were published in 1987 and 1992, each of these providing not only the 'facts and figures' needed by those concerned with exhibiting, but also revealing the current state of the exhibition business.

So what does this the fourth edition tell us? Well, first of all, it shows that despite the growth of public art and other more media-attractive activities, the exhibition form is alive and kicking. Sure, some of the commercial galleries have given up the struggle to survive, and some of the public ones haven't done so well either. It's perhaps no surprise to discover that since 1993 there's been a certain amount of 'rationalisation': for example, the Craft Centre and Design Gallery in Leeds is now more of a craft and gift shop, and the independent Northern Centre for Contemporary Art in Sunderland has been subsumed by the local authority who set up the brand-new City Gallery and Library in the former Binns department store instead.

Jostling for attention amongst the traditionally-run galleries is a growing band of artist-run spaces. The move by individual and groups of artists to set up such spaces is an indication of a new era in the status of artists. No longer content to wait to be offered exhibition opportunities, many artists now see promotion of work as part-and-parcel of producing it. They develop their own galleries not only to create a context for new work, but to try to reduce the commercial art market's grip by enabling collectors and curators to deal directly with them. And as artists move forward and appropriate all manner of other kinds of spaces for temporary 'exhibitions' – vault, coastline, city-centre wasteland, railway arch – and so on – how to include such activities in a publication like this will surely tax the brain of the next editor!

Importantly, this new edition covers the whole of Ireland – the last edition stopped at the border. This is not merely in acknowledgement of the cessation of hostilities in Ireland in 1994, but part of understanding that for the arts, such boundaries are superfluous. The gateway to Europe offered in 1992 means that cultural exchange – through exhibitions, visits and conferences – will be as much a part of the working life of artists and arts organisers in the future as locating the best galleries in which to show and sell in the UK.

Read this first!

Because there's an awful lot of information in this book, the following pages describe how we got it, as well as how it's been organised. We hope this makes it easier for each reader to find out what they particularly need to know, without having to wade through page-after-page of descriptions.

How do we get the information in the first place? We go to enormous lengths, is the simple answer. Because although this is a new edition, we effectively start from scratch to gather and collate information. We use a plethora of lists and publications to locate new galleries and send them each a questionnaire. We try hard to eliminate all those which have faded away. We do refer back to the original galleries database, but ask all galleries – new or old – to proof and agree their entry before it gets into print. Needless to say, and despite the fact that entry in the directory is free, a good few don't bother to respond, even after three reminders. As some of the very well-known galleries fall into this latter category, we have decided not to leave out galleries which we know exist, even though they've not confirmed the details. Because of this, readers are urged to use the information as a starting-point to their own exhibition research and not treat the entries as definitive profiles of each gallery.

Using the indexes

We've organised the directory by country – England, Northern Ireland, Republic of Ireland, Scotland and Wales – and then by town. In this way, you can quickly locate all the galleries in, say, Ashby-de-la Zouch without needing to know what part of the country it's in. But if you've only got the name of the gallery – Transmission for example – then look it up in the Gallery Index (on pages 27 to 48) which will lead you directly to the page on which it is listed.

And this index also gives a quick reference to the artforms each gallery shows and whether artists are welcome to apply for shows, whether the space is hired out and, last but not least, if exhibitors get a fee for showing work.

But if you're searching for galleries in a specific geographical location, you need to refer to the Region/County/Town Index. This is organised to coincide with the arts funding areas, that is the arts councils in Northern Ireland, Scotland and Wales, and the English regional arts boards. So, if you're planning a tour of galleries in the West Midlands, start by consulting this index to plan your itinerary.

Reading the entries

These begin with a number of symbols providing an at-a-glance way to check the artforms it shows or specialises in, whether applications from exhibitors are welcomed, if exhibitors receive a fee for showing, whether the space is hired out, and a description of how easy – or difficult – access is for people who have disabilities. See Key to Entries on page 8 for details.

Quick description

There follows a thumbnail sketch of the scope and nature of the gallery, for example "Artist-run gallery showing work by regional and national artists."

Contact

As might be supposed, this is the name of the person responsible for the exhibition programme, although they may not always be working full-time on that, and in some cases may need to contacted at an entirely different address. Although we made every effort to check all names, be aware that arts organisers are a mobile lot, and you'll need to check names for yourself before you write.

Open

This includes any information we have about when a gallery or exhibition space is open. Note however that some are only open during exhibitions or in term-time, and that limited opening times – perhaps two or three days a week – is a characteristic of many artist- or curator-run spaces. "By appointment" is still a commonly used epithet to describe the viewing mechanisms for galleries which aren't open full-time, or are run by people with other occupations too.

Space

The directory describes – where information is available – the number of separate exhibition spaces a gallery has, and whether these are used on a regular or occasional basis for temporary exhibitions of contemporary art. For example, an arts centre may mount shows in a main gallery, craft display space and in their coffee-bar, and a local authority gallery may only use some of their galleries for contemporary work. The directory also gives details of the total horizontal length of hanging space in linear metres, how much is additionally available on screens and also the total floor space for temporary shows in square metres.

Exhibitions

Because contemporary exhibitions may only be part of a gallery's annual programme, or an exhibition space may not be open all year round, the figure given in this category denotes the number of temporary exhibitions of contemporary art normally shown over a twelve-month period. What follows is a breakdown of how many are originated – that is researched, selected or otherwise put together – by the gallery, how many touring exhibitions are brought in, and how many exhibitions are organised on the basis of hiring space to artists.

Details

This contains an edited version of what each gallery wanted to say about their exhibition policy and audience for the shows. Sometimes, it includes other information, for example about their education programme, gallery talks or how they contribute to the local arts festival.

A word of advice

All listings in the *Directory of Exhibition Spaces* are published in good faith. However, as we have relied on the galleries' own descriptions, we urge all those using the book to form professional relationships – accepting an invitation to show, entering into any financial arrangements, touring or exchanging exhibitions and so on – to check the details fully for themselves. Artists seeking galleries and exhibition opportunities might also like to ponder advice given by artist and curator Maud Sulter:

"When trying to impress an exhibition organiser that your sole purpose in life is to show in their hallowed halls, please don't insult their intelligence by admitting you've never set foot in their gallery nor have a clue about their programme. Actually do your homework. It's imperative to keep up to date – and that goes for gallery organisers too. Never risk setting up a meeting with a gallery unless your proposal is so together, so hot that its haveability is unmistakable. The *Directory of Exhibition Spaces* needs to be part of your plan."

Key to entries

(£) Exhibition Payment Right (EPR) – venue pays a fee to exhibitors for showing their work to the public.

A Artists-run – venue or programme run by an artist group or cooperative.

Regional areas in England based on reional arts boards

EA	Eastern Arts
EMA	East Midlands Arts
LA	London Arts
NA	Northern Arts
NWA	North West Arts
SA	Southern Arts
SEA	South East Arts
SWA	South West Arts
WMA	West Midlands Arts
YHA	Yorkshire and Humberside Arts

* No updated information received from the gallery for this edition. Entry compiled from previous edition.

Alnwick
NORTHUMBERLAND (NA)

Bondgate Gallery *

Provides facilities for artists to exhibit work, usually in solo exhibitions, for the benefit of members, visitors, and local schools.

22 Narrowgate, Alnwick NE66 1JG, tel: 01665 577088

Contact: Peter Bolwell Andrews, Chairman

Space: A gallery with 23 lin m hanging space and 51 sq m floor space

Exhibitions: 10 a year all originated

Details: Run by members of the Anwick and District Arts Association, showing art and craft in wide variety of media every month. Illustrates history of art and encourages its appreciation, stimulates interest in contemporary art in area. Other activities include visits and lectures.

Artform

Pa Painting, drawing, illustration
Ph Photograph, holography
Pr Print
Cr Craft (all craft & applied art forms included)
Sc Sculpture and installation work
La Live or performance work

Symbols in reverse
Pa Ph Pr Cr Sc La indicate the venue treats these art forms as a speciality within its broader programme. It in no way denotes an editorial value judgement across the galleries.

✓ Applications welcomed – venue welcomes artists to contact them about exhibition possiblities. There may only be one exhibition slot in the year or for the entire programme.

H Available for hire. All or part of programme is made available by hiring space to individual or group exhibitors.

Exhibitions

The number of temporary exhibitions of contemporary art or craft normally displayed in a twelve month period. This is broken down into the number originated by the gallery, bought-in travelling exhibitions and the number hired out to exhibitors.

Facilities for disabled visitors

& Exhibition spaces accessible by wheelchair without assistance
(&) Wheelchair access with assistance
⊗ Wheelchair access inpossible
We Toilets suitable for wheelchair users
4 Gallery claims to deliver four out of the following five criteria:
  - encourages participation by disabled people
  - signing/induction loop used where appropriate
  - takes account of vision height of displays
  - promotes through media accessible by blind or partially sighted
  - staff aware of disabilty issues.

Space

Gallery	the number of separate exhibition spaces used regularly or occasionaly for temporary exhibitions of contemporary work.
Lin m	linear metres – the total horizontal length of the wall space available for hanging temporary exhibitions.
Sq m	square metres the total floor area of all the temporary exhibitions spaces.

Region/County/Town Index

This index groups galleries by region, county and town. The regions are based on the Republic of Ireland and the constituent countries making up the UK. England is further divided into the regions covered by the ten regional arts boards:

East Midlands
Eastern England
London
North West England
Northern England
South East England
South West England
Southern England
West Midlands
Yorkshire & Humberside

East Midlands

Counties of Leicestershire, Nottinghamshire, Northamptonshire and Derbyshire except the High Peaks District.

East Midlands Arts Board, Mountfields House, Epinal Way, Loughborough LE11 0QE, tel: 01509 218292

Derbyshire (except High Peak District)

Chesterfield:
Peacock Heritage Centre
Uno Gallery
Derby:
Arbor Darkrooms & Gallery
Atrium Gallery
Derby City Council House
Derby City General Hospital
Derby Community Arts
Derby Industrial Museum
Derby Museum & Art Gallery
Derby Playhouse
Derby Tertiary College: Wilmorton
Gallery 93
Guildhall Theatre
Metro Gallery
Montage Gallery
St Michael's Gallery
Sinfin Library
University of Derby (Concourse Gallery)
Ilkeston:
Erewash Museum
Ilkeston Community Hospital
Wirksworth:
Howard Gallery
Modern Print Gallery

Leicestershire

Ashby de la Zouch:
Ferrers Gallery
Desford:
Bosworth College Gallery
Hinckley:
Hinckley College of Further Education
Leicester:
27A Access Artspace
City Gallery
Craft Gallery

Gadsby Gallery
Haymarket Theatre
Leicester Print Workshop
Leicester Royal Infirmary
Leicestershire Museum & Art Gallery
Phoenix Art Centre
Picture House
Vaughan College
Woods Gallery
Loughborough:
Loughborough College of Art and Design
Rawlins School & Community College
Market Harborough:
Frank Haynes Gallery
Harborough Museum
Melton Mowbray:
Melton Mowbray Library
Rutland:
Goldmark Gallery
Rutland County Museum

Northamptonshire

Brackley:
Brackley Library
Corby:
Corby Library
Daventry:
Daventry Library
Moot Hall
Kettering:
Alfred East Art Gallery
Kettering Library
Rothwell Library
Lamport:
Lamport Hall
Northampton:
Derngate
Four Seasons Gallery
Northampton Local Education Authority
Northamptonshire Libraries
Onsight Gallery
University Centre Northampton
Weston Favell Library
Oundle:
Yarrow Gallery
Towcester:
Blakesley Gallery
Towcester Library
Wellingborough:
Gallery (The)
Wellingborough Library

Nottinghamshire

Belper:
Fleet Arts Project
Calverton:
Patchings Farm Arts Centre
Mansfield:
Mansfield Community Arts Centre

Mansfield Museum & Art Gallery
Newark:
Millgate Museum
Pierrepont Gallery
Rufford Craft Centre
Nottingham:
Angel Row Gallery
Arnold Library
Bonington Gallery
Broadway Media Centre
Byard Gallery
Carlton Library
Castle Museum & Art Gallery
Djanogly Art Gallery
EMACA Visual Arts
Focus Gallery
Hart Gallery
Longdale Gallery
Nottingham Community Arts
Nottingham Playhouse
Nottingham Society of Artists
Ravenshead Library
St Mary's Exhibition Centre
Worksop:
Harley Gallery
Priory Gatehouse

Eastern England

Counties of Bedfordshire,
Cambridgeshire, Essex, Hertfordshire,
Lincolnshire, Norfolk and Suffolk.

Eastern Arts Board, Cherry Hinton
Hall, Cherry Hinton Road, Cambridge
CB1 4DW, tel: 01223 215355

Bedfordshire

Bedford:
Bedford Central Library Gallery
Bedford Museum
Bromham Mill Gallery
Community Arts in Bedford
Dunstable:
Gallery (The)
Queensway Hall
Leighton Buzzard:
Leighton Buzzard Library Gallery
Luton:
33 Arts Centre
Luton Central Library
Luton Museum & Art Gallery
St George's Theatre
Woburn:
Clifford Gallery

Cambridgeshire

Cambridge:
Architecture Gallery
Bodilly Galleries
Broughton House Gallery
Cambridge Centre Library Exhibition
Room and Area
Cambridge Darkroom Gallery
CCA Galleries (Cambridge)
Conservatory Gallery
Eureka! The Float Place
Fitzwilliam Museum
Heffer Gallery
Jock Colville Hall
Junction (The)
Kettle's Yard
Pelican Gallery
Primavera
Trumpington Gallery
Wysing Arts
Ely:
Old Fire Engine House
Huntingdon:
Cottage Gallery
Peterborough:
David Holmes Contemporary art
Orton District Library
Peterborough Art Gallery
Peterborough Arts Centre
Peterborough Central Library
St Ives:
L'Bidi Studio
Whittlesford:
Peppin Brown Gallery
Wisbech:
Angles Centre
Hudson Gallery
Skylark Studios

Essex

Basildon:
Berlesduna Gallery
Braintree:
Braintree Town Hall Centre Gallery
Brentwood:
Brandler Galleries
Brentwood Library
Shenfield Library
Chelmsford:
Chelmsford Central Library
Chelmsford & Essex Museum
Essex Libraries
Gallery (The)
Clacton on Sea:
Clacton Library
Colchester:
Chappel Galleries
Colchester Institute, School of Art
Colchester Library
Craftsman (The)
Digby Gallery
Firstsite at the Minories
Hayletts Gallery
Pam Schomberg Gallery
Printworks
Trinity Street Studios
University Gallery

Grays:
Grays Library
Thameside Theatre Foyer
Harlow:
Harlow Library
Harlow Study Centre
Playhouse Gallery
Harwich:
Bodgeners
Hornchurch:
Queens Theatre
Loughton:
Loughton Library
Maldon:
Oakwood House
Old Harlow:
St John's Art & Recreation Centre
Romford:
Central Gallery
Saffron Walden:
Exchange Gallery
Fry Public Art Gallery
Saffron Walden Museum
Southend on Sea:
Focal Point Gallery
Waltham Abbey:
Epping Forest District Museum
Westcliff on Sea:
Beecroft Art Gallery
Wickford:
Wickford Library
Witham:
Witham Library

Hertfordshire

Hatfield:
Mill Green Museum & Mill
Hemel Hempstead:
Old Town Hall Arts Centre
Hertford:
Hertford Museum
Mill Bridge Rooms
Hitchin:
Hitchin Museum & Art Gallery
Rikki Harcourt Gallery at Phillips of
Hitchin
Hoddesdon:
Hoddesdon Library
Letchworth:
Letchworth Central Library
Letchworth Museum
Rickmansworth:
Watersmeet
Royston:
Royston Museum
St Albans:
C.R.A. Gallery
Museum of St Albans
St Albans Central Library
St Albans Town Hall
Stevenage:
Boxfield Gallery
Stevenage Library
Ware:
Trading Places Gallery
Watford:
Oxhey Library

London

Covers Greater London

London Arts Board, Elme House,
133 Long Acre, London WC2E 9AF,
tel: 0171 240 1313

North West England

Counties of Cheshire, Greater Manchester, Lancashire, Mersyside and the High Peak District of Derbyshire

North West Arts Board, 4th Floor, 12 Harter Street, Manchester M1 6HY, tel: 0161 228 3062

Cheshire

Alsager:
Alsager Gallery
Brimstage:
Voirrey Embroidery Centre
Chester:
Bishops' Gallery
Chester Library
Grosvenor Museum
Congleton:
Carters Gallery
Ellesmere Port:
Boat Museum
Frodsham:
Castle Park Arts Centre
Neston:
Ness Gardens
Prestbury:
Artizana
Runcorn:
Norton Priory Museum
& Gardens
Runcorn Shopping City Library
Sandbeach:
Dukes Oak Gallery
Stalybridge:
Astley Cheetham Art Gallery
Warrington:
Warrington Museum and Art Gallery
Winsford:
Vale Royal Community Arts Centre
Woodford Visual Art Centre

Derbyshire (High Peak District)

Buxton:
Buxton Museum & Art Gallery
David Russell

Greater Manchester

Bolton:
Bolton Library Service
Bolton Museum & Art Gallery
Turton Tower
Castlefield:
Dukes 92 Gallery
Leigh:
Turnpike Gallery
Manchester:
Castlefield Gallery
Chinese Arts Centre
Colin Jellicoe Gallery
Cornerhouse
Counter Image
Gallery Manchester's Art House
Generation X
Hacienda Club
Horniman Bar
Manchester Central Library
Manchester City Art Galleries
Manchester Craft Centre
Manto
Met Arts Centre
Metropolitan Galleries
Pankhurst Centre
Portico Library & Gallery
Royal Exchange Craft Centre & Foyer
Gallery
Tib Lane Gallery
Whitworth Art Gallery
Salford:
Chapman Gallery
City of Salford Cultural Services
Glass Box Gallery
Salford Museum & Art Gallery
Viewpoint Photography Gallery
Stockport:
Bramall Hall Café Gallery
Bramhall Library
Bredbury Library Gallery
Brinnington Library Gallery
Cheadle Library Gallery
Dialstone Library
Heatons Library Gallery
Marple Library
Stockport Art Gallery
Stockport Central Library
Uppermill:
Saddleworth Museum & Art Gallery

Lancashire

Accrington:
Haworth Art Gallery
Blackburn:
Blackburn Museum & Art Gallery
Lewis Textile Museum
Street (The)
Witton Country Park Visitor Centre
Blackpool:
Grundy Art Gallery
Burnley:
Mid Pennine Gallery
Towneley Hall Art Gallery
Carnforth:
Ingleborough Gallery
Chorley:
Chorley Central Library
Clitheroe:
Platform Gallery
Colne:
Barnoldswick Library
Colne Library
Trawden Library
Darwen:
Sunnyhurst Wood Visitor Centre
Fleetwood:
Fleetwood Library
Garstang:
Old Grammar School Arts Centre
Lancaster:
Lancaster City Museum
Lancaster Maritime Museum
Ludus 2D Gallery
Peter Scott Gallery
Storey Institute Art Gallery
Leyland:
South Ribble Museum and Exhibition
Centre
Nelson:
Barrowford Library
Brierfield Library
Nelson Library
Pendle Arts Gallery
Pendle Heritage Centre
Oldham:
Artisan
John McCombs Gallery
Oldham Art Gallery
Preston:
Brook Gallery
Harris Museum & Art Gallery
Samlesbury Hall
Vernon Gallery
Victoria Building
Rochdale:
Rochdale Art Gallery
Rossendale:
Haslingden Library
Rossendale Museum
Skelmersdale:
St Thomas the Apostle RC High School
Skelmersdale Arts Centre
Thornton Cleveleys:
Wryreside Ecology Centre
Wigan:
Drumcroon Art Centre
Metropolitan Borough of Wigan

Merseyside

Birkenhead:
Birkenhead Central Library
Williamson Art Gallery & Museum
Wirral Borough Council Department of
Leisure
Bootle:
Orrell Arts Centre
Heswall:
Dee Fine Arts
Huyton:
Knowsley Libraries
Liverpool:
Acorn Gallery
Ainscough Gallery
Art Cellar
Artreach
Blackie Gallery

Bluecoat Display Centre
Bluecoat Gallery
Bridewell Studios
Concord Gallery
Hanover Galleries
Harold House Jewish Youth &
Community Centre
Liverpool Central Library
Methodist Centre
Open Eye Gallery
Tate Gallery Liverpool
Unity Theatre
University of Liverpool Senate House
Exhibition Hall
Walker Art Gallery
St Helens:
Citadel Arts Centre
Pilkington Glass Museum
St Helens Museum & Art Gallery
Southport:
Atkinson Art Gallery
Birkdale Branch Library

Northern England

Counties of Cleveland, Cumbria,
Co Durham, Northumberland and
Tyne & Wear

Northern Arts Board, 9/10 Osborne
Terrace, Newcastle upon Tyne
NE2 1NZ, tel: 0191 281 6334

Cleveland

Billingham:
Billingham Art Gallery
Easington Village
Long Gallery
Guisborough:
Walton Galleries
Hartlepool:
Hartlepool Art Gallery
Middlesbrough:
Captain Cook Birthplace Museum
Cleveland Crafts Centre
Cleveland Gallery
Dorman Museum
Easterside Library
Middlesbrough Art Gallery
Ormesby Hall
University of Leeds Adult Education
Centre
Redcar:
Kirkleatham Old Hall Museum
Stockton on Tees:
Dovecot Arts Centre

Co Durham

Barnard Castle:
Bowes Museum
Castle Gallery
Priors
Bishop Auckland:
Bishop Auckland Town Hall
Crook:
Mall (The)
Darlington:
Bernhardt Gallery
Darlington Art Gallery
Darlington Arts Centre
Durham:
Almhouses Restaurant
Durham Art Gallery & DLI Museum
Stanley:
Stanley Civic Hall

Cumbria

Alston:
Gossipgate Gallery
Ambleside:
Dexterity
Gallery-in-the-Forest
Barrow in Furness:
Dock Museum
Forum 28
Bowness on Windermere:
Old Laundry
Brampton:
William Howard Gallery
Carlisle:
Manor Photographic Gallery
Sark Gallery
Tullie House
Cockermouth:
Castlegate House
Egremont:
Lowes Court Gallery
Kendal:
Abbot Hall Art Gallery
Brewery Arts Centre Photographic
Gallery
Warehouse Gallery
Keswick:
Keswick Museum & Art Gallery
Penrith:
Beck Mill Gallery
Isis Gallery
Laburnum Ceramics
Ulverston:
Welfare State International
Whitehaven:
Beacon (The)
Foyer Gallery
Workington:
Carnegie Theatre & Arts Centre

Northumberland

Alnmouth:
Riverbank Gallery
Alnwick:
Bondgate Gallery
Ashington:
Woodhorn Church Museum

Berwick upon Tweed:
Berwick Borough Museum & Art
Gallery
Berwick Gymnasium
Sallyport Gallery
Three Feathers Gallery
Windmill Hole Studio
Chatton:
Chatton Gallery
Corbridge:
Corbridge Gallery
Cramlington:
Forum Gallery
Haltwhistle:
Haltwhistle Library
Hexham:
Abbey Prints
Moothall Gallery
Queens Hall Arts Centre
Kielder:
Duchess Gallery
Morpeth:
Chantry Silver
Rothbury:
Coquetdale Gallery
Stocksfield:
Bewick Studios

Tyne & Wear

Gateshead:
Design Works
Gateshead Library Gallery
Portcullis Crafts Gallery
Shipley Art Gallery
Jarrow:
Bede Gallery
Bede's World
Newcastle upon Tyne:
Browns
Café Procope
Calouste Gulbenkian Gallery
Chameleon Gallery
Clayton Gallery
Denton Park Library
Hancock Museum
Hatton Gallery
Laing Art Gallery
Locus+
Newcastle Central Library
Newcastle Playhouse Galleries
Newcastle University Long Gallery
People's Gallery
Red Herring Café
Side Gallery
University Gallery
Waygood gallery & Studios
X-Site Gallery
Zone Gallery
North Shields:
Globe Gallery
Knotts Exhibition Centre
Northern Print Studio
Vicarage Cottage
South Shields:
Customs House Art Gallery
South Shields Museum & Art Gallery

Sunderland:
City Library and Arts Centre
Reg Vardy Arts Foundation Gallery
Sunderland Museum & Art Gallery
Wallsend:
Buddle (The)
Washington:
Arts Centre (Washington)

South East England

Counties of East Sussex, Kent, Surrey and West Sussex

South East Arts Board, 10 Mount Ephraim, Tunbridge Wells, TN4 8AS, tel: 01892 515210

East Sussex

Battle:
Davies Bailey Gallery
Bexhill on Sea
De La Warr Pavilion
Brighton:
5 Ways Studio
Brighton Museum & Art Gallery
Burstow Gallery
Craft Direct
Gardner Centre Gallery
Hugo Barclay
Markovitch Gallery
North Star Studios
Phoenix Gallery
Sanctuary (The)
University of Brighton Gallery
Window Gallery
ZAP Club
Crowborough:
Green Lane Gallery
Ditchling:
Craftsman Gallery
Eastbourne:
Central Library Exhibition Room
Towner Art Gallery
Hailsham:
Michelham Priory
Hastings:
Hastings Exhibitions
Hastings Museum & Art Gallery
Old Town Art Gallery
Riviera (The)
Stables Theatre Gallery
Horsham:
Christ's Hospital Theatre

Horsham Arts Centre Gallery
Hove:
Hove Museum & Art Gallery
Lewes:
Charleston Gallery
Hesketh Gallery
Rye:
Easton Rooms, Rye Art Gallery
Stormont Studio, Rye Art Gallery
Seaford:
Crypt Gallery

Kent

Ashford:
Ashford Library Gallery
Evegate Farm Art Gallery
Bexley:
Hall Place
Broadstairs:
Broadstairs Library Gallery
Canterbury:
Drew Gallery
Gibbs Gallery Canterbury
Graphics Gallery
Herbert Read Gallery
Nevill Gallery
Royal Museum & Art Gallery
Dartford:
Dartford Central Library Gallery
Deal:
Deal Library Gallery
Dover:
Dover Museum
Dover Town Hall
Eynsford:
Lullingstone Visitors Centre
Folkestone:
Platform Gallery
Sassoon Gallery
Sassoon Gallery
Gillingham:
Gillingham Library Gallery
Space Frame Gallery
Spiral Arts
Gravesend:
Gravesend Central Library Gallery
Maidstone:
County Hall Gallery
Gallery, Kent Institute of Art & Design at Maidstone
Hazlitt Theatre Foyer
Maidstone Library Gallery
Margate:
Margate Library Gallery
Salmestone Grange
Ramsgate:
Addington Street Studio & Gallery
Ramsgate Library Gallery
Rochester:
Gallery, Kent Institute of Art & Design at Rochester
Medway Gallery
Strood Library Gallery
Sandwich:
Hunt Gallery
Sevenoaks:
Bank Street Gallery

Pratt Contemporary Art
Sevenoaks Library Gallery
Tonbridge:
Angel Leisure Centre
Tonbridge Library Gallery
Tunbridge Wells:
Clare Gallery
Fairfax Gallery
Trinity Gallery
Tunbridge Wells Museum and Art Gallery
Whitstable:
Whitstable Museum & Gallery

Surrey

Chertsey:
Chertsey Museum
Chobham:
Bank Gallery
Cranleigh:
Cranleigh Arts Centre
Dorking:
Gentle Gallery
Westcott Gallery
East Molesey:
Molesey Gallery
Epsom:
Epsom Playhouse
Ewell:
Bourne Hall
Farnham:
Andrew Lloyd Gallery
CCA Galleries (Farnham)
James Hockey Gallery
New Ashgate Gallery
SC Johnson Gallery & Studio
Godalming:
Godalming Museum
Gomshall:
Gomshall Gallery
Great Bookham:
Kingsmead Gallery
Guildford:
Forest Contemporary Art
Guildford House Gallery
Harvey Gallery
Jonleigh Gallery
Library Gallery
Haslemere:
Haslemere Museum
Leatherhead:
Fire and Iron Gallery
Thorndike Theatre Gallery
Ockley:
Hannah Peschar Gallery and Sculpture Garden
Staines:
Old Town Hall Arts Centre
Walton on Thames:
Boathouse Gallery

West Sussex

Arundel:
Armstrong Davis Gallery
Little Gallery Bookshop

Chichester:
   Chichester Centre for the Arts
   Mitre Gallery
   Pallant House
Crawley:
   Hawth Theatre Foyer
East Grinstead:
   Autumn Art Show
Shoreham by Sea:
   Marlipins Museum Gallery
Worthing:
   Northbrook Photography Gallery and
   Theatre
   Terrace Gallery
   Worthing Museum and Art Gallery

South West England

Counties of Avon, Cornwall, Devon, Dorset (excluding the districts of Poole, Bournemouth and Christchurch), Gloucestershire and Somerset

South West Arts Board, Bradninch Place, Gandy Street, Exeter EX4 3LS, tel: 01392 218188

Avon

Bath:
   Anthony Hepworth Gallery
   Beaux Arts
   Bruton Gallery
   CCA Galleries (Bath)
   F. Stop Gallery & Darkroom
   Hitchcocks'
   Holburne Museum & Crafts Study
   Centre
   Hotbath Gallery
   Once A Tree Gallery
   Peter Hayes Contemporary Art
   Rooksmoor Gallery
   RPS National Centre of Photography
   St James's Gallery
   Six Chapel Row Contemporary Art
   Sladebrook House
   Underground Gallery
   Victoria Art Gallery
Bristol:
   35 King Street Gallery
   3D Gallery
   Alastair Gill Gallery
   Arnolfini
   Barton Hill Photography Project Gallery
   Bristol Museum & Art Gallery

Church House Designs
Croft Gallery
David Cross Gallery
Guild Gallery
Happening Gallery
Michael Stewart Galleries
Off-Centre Gallery
Patricia Wells Gallery
Praxis Gallery/Café
Royal West of England Academy
Unit 1 Clifton Down Centre
Watershed Gallery
Clevedon:
   Toll House Gallery
Gloucester:
   Glassbarn (The)

Cornwall

Bodmin:
   Cornwall Crafts Association at
   Pencarrow
Boscastle:
   Boscastle Gallery
Camelford:
   North Cornwall Museum & Gallery
Falmouth:
   Beside the Wave
   Falmouth Art Gallery
   Falmouth Arts Centre
   Falmouth College of Arts
Fowey:
   Cry of the Gulls Gallery
Helston:
   Cornwall Crafts Association at
   Trelowarren
   Mullion Gallery
Par:
   Mid-Cornwall Galleries
Penzance:
   Contemporary Gallery
   Jamieson Library
   Newlyn Art Gallery
   Victoria Studios
   Wolf at the Door
Polperro:
   Peak Rock Artists' Studios & Gallery
Redruth:
   Camborne School of Mines
St Austell:
   St Austell Arts Centre
   St Austell Library
St Ives:
   New Craftsman
   Penwith Galleries
   Plumbline Gallery
   Salthouse Gallery
   Tate Gallery St Ives
   Wills Lane Gallery
Saltash:
   Cotehele Quay Gallery
Truro:
   Gallery Portscatho
   Royal Cornwall Museum Galleries
   Tidelines
   Trelissick Gallery

Devon

Bideford:
   Appledore Crafts Company
   Appledore Gallery
   Burton Art Gallery & Museum
   Gallerie Marin
Bovey Tracey:
   Devon Guild of Craftsmen
Braunton:
   Elliott Gallery
Budleigh Salterton:
   Otterton Mill Gallery
Chagford:
   Stone Lane Gardens
Colyton:
   Dolphin House Gallery
Dartmouth:
   Facets
   Higher Street Gallery
   Simon Drew Gallery
Dawlish:
   Porch Galleries
   Vivian Gallery
Exeter:
   Exeter City Museums
   & Art Gallery
   Exeter & Devon Arts Centre
   Exeter University (Library)
   Spacex Gallery
   Vincent Gallery
Exmouth:
   Rolle Faculty Gallery (University of
   Plymouth)
Instow:
   Waterside Gallery
Okehampton:
   Salar Gallery
Plymouth:
   Barbican Theatre
   Plymouth Arts Centre
   Plymouth City Museum
   & Art Gallery
   Plymouth Theatre Royal
   White Lane Gallery
Princetown:
   Dartmoor Gallery
Shebbear:
   Shebbear College (Little Gallery)
Tiverton:
   Angel Gallery
Torquay:
   Torre Abbey Historic House
   & Gallery
Torrington:
   Plough Gallery
Totnes:
   Dartington Arts Gallery
   Dartington Cider Press Centre
   Marshall Arts Gallery
   Seymour Gallery

Dorset (excluding districts of Poole, Bournemouth & Christchurch – see Southern England)

Beaminster:
Parnham House
Blandford:
Hambledon Gallery
Bridport:
Bridport Arts Centre
Cranborne:
Cranborne Gallery
Dorchester:
Dorchester Gallery
Gallery Gilbert
Lytchett Minster:
Courtyard Centre
Portland:
Chesil Gallery
Shaftesbury:
Shaftesbury Arts Centre
Sherborne:
Alpha House Gallery
Melbury Gallery
Swanage:
Alpha Gallery
Wareham:
Peter Hedley Gallery
Trinity Art Gallery
Wimborne:
Walford Mill Craft Centre

Gloucestershire

Chalford:
Gallery Pangolin
Cheltenham:
Axiom Centre for the Arts
Cheltenham Art Gallery & Museum
Montpellier Gallery
Ogle Fine Arts
Pittville Gallery
Pittville Pump Room Museum
Turtle Fine Art
Cirencester:
Brewery Arts
Gloucester:
Gloucester City Museum & Art Gallery
Guildhall Arts Centre
Nailsworth:
Hand Prints & Watercolours Gallery
Stroud:
Yew Tree Gallery
Tetbury:
Gumstool Gallery
Uley:
Prema Arts Centre

Somerset

Bridgwater:
Admiral Blake Museum
Bridgwater Arts Centre
Dulverton:
Dulverton Guildhall Heritage & Arts Centre

Frome:
Black Swan Guild
Craft Movement (The)
Merlin Theatre
Glastonbury:
Somerset Rural Life Museum
Minehead:
Little Gallery
Taunton:
Albermarle Centre Gallery
Brewhouse Gallery
Byram Gallery
Makers
Wellington:
Pitminster Studio
Yeovil:
Yeovil Community Arts Centre

Southern England

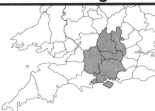

Counties of Berkshire, Buckinghamshire, Hampshire, Isle of Wight, Oxfordshire, Wiltshire and the Poole, Bournemouth and Christchurch districts of Dorset

Southern Arts Board, 13 St Clement Street, Winchester SO23 9DQ, tel: 01392 218188

Berkshire

Bracknell:
Bracknell Gallery
Eton:
Contemporary Fine Art Gallery Eton
CSK Gallery
Newbury:
Arts Workshop
Granary Exhibition Room
Reading:
Gallery 28
Hexagon
Jelly Leg'd Chicken Arts Gallery
Open Space
Rising Sun Institute
Town Hall
Windsor:
Old Court Gallery

Buckinghamshire

Aylesbury:
Buckinghamshire County Museum
Malt House Barn Gallery
Queen's Park Arts Centre Gallery

Bletchley:
Fenny Lodge Gallery
High Wycombe:
Spring Gardens Arts Centre
Milton Keynes:
Milton Keynes Exhibition Gallery
Winslow:
Redfield Exhibition Gallery

Dorset (see South West England for rest of Dorset)

Bournemouth:
Daler Gallery
Russell-Cotes Art Gallery and Museum
TZB Southbourne Gallery
Christchurch:
Red House Museum & Gardens
Poole:
Bournemouth University Gallery
Poole Arts Centre (Seldown Gallery)
Upstairs Gallery
Waterfront Museum

Hampshire

Aldershot:
West End Centre Gallery
Alresford:
Alresford Gallery
Candover Gallery
Alton:
Allen Gallery
Andover:
Andover Museum
Basingstoke:
Central Studio and The Street
Chapel House Gallery
Willis Museum
Calshot:
Calshot Crafts Centre
Eastleigh:
Beatrice Royal Art Gallery
Eastleigh Museum
Fareham:
Ashcroft Arts Centre
Fareham Library
Westbury Manor Museum
Gosport:
Gosport Museum
Hartley Wintney:
Century Galleries
Havant:
Havant Arts Active
Havant Museum
Liphook:
Working Tree
Lymington:
Solent Gallery
Petersfield:
Bedales Gallery
Portsmouth:
Aspex Gallery
Portsmouth Arts Centre
Portsmouth City Museum
Ringwood:
Bettles Gallery
Southampton:
First Gallery

Gantry (The)
Gutteridges
John Hansard Gallery
Lordshill Library
Nuffield Theatre Restaurant
On Line Gallery
Southampton City Art Gallery
Starlight Gallery
Visage
Stockbridge:
Courcoux & Courcoux
Winchester:
Circle Bar Gallery
Guildhall Gallery
Hampshire County Council Museums
Service
Winchester Gallery

Isle of Wight

Freshwater:
Freshwater Gallery
Newport:
Isle of Wight Cultural & Leisure
Services Department
Quay Arts Centre
Seely Gallery
Ryde:
Ryde Gallery
Ventnor:
Ventnor Library

Oxfordshire

Abingdon:
Abingdon Museum
Rocket Contemporary Art
Bampton:
West Oxfordshire Arts Association
Gallery
Banbury:
Banbury Museum Gallery
Mill Foyer Gallery
Burford:
Brian Sinfield Gallery
Chipping Norton:
Theatre (The)
Cropredy:
Old Coal Wharf Arts at Cropredy
Eynsham:
Gundry Gallery
Goring on Thames:
Goring Mill Gallery
Henley on Thames:
Barn Galleries
Henley on Thames:
Bohun Gallery
Century Galleries
Luxters Fine Art
Oxford:
Ashmolean Museum (McAlpine Gallery)
Bampton Arts Centre
Bloomin Arts
CCA Galleries (Oxford)
Christ Church Picture Gallery
Computer Corridor
Freud's
Museum of Modern Art

Museum of Oxford
Old Fire Station Theatre
Oxford Gallery
Photography Workshop
St Giles' Church
Thame:
Thame Sports & Arts Centre
Wallingford:
Julius Gottlieb Gallery
Witney:
We Three Kings
Woodstock:
Oxfordshire County Museum

Wiltshire

Amesbury:
Amesbury Library
Bradford on Avon:
Lailey's
Lacock:
Fox Talbot Museum
Marlborough:
Marlborough Studio Art Gallery
Mount House Gallery
Salisbury:
Bill Toop Gallery
Fisherton Mill
Salisbury Arts Centre
Salisbury Playhouse Gallery
Salisbury & South Wiltshire Museum
Swindon:
Swindon Arts Centre
Wyvern Theatre
Warminster:
Athenaeum

West Midlands

**Counties of Hereford & Worcester,
Shropshire, Staffordshire,
Warwickshire and West Midlands**

West Midlands Arts Board,
82 Granville Street, Birmingham
B1 2LH tel: 0121 631 3121

Hereford & Worcester

Bromsgrove:
Avoncroft Museum of Historic
Buildings
Jinney Ring Craft Centre
Droitwich:
Droitwich Heritage Centre
Droitwich Library

Evesham:
Evesham Library
Great Malvern:
Malvern Arts Workshop
Malvern Festival Theatre
Malvern Library Art Gallery
Winter Gardens Complex
Works of Art Gallery
Hereford:
Gallery at 89
Hatton Art Gallery
Hereford City Art Gallery
John McKellar Designer Jewellery
Kidderminster:
Hartlebury County Museum
Kington:
Penrhos Art Gallery
Ledbury:
Collection Gallery
Heritage Gallery
Leominster:
Farmers Gallery
Leominster Library
Ombersley:
Ombersley Gallery
Redditch:
Redditch Library
Ross on Wye:
Man of Ross Gallery
Tenbury Wells:
Tenbury Library
Worcester:
Framed
Hereford & Worcester LIbraries & Arts
Department
John Noott Galleries
Swan Theatre
Worcester Arts Workshop
Worcester City Museum & Art Gallery

Shropshire

Bishop's Castle:
Longhouse Gallery
Broseley:
Gallery 6
Ellesmere:
Ellesmere College Arts Centre
Ludlow:
Silk Top Hat Gallery
Oswestry:
Oswestry Heritage and Exhibition
Centre
Shrewsbury:
Gateway Galleries
Music Hall Photographic Gallery
Parade Shops
Rowley's House Museum
Shropshire County Library
Tower Gallery
Telford:
Elton Gallery
Gallery at Madeley Court School
New College Gallery
Spout Farm House Gallery

Staffordshire

Burton on Trent:
Brewhouse
Round House Gallery
Cannock:
Cannock Library
Valley Heritage Centre & Museum
Keele:
Keele University Art Exhibitions
Lichfield:
Lichfield Arts Centre
Newcastle under Lyme:
New Victoria Theatre
Newcastle under Lyme Museum & Art Gallery
Wavertree Gallery
Stafford:
Shire Hall Gallery
Stoke on Trent:
Edge City Gallery
Flaxman Gallery
Stoke on Trent City Museum & Art Gallery
Tamworth:
Palace Gallery
Palace Media Centre
Tamworth Arts Centre
Tamworth Central Library

Warwickshire

Henley in Arden:
Gallery Upstairs
Leamington Spa:
Earl of Smith Gallery
Griffin Gallery
Leamington Spa Art Gallery & Museum
North Lodge
Royal Spa Centre
South Town Gallery
Nuneaton:
Nuneaton Museum & Art Gallery
Rugby:
Rugby Exhibition Gallery
Stratford upon Avon:
Gallery (The)
Montpellier Gallery
Shakespeare Centre
Warwick:
Mill Gallery
Warwick Gallery
Warwickshire Museum

West Midlands

Bilston:
Bilston Museum & Art Gallery
Birmingham:
Angle Gallery
Birmingham Centre for Media Arts
Birmingham & Midland Institute
Birmingham Museum & Art Gallery
Birmingham University (Winterbourne House)
Bond Gallery
Cave (The)
Craftspace Touring
Custard Factory

Helios Gallery
Ikon Gallery
mac
Mill Gallery
Photopack
Picture Palace
Royal Birmingham Society of Artists
Sutton Coldfield Town Hall
Woodbridge Gallery
Wythall Library
Coventry:
Bug Gallery
Herbert Art Gallery and Museum
Lanchester Gallery
Mead Gallery
Dudley:
Dudley Art Gallery
Kingswinford:
Broadfield House Glass Museum
Solihull:
Solihull Arts Complex
Sutton Coldfield:
Artifex
Walsall:
Walsall Museum & Art Gallery
Wednesbury:
Wednesbury Museum & Art Gallery
Wolverhampton:
Eagle Works
Lighthouse Media Centre
University of Wolverhampton
Wolverhampton Museum & Art Gallery

Yorkshire and Humberside

Counties of Humberside and North, South and West Yorkshire

Yorkshire and Humberside Arts,
21 Bond Street, Dewsbury WF13 1AX,
tel: 01924 455555

Humberside

Barton upon Humber:
Baysgarth House Museum
Beverley:
Beverley Art Gallery & Museum
Bridlington:
Sewerby Hall
Goole:
Snaith Arts & Crafts
South Farm Craft Gallery
Grimsby:
Central Library

Grimsby College of Technology (Gallery One Hundred)
Hull:
Ferens Art Gallery
Spring Street Theatre
University of Hull Art Collection
Scunthorpe:
Scunthorpe Museum & Art Gallery
Thomas Sumpter Comprehensive School

North Yorkshire

Harrogate:
Godfrey & Twatt
Masai Mara
Mercer Art Gallery
Helmsley:
Look Gallery
Sissons William Gallery
Knaresborough:
Courthouse Museum (Little Gallery)
European Ceramics Gallery
Gordon Reece Gallery
Leyburn:
Chandler Gallery
Old School Arts Workshop
Pickering:
Green Man Gallery
Ripley:
Chantry House Gallery
Scarborough:
Crescent Arts Workshop
Scarborough Art Gallery
Settle:
Linton Court Gallery
Thirsk:
Zillah Bell Contemporary Art
Whitby:
Montage Studio Gallery
York:
AD Gallery
Burton Stone Community Centre
Impressions Gallery
Kentmere House Gallery
New York Gallery (The)
Priory Street Centre
Pyramid Gallery
Robert Feather Gallery
Shandy Hall
Stonegate Gallery
Wentworth Exhibition Area
York Arts Centre
York City Art Gallery

South Yorkshire

Barnsley:
Barnsley Central Library
Cooper Gallery
Doncaster:
Church View Gallery
Doncaster Museum & Art Gallery
Make Do and Mend Art Gallery and Exhibition Space
Museum of South Yorkshire Life
South Yorkshire Art Gallery

Rotherham:
Central Library Arts Centre
Rotherham Art Gallery
Rotherham College of Arts &
Technology Gallery
Sheffield:
Bishops' House Museum
Crucible Theatre Gallery
Cupola
Darnall Library
Graves Art Gallery
Mappin Art Gallery
Ora Gallery
Ruskin Craft Gallery
Sheffield City Art Galleries Touring
Exhibitions Service
Sheffield Hallam University Gallery
Site Gallery
Star Works Café
Stocksbridge Library
University of Sheffield (Library
Exhibition Area)
Walkley Centre
Waterhope Library
Woodhouse Community Education
Centre
Yorkshire Artspace Society

West Yorkshire

Addingham:
Helyg Pottery & Textiles Gallery
Batley:
Bagshaw Museum
Batley Art Gallery
Bingley:
Bingley Arts Centre
Bingley Library
Bradford:
Bolton Royd Gallery
Bradford Community Arts Centre
Bradford Design Exchange
Bradford Industrial Museum & Horses
at Work
Cartwright Hall
Gallery II
National Museum of Photography, Film
& Television
Brighouse:
Smith Art Gallery
Dewsbury:
Art Gallery at Dewsbury Museum
Halifax:
Bankfield Museum and Art Gallery
David Holmes Ceramics
Dean Clough Galleries
Henry Moore Sculpture Trust Studio
Piece Hall Art Gallery
Square Chapel Centre for the Arts
Throstle Nest Gallery
Huddersfield:
Booth House Gallery & Pottery
(Robison Ceramics)
Bryam Galleries
Huddersfield Art Gallery
Ilkley:
Lauron Gallery
Manor House Art Gallery & Museum

Keighley:
Cliffe Castle
Leeds:
Art & Design Movement
Benjamin Gott
BRAHM Gallery
Cookridge Street Gallery
Craft Centre & Design Gallery
Gilbert Scott Gallery
Henry Moore Institute
Leeds City Art Gallery
Leeds Design Innovation Centre
Leeds Metropolitan University Gallery
Lotherton Hall
Newlyn Gallery
Site (Architecture) Gallery
Space (The)
Terrace Gallery
University Gallery Leeds
Yorkshire Dance Centre
Mirfield:
Eastthorpe Gallery
Thornton:
South Square Gallery
Todmorden:
Red Water Arts
Wakefield:
Bothy Shop/Gallery
Elizabethan Exhibition Gallery
Lawrence Batley Centre
Marie Jordan Gallery
Wakefield Art Gallery
Wakefield College Arts Centre
Yorkshire Sculpture Park

Northern Ireland

Counties of Antrim, Armagh, Derry,
Down, Fermanagh and Tyrone.

Arts Council of Northern Ireland,
185 Stranmillis Road, Belfast BT9 5DU,
tel: 01232 381591

Co Antrim

Antrim:
Clotworthy House Arts Centre
Ballymena:
North Eastern Education & Library
Board
Belfast:
Belfast Public Libraries
Bell Gallery
Catalyst Arts
Cavehill Gallery
Crescent Arts Centre

Factory Gallery
Fenderesky Gallery at Queen's
Gallery (The)
Linen Hall Library
Magee Gallery
Old Museum Arts Centre
One Oxford Street
Ormeau Baths Gallery
Orpheus Gallery
Tom Caldwell Galleries
Ulster Arts Club Gallery
Ulster Museum
Lisburn:
Harmony Hill Arts Centre
Seymour Galleries
Portrush:
Portrush Gallery

Co Armagh

Armagh:
Adam Gallery
Armagh County Museum
Craigavon:
Brownlow Library Gallery
Pinebank House Arts Centre (Peacock
Gallery)
Demesne:
Hayloft Gallery
Lurgan:
Corridor Gallery
Portadown:
Roy Edwards Fine Arts

Co Derry

Coleraine:
Town House Gallery
University of Ulster (Riverside Gallery)
Derry:
Context Gallery
Foyle Arts Centre
Gordon Galleries
Orchard Gallery
Magherafelt:
Horner Gallery
Portstewart:
Flowerfield Arts Centre

Co Down

Bangor:
North Down Visitors and Heritage
Centre
Comber:
Castle Espie Gallery
Salem Gallery
Donaghadee:
Cleft Art Gallery
Downpatrick:
Down Arts Centre
Hillsborough:
Shambles Gallery
Holywood:
Priory Art Gallery
Newcastle:
Grant Fine Art
Newcastle Art Gallery

Newcastle Centre
Newry:
Carroll
Newtownards:
Ards Arts Centre

Co Fermanagh

Enniskillen:
Ardhowen Photographic Gallery
Enniskillen Castle

Republic of Ireland

Counties of Carlow, Cavan, Clare, Cork, Donegal, Dublin, Galway, Kerry, Kildare, Kilkenny, Laois, Leitrim, Limerick, Longford, Louth, Mayo, Meath, Monaghan, Offaly, Sligo, Tipperary, Waterford, Westmeath, Wexford, Wicklow.

Arts Council of Ireland, 70 Merrion Square, Dublin 2, tel: [00353] 1 661 1840, fax: [00 353] 1 676 1302

Co Carlow

Carlow:
Pembroke Studio Gallery

Co Cavan

Cavan:
Cavan County Arts Service

Co Clare

Ballyvaughan:
Dallan Gallery
Ennis:
De Valera Library
Ennistymon:
Ennistymon Branch Library
Kilshanny:
Atlantis Gallery
Shannon:
Seán Lemass Library

Co Cork

Bantry:
Bantry Library
O'Kane's Green Gallery

Charleville:
Charleville Library
Cobh:
Sirius Commemoration Trust
Cork:
Art Hive
Blackcombe Art Gallery
Crawford Municipal Art Gallery
Lavitt's Quay Gallery
Triskel Arts Centre
University College Cork (Boole Library)
Kinsale:
Keane-on-Ceramics
Macroom:
Vangard Gallery
Skibbereen:
West Cork Arts Centre

Co Donegal

Buncrana:
Tullyarvan Mill Culture & Exhibition Centre
Gleann Cholm Cille:
Foras Cultuir Uladh - Ulster Cultural Centre
Kilcar:
Ram's Head Gallery
Letterkenny:
Cristeph Gallery
Donegal County Arts Service
Donegal County Museum
Glebe House and Gallery
Port Gallery

Co Dublin

Ballsbridge:
Milmo-Penny Fine Art
Dalkey:
James Gallery
Dublin:
Andrews Lane Theatre
Anya Von Gösseln Gallery
Arts Council
City Arts Centre
Combridge Fine Arts
Crafts Council Gallery
Davis Gallery
Designyard
Douglas Hyde Gallery
Dublin Photographic Centre
Dublin Public Libraries
Dublin Writers Museum
Gallery of Photography
Gorry Gallery
Graphic Studio Dublin Gallery
Green on Red Gallery
Guinness Gallery
Guinness Hop Store
Hallward Gallery
Hugh Lane Municipal Gallery of Modern Art
Irish Life Exhibition Centre
Irish Museum of Modern Art
Jo Rains Gallery
Kennedy Gallery
Kerlin Gallery

Mansion House
New Apollo Gallery
Oisin Art Gallery (Marino Mart)
Oisin Art Gallery (Westland Row)
Oriel Gallery
Ormond Gallery
Project Arts Centre
RHA Gallagher Gallery
Royal Dublin Society
Rubicon Gallery
Solomon Gallery
Taylor Galleries
Temple Bar Gallery & Studios
Village Art Gallery
Wyvern Gallery
Dun Laoghaire:
Bobby Dawson Gallery
Howth:
Howth Harbour Gallery
Kilmainham:
Irish Museum of Modern Art
Lucan:
Phoenix Art Studio
Swords:
Swords Art and Craft Centre
Tallaght:
Old Bawn Community School

Co Galway

Ballinasloe:
Ballinasloe Library
Connemara:
Danlann (An)
Galway:
Dámhlann Kenny Gallery
Galway Arts Centre
Grainstore Gallery
Kenny Gallery
University College Galway
Oughterard:
West Shore Gallery

Co Kerry

Castleisland:
Ivyleaf Arts Centre
Dingle:
Simple Pleasures Art Gallery
Kenmare:
Iverni Gallery
Killarney:
Frank Lewis Gallery
Killarney Art Gallery
Killarney Branch Library
Killorglin:
Sheeog Art Gallery
Siamsa Tire Theatre/Arts Centre
Listowel:
St Johns Arts and Heritage Centre
Tralee:
Bín Bán Gallery
Tralee Library
Wellspring Gallery

Co Kildare

Athy:
Athy Community Library
Crookstown Mill Heritage Centre
Celbridge:
Celbridge Branch Library
Kilcock:
Kilcock Art Gallery
Maynooth:
Maynooth Exhibition Centre
Naas:
Naas Branch Library
Tuckmill Gallery

Co Kilkenny

Graiguenamanagh:
Kilkenny County Library
Kilkenny:
Butler Gallery
Thomastown:
Berkeley Gallery

Co Laois

Portlaoise:
Laois County Hall

Co Leitrim

Carrick on Shannon:
Old Barrel Store Arts Centre
Keshcarrigen:
Fionn Mc Cumhaill Centre

Co Limerick

Foynes:
Foynes Branch Library
Limerick:
Belltable Arts Centre
Chris Doswell's Gallery
Dolmen Gallery
Limerick City Gallery of Art
Muse Gallery
University of Limerick Gallery
Newcastle West:
Newcastle West Library

Co Longford

Longford:
Carroll Gallery

Co Louth

Ardee:
Ardee Branch Library
Carlingford:
Artistic Licence
Holy Trinity Heritage Centre
Drogheda:
Droichead Arts Centre
Dundalk:
Basement Gallery
County Museum Dundalk
TristAnn's Gallery

Co Mayo

Achill Island:
Western Light Art Gallery
Yawl Art Gallery
Castlebar:
Castlebar Public Library
Kirk Gallery
Linenhall Arts Centre
Claremorris:
Claremorris Gallery
Foxford:
Foxford Exhibition Centre
Louisburgh:
Aimhirgin Gallery
Westport:
Westport Pubic Library

Co Meath

Navan:
Meath County Library Service

Co Monaghan

Monaghan:
Market House Gallery
Monaghan County Museum

Co Offaly

Tullamore:
Offaly County Library Service

Co Sligo

Riverstown:
Taylor's Art Gallery
Sligo:
Hawk's Well Theatre
Model Arts Centre
Sligo Art Gallery

Co Tipperary

Birdhill:
Lucy Erridge Gallery
Carrick on Suir:
Carrick on Suir Heritage Centre
Clonmel:
Tipperary South Riding County
Museum
Nenagh:
Nenagh District Heritage Centre
Roscrea:
Roscrea Heritage Centre
Thurles:
Tipperary County Library Serice

Co Waterford

Lismore:
Lismore Library
Waterford:
Dyehouse Gallery
Garter Lane Arts Centre

Co Westmeath

Athlone:
Dolan Moore Gallery
Mullingar:
Midland Arts Resource Centre

Co Wexford

Bunclody:
Chantry Gallery
Gorey:
Woodland Arts & Crafts Gallery
Wexford:
Wexford Arts Centre

Co Wicklow

Bray:
Craft Art Gallery
Hangman Gallery
Signal Arts Centre
Wicklow:
Renaissance III Gallery

Scotland

**Regions of Borders, Central, Dumfries
& Galloway, Fife, Grampian,
Highland, Lothian, Orkney, Shetland,
Strathclyde, Tayside and Western Isles**

Scottish Arts Council,
12 Manor Place, Edinburgh EH3 7DO,
tel: 0131 226 6051

Borders

Biggar:
Broughton Gallery
Galashiels:
Christopher Boyd Gallery
Hawick:
Scott Art Gallery
Peebles:
Tweeddale Museum & Art Gallery
Selkirk:
Robson Gallery

Central

Alloa:
Alloa Museum & Gallery
Stirling:
Cowane Gallery
MacRobert Arts Centre Gallery
Smith Art Gallery & Museum

Dumfries & Galloway

Castle Douglas:
Castle Douglas Art Gallery
Dumfries:
Gracefield Arts Centre
Robert Burns Centre
Kirkcudbright:
Tolbooth Art Centre
Stranraer:
Stranraer Museum

Fife

Cardenden:
Arts in Fife
Dunfermline:
Small Gallery
Glenrothes:
Corridor Gallery
Rothes Halls
Kirkcaldy:
Kirkcaldy Museum & Art Gallery
Leven:
Loomshop Gallery
Lochgelly:
Lochgelly Centre Gallery
St Andrews:
Byre Theatre
Crawford Arts Centre

Grampian

Aberdeen:
Aberdeen Art Gallery
Aberdeen Arts Centre
Gallery Heinzel
Haddo Arts Trust
Lemon Tree
Peacock Printmakers
Scottish Sculpture Workshop
Banff:
Warehouse Gallery
Elgin:
Elgin Museum
Ellon:
Tolquhon Gallery
Macduff:
Macduff Arts Centre
Peterhead:
Arbuthnot Museum
Stonehaven:
Riverside Gallery

Highland

Inverness:
Culloden Library Mini Gallery
Eden Court
Highland Printmakers Workshop &
Gallery
Inverness Museum & Art Gallery
Isle of Skye
Tuireann Arts Centre (An)
ArtiZania
Orbost Gallery
Kingussie:
Iona Gallery

Thurso:
Swanson Gallery
Wick:
Lyth Arts Centre
St Fergus Gallery

Lothian

Bathgate:
Balbardie Gallery
Dalkeith:
Dalkeith Arts Centre
Edinburgh:
369 Gallery
Cameo Cinema
Carlyle's Gallery
Chessel Gallery
Citizens Studios
City Art Centre
Collective Gallery
Commonwealth Institute, Scotland
Contact Gallery
Craigmillar Festival Society Arts Centre
Danish Cultural Institute
Designer Frames & Gallery La Belle
Angele
Eastern General Hospital
Edinburgh City Libraries
Edinburgh College of Art
Edinburgh Gallery
Edinburgh Printmakers Workshop &
Gallery
Edinburgh Sculpture Workshop
ESU Gallery
Firth Gallery
French Institute
Fruitmarket Gallery
Galerie Mirages
Hanover Fine Arts
Inverleith House/Royal Botanic Garden
Edinburgh
Kingfisher Gallery
Leith Gallery
Malcolm Innes Gallery
Matthew Architecture Gallery
Moray House Institute of Education
National Library of Scotland
Netherbow Art Centre
Open Eye Gallery
Out of the Blue Artspace
Portfolio Gallery
Queen's Hall
RIAS Gallery
Royal Scottish Academy
Scottish Gallery
Scottish National Gallery of Modern Art
Scottish National Portrait Gallery
Scottish Photographic Works
Seeds Wholefood Café
Stills Gallery
Talbot Rice Gallery
Theatre Workshop
Torrance Gallery
Traverse Theatre
Ware on Earth
WASPS Studios Gallery
Gullane:
Norrie Toch Studios

Haddington:
Peter Potter Gallery Trust
Livingston:
Inveralmond Community Education
Centre
Musselburgh:
Brunton Theatre

Orkney

Kirkwall:
Tankerness House Museum
Stromness:
Pier Arts Centre

Shetland

Lerwick:
Shetland Museum
Weisdale:
Bonhoga Gallery

Strathclyde

Ayr:
Maclaurin Art Gallery
Cleland:
Cleland Arts Schoolhouse
Clydebank:
Dalmuir Branch Library
Coatbridge:
Ironworks Gallery
Cumnock:
District History Centre & Baird
Institute Museum
Dumbarton:
Dumbarton Public Library
Girvan:
McKechnie Institute
Glasgow:
Art Gallery & Museum, Kelvingrove
Barclay Lennie Fine Art
Centre for Contemporary Arts
Centre for Developmental Arts Gallery
Collins Gallery
Compass Gallery
Cyril Gerber Fine Art
Eastwood House
Ewan Mundy Fine Art
Gatehouse Gallery
Glasgow Museums
Glasgow Print Studio
Glasgow School of Art
Haggs Castle Museum
Hillhead Underground Gallery
Hunterian Art Gallery
Interdec Gallery
Intermedia Gallery
Kelly Gallery
Lillie Art Gallery
McLennan Gallery
Michael Main Gallery
Mitchell Library
Pearce Institute
Roger Billcliffe Fine Art
Rowan Gallery
Royal Scottish Academy of Music and
Drama

Springburn Museum
Strathclyde Arts Centre
Street Level Photography Gallery and
Workshop
t.Garner Gallery
T & R Annan & Sons
Tramway
Transmission Gallery
William Hardie Gallery
Greenock:
Greenock Arts Guild
McLean Museum & Art Gallery
Irvine:
Harbour Arts Centre
Kilmarnock:
Dean Castle
Dick Institute (The)
Kirkintilloch:
Auld Kirk Museum
Paisley:
Paisley Arts Centre
Paisley Museum & Art Galleries

Tayside

Arbroath:
Arbroath Library Art Gallery
Carnoustie:
Carnoustie Library Art Gallery
Crieff:
Strathern Gallery
Dundee:
Barrack Street Museum
Bonar Hall
Duncan of Jordanstone College of Art
Dundee Rep Gallery
McManus Galleries
Roseangle Gallery
Seagate Gallery
Forfar:
Meffan Museum & Art Gallery
Montrose:
Montrose Library Art Gallery
Perth:
Perth Theatre Gallery

Western Isles

North Uist
Taigh Chearsabhagh
Stornoway:
Lanntair (An)

Wales

Clwyd, Dyfed, Gwent, Gwynedd, Mid-Glamorgan, Powys, South Glamorgan and West Glamorgan

Welsh Arts Council, Museum Place, Cardiff CF1 3NX, tel: 01222 394711.
Regional Offices: North East Wales Office, Daniel Owen Centre, Earl Road, Mold, Clwyd CH7 1AP, tel: 01352 758403, fax: 01352 700236; North Wales Office, 10 Wellfield House, Bangor, Gwynedd LL57 1ER, tel: 01248 353248; South East Wales Office, Victoria Street, Cwmbran NP44 3YT, tel: 01633 875075.

Clwyd

Abergele:
Abergele Library
Caergwrle:
Caegwrle Library
Colwyn Bay:
Colwyn Bay Library
Denbigh:
Denbigh Library Museum and Gallery
Hawarden:
Hawarden Library
Holywell:
Holywell Library
Llanfihangel GM:
Mariers Pictures
Llangollen:
ECTARC
Llangollen Library
Mancot:
Mancot Library
Mold:
Daniel Owen Centre, Exhibition Room
Oriel Theatr Clwyd
Wern Mill Gallery
Prestatyn:
Prestatyn Library
Rhuddlan:
Rhuddlan Library
Rhyl:
Rhyl Library, Museum and Arts Centre
Ruthin:
Ruffin Craft Centre Gallery
St Asaph:
St Asaph Library
Tenby:
Boathouse Gallery
Wrexham:
Bersham Heritage Centre
Cefn Mawr

Clwyd County Art & Exhibition
Division
Rhosllanerchrugog Library
Wrexham Library Arts Centre

Dyfed

Aberystwyth:
Aberystwyth Arts Centre
Ceredigion Museum
National Library of Wales
Cardigan:
Chelini
Frame by Frame Gallery & Workshop
Theatr Mwldan
Carmarthen:
Carmarthen Library
Henry Thomas Gallery
Oriel Myrddin Gallery
Fishguard:
Fishguard Branch Library
West Wales Arts Centre
Haverfordwest:
Graham Sutherland Gallery
Haverfordwest Library
Laugharne:
Three Market Street Gallery
Lampeter:
Galeri (Y)
St David's University College
Theatr Felinfach
Llandeilo:
Country Fine Arts
Fountain Fine Art
Llandysul:
Museum of Welsh Woolen Industry
Llanelli:
Llanelli Borough Library
Mansion House
Park Howard Mansion
Milford Haven:
Torch Theatre
Narberth:
Gallery at Colby
Newport:
Pauline Harries Gallery
Sessions House
Pembroke Dock:
Pembroke Dock Library
Penglais:
Catherine Lewis Gallery
Tenby:
Tenby Museum & Art Gallery
Whitland:
Studio in the Church

Gwent

Abergavenny:
Abergavenny Museum
Blackwood:
Holmlands Studio Gallery
Blaenavon:
Big Pit Museum Trust
Caldicot:
Tower Gallery
Chepstow:
Art Approach
Chepstow Museum

Workshop Gallery
Cwmbran:
Llantarnam Grange Arts Centre
Moving Pictures
Monmouth:
Art Centre (Monmouth)
Pat Yallup Studio Gallery
Newport:
Brynglas Adult Education Centre
Newport Museum & Art Gallery
Pontypool:
Valley Inheritance Museum

Gwynedd

Bala:
Bala Heritage Centre
Bangor:
Bangor Museum & Art Gallery
Theatr Gwynedd
Beaumaris:
David Hughes Community Centre
Blaenau Ffestiniog:
Blaenau Ffestiniog Library
Oriel y Ddraig
Caernarfon:
Arfon Gallery
Caernarfon Library
Gwynedd County Libraries
Oriel Pendeitsh
Conwy:
Royal Cambrian Academy of Art
Dolgellau:
Library Art Gallery
Harlech:
Theatr Ardudwy
White Room Gallery at Harlech Pottery
Holyhead:
Ucheldre Centre
Llandudno:
Fulmar Gallery
Oriel Mostyn
Llangefni:
Nant yr Odin
Oriel Ynys Mon
Menai Bridge:
Tegfryn Art Gallery
Porthmadog:
Flour Shed Gallery
Porthmadog Community Centre
Stiwdio Garreg Wen
Pwllheli:
Bodvel Hall Craft Centre
Plas Glyn-y-Weddw Gallery

Mid-Glamorgan

Aberdare:
Aberdare Central Library
Dare Valley Country Park (Visitor Centre)
Blaengarw:
Blaengarw Workmens Hall
Bridgend:
Berwyn Centre
Mid Glamorgan County Libraries
Nolton Gallery

Caerphilly:
Coach House Gallery
Llantrisant:
Butchers Arms Gallery
Model House Craft & Design Centre
Maesteg:
Oriel Plasnewydd Gallery
Merthyr Tydfil:
Cefn Community Centre
Cyfarthfa Castle Museum & Art Gallery
Pontypridd:
Circle Gallery
Oriel y Bont
Pontypridd Heritage Centre
Rhondda:
Rhondda Community Arts
Trehafod:
Rhondda Heritage Park Centre Gallery
Treorchy:
Parc & Dare Theatre

Powys

Brecon:
Beacons Fine Art Gallery
Brecknock Museum
Brecon Library
Sable & Hogg Gallery
Builth Wells:
Builth Wells Library
Wyeside Gallery
Hay on Wye:
Kilvert Gallery
Meridian Contemporary Arts
Rogues Gallery
Knighton:
Knighton Library
Old School Gallery
Llandrindod Wells:
Porticus
Llanidloes:
Studio 13
Machynlleth:
Museum of Modern Art, Wales
Spectrum Gallery
Montgomery:
Country Works
Montgomeryshire:
Museum of Modern Art Wales
Newtown:
Gwasg Gregynog Gallery
Oriel 31
Phoenix Gallery
Presteigne:
MBCA Gallery (Mid Border Community Arts)
Rhayader:
Elan Valley Visitor Centre
Rhayader Library
Welshpool:
Oriel 31
Welshpool Library

South Glamorgan

Barry:
Living Archive Centre

Cardiff:
Albany Gallery
Art Education Gallery
Canton Library
Cardiff Central Library
Chapter
Ely Branch Library
Ffotogallery
Gallery (The)
Llanover Hall Oriel Llanover
Makers Gallery
Manor House Fine Arts
Martin Tinney Gallery
National Museum of Wales (Department of Art)
Norwegian Church Centre
Old Library
Oriel
St David's Hall
Welsh Industrial & Maritime Museum
Cowbridge:
Cowbridge Old Hall Gallery
John Owen Gallery
Llandough:
Llandough Exhibition Space
Llantwit Major:
St Donat's Arts Centre
Penarth:
Turner House

West Glamorgan

Neath:
Cefn Coed Colliery Museum
Pontardawe:
Cross Gallery
Port Talbot:
Margam Orangery
Swansea:
Attic Gallery
Ceri Richards Gallery
Craftsman Gallery
Glynn Vivian Art Gallery
Gorseinon Institute
Mumbles Gallery
New Gallery
Ocean Gallery
Swansea Arts Workshop Gallery
Swansea Maritime & Industrial Museum
Swansea Museum

Channel Islands

Guernsey

St Martins:
Studio Renoir
St Peter Port:
Guernsey Museum & Art Gallery
St Peters:
Coach House Gallery

Jersey

St Helier:
Studio 18

Gallery Index

**Blackthorpe Barn, Rougham,
Suffolk**

Installation of *Time Spiral* by
Micheal Pinsky, 1994
Photo: Dona Haycraft

England

Abingdon
OXFORDSHIRE SA

Abingdon Museum
[Pa][Ph][Pr][Cr][Sc][LA] ✔

Museum with permanent displays and exhibitions of contemporary craftwork.
County Hall, Market Place, Abingdon OX14 3JE, tel: 01235 523703
Contact: Sally Heartshorne, Crafts Officer, Oxfordshire County Museum, Fletcher's House, Park Street, Woodstock, OX20 1SN
Space: 1 gallery
Details: In County Hall designed by Sir Christopher Wren. Displays local history and archaeology of the town and surrounding area. Gallery shows contemporary craftwork and houses Southern Arts Craft Collection. Educational study and workshop facilities in newly converted basement area.

Rocket Contemporary Art
[Pa][Ph][Pr] ✔

Displays work by artists associated with the Rocket Press.
The Rocket Press, The Grain Store, Church Lane, Steventon, Abingdon OX13 6SW, tel: 01235 835525
Contact: Jonathan or David Stephenson, Directors
Space: 186 sq m floor space
Exhibitions: 2 a year both originated
Details: All the walls of the Rocket Press building used for displays. Special open days and weekends are organised to attract the public. Commission variable.

Accrington
LANCASHIRE NWA

Haworth Art Gallery
[Pa][Cr][Sc] ✔ ♿

Edwardian Tudor house with collections of C19th paintings and Tiffany Glass, and temporary exhibitions mainly of work by local/amateur artists and craftspeople.
Haworth Park, Manchester Road, Accrington BB5 2JS, tel: 01254 233782, fax: 01254 380291
Contact: Jennifer Rennie, Curator
Open: Sat-Thurs 2-5; closed BH
Space: 7 galleries with 114 lin m hanging space plus 27 lin m on screens and 211 sq m floor space
Exhibitions: 40 a year of which 36 originated, 4 touring
Details: Current programme mainly shows work by groups of local amateur artists. However aims to include more professional, historic and culturally diverse exhibitions; to stress significance of crafts and show more 3D work; to use house and collections as source for Artists in Residence/site specific work. Sales not a priority. Will pay exhibition fee in future.

Addingham
WEST YORKSHIRE YHA

Helyg Pottery & Textiles Gallery
[Pa][Cr]

Permanent workshops open to public with one or two exhibitions a year.
2 Bolton Road, Addingham LS29 0NR, tel: 01943 830165
Contact: Meira Stockl
Space: 3 galleries
Exhibitions: 1 a year originated
Details: Craft workers with own work on permanent display interested in encouraging other makers

Aldeburgh
SUFFOLK EA

Aldeburgh Cinema Gallery
[Pa][Pr][Cr][Sc] ✔ [H] ♿ [WC]

First-floor exhibition space, mainly hired to selected exhibitors, plus small sculpture garden.
High Street, Aldeburgh IP15 5AU, tel: 01728 452996, fax: 01728 454026
Contact: Mr Reiss
Open: Daily 10-5.30
Space: 1 gallery with 21 lin m hanging space plus 5 lin m on screens and 48 sq m floor space
Exhibitions: 12 a year of which 2 originated, 10 on a hire basis
Details: Gallery available for hire by selected exhibitors except when gallery collaborates with Aldeburgh Foundation during June Festival. Sales primary role of gallery.

Peter Pears Gallery
[Pa][Pr][Cr][Sc][LA] ✔ [H] ♿

Supports the Aldeburgh Festival as a venue for specialist exhibitions, also hosting the Suffolk Craft Society.
Aldeburgh Foundation, High Street, Aldeburgh IP15 5AX, tel: 01728 852935, fax: 01728 452715
Contact: Exhibition Organiser
Space: 1 gallery
Exhibitions: 2 a year both originated
Details: Available for hire.

Tudor House Gallery
[Pa][Cr][Sc] ✔ £ [H] ♿

Small commercial gallery showing work by artists living within and outside the area.
143 High Street, Aldeburgh IP15 5HW, tel: 01278 454280
Contact: Exhibitions Organiser
Open: Daily 10-5
Space: 1 gallery with 17 lin m hanging space and 15 sq m floor space
Exhibitions: 11 a year
Details: Gallery opened April 1994. Weekly or fortnightly shows. Aims to promote artists' work in informal and relaxed atmosphere. Plinths and screens available. Plans to be part of Aldeburgh Festival and arts network. Sales priority but no commission taken. Artists pay weekly booking charge.

Aldershot
HAMPSHIRE SA

West End Centre Gallery
[Pa][Ph][Pr][Cr][Sc] ✔ £ ♿ [WC]

Dedicated exhibition space for innovative and challenging contemporary art and craft in arts centre.
Queens Road, Aldershot GU11 3JD, tel: 01252 21158, fax: 01252 342832
Contact: Susan Ryland, Visual Arts & Crafts Director
Open: Mon-Fri 10-5.30, 7-9; Sat 10-1; other times on request
Space: 1 gallery with 35 lin m hanging space and 256 sq m floor space
Exhibitions: 6 a year all originated
Details: Programme of mixed theme, group and one-person exhibitions. Provides younger artists opportunity to present innovative work to receptive audience in supportive environment. Artists invited to participate in educational programme of workshops, talks, etc. Sales encouraged but not primary motive.

Alnmouth
NORTHUMBERLAND NA

Riverbank Gallery
[Pa][Ph][Pr][Cr][Sc] ✔ ♿

Commercial gallery with emphasis on work by local artists and craftspeople.
57 Northumberland Street, Alnmouth NE66 2RS, tel: 01665 830333
Contact: Mrs Claire Ford-Hutchinson, Owner/Manager
Open: (Summer) Daily 10-5.30 plus some evenings; (Winter) Most days 11-3 and longer at weekends.
Space: 1 gallery with 27 lin m hanging space and 26 sq m floor space
Details: Gallery with continuous changing display. Encourages local artists and craftspeople to bring in their work with a view to exhibit it for sale, for six-month period, on understanding that gallery or artists may withdraw at any time. Gallery takes a third of retail price. Framing service and arranges commissions. Meeting place for local artists.

Alnwick
NORTHUMBERLAND NA

Bondgate Gallery
Pa Ph Pr Cr Sc ✓ ⊕ ⚫⚫

Provides facilities for artists to exhibit work, usually in solo exhibitions, for the benefit of members, visitors, and local schools.
22 Narrowgate, Alnwick NE66 1JG, tel: 01665 577088
Contact: Peter Bolwell Andrews, Chairman
Space: 1 gallery with 23 lin m hanging space and 51 sq m floor space
Exhibitions: 10 a year all originated
Details: Run by members of the Anwick and District Arts Association, showing art and craft in wide variety of media every month. Illustrates history of art and encourages its appreciation, stimulates interest in contemporary art in area. Other activities include visits and lectures.

Alresford
HAMPSHIRE SA

Alresford Gallery *
Pa Sc ✓

Commercial gallery competing in the same general market as London galleries.
36 West Street, Alresford SO24 9AU, tel: 01962 735286, fax: 01962 735295
Contact: The Gallery Director
Space: 3 galleries
Exhibitions: 10 a year all originated
Details: Aims to show and sell the best of work by living artists in variety of single, group and mixed shows. Artists range from those of established reputation to younger emerging painters and sculptors. One large area which can be divided into 3 smaller spaces. Commission on sales.

Candover Gallery
Pa Cr ⓔ ⚫

Commercial allery in 200 year old building selling contemporary ceramics, glass and paintings mostly by well-known British craftspeople and artists.
22 West Street, Alresford SO24 9AE, tel: 01962 733200, fax: 01256 812864
Contact: Barbara Ling, Owner
Open: Mon-Sat 9.30-5.30
Space: 1 gallery with 37 lin m hanging space and 84 sq m floor space
Exhibitions: 4 a year all originated
Details: Displays contemporary ceramics and glass by more than 30 of the best craftspeople in Britain. Four exhibitions lasting a month held each year, one or two of these are one-person exhibitions. Rapid turn-over of work throughout the year. Independent access for wheelchair users to first-floor only.

Alsager
CHESHIRE NWA

Alsager Gallery
Pa Ph Pr Cr Sc LA ✓ ⚫

Manchester Metropolitan University, Crewe + Alsager Faculty, Hassall Road, Alsager ST7 2HL, tel: 0161 247 5302, fax: 0161 247 6377
Contact: Dorothy Pickering, Senior Lecturer
Space: 1 gallery with 240 lin m hanging space plus 16 lin m on screens and 96 sq m floor space
Exhibitions: 9 a year all originated
Details: Provides wide range of arts activities and events for students and general public. Exhibitions of work by living artists and makers, often in conjunction with lectures and workshops. Exhibitions include touring shows, work by members of staff and shows reflecting interest in historical, ethnic and current issues.

Alston
CUMBRIA NA

Gossipgate Gallery
Pa Ph Pr Cr Sc ✓

Specialises in work of contemporary artists and craftspeople from North of England and the Borders with equal emphasis on art and craft.
The Butts, Alston CA9 3JU, tel: 01434 381806
Contact: Sonia Kempsey, Proprietor
Open: (Mid Feb-Mar & Nov-Dec) Sat 10-5, Sun-Fri 11-4.30; (Apr-Oct) Daily 10-5; closed Jan
Space: 1 gallery with 17 lin m hanging space and 19 sq m floor space
Exhibitions: 9 a year all originated
Details: In addition, a permanent display of work from this region. Programme consists of consecutive exhibitions of at least four weeks duration. Exhibitions are themed usually combining art and crafts with about half a dozen contributors.

Alton
HAMPSHIRE SA

Allen Gallery
Pa Ph Pr Cr Sc ✓ⓔ ⚫4

Local museum showing varied programme including contemporary and historical art and craft.
Church Street, Alton GU34 2BW, tel: 01420 82802, fax: 01962 869836
Contact: Carol Littlefair, Exhibition Officer, Hampshire County Council Museums Service, Chilcomb House, Chilcomb Lane, Winchester, SO23 8RD, tel: 01962 846315, fax: 01962 869836

Open: Tues-Sat 10-5
Space: 1 gallery with 25 lin m hanging space and 44 sq m floor space
Exhibitions: 8 a year of which 7 originated, 1 touring
Details: See entry for Hampshire County Council Museums, Winchester for policy

Ambleside
CUMBRIA NA

Dexterity
Pa Ph Pr Cr ✓ ⓖ

Changing selection of contemporary art and craftwork from UK artists with work of a specific artist specially featured from time to time.
Kelsick Road, Ambleside LA22 0BZ, tel: 015394 34045
Contact: Mrs Gillean Bell, Proprietor
Open: Mon-Sun 9.30-6; closed Xmas & Boxing Days
Space: 1 gallery with 8 lin m hanging space and 45 sq m floor space
Exhibitions: 3 a year all originated
Details: Work displayed includes original paintings and drawings, limited edition prints, ceramics, jewellery, wood, glass, textiles and sculpture. All work is insured whilst in the gallery. Sale of work is a priority.

Gallery-in-the-Forest
Pa Pr Cr Sc ✓ ⚫⚫⚫4

Two exhibition spaces: theatre foyer for changing displays of 2D work and Gallery-in-the-Forest for didactic exhibitions of work made at Grizedale during artists' residencies.
Grizedale Society, Theatre-in-the-Forest, Grizedale, Nr Hawkshead, Ambleside LA22 0QJ, tel: 01229 860291
Contact: Bill Grant, Director
Open: (Easter-mid Nov) daily 11-5; otherwise by appointment
Space: 2 galleries with 610 lin m hanging space and 293 sq m floor space
Exhibitions: 8 a year all originated
Details: Shows eight temporary exhibitions a year in the theatre foyer, exhibiting mainly painting but also hangings, weavings and ceramics. Gallery-in-the-Forest is reserved for semi-permanent indigenous exhibitions of work executed during artists' residencies. Sales not main function of gallery.

Amesbury
WILTSHIRE SA

Amesbury Library
Pa Ph Pr Cr Sc ✓ ⚫

Exhibition space for use by local artists, craftspeople, photographic groups and other cultural organisations.

Smithfield Street, Amesbury SP4 7AL,
tel: 01980 623491
Contact: Librarian
Open: Mon, Thurs 2-7; Tues 10-5; Fri 10-7; Sat 10-4
Details: Run by Wiltshire Library and Museum Service. Selling work isn't gallery's main aim. 18% commission on sales.

Andover
HAMPSHIRE SA

Andover Museum

Local museum showing varied programme including contemporary and historical art and craft.
6 Church Close, Andover SP10 1DP, tel: 01264 366283, fax: 01962 869836
Contact: Carol Littlefair, Exhibitions Officer, Hampshire County Council Museums Service, Chilcomb House, Chilcomb Lane, Winchester, SO23 8RD, tel: 01962 846315, fax: 01962 869836
Open: Tues-Sat 10-5; (Apr-Sept) Sun 2-5
Space: 1 gallery with 22 lin m hanging space and 46 sq m floor space
Exhibitions: 8 a year of which 6 originated, 2 touring
Details: See entry for Hampshire County Council Museums, Winchester for policy.

Arundel
WEST SUSSEX SEA

Armstrong Davis Gallery *

International reputation for exhibiting only sculpture and drawings by sculptors.
The Square, Arundel BN18 9AB, tel: 01903 882 752
Contact: Laurence Davis
Space: 3 galleries with 237 sq m floor space
Details: Changing programme of C18th, C19th, C20th sculpture, predominantly in mixed international shows, occasionally solo shows. Supplies many collectors, museums and public galleries world-wide.

Little Gallery Bookshop *

Three large elegant rooms with plenty of natural lighting and spots.
32a High Street, Arundel BN18 9AB, tel: 01903 882 642
Contact: Mr M Hatley
Space: 4 galleries with 40 lin m hanging space and 800 sq m floor space
Exhibitions: 8 a year all originated
Details: Exhibitions generally last for 2 weeks.

Ashby de la Zouch
LEICESTERSHIRE EMA

Ferrers Gallery

Crafts Council selected shop/galleries in granary building.
Ferrers Centre for Art & Crafts, Staunton Harold, Ashby de la Zouch LE6 1RU, tel: 01332 863 337
Contact: Jackie Blunt, Director
Open: Tues-Sun 11-5; open BH
Space: 2 galleries with 39 lin m hanging space and 60 sq m floor space
Exhibitions: 3 a year all originated
Details: Showing mixed media, thematic, group and one-person shows, gallery aims to increase awareness and appreciation of British craftsmanship in thriving tourist area. Selling venue operating Art Purchase Scheme in conjunction with East Midlands Arts. Ground-floor gallery/shop accessible to wheelchair users; two upper exhibition floors not accessible.

Ashford
KENT SEA

Ashford Library Gallery

Gallery offering broad-based visual arts and crafts programme of exhibitions and events by individuals and groups from the region.
Church Road, Ashford TN23 1QX, tel: 01233 620649, fax: 01233 620295
Contact: Linda Robards, Arts and Heritage Officer
Open: Mon, Tues 9.30-6; Wed 9.30-5; Thurs, Fri 9.30-7; Sat 9-5
Space: 1 gallery with 30 lin m hanging space plus 36 lin m on screens and 114 sq m floor space
Exhibitions: 19 a year of which 1 originated, 4 touring, 14 on a hire basis
Details: Promotes the work of regional artists in shows lasting approximately 3 weeks. Aims to educate, inform and entertain. Exhibitions target an audience drawn from cross-section of residents and visitors. Sales not primary role of gallery. Lift to gallery level being installed 1995/96.

Evegate Farm Art Gallery

Gallery presenting work by professional and amateur artists.
Station Road, Smeeth, Ashford TN25 6SX, tel: 01303 813687
Contact: Jean Orman
Open: Tues-Sat 9-5
Space: 2 galleries
Exhibitions: 14 a year all originated
Details: Housed in an old barn and two oast houses. Atmosphere is relaxed and welcoming. Exhibitions by local artists presented in mainly solo shows. Popular

with the local audience and has many regular visitors. Art tuition/demos by professional artists. Range of art materials sold.

Ashington
NORTHUMBERLAND NA

Woodhorn Church Museum

Programme of temporary exhibitions in art, craft and local history.
Woodhorn Village, Ashington, tel: 01670 817371
Contact: Barry Mead, Director, Leisure Department, Wansbeck District Council, Wansbeck Square, Ashington, NE63 9XL, tel: 01670 814444/ 520056, fax: 01670 520136
Open: May-Aug: Wed-Sun 11-12.30, 1-5; Sept-April: Wed-Sun 10-12.30, 1-4
Space: 1 gallery with 27 lin m hanging space and 48 sq m floor space
Exhibitions: 9 a year of which 1 originated, 8 touring
Details: Many exhibitions accompanied by demonstrations and events from kite flying to weaving. Local and regional artists particularly welcome to apply. Selling work not primary function of gallery.

Aylesbury
BUCKINGHAMSHIRE SA

Buckinghamshire County Museum

Museum with contemporary art exhibition.
Church Street, Aylesbury HP20 2QP, tel: 01296 88849
Contact: Emma Gregory, Exhibition Officer, Milton Keynes Exhibition Gallery, 555 Silbury Boulevard, Milton Keynes, MK9 3HL, tel: 01908 835025
Space: 1 gallery with 30 lin m hanging space and 65 sq m floor space
Exhibitions: 10 a year
Details: Housed in County Museum headquarters. Programme covers wide range of topics, history, natural history, scientific exhibitions, contemporary and historical art exhibitions. Approximately a quarter of exhibitions feature the work of contemporary artists and makers.

Malt House Barn Gallery *

Only remaining barn of a C17th malting house.
Walton Road, Aylesbury HP21 7SR, tel: 01296 89375
Contact: Frances Mace
Space: 3 galleries
Exhibitions: 2 a year both originated

Details: Barn is small with ancient ship's beams and old brickwork. During exhibitions walled garden and conservatory also used as display areas. Allows work of a diversity of styles to be shown in sympathetic environment. Exhibitions of local and internationally known artists in range of media.

Queen's Park Arts Centre Gallery

 ○ ○○

Exhibition space for new artists.
Queens Park Road, Aylesbury HP21 7RT, tel: 01296 24332
Contact: Mr M.D. Thackwray, Director
Open: Mon & Fri 10-4; Tues-Thurs 10-9; Sat 10-10
Space: 2 galleries with 40 lin m hanging space plus 10 lin m on screens and 50 sq m floor space
Exhibitions: 12 a year all originated
Details: Principally a 'starter' gallery. Space is free, exhibitions selected by fine arts staff for interest, quality, mix and appropriateness. Exhibitions generally four weeks duration, mixed, continuous programme through year. Audience mostly general public, limited sales mainly in lower price range. Educational rather than a commercial gallery. Good space and support/advice for artists early in their exhibiting careers.

Aylsham
NORFOLK   EA

Gallery at Bacon's Bookshop

Pa Pr SC

Local commercial gallery, but artists coming from an increasingly wide area.
17 White Hart Street, Aylsham NR11 6HG, tel: 01263 734240
Contact: Helen Bacon, Partner
Open: Mon-Sat 9-1, 2-5; Wed 9-1
Space: 1 gallery with 15 lin m hanging space and 600 sq m floor space
Exhibitions: 12 a year all originated
Details: All types of work considered but the gallery has not been successful selling abstract paintings. Continuing programme of three-week exhibitions by living artists. Commission is negotiable.

Red Lion Gallery

Pa Ph Pr Cr SC   ○○   ○○

Commercial gallery promoting work by local artists.
Market Place, Aylsham NR11 6EJ. tel: 01263 732115
Contact: Liz Butler, Proprietor
Open: Mon-Sat 9-5
Space: 1 gallery with 63 lin m hanging space plus 6 lin m on screens and 70 sq m floor space

Details: Work by East Anglian artists; watercolours, oils, pastels, prints, sculpture, wood, studio pottery. Resident artist Anthony B. Butler watercolourist – house portraits a speciality.

Bampton
OXFORDSHIRE SA

West Oxfordshire Arts Association Gallery

A Pa Ph Pr Cr SC   ○○   ○

Open plan gallery used primarily to promote work of West Oxfordshire artists.
Bampton Town Hall, Bampton OX18 2JH, tel: 01993 850137
Contact: Sarah Edwards
Open: Tues-Sat 10.30-12.30, 2-4; Sun 2-4; closed between exhibitions
Space: 1 gallery with 20 lin m hanging space plus 10 lin m on screens and 60 sq m floor space
Exhibitions: 10 a year of which 8 originated, 2 on a hire basis
Details: Large single room used to exhibit work by members and non-members. Reduced rate of commission charged on sales by Association members. Audience of local inhabitants and tourists. Classes and workshops organised throughout the year. Sale of work is a priority.

Banbury
OXFORDSHIRE SA

Banbury Museum Gallery

Pa Ph Pr Cr SC   ○○   ○

Small gallery for temporary exhibitions of contemporary arts and crafts.
8 Horse Fair, Banbury OX16 0AA, tel: 01295 259855, fax: 01295 270556
Contact: Vicky Hope-Walker, Arts & Tourism Manager, Cherwell District Council, Bodicote House, Bodicote, Banbury, OX15 4AA, tel: 01295 252535 ext 4348
Open: (April-Sept) daily 9.30-5
Space: 1 gallery with 22 lin m hanging space plus 3 lin m on screens
Details: Diverse exhibitions linked with projects and workshops to increase public access to the work of professional artists and craftspeople. Developing innovative education projects that outreach into the community. Exhibitions include photography, animation, installations and some historically-based exhibitions. Sale of work not gallery's primary function.

Mill Foyer Gallery

Pa Ph Pr Cr SC IA   ○   ○○

Resource for use by local community where development of the arts is seen as a priority.
Mill Arts & Community Education Centre, Spiceball Park, Banbury OX16 8QE, tel: 01295 252050

Contact: Polly Foster, Gallery Co-ordinator
Open: Open most day times and evenings; closed Christmas Day & New Year's Day
Space: 1 gallery with 246 sq m floor space
Exhibitions: 6 a year all originated
Details: Support, encouragement and guidance offered by the staff. Exhibitions last six weeks. Exhibitors encouraged to take part in workshops, talks and demonstrations. Centre also houses meetings of local clubs and societies. Sale of work is primary function of gallery.

Barnard Castle
CO DURHAM NA

Bowes Museum

Pa Ph Pr Cr SC   ○

Museum with fine and decorative arts collections and temporary exhibition programme.
Barnard Castle DL12 8NP, tel: 01833 690606, fax: 01833 37163
Contact: Elizabeth Conran, Curator
Space: 1 gallery with 25 lin m hanging space plus 4 lin m on screens and 85 sq m floor space
Exhibitions: 4 a year all originated
Details: Large collection of European paintings with extensive decorative art collection. Concentrates on fine and decorative arts up to 1900 but exhibitions of C20th art are held. These are regional group exhibitions or solo shows by artists and makers working in Teesdale. Four main exhibitions a year.

Castle Gallery

Pa Ph Cr   ○○

Gallery in busy market town in holiday area available for hire.
Witham Hall, Horsemarket, Barnard Castle
Contact: Mrs J McLean, Secretary, Croft House, Cotherstone, Barnard Castle, DL12 9PB, tel: 01833 650612
Open: (Summer) 10-5; (Winter) 10-4; or at artist's discretion
Space: 1 gallery with 20 lin m hanging space and 33 sq m floor space
Details: Aims to provide low cost selling exhibition space for artists. Non profit making. Also encourages local art clubs and photographic societies and provides free weeks for displays of work from local schools, prisons and youth groups.

Priors

Pa Ph Pr Cr   ○   ○

Shop selling contemporary art and crafts by Northern professional artists and makers.
7 The Bank, Barnard Castle DL12 8PH, tel: 01833 638141
Contact: Mark Prior
Open: Mon-Fri 10-5; Sat 10-5.30; (New

Year-Easter) Sun 12-5, (Easter-New Year)
Sun 12-5.30
Space: 1 gallery
Details: Fronts a popular vegetarian
restaurant with large captive audience.
Retail outlet for professional artists and
craftspeople working in the north of
England. Established clientele from far and
wide, who come to buy contemporary work
in friendly and lively surroundings. Always
keen to see new work.

Barnsley
SOUTH YORKSHIRE YHA

Barnsley Central Library

Pa Ph Cr SE LA ✔ ⊕ ⓖ

*Multi-purpose lecture theatre which can be
adapted for exhibition use.*
**Shambles Street, Barnsley S70 2JF, tel:
01226 773930, fax: 01226 773955**
Contact: Ron Collier
Open: Mon, Wed 9.30-8; Tues, Thurs, Fri
9.30-6; Sat 9.30-5
Space: 4 galleries with 110 lin m hanging
space plus 79 lin m on screens and 355 sq
m floor space
Details: The lecture theatre in the central
library may be hired from Mon-Sat. The
premises may be used for exhibition
purposes or as a theatre with a seating
capacity for 160 persons. Selling work not
considered important.

Cooper Gallery

Pa Ph Cr SE LA ✔ ⓖ

*Five display galleries for touring exhibitions
and selections from permanent collection.*
**Church Street, Barnsley S70 2AH, tel:
01226 242905**
Contact: Mr D Bashforth, Assistant Keeper
Open: Tues-Fri 12.30-4.30; Sat 10-1.30
Space: 5 galleries with 110 lin m hanging
space plus 18 lin m on screens and 256 sq
m floor space
Exhibitions: 7 a year of which 4
originated, 3 touring
Details: Permanent collection with
programme of touring exhibitions of local,
national and international significance.
Encourages work from groups and
individuals with strong element of social
relevance; emphasis on thematic shows.
Exhibitions supplemented by educational
workshops and performances as
appropriate. Programme of chamber
concerts. Sales not a priority. Disabled
access with assistance to ground floor only.

Barrow in Furness
CUMBRIA NA

Dock Museum

Pa Ph Pr Cr SE ✔ ⓖ ⓦ

*Local authority run museum housing
broad-based collections and with varied
temporary exhibition programme.*
**North Road, Barrow in Furness LA14
2PW, tel: 01229 870871**
Contact: Emma Chaplain, Collections
Manager
Open: (Mar-Oct) Tues-Fri 10-5, Sat-Sun
10-6; (Nov-Feb) Wed-Sat 10-4.30
Space: 1 gallery with 2 lin m hanging space
and 20 sq m floor space
Exhibitions: 1 a year originated
Details: Historical and contemporary
shows (fine and applied art) included in
programme with commitment to exhibiting
contemporary work. Complementary range
of educational activities and events
organised. Sales not a priority.

Forum 28

Pa Ph Cr ✔ ⓖ ⓦ

Gallery showing one-person exhibitions.
**28 Duke Street, Barrow in Furness LA14
1HU, tel: 01229 820000, fax: 01229
432289**
Contact: Sue Jenkins, Arts and Museums
Manager, Barrow Borough Council, Town
Hall, Barrow in Furness, LA14 2LD, tel:
01229 842335
Open: Mon-Wed, Fri & Sat 9.30-5; Thurs
10.30-5
Space: 1 gallery with 21 lin m hanging
space
Exhibitions: 6 a year all originated
Details: Work for exhibition is chosen
from within the area and nationally. Shows
last 6 weeks to 2 months.

Barton upon Humber
HUMBERSIDE YHA

Baysgarth House Museum

Pa

*C18th house and park with permanent
displays and changing exhibitions.*
**Baysgarth Park, Caistor Road, Barton
upon Humber DN18 6AH, tel: 01652
632318**
Contact: D. Williams, Curator
Space: 1 gallery with plus 24 lin m on
screens
Exhibitions: 4 a year
Details: Run by Glanford Borough
Council.

Basildon
ESSEX EA

Berlesduna Gallery

Pa Pr SE ✔ ⊕

*Ground floor space in public library which
artists may hire to sell work.*
**Basildon Library, The Basildon Centre,
Pagel Mead, Basildon SS14 1EE, tel:
01268 288533, fax: 01286 286326**
Contact: Sue Facey
Space: 1 gallery with 3 lin m hanging space
Exhibitions: 8 a year all on a hire basis
Details: Usually one/two-person shows.
Exhibitions are chosen on an annual basis
by a selection panel.

Basingstoke
HAMPSHIRE SA

Central Studio and The Street

Pa Ph Pr SE ✔ ⊕

*In sixth-form college arts centre and theatre
showing Southern Arts touring exhibitions
and other temporary exhibitions.*
**Cliddesden Road, Basingstoke RG21
3HF, tel: 01256 20861, fax: 01256
26097**
Contact: Jennie Gettens, Exhibitions
Organiser
Space: 2 galleries with 100 lin m hanging
space and 190 sq m floor space
Exhibitions: 8 a year of which 7
originated, 1 on a hire basis
Details: Shows work by living artists and
makers working in variety of media and
contexts including professionals as well as
amateurs and students. Open to general
public, theatre-goers and sixth-form
students. Close links with local community.
National reputation for theatre and
performance.

Chapel House Gallery

Pa Pr Cr ✔ ⓖ

*Small commercial gallery in converted
methodist chapel selling paintings and
prints by professional artists.*
**Down Street , Dummer, Basingstoke
RG25 2AD, tel: 01256 397295**
Contact: David Dean-Saunders, Director
Open: Mon-Sat 10-1, 2-5
Space: 1 gallery with 27 lin m hanging
space and 33 sq m floor space
Exhibitions: 5 a year all originated
Details: Promotes professional artists not
well known in area. Group and individual
shows. Exhibitions loosely connected with
seasons. Figurative work. Sales good
especially watercolour landscapes/seascapes.
Maximum size 4'x3'. Also gallery shop with
cards, framing.

Willis Museum

Local museum with varied exhibition programme including contemporary and historical art and craft.
Market Place, Basingstoke RG21 1QD, tel: 01256 465902, fax: 01962 869836
Contact: Carol Littlefair, Exhibitions Officer, Hampshire County Council Museums Service, Chilcomb House, Chilcomb Lane, Winchester, SO23 8RD, tel: 01962 846315, fax: 01962 869836
Open: Tues-Fri 10-5; Sat 10-4
Space: 1 gallery with 24 lin m hanging space and 45 sq m floor space
Exhibitions: 8 a year of which 6 originated, 2 touring
Details: See entry for Hampshire County Council Museums, Winchester for policy.

Bath
AVON SWA

Anthony Hepworth Gallery

Privately owned and unfunded gallery specialising in post war and contemporary British art which is for sale.
15 York Street, Bath BA1 1NG, tel: 01225 442917
Contact: Anthony & Rose Hepworth, Proprietors
Open: Tues-Sat 10-5
Space: 2 galleries with 31 lin m hanging space and 56 sq m floor space
Exhibitions: 8 a year all originated
Details: Aims to show variety of work, non-figurative as well as figurative. No definite policy; proprietors select work they like. Sales a priority and commission taken.

Beaux Arts

Commercial gallery dealing in C20th British paintings, sculpture, ceramics.
12/13 York Street, Bath BA1 1NG, tel: 01225 464850, fax: 01225 422256
Contact: Reg and Patricia Singh, Mary Wilkinson
Open: Mon-Sat 10-5
Space: 1 gallery
Exhibitions: 8 a year
Details: Changing stock of work by prominent painters, sculptors and potters plus solo exhibitions by well-known and up-and-coming artists.

Bruton Gallery

35 Gay Street, Queen Square, Bath BA1 2NT, tel: 01225 466292, fax: 01225 461294
Contact: Mrs Sandra Le Marchant, Director, Bruton Gallery, Stockwell House, High Street, Bruton, tel: 01749 812205

Space: 3 galleries with 195 sq m floor space
Exhibitions: 5 a year all originated
Details: Contemporary work by international artists and European figurative sculptors from Rodin to the present. 1 large and 2 formal rooms for exhibitions. Audience drawn from general public as well as international visitors. Also galleries in New York and in Bruton, Somerset.

CCA Galleries (Bath)

One of a network of commercial galleries in South of England specialising in original prints.
5 George Street, Bath BA1 2EH, tel: 01225 448121, fax: 01225 447421
Contact: Alex Murdin
Open: Mon-Sat 9-5.30
Space: 3 galleries with 65 lin m hanging space and 120 sq m floor space
Exhibitions: 12 a year all originated
Details: CCA Galleries is a leading publisher of original limited edition prints with other galleries in London, Farnham, Oxford and Cambridge (see separate entries for these). Each gallery selects its own work. Primary aim is to promote hand-made prints by CCA artists.

F. Stop Gallery & Darkroom

A small public-funded organisation promoting innovative exhibitions and education outreach projects.
Green Park Station, Bath BA1 1JB, tel: 01225 316922, fax: 01225 465135
Contact: Philip Smith, Manager
Open: Tues, Thurs 10-9; Wed, Fri 10-6; Sat 10-6
Space: 1 gallery with 40 lin m hanging space and 80 sq m floor space
Exhibitions: 9 a year of which 6 originated, 3 touring
Details: Exhibits contemporary photographic work including related media (video, electronic imagery, installation work) on a continuous basis, promoting the work of young and emerging artists. Exhibitions are supported by talks and workshops, and an outreach programme that includes educational events and touring exhibitions. Sales not a priority.

Hitchcocks'

Commercial gallery above craft shop showing high-quality craftwork by contemporary makers.
10 Chapel Row, Off Queens Square, Bath BA1 1HN, tel: 01225 330646
Contact: Fleur Hitchcock
Open: Mon-Sat 10-5.30
Space: 3 galleries
Exhibitions: 4 a year

Details: Varied programme of thematic and group exhibitions. (See entry for Hitchcocks', Alresford.) Exhibition artists by invitation only.

Holburne Museum & Crafts Study Centre

Collection of C20th arts and crafts with additional temporary exhibition programme.
Great Pulteney Street, Bath BA2 4DB, tel: 01225 466669
Contact: Barley Roscoe, Curator
Open: Mon-Sat 11-5; Sun 2.30-5.30; closed mid-Dec – mid-Feb & Mon Nov-Easter
Space: 84 lin m hanging space and 151 sq m floor space
Exhibitions: 3 a year of which 2 touring, 1 on a hire basis
Details: Contains work by C20th artists/craftspeople in textiles, ceramics, calligraphy and wood, together with the fine and decorative art collections of Sir Thomas William Holburne. Exhibition programme complements these areas attracting a wide audience including students, children, craftspeople, specialists and senior citizens. Temporary exhibition area is without natural daylight. Some display cases available.

Hotbath Gallery

College and community resource displaying contemporary visual arts encompassing student shows and artists of international stature.
City of Bath College, Avon Street, Bath BA1 1UP, tel: 01225 312191
Contact: Bob Briggs, Deputy Head of School, Creative & Performing Arts
Open: Mon-Sat 10-4
Space: 3 galleries with 75 lin m hanging space and 262 sq m floor space
Exhibitions: 3 a year all originated
Details: Gallery opened1994; plans to show 12-15 exhibitions a year. Broad programme with associated educational activities and events. It is intended to develop gallery as focus for the arts in the community as well as the college with informal café area and sales point. Sales not priority but welcomed; 30% commission taken.

Once a Tree Gallery

Exhibition space on first floor above shop available for hire to selected exhibitors.
5 Saracen Street, Bath BA1 5BR, tel: 01225 442680
Contact: Ruth Evans, Manager
Open: Mon-Sat 9.30-5.30
Space: 1 gallery with 14 lin m hanging space

Exhibitions: 2 a year both on a hire basis
Details: Shop is part of group that promotes forest sustainability and products sold, wooden gift items, reflect this. Exhibitors in gallery would be required to reinforce this environmental practice. Display areas in gallery in addition to hanging space.

Peter Hayes Contemporary Art

Commercial gallery with working studio.
2 Cleveland Bridge, Bath BA1 5DH, tel: 01225 466215
Contact: Peter Hayes, Exhibition Organiser
Space: 2 galleries with plus 15 lin m on screens and 450 sq m floor space
Exhibitions: 4 a year all originated

Rooksmoor Gallery

Selling gallery on two floors with mostly one-person shows by gallery artists; also ceramics and ceramic sculpture.
31 Brock Street, Bath BA1 2LN, tel: 01225 420495
Contact: Connie Herring, Owner
Open: Mon-Sat 10-5.30
Space: 3 galleries with 30 lin m hanging space and 60 sq m floor space
Exhibitions: 8 a year all originated
Details: All work shown by living artists with clearly-developed personal style. Shelves and display cabinets for ceramics and sculptures.

RPS National Centre of Photography

Headquarters of the Royal Photographic Society.
Milsom Street, Bath BA1 1DN, tel: 01225 462841, fax: 01225 448688
Contact: Carole Sartain, Exhibition Officer
Space: 6 galleries
Exhibitions: 23 a year
Details: Permanent collection of mainly C19th work, plus temporary exhibitions of contemporary greats, classical solo shows, touring exhibitions from major galleries, historical, theme/educational and young photographers. Programme of talks, lectures, films and workshops. Darkroom facilities available.

Sladebrook House

Gallery shows exhibitions from home and abroad as well as permanent display of prints and paintings of resident artist.
222 Englishcombe Lane, Bath BA2 2EP, tel: 01225 420160
Contact: Wendy Trentham
Open: Daily; for details please ring

Space: 3 galleries with 50 lin m hanging space and 55 sq m floor space
Exhibitions: 2 a year both originated
Details: A country house gallery showing mainly figurative work. Includes print studio of resident artist John Trentham. Ample parking and on bus routes from city centre. Sales a priority.

St James's Gallery

Commercial art and crafts gallery.
9B Margarets Buildings, Bath BA1 2LP, tel: 01225 319197
Contact: Mr R.E. Sloman, Owner
Open: Mon-Sat 10-5.30
Space: 2 galleries with 20 lin m hanging space and 50 sq m floor space
Exhibitions: 3 a year all originated
Details: Three group exhibitions a year with a changing display of work. Stocks a large range of contemporary ceramics, handmade jewellery and paintings by chosen artists.

Six Chapel Row Contemporary Art

Commercial gallery specialising in contemporary fine art and applied arts.
6 Chapel Row, Bath BA1 1HN, tel: 01225 337900, fax: 01225 336577
Contact: Josie Reed
Details: Programme of group exhibitions which show similar concerns of artists working in different media.

Underground Gallery *

Gallery occasionally shows young local artists and craft makers.
72-74 Walcot Street, Bath BA1 5BD, tel: 01225 448265, fax: 01225 774138
Contact: Mickey Houston, Director
Space: 3 galleries with 30 lin m hanging space and 50 sq m floor space
Exhibitions: 4 a year all originated

Victoria Art Gallery

City art gallery with major touring exhibitions, together with shows by contemporary artists of the South West.
Bridge Street, Bath BA2 4AT, tel: 01225 477772, fax: 01225 477231
Contact: Mrs Victoria Barwell, Arts Officer
Open: Mon-Fri 10-5.30; Sat 10-5; closed B/H
Space: 2 galleries with 92 lin m hanging space plus 29 lin m on screens and 220 sq m floor space
Exhibitions: 8 a year of which 2 originated, 6 touring
Details: Displays from permanent collection of C17– C20th British and European art. The larger of the two

temporary exhibition galleries houses large scale touring exhibitions and the smaller gallery is devoted to work by contemporary artists, predominantly of the South West region. Not available for hire. Admission free. Lectures and workshops organised alongside exhibitions including workshops for children and adults with special needs. Sales not a priority.

Batley
WEST YORKSHIRE YHA

Bagshaw Museum

Venue for local artists and craftspeople providing comparisons with permanent collections which may also be inspiration for works of art.
Wilton Park, Batley WF17 0AS, tel: 01924 472514, fax: 01924 420017
Contact: Brian Haigh, Senior Museums Officer
Open: Mon-Fri 11-5; Sat & Sun 12-5
Space: 1 gallery with 30 lin m hanging space plus 20 lin m on screens and 70 sq m floor space
Exhibitions: 1 a year originated
Details: Collections of ethnography, Egyptology, oriental, fine and decorative arts and natural history. Two galleries for temporary exhibitions drawn from collections and occasional exhibitions by contemporary artists. Lectures, demonstrations, craft workshops and general educational activities. Sales not a priority.

Batley Art Gallery

Town centre art gallery featuring wide range of contemporary art exhibitions in all media, from local and regional artists.
Market Place, Batley WF17 5DA, tel: 01924 423205, fax: 01924 477375
Contact: Helen Robinson, Galleries Officer, Kirklees Cultural Services
Open: Mon, Wed, Fri 10-6; Tues 10-1; Thurs 10-5; Sat 10-4
Space: 1 gallery with 40 lin m hanging space and 100 sq m floor space
Exhibitions: 10 a year of which 7 originated, 3 touring
Details: Exhibitions vary from local, regional and some national artists. Solo and group shows in all media, art, craft and photography. Education programme organised to complement displays. Promotes all forms of visual art to help create better understanding of contemporary art. Applications particularly welcomed from black and women artists. Sales not a priority. Lift proposed for 1995 will enable full access.

Battle
EAST SUSSEX SEA

Davies Bailey Gallery

12-13 High Street, Battle TN33 0AE, tel:
01424 772477, fax: 01424 775327

Beaminster
DORSET SWA

Parnham House

Pa Ph Cr Sc LA ● ● Wc 4

*An historic venue for displays of
contemporary art, craftwork in wood,
textiles and ceramics.*
Beaminster DT8 3NA, tel: 01308
862204, fax: 01308 863494
Contact: Bruce Hunter-Inglis, House
Manager
Open: (April-Oct) Wed, Sun & BH 10-5
Space: 2 galleries with 31 lin m hanging
space plus 4 lin m on screens and 122 sq m
floor space
Exhibitions: 6 a year all originated
Details: Elizabethan Manor house, restored
and devoted to displaying work by British
contemporary artists and makers. Two
main spaces in the drawing room and Great
Hall. Other rooms and garden can stage
special events and shows. For the most part,
floor space used to display modern
furniture in wood. Craft shop sells work
chosen from Chelsea Craft Fair. Selling
work is gallery's primary role.

Bedford
BEDFORDSHIRE EA

Bedford Central Library Gallery

Pa Ph Pr Cr Sc ●

*Temporary exhibitions covering all aspects
of visual arts in dedicated exhibition space
on first floor of library.*
Harpur Street, Bedford MK40 1PG, tel:
01234 350931, fax: 01234 342163
Contact: County Arts Officer, South and
Luton, Bedfordshire County Council
Leisure Services, Luton Central Library, St
Georges Square, Luton, LU1 2NG, tel:
01582 30161 ext 217
Open: Mon-Fri 9.30-7; Sat 9.30-4
Space: 1 gallery with 27 lin m hanging
space and 330 sq m floor space
Exhibitions: 16 a year of which 11
originated, 5 touring
Details: Gallery in public library which has
an average of 45,000 visitors per month.
International and national artists exhibited,
as well as artists resident in the county.
Provides opportunity for work of artist or
group of artists resident in County to tour
libraries in Bedfordshire.

Bedford Museum

Pa Ph Pr Cr Sc ● ● ● Wc

*Ground-floor gallery offers space for
temporary exhibitions, mainly museum
related topics but also a few contemporary
art.*
Castle Lane, Bedford MK40 3XD, tel:
01234 353323, fax: 01234 214599
Contact: General Office
Space: 1 gallery with 20 lin m hanging
space plus 11 lin m on screens and 40 sq m
floor space
Exhibitions: 2 a year both originated
Details: General interest in topographical
art but full programme means confirmed
space for only 2 contemporary shows a
year. (Some possibility of occasional shows
in spare time.) Artists welcome to apply if
they feel their work comes within bounds
of Museum's subject areas. Sales not a
priority.

Bromham Mill Gallery

Pa Ph Pr Cr ● ● ●

*Small-first floor gallery offering varied
programme of monthly exhibitions
particularly from young non-commercial
artists from region.*
Bromham Mill, Bridgend, Bromham,
Bedford, tel: 01234 824330
Contact: Sally Wileman, Visitor Services
Manager, Bedfordshire County Council,
Cauldwell Street, Bedford, MK42 9AP, tel:
01234 228330, fax: 01234 228921
Open: Wed-Fri 10.30-4.30; Sat-Sun & BH
11.30-6.00
Space: 1 gallery with 20 lin m hanging
space and 43 sq m floor space
Exhibitions: 7 a year of which 1
originated, 6 on a hire basis
Details: Owned by Bedfordshire County
Council, situated within working watermill.
Favours younger professional artists from
Bedfordshire and surrounding counties.
High proportion women artists, work
shown very varied, try not to play too safe.
Audience local but expanding. Craft
cabinets on ground floor carry work from
Crafts Council gallery. Exhibition/sale
facilities developed in conjunction with
Eastern Arts Board. Workshops,
demonstrations & talks. Sales not high
priority. Chair lift is planned to make
gallery fully accessible. Where space is hired
out this is on commission only basis.

Community Arts in Bedford

Pa Ph Pr Cr Sc LA ● ● Wc 4

*Exhibition space in busy meeting room used
by people attending workshops and courses.*
The Gatehouse, Foster Hill Road,
Bedford MK41 7TD, tel: 01234 355870,
fax: 01234 212388
Contact: Gilly Love, Community Arts
Development Officer
Open: Mon-Thurs 9-4; Fri 9-12.30

Space: 1 gallery with 30 lin m hanging
space and 28 sq m floor space
Exhibitions: 3 a year all originated
Details: Artists can utilise this exhibition
space, usually for small scale craft and
photography. Open to approaches from
local artists working in other media. Sale of
work not gallery's primary role.

Belper
NOTTINGHAMSHIRE EMA

Fleet Arts Project

Pa Ph Pr ● ● ● Wc

*Community arts project offering a variety
of art activities and projects including
exhibitions.*
The Old School, The Fleet, Belper DE56
1NU, tel: 01773 820484
Contact: Sarah Laman, Coordinator
Space: 1 gallery with 21 lin m hanging
space
Exhibitions: 6 a year of which 3
originated, 3 on a hire basis
Details: Exhibitions either an integral part
of the project programme, of particular
local community interest or an opportunity
to local artists who would not otherwise
exhibit.

Berwick upon Tweed
NORTHUMBERLAND NA

Berwick Borough Museum & Art Gallery

Pa Ph Pr Cr Sc LA ● ● Wc

*Display space in museum for contemporary
and historical arts and science.*
Barracks, Ravensdowne, Berwick upon
Tweed TD15 1DQ, tel: 01289 330933,
fax: 01289 330540
Contact: Chris Green, Curator
Open: (Apr-Nov) daily 10-6; (Nov-Apr)
Wed-Sun 10-4
Space: 2 galleries with plus 89 lin m on
screens and 240 sq m floor space
Exhibitions: 6 a year of which 2
originated, 4 touring
Details: Two adjoining clear spaces,
flexible hanging and lighting, enable the
Museum to create either traditional 'white
wall' gallery space or more intricate
patterns. Additional area of fixed screens on
an upper floor sometimes used in the
winter. All art styles welcomed. Borough
Museum is one of three on the same site.
An entrance charge is made by English
Heritage.

Berwick Gymnasium

Pa Pr Cr Sc ● ●

*A new gallery used as a studio for 6 months
each winter and as a temporary exhibition
venue in the summer months.*
The Barracks, Berwick upon Tweed, tel:
01289 330933, fax: 01289 330540

Contact: Visual Art Project Officer, Central Library, The Willows, Morpeth, NE61 1TA
Open: (April-Sept) Tues-Sun 11-5
Space: 1 gallery with 76 lin m hanging space and 279 sq m floor space
Exhibitions: 3 a year all originated
Details: Each winter the venue is used as a studio by the artist holding the Berwick Gymnasium Fellowship. An exhibition of work resulting from this fellowship forms one exhibition, the other two exhibitions are initiated by the gallery's steering group, by invitation only. Sale of work is not the gallery's primary function.

Sallyport Gallery

Pa Pr ● &

A commercial gallery with one room set aside for suggested exhibitions.
48 Bridge Street, Berwick upon Tweed TD15 1AQ, tel: 01289 307749
Contact: Derek Jones, Director
Open: (Winter) Mon-Wed, Fri & Sat 10-5; (Summer) Mon-Wed, Fri & Sat 10-5, Thurs 10-1
Space: 1 gallery with 11 lin m hanging space
Exhibitions: 4 a year all originated
Details: Gallery that has not had separate shows for some years but 'merged' invited artists' work into permanent display. Now has small room available for shows; small works about colour, figure with interest also in printmaking. Nature of building makes wheelchair access difficult.

Three Feathers Gallery

Pa Ph Pr Cr Sc ●

Commercial gallery showing local professional artists.
83c Mary Gate, Berwick upon Tweed TD15 1BA, tel: 01289 307642
Contact: Brian Martin, Owner
Open: Mon-Wed, Fri & Sat 9-5; Thurs 9-12
Space: 2 galleries with 20 lin m hanging space
Exhibitions: 1 a year originated
Details: Has built up a mailing list of over 500.

Windmill Hole Studio

Pa Ph Pr Cr Sc &

Gallery's main purpose is to increase public awareness and appreciation of modern and especially abstract art.
9 Railway Street, Berwick upon Tweed TD15 1NF, tel: 01289 307135
Contact: Inger Lawrance
Open: Tues & Fri 11-4; Sat for special exhibition 10-1; other times by appointment
Space: 2 galleries with 12 lin m hanging space and 16 sq m floor space
Exhibitions: 3 a year all originated
Details: Gallery in entrance hall and downstairs room. Walled-in court for outdoor sculpture. Concentrates on showing abstract art by mainly Northern contemporary artists. About 3 special exhibitions a year by one or two artists, each 6-8 weeks (by invitation only). Member of Northern Arts purchase plan. 20% commission, no VAT. Gallery pays for private view , advertising and insurance. Occasional printmaking demonstrations in print workshop. Sales are important to the gallery.

Beverley
HUMBERSIDE YHA

Beverley Art Gallery & Museum *

Pa Pr Cr Sc ● H

Shows contemporary exhibitions alongside work by schools, local artists and loan exhibitions.
Champney Road, Beverley HU17 9BQ, tel: 01482 882255, fax: 01482 883913
Contact: Miss Nicholson, Exhibition Organiser, Beverley Borough Council, The Hall, Lairgate, Beverley, HU17 8HL
Space: 1 gallery
Exhibitions: 6 a year of which 2 originated, 4 on a hire basis

Bexhill on Sea
EAST SUSSEX SEA

De La Warr Pavilion

Marina, Bexhill on Sea TN40 1DP, tel: 01424 212023

Bexley
KENT SEA

Hall Place

Pa Ph Pr Cr Sc ● &

Great Hall of Tudor house used for various exhibitions.
Bourne Road, Bexley DA5 1PQ, tel: 01322 526 574, fax: 01322 522921
Contact: Lilian Booker, Exhibitions Officer
Open: (GMT) Mon-Sat 10-dusk; (BST) Mon-Sat 10-5; every Sun & BH 2-6
Space: 1 gallery with 78 sq m floor space
Exhibitions: 8 a year of which 2 originated, 6 touring
Details: Hall Place is administered by Bexley Libraries and Museums Department and presents a varied programme of visual arts and crafts exhibitions, normally shown for three to six weeks. Some exhibitions targeted towards particular groups of children or schools, most are for the general public. Sales not a priority.

Bideford
DEVON SWA

Appledore Crafts Company

Pa Ph Cr Sc ●

A gallery run co-operatively by craftworkers in North Devon to display and sell their work.
5 Bude Street, Appledore, Bideford, tel: 01237 423547
Contact: Penny Lucraft
Open: (Apr-Oct) Daily 10-6; (Nov-Mar) Wed-Sat 10-4
Space: 3 galleries with 21 lin m hanging space and 35 sq m floor space
Exhibitions: 2 a year both originated
Details: Gallery sells craftwork, including furniture, by its members. Accepts commissions from customers. Work is accepted from associate members and sold on commission basis.

Appledore Gallery

Pa Cr Sc ● & 4

Small commercial gallery specialising in local watercolours, batiks, pottery, jewellery, etc.
31 Bude Street, Appledore, Bideford EX39 1PS, tel: 01237 476729
Contact: Mrs Heather Sedge
Open: Mon-Sat 10-1, 2-5
Space: 1 gallery with 15 lin m hanging space and 6 sq m floor space
Exhibitions: 4 a year all originated
Details: Sales are considered a priority and a commission is taken on works sold.

Burton Art Gallery & Museum

Pa Ph Pr Cr Sc ● H & W

Three temporary exhibition galleries and workshop within museum with permanent collection.
Kingsley Road, Bideford EX39 2QQ, tel: 01237 471455
Contact: Emma Bond, Museums Officer
Open: Tues-Sat 10-4; Sun 2-4
Space: 3 galleries with 160 lin m hanging space and 311 sq m floor space
Exhibitions: 11 a year of which 6 originated, 5 touring
Details: Varied exhibition programme balanced between travelling exhibitions and originated shows of individual artists' work. Workshops, lectures and educational activities. Craft gallery.

Gallerie Marin

Pa ⊘

Gallery selling marine art, landscapes and seascapes by well-known artists.
31 Market Street, Appledore, Bideford EX39 1PP, tel: 01237 473679/01237 472576
Contact: Audrey Hinks, Proprietor

Open: Mon-Sat 10.30-12 & 2-4 (4.30 in summer); Sun by appointment
Space: 56 lin m hanging space and 56 sq m floor space
Exhibitions: 2 a year both originated
Details: Gallery specialises in marine art. Exhibition costs paid by gallery.

Billingham
CLEVELAND NA

Billingham Art Gallery

Venue for temporary and travelling exhibitions, mostly art, craft and local history.
Queens Way, Billingham TS23 2LN, tel: 01642 555443, fax: 01642 616315
Contact: Mrs Jones, Gallery Manager
Open: Mon-Sat 9-5; closed BH
Space: 2 galleries with 64 lin m hanging space plus 63 lin m on screens and 264 sq m floor space
Exhibitions: 15 a year of which 14 originated, 1 touring
Details: Programme of changing exhibitions, each lasting 2-5 weeks. Provides mixed media exhibition programme featuring work from local area, national and international touring exhibitions. School and educational displays. Workshops based on exhibitions of particular interest to schools and art students. Talks by exhibiting artists. Art Society meetings, lectures, craft fairs. Sales not primary role of gallery.

Bilston
WEST MIDLANDS WMA

Bilston Museum & Art Gallery

Operated by Wolverhampton Museum and Art Gallery showing mainly local and regional artists and makers.
Mount Pleasant, Bilston WV14 7LU, tel: 01902 409143
Contact: Arts Development Officer
Open: Mon-Thurs 10-5; Sat 10-4
Space: 1 gallery with 75 lin m hanging space and 50 sq m floor space
Exhibitions: 3 a year all originated
Details: The space is reputably one of the best in West Midlands and houses a permanent collection of C19th enamels.

Bingley
WEST YORKSHIRE YHA

Bingley Arts Centre

Gallery available for hire to artists or groups wishing to put on shows.

Main Street, Bingley BD16 2LZ, tel: 01274 751576
Contact: Manager
Details: Founded to provide local venue for mounting shows and exhibitions.

Bingley Library

Two exhibition spaces in library primarily for local artists to exhibit their talents and for promotion of organisations.
Myrtle Walk, Bingley BD16 1AW, tel: 01274 758780
Contact: Mrs P Booth, Supervisor
Open: Mon 9.30-7; Wed-Fri 9-7; Sat 9-5
Space: 2 galleries with 35 lin m hanging space and 49 sq m floor space
Exhibitions: 40 a year
Details: Hanging space suitable for 2D work with cases for crafts. Source of inspiration and interest for the public. Mixed and solo exhibitions. Selling work not main aim of gallery.

Birkenhead
MERSEYSIDE NWA

Birkenhead Central Library

Exhibition space in library for work of local painters and craftspeople.
Borough Road, Birkenhead L41 2XB, tel: 0151 652 6106, fax: 0151 653 7320
Contact: L.J. Sharp, Senior Librarian
Space: 5 lin m hanging space plus 29 lin m on screens and 55 sq m floor space
Exhibitions: 4 a year of which 2 touring, 2 on a hire basis
Details: Marler Hayley 6' x 4' exhibition boards with cases and also 2 exhibition glass cases approx 6' x 4' x 3'. Operated by Wirral Borough Council Department of Leisure (see separate entry).

Williamson Art Gallery & Museum

Municipal gallery with mostly local based programme.
Slatey Road, Birkenhead L43 4UE, tel: 0151 652 4177
Contact: Colin Simpson, Curator
Open: Tues-Sat 10-5; Sun 2-5
Space: 4 galleries with 130 lin m hanging space and 366 sq m floor space
Exhibitions: 10 a year of which 7 originated, 3 touring
Details: Traditional purpose-built gallery with mixed collections. 1 or 2 solo shows a year. 90% of visitors from Merseyside. Programme is run on small budget and is accessory to policy of providing for the local public, both visitors and artists.

Wirral Borough Council Department of Leisure *

Wirral Libraries bring in exhibitions from Merseyside Exhibitions and North West Museum and Art Gallery Service to tour libraries with occasional self-generated shows.
Westminster House, Hamilton Street, Birkenhead L41 5FN, tel: 0151 647 2366, fax: 0151 666 1343
Contact: Ian Coles, Assistant Director Libraries & Arts
Details: Branch libraries at Bromborough, Eastham, Greasby, Heswell, Hoylake, Moreton, Rock Ferry, Seacombe, St James, Upton, West Kirby and Wallasey Central Library, Bebington Central Library and Birkenhead Central Library all have temporary exhibition space and are part of the touring network. (See also entry for Birkenhead Central Library).

Birmingham
WEST MIDLANDS WMA

Angle Gallery

Anti-censorship art space showing work which might not otherwise be seen and giving new artists, photographers and performers first opportunity to exhibit.
Dakota Buildings, James Street, off St Paul's Square, Birmingham B3 1SD, tel: 0121 233 9260, fax: 0121 233 9275
Contact: Ceri Dingle, Co-ordinator
Open: Mon-Sat 11-7
Space: 5 galleries with 108 lin m hanging space and 558 sq m floor space
Exhibitions: 14 a year all originated
Details: Gallery committed to equal rights for all and opposed to all forms of censorship. Staffed by artists and volunteers and funded mostly by denotations. All five galleries comprise flexible exhibiting space. Seminars, films and round table discussions often accompany shows. Café and artshop for sale of work. Gallery is also available for hire.

Birmingham Centre for Media Arts

Temporary exhibition space within resource centre for photographers, film and video makers, and animators.
Trade Union Resource Centre, Victoria Works, 7 Frederick Street, Birmingham B1 3HE, tel: 0121 233 4061, fax: 0121 212 1784
Contact: Nicky Edmonds, Director
Open: Mon, Wed & Thurs 10-9; Tues & Fri 10-6
Exhibitions: 1 a year
Details: Walls and boards in exhibition space within centre made available for

occasional exhibitions. Boards and frames for hire. Exhibitions also organised at other venues of work by centre users. Sales not a priority.

Birmingham & Midland Institute

Display areas are ancillary to the activities of a busy cultural centre and consist of wall space in reception and mezzanine floor.
Margaret Street, Birmingham B3 3BS, tel: 0121 236 3591
Contact: Mr Philip Fisher, Administrator
Open: Mon-Fri 9.30-6.30
Space: 2 galleries with 50 lin m hanging space plus 30 lin m on screens
Exhibitions: 30 a year of which 10 originated, 2 touring, 18 on a hire basis
Details: Offered free of charge but commission of 15% taken. Encourages young artists by giving them an opportunity to advertise their talents. Display areas staffed and building protected by alarm system.

Birmingham Museum & Art Gallery

Two temporary exhibition spaces; Gas Hall and gallery adjoining Museum and Art Gallery.
Chamberlain Square, Birmingham B3 3DH, tel: 0121 235 2834, fax: 0121 236 6227
Contact: Exhibition & Display Officer
Open: Mon-Sat 10-5; Sun 12.30-5
Space: 2 galleries with 1250 sq m floor space
Exhibitions: 11 a year
Details: Victorian museum/gallery with extensive collections of archaeological, historical, natural, fine and applied art material. Audience of about 500-700,000 p.a. from broad cross-section of the population. Programme aims to broaden access to all cultural and social groups. Contemporary art/craft takes between 20-30% exhibition slots. Gas Hall designed to take large, flexible multi-media shows including occasional contemporary art exhibitions while technical and spatial flexibility of smaller space is limited. Admission charge to Gas Hall. Sales not a priority.

Birmingham University (Winterbourne House)

Space in foyer of Department of Education and Continuing Studies showing mainly work by West Midlands artists and makers.
School of Continuing Studies, 58 Edgbaston Park Road, University of Birmingham, Birmingham B15 2TT, tel: 0121 414 5613

Contact: Dianne Barre, Exhibition Organiser
Open: (Term-time) Mon-Thurs 9-9; Fri 9-5
Space: 1 gallery with 12 lin m hanging space
Exhibitions: 6 a year all originated
Details: Two exhibitions held each term, usually solo exhibitions. Open to public as well as those at the university. Sales not a priority.

Bond Gallery

Two galleries with lobby and exterior covered space for live art with funded programme for Midland artists.
180-182 Fazeley Street, Digbeth, Birmingham B55 SE, tel: 0121 753 2065, fax: 0121 766 8744
Contact: Exhibition Organiser
Open: Tues-Fri 10.30-5.30; Sat 10.30-4
Space: 2 galleries with 69 lin m hanging space and 74 sq m floor space
Exhibitions: 16 a year of which 6 originated, 10 on a hire basis
Details: Gallery which holds a variety of exhibitions including student degree shows. One main gallery and a smaller space for overspill. New covered outdoor space for live art, installation and performance. Sales not gallery's primary function. Exhibition fee paid to artists in gallery-funded shows only.

Cave (The) *

Multi-purpose art centre, concentrating on art from South Asia, Africa and the Caribbean.
516 Moseley Road, Balsall Heath, Birmingham B12 9AH, tel: 0121 440 0288/ 03881, fax: 0121 440 3742
Contact: Ms H. McIntosh, Director
Space: 1 gallery with 24 lin m hanging space and 92 sq m floor space
Exhibitions: 2 a year both originated
Details: Performances in drama, dance, music, and poetry as well as exhibitions

Craftspace Touring

Custard Factory, Gibb Street, Digbeth, Birmingham B9 4AA, tel: 0121 608 6668

Custard Factory

Exhibition space showing innovative work by young artists.
Gibb Street, Digbeth, Birmingham B9 4AA, tel: 0121 604 7777, fax: 0121 604 8888
Contact: Ruth Thomas-Roe, Director of Marketing & Events
Open: Daily 10-10
Space: 2 galleries with 558 sq m floor space
Exhibitions: 24 a year all originated
Details: Provides platform for grass roots

artists in all disciplines. One-person and group exhibitions. Degree shows held in effort to encourage London gallery visitors to travel to Birmingham as well as using space as alternative venue. Sales not priority.

Helios Gallery *

Exhibits and sells contemporary work from local and regional sources.
25 Valentine Road, Kings Heath, Birmingham B14 7AN, tel: 0121 444 1585
Contact: John Palmer, Exhibitions Organiser
Exhibitions: 5 a year all originated
Details: Programme of exhibitions throughout the year. Exhibitions mostly by local artists. Framing service.

Ikon Gallery

Ikon Gallery promotes the work of living artists from the UK and abroad, within a context of debate and participation.
58-72 John Bright Street, Birmingham B1 1BN, tel: 0121 643 0708, fax: 0121 643 2254
Contact: Elizabeth A. MacGregor, Director
Open: Tues-Wed & Fri-Sat 11-6; Thurs 11-8
Space: 2 galleries with 133 lin m hanging space plus 40 lin m on screens and 540 sq m floor space
Exhibitions: 13 a year of which 9 originated, 4 touring
Details: Promotes the work of contemporary artists through exhibitions and other activities which facilitate contact between artists and public. Has no permanent collection. Exhibitions include a wide variety of work from Britain and abroad including painting, sculpture, photography, film, video and performance. Touring shows available. Runs comprehensive in house and outreach education programme and regional touring exhibitions service. Sales not a priority.

mac

Arts centre housing exhibition spaces, theatres, cinema, studios, bar and restaurant, and offering broad programme of presentation and participation to general public.
Cannon Hill Park, Birmingham B12 9QH, tel: 0121 440 4221, fax: 0121 446 4372
Contact: Judy Dames, Exhibitions Programmer
Open: Main galleries, daily 12-8; other gallery spaces, daily 9am-10pm
Space: 6 galleries with 194 lin m hanging space and 205 sq m floor space

Exhibitions: 38 a year of which 20 originated, 18 touring
Details: Fine art, photography and craft form equal components of programme. Shows work of both established artists and those in early stages of a promising career. Relates exhibitions to events in MAC and with regional and national festivals. Workshops, lectures and occasional residencies support exhibitions programme. Only one space does not have disabled access. Sales not primary role.

Mill Gallery

Exhibition space broken by panels and columns housing permanent work, prints and mirrors.
580 Pershore Road, Selly Park, Birmingham B29 7EN, tel: 0121 4141005
Contact: Steve Maddox, Proprietor
Open: Mon, Tues, Thurs-Sat 9.30-5.30
Space: 1 gallery with 21 lin m hanging space plus 1484 lin m on screens and 42 sq m floor space
Exhibitions: 7 a year of which 6 originated, 1 touring
Details: Gallery selects artists for sales potential, quality and interest. Catalogues produced to help visitors view work. Frames may be available if necessary for promising artists. Gallery may be available for hire. Sales of work not primary function.

Photopack

Sets up and manages partnerships which bring people and photography together in a range of educations settings (formerly called Building Sights).
Custard Factory 1, Gibb Street, Digbeth, Birmingham B9 4AA, tel: 0121 608 7006
Contact: Su Richardson, Director, Building Sights
Space: 1 gallery with 10 lin m hanging space plus 5 lin m on screens
Exhibitions: 6 a year of which 1 originated, 5 touring
Details: Manages photography commission, placements and projects in community/educational settings; acts as advisory and networking agency to community and educational organisations; developes innovative approaches to photography education and photography in community settings, as models of good practice; disseminates information and resources around photography and education.

Picture Palace *

Mainly photography, both contemporary and 'past'. Concerned with innovation and anti-racist and anti-sexist work.
Balsall Heath Library, 497 Moseley Road, Birmingham B12 9BX, tel: 0121 440 1962, fax: 0121 446 4149
Contact: Su Richardson
Space: 1 gallery with 8 lin m hanging space
Exhibitions: 12 a year of which 11 originated, 1 touring
Details: Well-lit space in a beautiful C19th library. Jointly run by Building Sights Photography Project and Birmingham Library Services. Aims to develop community education through programme of issue-based exhibitions and events targeted at all sections of local community.

Royal Birmingham Society of Artists

Gallery run by the society for its members and available for hire.
69a New Street, Birmingham B2 4DU, tel: 0121 643 3768
Contact: Brian Singler, RBSA, Secretary, RBSA
Open: Mon-Sat 10.30-5
Space: 3 galleries with 500 sq m floor space
Exhibitions: 7 a year of which 4 originated, 3 on a hire basis
Details: Varied yearly programme of society exhibitions, shows by individuals and two open exhibitions a year (March/June). Applications to submit welcome. Talks, seminars, demonstrations and trips organised. Sale of work not gallery's primary function.

Sutton Coldfield Town Hall

Multi-purpose facility for hire.
Upper Clifton Road, Sutton Coldfield, Birmingham B23 6DR, tel: 0121 355 8990, fax: 0121 355 8255
Contact: Lynette Skinner, Manager
Open: flexible, on request.
Exhibitions: 12 a year all on a hire basis
Details: Venue for hire to artists and others for exhibitions/events. All aspects of exhibition to be organised by hirer.

Woodbridge Gallery

Two linked rooms in converted Victorian school offering exhibition space to local artists/makers and groups.
47 Woodbridge Road, Moseley, Birmingham B13 9DZ, tel: 0121 449 0123
Contact: Liz Williams, Owner/Director
Open: (During exhibitions only) Mon-Fri 10-6, Sun 2-6

Space: 2 galleries with 40 lin m hanging space and 84 sq m floor space
Exhibitions: 6 a year of which 2 originated, 4 on a hire basis
Details: Gallery aims to provide good-quality exhibition space at low cost for benefit of local artists and local community. In addition to 6 exhibitions per year, gallery also hosts annual craft fair. Sales a priority. Artists pay for private view and publicity. Access for wheelchair users with assistance to lower gallery only.

Wythall Library

Small library in lively community with purpose-built exhibition space in square room.
May Lane, Hollywood, Birmingham B47 5PD, tel: 01564 822980
Contact: Mrs L Downes, Librarian
Open: Mon, Wed, Fri 10-1, 2-5.30; Tues 2-8; Sat 10-1, 2-4
Space: 1 gallery with 37 sq m floor space
Exhibitions: 17 a year of which 3 touring, 14 on a hire basis
Details: Presents varied selection of exhibitions, appealing to wide audience, aiming to attract local community towards art in general. Reflects local talents and interests, but not exclusively. Heavily booked. 20% commission on sales + VAT. Hire fee £10 for individuals, £25 for group.

Bishop Auckland
CO DURHAM NA

Bishop Auckland Town Hall

Run by Durham County Council's Arts, Libraries and Museums Department, the programme includes exhibitions from artists with a regional and national reputation.
Market Place, Bishop Auckland DL14 7NP, tel: 01388 604922, fax: 01388 604960
Contact: Gillian Wales, Centre Manager
Open: Mon-Fri 10-7; Sat 9-4
Space: 1 gallery with 19 lin m hanging space plus 18 lin m on screens
Exhibitions: 12 a year
Details: Gallery opened 1994. Aims to establish reputation as secure venue for exhibitions of particular interest to visitors and local residents. Plans to hold 12 exhibitions a year including textiles, illustration, ethnography, architecture and natural history. Hopes to host artist in residence schemes.

Bishop's Castle
SHROPSHIRE WMA

Longhouse Gallery

Small commercial gallery bringing art into Shropshire as well as promoting local artists.
25 The High Street, Bishop's Castle SY9 5BT, tel: 01588 638147
Contact: Dawn McBarnet, Owner
Open: Mon-Sat 10-4.30; some Suns
Space: 1 gallery with 23 sq m floor space
Exhibitions: 11 a year
Details: Mixed and one-person exhibitions showing craft, sculpture, embroidery and paintings offering scope to young and established artists from all over the country.

Blackburn
LANCASHIRE NWA

Blackburn Museum & Art Gallery

Exhibitions with mixed themes, from local groups to professional artists, to entertain, educate and increase art awareness.
Museum Street, Blackburn BB1 7AH, tel: 01254 667130, fax: 01254 680870
Contact: Steve Morris, Exhibitions Officer
Open: Tues-Sat 9.45-4.45
Space: 1 gallery with 36 lin m hanging space plus 20 lin m on screens and 100 sq m floor space
Exhibitions: 12 a year of which 6 originated, 2 touring, 4 on a hire basis
Details: Permanent collection of fine and decorative arts Programme based around a few regular annual exhibitions. Others selected more often from applications than by invitation. Where space is hired out this is free. (See also entries for Lewis Textile Museum, Sunnyhurst Wood Visitor Centre and Witton Country Park Visitor Centre.) Selling work not principal role of gallery.

Lewis Textile Museum

Regular programme of temporary exhibitions held throughout the year.
Exchange Street, Blackburn BB1 7JN, , fax: 01254 680870
Contact: Exhibitions Officer, Blackburn Museum & Art Gallery, Museum Street, Blackburn, tel: 01254 667130
Space: 1 gallery with 36 lin m hanging space plus 45 lin m on screens and 75 sq m floor space
Exhibitions: 12 a year of which 1 originated, 3 touring, 8 on a hire basis
Details: Demonstrates the inventions of Kay, Hargreaves and Arkwright. (See also entry for Blackburn Museum & Art Gallery.)

Street (The)

Part of Blackburn Central Library and concentrates on showing work of local artists.
Blackburn Central Library, Town Hall Street, Blackburn BB2 1AH, tel: 01254 661221, fax: 01254 690539
Contact: Mrs N L Monks, Divisional Librarian
Details: Generally shows ten exhibitions a year. Venue for local artists to show work and focal point for public interest in local visual arts.

Witton Country Park Visitor Centre

Gallery housed in restored hay loft providing space for exhibitors from Lancashire in general and East Lancashire in particular.
Preston Old Road, Blackburn BB2 2TP, tel: 01254 55423
Contact: Mr Robert Wilson, Senior Warden
Open: (Apr-Oct) Mon-Sat 1-5, Sun & BH 11-5; (Nov-Mar) Thurs-Sat 1-5, Sun & BH 11-5
Space: 1 gallery with 19 lin m hanging space plus 6 lin m on screens and 42 sq m floor space
Exhibitions: 3 a year all on a hire basis
Details: Gallery forms part of a stable block now converted to a Visitor Centre. Exhibitions vary widely – local history, natural history, paintings, photography, local societies, etc. Visitors are drawn from throughout Lancashire as well as locally. 15% commission on sales. All publicity handled and paid for by Blackburn Borough Council.

Blackpool
LANCASHIRE NWA

Grundy Art Gallery

Purpose-built gallery opened 1911 with permanent collections and programme of regular travelling and contemporary exhibitions.
Queen Street, Blackpool FY1 1PX, tel: 01253 751701
Contact: Lynn Fade, Curator
Open: Mon-Sat 10-5; BH closed
Space: 4 galleries
Exhibitions: 4 a year
Details: Permanent collection of C19th and C20th paintings, watercolours and drawings, British and French sculpture, British C20th prints, oriental ivories and a contemporary jewellery collection. Dedicated audience of local people. Working relationship with local art societies. Sales not gallery's primary role.

Blandford
DORSET SWA

Hambledon Gallery *

Gallery presenting mainly solo shows by established artists.
42-44 Salisbury Street, Blandford DT11 7PR, tel: 01258 452880
Contact: Wendy Suffield
Space: 1 gallery with 29 lin m hanging space plus 28 lin m on screens and 57 sq m floor space
Exhibitions: 8 a year all originated
Details: White space with beech floor and eight skylights. In addition to regular shows one special thematic exhibition each year with open submission. Audience of local people and visitors.

Bletchley
BUCKINGHAMSHIRE SA

Fenny Lodge Gallery

Commercial gallery in C18th house on banks of Grand Union Canal showing selection of work and with 2-3 exhibitions a year.
Simpson Road, Fenny Stratford, Bletchley MK1 1BD, tel: 01908 642207, fax: 01908 647840
Contact: Sophie Miller, Manager
Open: Mon-Fri 9-5; Sat 9-4
Exhibitions: 3 a year all originated
Details: Selection of watercolours, oils, pastels and limited edition prints, as well as decorative applied art shown. Shows invited artists' work only.

Bodmin
CORNWALL SWA

Cornwall Crafts Association at Pencarrow

Small craft gallery in grounds of Pencarrow House, devoted to work by Cornwall Crafts Association members.
Pencarrow House, Washaway, Bodmin PL30 3AG, tel: 0120 884 465
Contact: Jenny Welch, Secretary
Open: Sun-Thurs: (15 Apr – Jun) 1.30-6; (4 Jun – 7 Sep) 11-6; (10 Sep – 15 Oct) 1.30-6
Details: (See also Cornwall Crafts Association at Trelowarren, Helston and Trelissick Gallery, Truro.)

Bolton
GREATER
MANCHESTER NWA

Bolton Library Service
Pa Pr Cr SE ✪

Various small-scale exhibition spaces in libraries, particularly aimed at local and/or amateur artists.
Bolton Central Library, Le Mans Crescent, Bolton BL1 1SE, tel: 01204 522311, fax: 01204 363224
Contact: Chief Librarian
Open: 5 days each week, including some evenings and Sat mornings.
Space: 3 galleries with 20 lin m hanging space plus 5 lin m on screens and 100 sq m floor space
Details: No facilities at Central Library for showing exhibitions but small spaces available at Farnworth, Harwood and Westhoughton Libraries with overall policy of exhibiting work with local theme or produced by local artists. Target audiences library users and school and college groups. Month-long exhibitions of which half are solo shows. Selling work is not Library Service's primary aim in making exhibition space available. Access and facilities vary; Farnworth Library has independent access for wheelchair users, adapted toilets and induction loop system.

Bolton Museum & Art Gallery
Pa Ph Pr Cr SE ✪ ⓔ ⓖ Wc ④

Local authority gallery housing collections of fine and applied arts and running historical and contemporary exhibitions.
Le Mans Crescent, Bolton BL1 1SE, tel: 01204 522311, fax: 01204 391352
Contact: David Morris, Senior Keeper of Art
Open: Mon, Tues, Thurs, Fri 9.30-5.30; Sat 10-5
Space: 1 gallery with 49 lin m hanging space plus 12 lin m on screens and 156 sq m floor space
Exhibitions: 4 a year of which 2 originated, 2 touring
Details: Seeks to show work of the highest quality, both aesthetically and technically, with regional or national significance. Exhibitions generated by staff, or touring exhibitions from national or regional sources. Education programme to complement displays and exhibitions.

Turton Tower
Pa Cr SE ⓗ

Historic house run by Lancashire County Council Museum service which organises 2 shows a year on contemporary crafts or a local theme.
Chapeltown Road, Bolton BL7 0HG, tel: 01204 852 203, fax: 01204 853759

Contact: Martin Robinson Dowland, Keeper
Space: 2 galleries with 100 sq m floor space
Exhibitions: 2 a year both originated
Details: Contains number of period rooms arranged to display domestic design during the C17th – C19th. Permanent collection of furniture, arms, armour and contemporary crafts.

Bootle
MERSEYSIDE NWA

Orrell Arts Centre
Pa Pr Cr ✪ ⓖ

Changing exhibitions of 2D work in community arts centre.
Linacre Lane, Bootle L20 6EG, tel: 0151 922 0006, fax: 0151 524 0216
Contact: Philip Wroe, Arts Project Officer, Sefton MBC (Arts Development), Netherton Arts Centre, Glovers Lane, Netherton, L30 3TL, tel: 0151 525 0417, fax: 0151 524 0216
Open: Mon-Thurs 1-4; Sat 10-2
Space: 1 gallery with 22 lin m hanging space and 60 sq m floor space
Exhibitions: 9 a year all originated
Details: Gallery converted from old library aiming to give Merseyside-based contemporary artists exhibition opportunities. Usually one-person shows. No facility to show 3D work. Gallery space used for weekly painting and craft classes. Sales not a priority.

Boscastle
CORNWALL SWA

Boscastle Gallery
Pa Ph Pr Cr SE ✪ ⓖ

Small gallery in beautiful harbour village visited by large number of tourists.
Dunn Street, Boscastle PL35 0AA, tel: 01840 250259
Contact: Bridget Pentecost, Director
Open: (Holidays and Summer) daily 9-5.30; (Winter) Mon-Sat 10-4
Space: 1 gallery with 37 sq m floor space
Exhibitions: 5 a year all originated
Details: Gallery policy to exhibit and sell work of a high standard from as many different fields as possible. Also shows by Falmouth art students who organise exhibitions to learn about sales and business. Local schools use gallery for art lessons. Sales a priority. Artists sometimes contribute to exhibition costs.

Boston
LINCOLNSHIRE EA

Blackfriars Arts Centre
Pa Ph Pr Cr SE LA ✪ⓔ ⓖ④

Arts centre foyer gallery exhibiting a varied programme of local, regional and national work.
Spain Lane, Boston PE21 6HP, tel: 01205 363108
Contact: Susan McCormick, Director
Space: 1 gallery with 30 lin m hanging space
Exhibitions: 12 a year of which 10 originated, 2 touring
Details: Multi-programme arts centre. Mixture of solo and touring shows and local amateur work, including sculpture and 3D craftwork. Intended to provide lively, changing selection of local, regional, national and international artists and craftspeople. Recently opened community exhibitions gallery. Selling work not primary role of gallery.

Guildhall Museum
Pa Ph Pr Cr SE ✪ ⓖ Wc

Small gallery offering a wide variety of exhibitions providing a public venue for the region's artists and craftworkers.
South Street, Boston PE21 6HT, tel: 01205 365954
Contact: Andrew Crabtree, Curator
Open: (April-Sept) Mon-Sat 10-5, Sun 1.30-5; (Oct-March) Mon-Sat 10-5
Space: 1 gallery with 15 lin m hanging space plus 15 lin m on screens and 75 sq m floor space
Exhibitions: 12 a year of which 11 originated, 1 touring
Details: Small intimate gallery which attracts local artist and craftspeople from (mainly) the south Lincolnshire area. Sale of work not gallery's primary role.

Bournemouth
DORSET SA

Daler Gallery
Pa Pr SE ✪

Aims to promote diverse range of contemporary work, particularly by local artists who haven't exhibited before.
4 Westover Road, Bournemouth BH1 2BY, tel: 01202 297682
Contact: Sue Watton
Open: Mon-Sat 9-5.30
Space: 1 gallery with 42 lin m hanging space and 126 sq m floor space
Details: Large selection of prints and etchings for sale by international artists. Art shop downstairs which displays work in windows. Exhibitions last 1-2 weeks and gallery welcomes written applications from all areas of the country.

Russell-Cotes Art Gallery and Museum

Pa Ph Pr Cr S/E LA ● ⊕ & wc 4

Gallery aims to provide an arts exhibition programme which reflects diversity, innovation and debate through historical, contemporary and multi-cultural themes.
East Cliff, Bournemouth BH1 3AA, tel: 01202 551009, fax: 01202 295644
Contact: Victoria Pirie/Mark Bills, Arts Officer/Visual Arts Officer
Open: Tues-Sun 10-5; closed Xmas & Easter
Space: 3 galleries
Exhibitions: 4 a year of which 3 originated, 1 touring
Details: Welcomes applications to exhibit and plans annual programme up to 18 months ahead. Gallery pays artists in line with EPR. Commission negotiable. Sale of work not gallery's primary role.

TZB Southbourne Gallery

Pa Ph Cr S/E ● &

Gallery exhibiting and selling owner/artist's own work and that of other artists.
2 Carbery Row, off Southbourne Road, Bournemouth BH6 3QR, tel: 01202 426967
Contact: Teresa Zwounska-Brzeski, Owner
Open: Wed-Fri 10-5.30
Space: 1 gallery with 56 lin m hanging space and 38 sq m floor space
Exhibitions: 3 a year
Details: Paintings, sculpture and pottery regularly exhibited. Aims to encourage young artists by showing their work. Shelving provided for display of pottery. Sales a priority. Gallery available for hire at £125 a week. Artists contribute to exhibition costs.

Bovey Tracey
DEVON SWA

Devon Guild of Craftsmen

Pa Ph Pr Cr S/E LA ● ⊘

Large upstairs gallery featuring changing thematic exhibitions throughout the year, showing work of contemporary artists and makers.
Riverside Mill, Bovey Tracey TQ13 9AF, tel: 01626 832223
Contact: Andy Christian, Director
Open: Daily 10-5.30
Space: 2 galleries with 100 lin m hanging space plus 15 lin m on screens and 250 sq m floor space
Exhibitions: 7 a year all originated
Details: Charitable organisation promoting the best of craftwork in the South West with exhibitions, lectures, workshops and sales through shop and café. Range of activities to promote the crafts, including library, collection, demonstrations, workshops and exhibitions. Exhibitions

feature wide range of work from regional, national and international makers as well as touring shows. Sales a priority. Independent access for wheelchair users to shop; access to exhibition not possible.

Bowness on Windermere
CUMBRIA NA

Old Laundry

Pa Ph Pr Cr LA ● & wc

Situated next to World of Beatrix Potter Exhibition, Old Laundry looks for exhibitions with childhood or family theme and popular appeal.
Crag Brow, Bowness on Windermere LA23 3EX, tel: 015394 88444
Contact: Richard Foster, Centre Manager
Open: (April-Sept) daily 10-6; (Oct-March) daily 10-4
Space: 2 galleries with 44 lin m hanging space and 120 sq m floor space
Exhibitions: 3 a year of which 1 originated, 2 touring
Details: Popular appeal of exhibitions important as gallery receives no grant aid or sponsorship. Space has air/environmental control system. Walls and floors can be painted/adapted to suit individual needs. Screens can be used. Theatre lighting rig and space used for theatre as well as exhibitions. Sales of work not primary role of gallery.

Boxford
SUFFOLK EA

Laurimore Gallery

Pa Pr Cr S/E ● &

Small gallery dedicated to showing and selling one-off contemporary applied art produced by new and established makers.
The Mews, 29 Swan Street, Boxford CO10 5NZ, tel: 01787 210138
Contact: Jon Laurimore, Exhibition Organiser
Open: Various (according to exhibition)
Space: 70 lin m hanging space and 100 sq m floor space
Exhibitions: 3 a year all originated
Details: Series of short private exhibitions, invitations limited to exclusive mailing list. Reputation for selling paintings and craft of the highest quality. Specialises in one-off work with a contemporary/figurative feel, particularly glass and ceramics. Submissions to exhibit welcome. Descriptions, photos, etc should include indication of wholesale prices. SAE appreciated.

Brackley
NORTHAMPTONSHIRE EMA

Brackley Library *

Pa Ph Pr Cr S/E ●

Exhibition area in library.
Manor Road, Brackley NN13 6AJ, tel: 01280 703455
Contact: Community Services Librarian
Details: (See Northamptonshire Libraries.)

Bracknell
BERKSHIRE SA

Bracknell Gallery

Pa Ph Pr Cr S/E ● ⊕ & wc

Gallery within publicly-funded multi-media arts centre and theatre showing mainly 2D work from region and elsewhere.
South Hill Park Arts Centre, Ringmead, Bracknell RG12 7PA, tel: 01344 427272, fax: 01344 411427
Contact: Kate Draper, Visual Arts Assistant
Open: Gallery: Tues-Sat 12.30-2.30, 6.30-9; Stairs & Meeting rooms: daily 9am-10.30pm
Space: 1 gallery with 62 lin m hanging space and 153 sq m floor space
Exhibitions: 10 a year of which 8 originated, 2 touring
Details: Broad policy and responsibility to local community to present contemporary work of quality. Difficult exhibitions counter-balanced with more accessible work. Exhibitions linked to drama, music, live art, workshops, artists in schools projects & gallery talks. Courses in visual arts and crafts. Two other smaller spaces showing 2D work by regional artists on regular basis. Sales not primary function of gallery.

Bradford
WEST YORKSHIRE YHA

Bolton Royd Gallery

Pa Ph Pr Cr S/E LA ● & 4

Glass-roofed former courtyard with sandstone walls and flagged floor promoting work in all artforms by lesser known artists.
Bradford & Ilkley Community College, Manningham Lane, Bradford BD8 7BB, tel: 01274 546 812
Contact: Harry Harrison, Lecturer in Art & Design
Open: (Term-time) Mon-Thurs 9am-9pm, Fri 9-4
Space: 1 gallery with 22 lin m hanging space plus 20 lin m on screens and 65 sq m floor space
Exhibitions: 6 a year
Details: Exhibition space has to be passed through to reach thriving art department which has very wide scope. Public awareness of gallery is growing and

intention is to not only enlighten but to encourage participation in the arts.

Bradford Community Arts Centre

Pa Ph Pr Cr Sc LA ✔ ⚹ Wc 4

Large gallery and café space within arts centre providing range of facilities; recording studio, darkroom, DTP, performance space, workshops.
The Old Quaker School, 17-21 Chapel Street, Bradford BD1 5DT, tel: 01274 721372, fax: 01274 742066
Contact: Caro Blount-Shah, Community Arts Worker
Open: Tues-Fri 10-4; open occasional weekends
Space: 2 galleries with 46 lin m hanging space plus 5 lin m on screens
Exhibitions: 6 a year all originated
Details: Exhibition space in cafe area on ground floor and also in large multi-purpose space on first floor; the main purpose of both is to show work by community groups and local individuals. Attracts broad cross-section of local and regional population. Organises workshops and projects in drama, photography and textiles in the community as well as in the building. Sales not a priority.

Bradford Design Exchange

Pa Ph Pr Cr Sc ✔ ⚹ Wc 4

Combination of studios and exhibitions space promoting good design for benefit of its tenants, local companies and schools.
34 Peckover Street, Little Germany, Bradford BD1 5BD, tel: 01274 729707, fax: 01274 729680
Contact: Neil Heavens, Manager
Open: Mon-Fri 9-5; weekends as appropriate
Space: 3 galleries with 604 sq m floor space
Exhibitions: 6 a year of which 5 originated, 1 touring
Details: Exhibition space comprises entrance reception, bar area and 3 galleries. All 2D work displayed on hanging boards, 3D work on "A" frames. Full education programme organised to complement design programme; school workshops, seminars and conferences for business. Range of meeting rooms. Sales not high priority. 30% commission taken.

Bradford Industrial Museum & Horses at Work

Pa Ph Pr Cr Sc ✔ ⚹ Wc

Flexible space for exhibitions of contemporary craft, design & technology, together with thematic social history subjects that may reflect the industrial and textile history context of the museum.
Moorside Road, Bradford BD2 3HP, tel: 01274 631756, fax: 01274 636362
Contact: Caroline Krzesinska, Keeper Arts & Exhibitions, Cartwright Hall, Lister

Park, Bradford, BD9 4NS, tel: 01274 493313, fax: 01274 481045
Open: Tues-Sun 10-5; Mon closed except BH
Space: 1 gallery with 40 lin m hanging space and 214 sq m floor space
Exhibitions: 6 a year all touring
Details: Where possible exhibitions relate to the social history/textile technology context of the museum. Education/interpretative policy extends beyond formal education groups using reminiscence techniques, role play and hands-on demonstrations – techniques used wherever possible with temporary exhibitions. Sales not a priority.

Cartwright Hall

Pa Ph Pr Cr Sc LA ✔ ⚹ Wc 4

Aims for a balanced programme of contemporary and historical exhibitions with particular emphasis on cultural diversity and popular accessibility, accommodated within four versatile modern exhibition galleries.
Lister Park, Bradford BD9 4NS, tel: 01274 493313, fax: 01274 481045
Contact: Steve Manthorp, Assistant Keeper, Exhibitions
Open: (Summer) Tues-Sun 10-6; (Winter) Tues-Sun 10-5; open BH
Space: 5 galleries with 250 lin m hanging space plus 300 lin m on screens and 1065 sq m floor space
Exhibitions: 18 a year of which 15 originated, 3 touring
Details: Built in 1904 as a splendid gallery in the Baroque style. The historical galleries have changing displays from the collections of C19th and C20th British art. An exciting exhibitions programme is arranged throughout the year. Sale of work not considered a priority.

Gallery II

Pa Ph Pr Cr Sc ✔ ⚹ Wc

Gallery aims to promote contemporary art mainly by younger artists across a wide range of artforms.
Chesham Building, off Great Horton Road, University of Bradford, Bradford BD7 1DP, tel: 01274 383365
Contact: Visual Arts Coordinator
Open: Times vary depending on exhibition
Space: 1 gallery with 36 lin m hanging space
Exhibitions: 8 a year of which 6 originated, 2 touring
Details: Gallery fully refurbished in 1994. Track lighting on dimmer circuits, full intruder and fire alarm system. Exhibitions held during term-time. Most exhibitions have complementary programme of talks and workshops, to which artists are encouraged to contribute (fees paid). Contracts issued for all exhibitors. Operates an equal opportunities policy.

National Museum of Photography, Film & Television

Pa Ph Pr Cr LA ✔ ⚹ Wc 4

Exhibitions help promote, explore and inspire interest in science and art of film, photography or television with broad range of contemporary and traditional exhibitions.
Pictureville, Bradford BD1 1NQ, tel: 01274 727488, fax: 01274 723155
Contact: Greg Hobson, Exhibitions Organiser
Open: Tues-Sun 10.30-7.30
Space: 4 galleries with 90 lin m hanging space plus 28 lin m on screens and 170 sq m floor space
Exhibitions: 12 a year of which 8 originated, 4 touring
Details: Two large galleries usually showing exhibitions themed and related to one another in some way. One small space for showing work by new artists selected for portfolio reviews. One space for installation/performance. Exhibitions last between 2-9 months. Exhibition fees paid in certain circumstances. Sales not a priority.

Bradford on Avon
WILTSHIRE SA

Lailey's

Pa Ph ✔ ⚹ ⚹

Exhibition area on three floors providing variety of exhibitions within arts centre converted from old forge
24 Bridge Street, Bradford on Avon BA15 1BY, tel: 01225 868569
Contact: Lyn Latham, Director
Open: Tues-Sat 10-5; or by appointment
Space: 1 gallery with 186 sq m floor space
Exhibitions: 4 a year of which 3 originated, 1 on a hire basis
Details: Gallery aims to bring varied art programme to area whilst maintaining friendly 'art for all' atmosphere. 4 major exhibitions a year plus permanent Russell Flint display. Mixed exhibition of local artists in summer caters for visitors. Sales a priority.

Braintree
ESSEX EA

Braintree Town Hall Centre Gallery

Pa Pr Cr Sc ✔ ⚹

Wide variety of exhibitions by local and national artists, makers, sculptors and photographers.
Market Square, Braintree CM7 6YG, tel: 01376 552525 ext 2333, fax: 01376 552626

Contact: Mrs Jean Grice, Head of Museum Services
Space: 1 gallery with 45 lin m hanging space plus 12 lin m on screens and 84 sq m floor space
Exhibitions: 12 a year
Details: Grade II listed building with public rooms, situated opposite the District Museum. Touring exhibitions also part of programme.

Brampton
CUMBRIA NA

William Howard Gallery
Pa Ph Pr Cr Sc LA ● ● Wc

Gallery aiming to provide community with exhibitions of quality contemporary art and of local interest.
William Howard Centre, Longtown Road, Brampton, tel: 016977 2212
Contact: Jeremy Latimer, Exhibitions Organiser, The 3 Beck Studios, Lowood, Armathwaite, Carlisle, CA4 9RB, tel: 01768 896479
Open: Mon-Fri 9-6
Space: 2 galleries with 43 lin m hanging space and 147 sq m floor space
Exhibitions: 11 a year of which 6 originated, 5 touring
Details: Aims to bring talented artists to the area and exhibit best artists in the area. Allows artists to create exhibitions with relative freedom. Gallery is in a school so talks to children are common. Gallery fully alarmed and continually supervised. Hanging by mirror plates or rods. Walls 12' high, white and lighting by spots.

Braunton
DEVON SWA

Elliott Gallery
Pa Ph Pr Cr Sc ● ● ●

Selling gallery promoting wide spectrum of visual arts and crafts through exhibitions, lectures, demonstrations, etc
Arts and Crafts Centre, Hillsview, Braunton EX33 2LA, tel: 01271 812100
Contact: Walter Elliott, Artist/Gallery owner
Open: (April-Oct) daily 10.30-5; (Oct-March) daily 10.30-4.30
Space: 4 galleries with 576 lin m hanging space plus 43 lin m on screens and 326 sq m floor space
Exhibitions: 8 a year of which 2 originated, 6 on a hire basis
Details: Two of four galleries usually devoted to one-person exhibitions which can be held concurrently. Special areas are designed to display sculpture, craftwork and other specialities. Daily art demonstrations via video and talks and demonstrations by artists often held. Sales a priority and commission taken.

Brentwood
ESSEX EA

Brandler Galleries
Pa Pr Cr Sc ●

Commercial gallery showing representational art.
1 Coptfold Road, Brentwood CM14 4BM, tel: 01277 222269, **fax:** 01277 222786
Contact: John Brandler
Open: Tues-Sat 10-5.30
Space: 3 galleries with 420 lin m hanging space plus 100 lin m on screens
Exhibitions: 3 a year all originated
Details: Representational art, value and quality foremost. Students work if above criteria met.

Brentwood Library
Pa Ph Pr Cr Sc ● ● ● ●

Exhibition space promoting arts in the community.
New Road, Brentwood CM14 4BP, tel: 01277 264290
Contact: Senior Library Assistant – Graphics
Open: Mon, Tues, Thurs & Fri 9-7.30; Sat 9-5
Space: 1 gallery with plus 40 lin m on screens and 56 sq m floor space
Exhibitions: 10 a year of which 1 originated, 2 touring, 7 on a hire basis
Details: To encourage the arts in the local community so that they are available to those who might not normally be exposed to them. All hanging space is on Marler Haley screens.

Shenfield Library
Pa Ph Pr Cr ● ● ●

One wall in library available for hire for exhibitions.
Hutton Road, Shenfield, Brentwood CM15 8NJ, tel: 01277 225540, **fax:** 01277 201275
Contact: Jeanne Cane, Library Assistant
Open: Mon, Tues, Thurs & Fri 9-7; Sat 9-5
Space: 1 gallery with 12 lin m hanging space plus 1 lin m on screens
Exhibitions: 14 a year all on a hire basis
Details: Wall with boards and rail above, hanging space 40'x 4'. Exhibitions of art, craft, photography, painted china, etc. Wall area only. Sales not a priority.

Bridgwater
SOMERSET SWA

Admiral Blake Museum
Pa Ph ● ●

Picture Gallery showing work by local artists and photographers to local audience.

Blake Street, Bridgwater TA5 3NB, tel: 01278 456127, **fax:** 01278 444076
Contact: Mary Thyne, Collections Manager
Open: Mon-Sat 11-5; Sun 2-5
Space: 1 gallery with 8 lin m hanging space
Details: Exhibitions last 2 weeks to one month. Aim is to allow work by local artists and groups to be exhibited to local audience. Sales not primary role of gallery.

Bridgwater Arts Centre
Pa Ph Pr Cr Sc LA ● ● ●

Arts centre promotes live events, theatre and visual arts exhibitions.
11-13 Castle Street, Bridgwater TA6 3DD, tel: 01278 422700/1
Contact: Alison Duthie, Centre Director
Open: Mon 7pm-11pm; Tues-Sat 10.30-5, 7-11
Space: 2 galleries
Exhibitions: 12 a year
Details: Centre situated in two Georgian houses in the centre of Bridgwater. Main Gallery and Centre Bar Gallery. Main Gallery has natural and spot-lighting. Programme run by visual arts committee. Monthly exhibitions include established artists as well as the up-and-coming. Programme includes one exhibition of work by schools, one open exhibition, one by local artists' group, one of photographic work and one of applied art & craft, eg textiles, wood, ceramic, glass.

Bridlington
HUMBERSIDE YHA

Sewerby Hall
Pa Ph Cr Sc LA ●

Local authority-run gallery with varied exhibition programme.
Sewerby, Bridlington YO15 1EA, tel: 01262 677874, **fax:** 01262 674265
Contact: Nial Adams, Museums Officer, East Yorkshire Borough Council, Dept ECS, 93 Quay Road, Bridlington, YO16 4ES, tel: 01262 606719, fax: 01262 400344
Space: 7 galleries with 100 lin m hanging space and 175 sq m floor space
Exhibitions: 24 a year of which 16 originated
Details: Mix throughout the year of paintings, photography, ceramics, 'A' level art and major touring exhibitions. Being a holiday resort visitors are mostly holiday-makers from all over Britain, and increasingly from Europe. Good mix of audience.

Bridport
DORSET SWA

Bridport Arts Centre

Pa Ph Pr Cr Sc LA ● ⊕

Mixed programme of professional and amateur work
**South Street, Bridport DT6 3NR, tel:
01308 427183**
Contact: Chris Huxley, Director
Open: Mon-Sat 10-4
Space: 2 galleries with 35 lin m hanging space plus 7 lin m on screens and 124 sq m floor space
Exhibitions: 12 a year all on a hire basis
Details: Spacious light gallery, access limited by stairs. Panelled walls for easy hanging. Sculpture, paintings, prints - all media welcomed. Audience – tourists in summer, regulars and members all year. Limited sales to unknown artists. Local and top professional artists very popular.

Brigg
LINCOLNSHIRE EA

Wrawby Moor Art Gallery

Pa

Converted stable block gallery with education, figurative art and national art profile.
Elsham Hall Country & Wildlife Park, Estate Office, Elsham, Brigg DN20 0RA, tel: 01652 688698, fax: 01652 688 708
Contact: Gervese Elwes, Curator
Space: 94 lin m hanging space plus 240 lin m on screens and 170 sq m floor space
Exhibitions: 8 a year of which 2 originated, 6 touring
Details: Owned and managed by the Elwes family as part of Elsham Hall Country Wildlife Park. Displays change every ten weeks between Easter and end of September. Craft shop, New Barn Theatre and restaurant adjacent.

Brighouse
WEST YORKSHIRE YHA

Smith Art Gallery

Pa Ph Pr Cr Sc ● ⓑ ④

Exhibition space within library building with varied programme which features artists that have particular relevance to the area.
Halifax Road, Brighouse HD6 2AF, tel: 01484 719222
Contact: Hazel McHugh, Exhibitions Officer, Calderdale Museums & Arts, Piece Hall, Halifax, HX1 1RE, tel: 01422 358087, fax: 01422 349310
Open: Mon, Tues, Thurs, Fri 10-12.30, 1-6; Sat 10-12.30, 1-4; closed BH
Space: 1 gallery with 31 lin m hanging space

Exhibitions: 8 a year of which 7 originated, 1 touring
Details: Municipal gallery and museum housing the Smith collection of 19th century oil paintings and playing host to a programme of changing exhibitions. Selling work is not gallery's primary function.

Brighton
EAST SUSSEX SEA

5 Ways Studio *

Pa Ph Pr Cr Sc ●

Private home turned into gallery during Brighton Festival.
Hollingbury Park Avenue, Brighton BN1 7JP, tel: 01273 505452
Contact: Helen Collis
Space: 1 gallery
Exhibitions: 1 a year originated
Details: An open exhibition that aims to be different. No compromise with quality but aims to present new and unusual art. May be any single or combination of media, and if large-scale the garden is used. Artists are expected to be present. Has established a reputation for attracting genuinely broad range of artists from beginners to mature professionals. Commission of 15% on sales.

Brighton Museum & Art Gallery

Pa Ph Pr Cr Sc ●

Three interconnecting galleries showing range of visual arts and design within museum with permanent collection.
Church Street, Brighton BN1 1UE, tel: 01273 603005, fax: 01273 779108
Contact: Nicola Coleby, Exhibitions Officer
Open: Mon, Tues, Thurs-Sat 10-5; Sun 2-5
Space: 105 lin m hanging space and 289 sq m floor space
Exhibitions: 6 a year of which 1 originated, 5 touring
Details: Policy to show range of visual arts, crafts and design; textiles, non-Western art items and visual arts from all periods. Permanent collection includes; fine arts, decorative arts, local history, fashion, non-Western art and archaeology of Sussex. Each May exhibition linked to Brighton Festival. Of 6 temporary exhibitions a year, around a third by living artists and makers. Selling work is not considered gallery's primary function.

Burstow Gallery

Pa Ph Pr Cr Sc LA ● ⓑ

Exhibits a variety of visual arts.
Brighton College, Eastern Road, Brighton BN2 2AL, tel: 01273 697131, fax: 01273 682342
Contact: Nicholas Bremer, Director of Art

Space: 2 galleries with 50 lin m hanging space plus 26 lin m on screens
Exhibitions: 4 a year
Details: Situated next to college's main hall with seating for up to 400. Exhibitions can be arranged to coincide with concerts, seminars, etc. Includes touring shows as well as solo and group shows, often by local artists. Internal shows of students' work. Four exhibitions open to public, one forming part of Brighton Festival.

Craft Direct

Pa Ph Pr Cr ● ⊕ ⓑ Wc

Small craft gallery, run by non profit-making arts company, dedicated to enabling artists to present their work professionally to the public.
Brighton Marina Village Square, 7 Village Square, Brighton BN2 5WA, tel: 01273 818368, fax: 01273 818363
Contact: Frazer Streames, Project Director
Space: 1 gallery with 20 lin m hanging space plus 4 lin m on screens and 21 sq m floor space
Exhibitions: 11 a year of which 10 originated, 1 on a hire basis
Details: Aims to provide opportunity for artists, whether professional, newly-graduated or amateur either in Craft Direct or in other exhibitions. Also runs scheme which keeps artists informed of all local opportunities, venues and exhibitions. Sale of work not gallery's primary role.

Gardner Centre Gallery *

Pa Ph Pr Cr Sc LA ●

Exhibition programme committed to showing works by contemporary artists in all media.
Gardner Centre, University of Sussex, Falmer, Brighton BN1 9RA, tel: 01273 685447, fax: 01273 678335
Contact: Jim Latter, Visual Arts Adviser
Space: 3 galleries with 72 lin m hanging space and 157 sq m floor space
Exhibitions: 13 a year all originated
Details: Function is to bring into the region the highest standard of work produced by living artists as well as providing a platform for the region's artists.

Hugo Barclay

Pr Cr ● ⓑ

Retail gallery on Crafts Council selected list showing individual pieces selected from UK makers, concentrating on glass, jewellery, ceramics, wood and work of original printmakers.
7 East Street, Brighton BN1 1HP, tel: 01273 321694
Contact: Hugo Barclay, Exhibition Organiser
Open: Mon-Sat 10-1, 2-5.30
Space: 2 galleries with 20 lin m hanging space and 60 sq m floor space
Exhibitions: 2 a year both originated

Details: Changing display of work by selected artists, both established and up and coming, plus solo or group shows. About 125 makers represented with two major exhibitions a year. Large group Summer Show and jewellery promotion held during the Christmas period.

Markovitch Gallery

Po Ph Pr Sc ✓ ⊕ &

New commercial gallery specialising in limited edition prints by both local and internationally acclaimed artists.
37 Bond Street, Brighton BN1 1RD, tel: 01273 772289, fax: 01273 625223
Contact: Steve Marlow
Space: 1 gallery with 14 lin m hanging space
Details: Also shows prototype furniture and other three-dimensional works. Willing to hire gallery space though generally works are hired from artist or supplier.

North Star Studios *

Ph Pr

Printmaking studio for local artists who display their work within.
65 Ditchling Road, Brighton BN1 4S, tel: 01273 601041
Contact: Nicholas Sinclair, Chairman
Details: Various forms of printmaking undertaken, ie screen, litho, etching, relief and photography.

Phoenix Gallery

A Po Ph Pr Cr Sc LA ✓ ⊕ &

Large artist-run space in building with studios and workshops showing new works of contemporary fine art in all media.
10-14 Waterloo Place, Brighton BN2 2NB, tel: 01273 603700
Contact: Gallery Co-ordinator
Open: Mon-Sat 11-6; Sun 12-4
Space: 2 galleries with 40 lin m hanging space plus 10 lin m on screens and 157 sq m floor space
Exhibitions: 25 a year all on a hire basis
Details: Programme of work by artists living in Brighton and elsewhere. Exhibition proposals viewed by studio members three times a year. Selected exhibitors hire space at subsidised rate and are responsible for organising, presenting and invigilating their shows. Because of organisation's charitable and educational aims, gallery can show challenging and informative work which might not normally be seen in commercial venues. Education programme involving artists and community through exhibitions, workshops, talks etc. For application information send SAE to Gallery Coordinator. Sale of work not gallery's primary function.

Sanctuary (The)

Po Ph Sc LA ✓ & Vc

A busy café utilising all wall space for exhibitions of contemporary work.
51-55 Brunswick Street East, Brighton BN13 1AV, tel: 01273 770002
Contact: Fiona Denning, Exhibition Organiser
Open: Daily 10am-11pm
Space: 3 galleries with 31 lin m hanging space and 149 sq m floor space
Exhibitions: 12 a year all originated
Details: Offer artists a much needed venue in Brighton with opportunity to sell work. Wall space on 3 floors. As this is a café all walls are coloured. Lighting more cafe-like than gallery – but atmospheric. 15% commission. Separate basement available for performance/live art. Independent access for wheelchair users to 2 rooms.

University of Brighton Gallery

Po Ph Pr Cr Sc ✓

Geared to a wide range of exhibitions which aim to attract a wider audience than users.
Grand Parade, Brighton BN2 2JY, tel: 01273 643012, fax: 01273 643128
Contact: Colin Matthews, Exhibitions Officer
Open: Mon-Fri 10-6; ring for weekend openings
Space: 2 galleries with 24 lin m hanging space plus 70 lin m on screens and 251 sq m floor space
Exhibitions: 20 a year of which 16 originated, 4 touring
Details: Exhibitions run for three to four weeks. Include solo shows by living artists and makers. Linked with historical exhibitions and shows of particular community interest.

Window Gallery

Po Pr Sc

Gallery showing and selling contemporary paintings, prints and sculpture, some by local artists.
69 Ship Street, Brighton BN1 1AE, tel: 01273 726190
Contact: Carole-Anne White, Proprietor
Space: 1 gallery with 70 lin m hanging space and 50 sq m floor space
Exhibitions: 3 a year all originated
Details: Publishes own original prints and reproductions and offers competitive framing service. Artists include: Philip Dunn, Ken Fleming, Susan Jameson, Brenda Hartill, Ilana Richardson, Shirley Trevena.

ZAP Club *

 LA

Renowned beach-front nightclub with occasional live art performances.

188-191 Kings Road Arches, Brighton BN1 1NB, tel: 01273 821588, fax: 01273 206960
Details: Live art venue which does not have any permanent gallery facilities. Commission specific installations which are suited to the venue from time to time.

Brimstage
CHESHIRE NWA

Voirrey Embroidery Centre

Cr ✓

Exhibitions in embroidery retail centre intended to provide focus, generate ideas and encourage sales.
Brimstage Hall, Brimstage L63 6JA, tel: 0151 342 3514, fax: 0151 342 5161
Contact: Mrs Voirrey Branthwaite, Partner
Space: 1 gallery with 31 lin m hanging space plus 2 lin m on screens and 47 sq m floor space
Exhibitions: 12 a year all originated
Details: Embroidery centre sells large range of specialist goods and runs workshops and courses. Exhibitions illustrate the many facets of embroidery and tapestry and aim to stretch the imagination of visitors. Programme changes monthly, and covers work from past and present, designers, manufacturers, professional makers. Also annual summer exhibition of work by 'customers'. Most exhibitions group shows and feature 3D approach to display rather than traditional 2D presentation.

Bristol
AVON SWA

35 King Street Gallery

A Po Ph Pr Sc ✓ & 4

Artist-led gallery with exhibitions promoting work of emerging artists based in Bristol area and their contemporaries on national and international level.
35 King Street, Bristol BS1 4DZ, tel: 0117 929 4071, fax: 0117 929 4173
Contact: Gallery Co-ordinator
Open: Tues-Sat 12-6
Space: 1 gallery with 30 lin m hanging space and 400 sq m floor space
Exhibitions: 20 a year all originated
Details: Platform for innovative locally-produced contemporary art which would not otherwise be seen in the city. Introduces city's wider community to visual arts, encourages artist initiated schemes, develops support network for artists. Part of Artspace Bristol. Sales not a priority.

3D Gallery

Po Pr Cr Sc ✓

Commercial gallery providing a showcase for contemporary artists and craftspeople.

13 Perry Road, Bristol BS1 5BG, tel:
0117 929 1363
Contact: Annette Guck, Owner
Space: 1 gallery with 74 sq m floor space
Exhibitions: 3 a year
Details: 3 linked spaces with rear
mezzanine area. Varied collection of work
on display by a cross-section of the artists
represented by gallery. Framing services,
commissions negotiated, group exhibitions
considered.

Alastair Gill Gallery

Showcase for contemporary furniture,
textiles, jewellery and fine bookbinding.
4 Christmas Steps, Bristol BS1 5BS, tel:
0117 922 1204
Contact: Alastair Gill, Gallery Proprietor
Space: 2 galleries with 20 lin m hanging
space and 42 sq m floor space
Exhibitions: 1 a year originated
Details: Showcase for contemporary
designer-makers working in the fields of
furniture, textiles (wall hangings, weavings
and embroideries), jewellery and fine
bookbinding. Promotes awareness of and
facilitates access to such work through the
process of direct retail and through
arrangements for commissions.

Arnolfini *

Major Arts Council of England funded
gallery.
16 Narrow Quay, Bristol BS1 4QA, tel:
0117 929 9191, fax: 0117 925 3876
Contact: Kate Bush, Senior Exhibitions
Officer
Space: 4 galleries with 122 lin m hanging
space and 405 sq m floor space
Exhibitions: 8 a year of which 7
originated, 1 touring
Details: Presents new and exciting
developments in contemporary visual arts
in a local, national and international
context. Brings the visual arts to a wider
audience. Extensive education
contextualises and expands on the work on
show. Conferences and other events are
organised for the gallery and outside.

Barton Hill Photography Project Gallery

Small display space in café of busy
community centre specialising in
community photography.
Bristol Settlement, 43 Ducie Road,
Barton Hill, Bristol BS5 0AX, tel: 0117
955 6971
Contact: Carrie Hitchcock, Project Worker
Open: Mon-Fri 10-2
Space: 1 gallery with 15 lin m hanging
space plus 2 lin m on screens
Exhibitions: 12 a year of which 10
originated, 2 touring

Details: Shows mainly laminated
exhibitions of group and individual work
by local community photography project
members and local groups. Would like to
show work by other photography groups
and individuals around the country.
Welcomes speakers (small fee available).
Space not suited to glass framed
exhibitions. Selling work not a main aim.

Bristol Museum & Art Gallery

The temporary exhibition gallery is one of
the museum's focal points, showing new
work and existing collections in a new way.
Queen's Road, Bristol BS8 1RL, tel:
0117 922 3571, fax: 0117 922 2047
Contact: Alison Hems, Collections
Manager
Open: Daily 10-5; BH openings vary
Space: 1 gallery with 56 lin m hanging
space plus 65 lin m on screens and 200 sq
m floor space
Exhibitions: 3 a year of which 1
originated, 2 touring
Details: Exhibitions programme designed
to reflect strengths of permanent
collections, building on or contrasting with
existing material as appropriate.
Contemporary work shown within this
context. Education programme formally
intended to encourage use by schools and
informally to enhance wider public access.
Sales not a priority but selling exhibitions
do take place.

Church House Designs

Small private gallery promoting high-
quality contemporary ceramics, glass, prints
and paintings.
Broad Street, Congresbury, Bristol BS19
5DG, tel: 0117 983 3660
Contact: Lorraine Coles, Proprietor
Open: Mon-Sat 10-1, 2.15-5.30
Space: 1 gallery with 12 lin m hanging
space and 28 sq m floor space
Exhibitions: 4 a year all originated
Details: To complement display of
contemporary craftwork by regional and
national makers, gallery runs on-going
programme of month-long exhibitions
featuring one of following; ceramics,
woodturning, textiles, glass, work by
graphic artists. Sales a priority.

Croft Gallery

Gallery near Bristol city centre available for
hire for exhibitions.
26 Stokes Croft, Bristol BS1 3QD, tel:
0117 942 2213, fax: 0117 942 3016
Contact: Richard Hart
Space: 35 lin m hanging space plus 10 lin
m on screens and 75 sq m floor space
Exhibitions: 10 a year all on a hire basis

David Cross Gallery

Specialises in traditional British painting;
marine, landscape, figurative, sporting
subjects particularly those relating to Bristol
and South West.
7a Boyces Avenue, Bristol BS8 4AA, tel:
0117 973 2614
Contact: Carole Innocent, Exhibition
Organiser
Open: Mon-Sat 9-6
Space: 1 gallery
Exhibitions: 6 a year all originated
Details: Period and contemporary work
shown on two floors with contemporary
exhibitions in Cellar Gallery. Restoration
studio and framing.

Guild Gallery

Monthly exhibitions of work by mainly
West Country artists and craftspeople.
68 Park Street, Bristol BS1 5JY, tel: 0117
926 5548
Contact: John Stops
Open: Mon-Sat 9.30-5; closed BH
Space: 1 gallery with 30 lin m hanging
space and 50 sq m floor space
Exhibitions: 9 a year of which 1
originated, 8 on a hire basis
Details: Gallery rented to exhibitors for
exhibitions usually lasting 3 week when no
commission charged on sales. Over the
Christmas period organises a large multi-
media exhibition by invited artists and
craftspeople.

Happening Gallery

Gallery aiming to make contemporary art
accessible to public in informal, friendly
space.
6 Cotham Hill, Cotham, Bristol BS6
6LF, tel: 0117 973 2792
Contact: John Wreyford
Open: Mon-Sat 10-6; Sun 11-4
Space: 1 gallery with 26 lin m hanging
space and 56 sq m floor space
Exhibitions: 24 a year of which 4
originated, 20 on a hire basis
Details: No specific policy other than
making contemporary work accessible and
eliminating elitism. Aims to enable artists
to show work with as few restrictions as
possible. Artists hire space and staff own
shows. No commission taken.

Michael Stewart Galleries

Commercial gallery with few major
exhibitions and number of smaller mixed
exhibitions.
24 The Mall, Clifton, Bristol BS8 4DS,
tel: 0117 970 6265, fax: 0117 970 6268
Contact: Nigel Clark & Justin Gardner,
Directors

Open: Mon-Sat 9.30-5.30
Space: 1 gallery with 35 lin m hanging space and 89 sq m floor space
Exhibitions: 5 a year all originated
Details: Can be split in to three sections, each holding a different exhibition. Extensive client list continually updated with new members who are kept informed of all exhibitions, new artists etc. Artists welcome to come and show work to the directors, if successful will be invited to hold an exhibition.

Off-Centre Gallery

Commercial gallery with changing display and one annual exhibition; other exhibitions held in more accessible venues (gallery up two flights of stairs).
13 Cotswold Road, Windmill Hill, Bedminster, Bristol BS3 4NX, tel: 0117 966 1782
Contact: Christine Higgott and Peter Ford
Open: by appointment
Space: 2 galleries with 30 lin m hanging space and 33 sq m floor space
Exhibitions: 4 a year all originated
Details: Aims to demonstrate the interest and versatility of contemporary prints through a series of exhibitions, some organised to tour. Drawing, painting and 3D work may also be shown. Selling is important, so is showing stimulating work to all visitors. Illustrated talks and demonstrations are offered with touring exhibitions.

Patricia Wells Gallery *

Hire gallery for solo and mixed exhibitions.
Morton House, Lower Morton, Thornbury, Bristol BS12 1RA, tel: 01454 412288
Contact: Mrs Patricia J.O. Wells, Owner
Space: 4 galleries with 139 lin m hanging space plus 48 lin m on screens and 284 sq m floor space
Exhibitions: 3 a year all on a hire basis
Details: Special promotional service through advertising. Attentive advice on framing and restoration. Open all year by telephone appointment, during exhibitions 10-1 and 2-5. Mailing list of over 1000 personal guests.

Praxis Gallery/Café

Exhibition space, often hired out, with aim of promoting work of younger artists.
90 Colston Street, Bristol BS1 5BB, tel: 0117 929 1538
Contact: Alan Greenway, Owner/Director
Space: 3 galleries with 65 lin m hanging space and 1250 sq m floor space
Exhibitions: 21 a year of which 7 originated, 14 on a hire basis
Details: Rooms are spacious and well-lit.

Situated very near town centre. Ground floor café provides a lively accessible environment for art .

Royal West of England Academy

Exhibiting mainly contemporary art, as arranged by the Academy's Council.
Queens Road, Clifton, Bristol BS8 1PX, tel: 0117 973 5129, fax: 0117 923 7874
Contact: Academy Secretary
Open: Mon-Sat 10-5.30; Sun 2-5
Space: 5 galleries
Exhibitions: 12 a year
Details: Self-supporting society of artists with permanent collection of painting and sculpture of elected members' work, and temporary exhibition programme. Aims to show work by distinguished artists, both members and others, and to encourage non-members to submit works for selection during open exhibitions. Sales of work important but not always primary function of exhibitions. Exhibition fee occasionally paid to artists.

Watershed Gallery

Large photographic gallery and three/four other spaces in which photography is constantly exhibited to a diverse and large audience.
Watershed Media Centre, 1 Canons Road, Bristol BS15TX, tel: 0117 927 6444, fax: 0117 921 3958
Contact: Philippa Goodall, Programming Director for Photography
Open: Mon-Sun 11-7
Space: 5 galleries with 98 lin m hanging space plus 14 lin m on screens and 100 sq m floor space
Exhibitions: 20 a year of which 10 originated, 6 touring, 4 on a hire basis
Details: Main gallery plus hanging space in Concourse 1 & 2 and on walls of café and sandwich bar. Leading regional centre for photography and media-related events and exhibitions in the South West. Specialises in contemporary work by living practitioners, generating touring shows and publications. Has no brief to include traditional fine arts, painting, sculpture, etc though applications are welcome from artists working in multi-disciplinary, multi-media, installations and events. Sale of work not gallery's primary role.

Broadstairs
KENT SEA

Broadstairs Library Gallery

Library foyer space promoting all forms and aspects of visual arts and crafts.

The Broadway, Broadstairs CT10 2BS, tel: 01843 862994
Contact: Sheena Watson, Arts Promotion Officer, Margate Library, Cecil Square, Margate, CT9 1RE, tel: 01843 223626
Open: Mon-Fri 9.30-6; Sat 9.30-5
Space: 1 gallery with 20 lin m hanging space and 28 sq m floor space
Exhibitions: 12 a year all originated
Details: Gains its audience from local schools, colleges, groups, societies and residents. Alongside exhibitions are occasional shows of museum or archive material. Sale of work not a main objective.

Bromsgrove
HEREFORD & WORCESTER WMA

Avoncroft Museum of Historic Buildings

Two galleries which, between them, hold a variety of exhibitions, workshops and events.
Stoke Heath, Bromsgrove B60 4JR, tel: 01527 831363/ 831886, fax: 01527 876934
Contact: Dr Simon Penn, Curator
Space: 2 galleries with 220 sq m floor space
Exhibitions: 6 a year of which 3 originated, 1 touring, 2 on a hire basis
Details: Smaller gallery is a room housed within rebuilt C16th public house used as a venue for small scale photographic exhibitions, craft workshops by individual crafts workers, etc. Larger venue is the New Guesten Hall, incorporating a mediaeval roof from Worcester, housing a variety of events including craft exhibitions, touring object-based exhibitions, lectures and concerts.

Jinney Ring Craft Centre

Selling gallery exhibiting work by both new and established artists and craftspeople.
Hanbury, Bromsgrove B60 4BU, tel: 01527 821272
Contact: Richard and Jenny Greatwood, Joint Proprietors
Open: Tues-Sat 10.30-5; Sun 11.30-5.30
Space: 1 gallery with 6 lin m hanging space and 140 sq m floor space
Details: Gallery aiming to hold monthly exhibitions of cross section of art and craft. 150,000 visitors to the centre a year. Always looking for new and exciting exhibitors. Gallery mainly shows crafts that can be displayed on stands/in cases as there is little hanging space in old barn.

Broseley
SHROPSHIRE WMA

Gallery 6

Selling gallery occupies ground floor and cellar space of converted Victorian building and exhibits paintings and prints by wide range of young and well-known contemporary artists.
6 Church Street, Broseley TF12 5DG, tel: 01952 882860
Contact: John Boulton
Open: Mon-Fri 9-5; may vary
Space: 4 galleries with 31 lin m hanging space and 37 sq m floor space
Exhibitions: 4 a year all originated
Details: Four gallery spaces each about 10 ft x 10 ft. Sales of work essential.

Budleigh Salterton
DEVON SWA

Otterton Mill Gallery

One room gallery in old mill still in use with programme designed to benefit from unusual environment.
Budleigh Salterton EX9 7HG, tel: 01395 68521
Contact: Desna Greenhow
Space: 1 gallery with 18 lin m hanging space plus 15 lin m on screens and 78 sq m floor space
Exhibitions: 9 a year all originated
Details: Programme has included contemporary sculpture, naive paintings and modern furniture. Most exhibitions by invitation but some applications may be considered. Attracts a wide audience and has many established visitors.

Burford
OXFORDSHIRE SA

Brian Sinfield Gallery *

High street gallery showing mainly contemporary paintings by distinguished artists.
128 High Street, Burford OX18 4GU, tel: 01993 822603
Contact: Brian Sinfield
Space: 2 galleries with 40 lin m hanging space and 67 sq m floor space
Exhibitions: 8 a year all originated
Details: The gallery covers two floors and draws clients from all over the U.K.

Burnley
LANCASHIRE NWA

Mid Pennine Gallery

Key exhibition venue for Mid Pennine Arts providing programme of events and activities covering all aspects of the arts throughout East Lancashire.
Mid Pennine Arts Association, Yorke Street, Burnley BB11 1HD, tel: 01282 21986
Contact: Sheenagh Mayo, Visual Arts Officer
Open: Mon-Sat 10-5; Thurs 1-5; (Educational groups only) Thurs 10-1
Space: 1 gallery with 42 lin m hanging space plus 61 lin m on screens and 150 sq m floor space
Exhibitions: 10 a year of which 8 originated, 2 touring
Details: Aims for a varied programme of contemporary visual arts and crafts, increasing awareness and accessibility of work by professional artists and makers. Provides an educational resource to public and schools within the area. Also craft showcase and jewellery shop. Pleased to see the work of local artists and makers. Sale of work not considered gallery's primary role.

Towneley Hall Art Gallery

Gallery with temporary exhibitions covering many subjects including contemporary art and museum with permanent collections.
Towneley Park, Burnley BB11 3RQ, tel: 01282 424213
Contact: Susan Bourne, Curator
Open: Mon-Fri 10-5; Sun 12-5
Space: 2 galleries with 56 lin m hanging space and 195 sq m floor space
Exhibitions: 12 a year of which 4 originated, 6 touring, 2 on a hire basis
Details: Art gallery and museum with own collections of fine and decorative arts, social and natural history. Housed in an historic house two miles from the town centre. Around 120,000 visitors per year. Admission free. Hanging space in main gallery is interrupted by three doors and window. Single line tracking system with dimmable fluorescent lighting and spots. Selling work is not gallery's primary function.

Burton on Trent
STAFFORDSHIRE WMA

Brewhouse

Small gallery in multi-purpose arts centre showing range of work by amateur and professional artists and community groups.
Union Street, Burton on Trent DE14 1EB, tel: 01283 567720

Contact: Gallery Co-ordinator
Open: Tues-Sat 10am-11pm
Space: 1 gallery with 27 lin m hanging space and 672 sq m floor space
Exhibitions: 9 a year all originated
Details: One-person, group and collective shows. One open submission exhibition a year. Sales not main purpose of gallery.

Round House Gallery *

Sells contemporary studio ceramics, studio glass and wood crafts.
38 High Street, Tutbury, Burton on Trent DE13 9LS
Contact: Leah or Philip John Evans
Space: 10 lin m hanging space
Exhibitions: 1 a year originated

Bury St Edmunds
SUFFOLK EA

Blackthorpe Barn

Provides venue and some funding for challenging contemporary art, especially installation work.
Rougham, Bury St Edmunds IP30 1LZ, tel: 01359 270238, fax: 01359 271555
Contact: George Agnew, Director, The Estate Office, Rougham, Bury St Edmunds, IP30 9LZ, tel: 01359 270238, fax: 01359 271555
Open: By arrangement
Space: 1 gallery with 65 lin m hanging space and 350 sq m floor space
Exhibitions: 1 a year originated
Details: Dates back to mediaeval times, still has timber frame from C16th. Gallery space now an excellent contemporary arena for large-scale paintings and sculpture and installations by new and nationally known artists. Standard is high and draws interested visitors from all over the region. Sale of work is not gallery's primary function.

Cathedral Cloister Gallery

Gallery connects the church to the new conference centre and Cathedral coffee shop.
St Edmundsbury Cathedral, Angel Hill, Bury St Edmunds IP33 1LS, tel: 01284 754933, fax: 01284 768655
Contact: Mrs Margaret Lee, Arts Co-ordinator
Open: (Easter-Nov) daily 10-4; other times by arrangement;
Space: 1 gallery with 24 lin m hanging space
Exhibitions: 14 a year of which 2 originated, 12 on a hire basis
Details: Sale of work not gallery's primary role. Commission structure (20%) aims to encourage established artists and facilitate non-discriminatory approach.

Chimney Mill Galleries

 Pa Pr Sc

Commercial gallery showing small number of mixed exhibitions with changing display.
Chimney Mill, West Stow, Bury St Edmunds IP28 6ER, tel: 01284 728234
Contact: Hilary Murfitt, Exhibition Organiser
Open: Daily except Mon 11-5
Details: Also selling antique pine and country furniture.

St John's Gallery *

Pa Pr ✓

Commercial art gallery providing contemporary art at reasonable prices.
67b St John's Street, Bury St Edmunds IP33 1SJ, tel: 01284 769573
Contact: Paul Henly, Director
Space: 1 gallery with 55 lin m hanging space and 21 sq m floor space
Exhibitions: 6 a year all originated
Details: Shows contemporary prints and watercolours between exhibitions. Most exhibitions are one person.

Buxton
DERBYSHIRE NWA

Buxton Museum & Art Gallery

Pa Ph Pr Sc LA ✓ 🗓 Wc

Local authority museum displaying wide range of 2D and 3D work by local, national and international artists.
Terrace Road, Buxton SK17 6DJ, tel: 01298 24658
Contact: D Harding, Curator
Open: Tues-Fri 9.30-5.30; Sat 9.30-5
Space: 1 gallery with 30 lin m hanging space and 150 sq m floor space
Exhibitions: 21 a year all originated
Details: Gallery and foyer exhibitions both changed monthly show local, national and international works, some of which are for sale. No fee for exhibitions. Sales not a priority.

David Russell *

Pa Ph Pr Cr Sc ✓

Small art shop with limited exhibition space specialising in work of living artists from the region.
10 Hall Bank, Buxton SK17 6EW, tel: 01298 24510
Contact: David Russell, Exhibition Organiser
Space: 1 gallery with plus 12 lin m on screens and 10 sq m floor space
Exhibitions: 12 a year all originated
Details: Emphasis on paintings and pottery. Framing service.

Calshot
HAMPSHIRE SA

Calshot Crafts Centre *

Cr

Craftshop and gallery.
Badminster Farm, Calshot SO4 1BB, tel: 01703 898846
Contact: Exhibition Organiser
Space: 9 sq m floor space
Exhibitions: 3 a year all originated
Details: Exhibitions of craftwork. Restaurant and nature trail.

Calverton
NOTTINGHAMSHIRE EMA

Patchings Farm Arts Centre *

Pa Ph Pr Cr Sc ✓

Independent art centre in restored C18th farm buildings.
Oxton Road, Calverton NG14 6NU, tel: 0115 965 3479, fax: 0115 965 3081
Contact: Miss Liz Wood, Co-Proprietor
Space: 2 galleries with 100 lin m hanging space plus 40 lin m on screens
Exhibitions: 18 a year all originated
Details: Independent art centre in restored C18th farm buildings. Two galleries, art and pottery studios, art materials and framing shop, licensed restaurant. 38 acres of landscaped grounds fashioned for the artist, with lake area and 'Monet' bridge. 10 studios and clubhouse provide additional facilities. Aims to be an accessible outlet for artists of all ages, stimulating interest and participation in art. East Midlands Artist of the Year – open competition. Courses and workshops.

Cambridge
CAMBRIDGESHIRE EA

Architecture Gallery

✓ ⊗

Part of regional architecture centre dedicated to presenting architecture and urbanism to public and related professions.
6 King's Parade, Cambridge CB2 1SJ, tel: 01223 324157, fax: 01223 357049
Contact: Colen Lumley, RIBA Hon Exhibitions Organiser, Lumley Architects, Trumpington Mews, Trumpington, Cambridge, CB2 2LS, tel: 01223 843931
Open: Mon-Sat 9.30-6
Space: 1 gallery with 26 lin m hanging space and 30 sq m floor space
Exhibitions: 8 a year of which 7 originated, 1 touring
Details: Four main exhibits a year interleaved with supplementary exhibitions. Talks and events linked to programme. Features regional, national and international contemporary architectural

projects; architecture photography and representation. Gallery available for hire for relevant uses. Sales not priority.

Bodilly Galleries

Pa Ph Pr ✓ 🗓

Purpose-built commercial gallery near Fitzwilliam Museum.
71 Lensfield Road, Cambridge CB2 1EN, tel: 01223 566555, fax: 01223 566552
Contact: Tim Halket, Director
Open: Mon-Fri 10-6; Sat 10-6
Space: 1 gallery with 28 sq m floor space
Exhibitions: 8 a year all originated
Details: Gallery shows abstract and figurative work. 80% from established artists; rest from promising young artists.

Broughton House Gallery

Pa Pr ✓ H 🗓

Lively centrally located gallery for contemporary work, welcoming to young artists, students and children, with regular buyers.
98 King Street, Cambridge CB1 1LN, tel: 01223 314960
Contact: Rosemary Davidson, Proprietor
Open: Tues-Sat 10.30-5.30
Space: 1 gallery with 22 lin m hanging space and 24 sq m floor space
Exhibitions: 10 a year of which 9 originated, 1 on a hire basis
Details: Small, friendly gallery with strong local following, some of whose exhibitions create national interest. Solo and mixed exhibitions of a range of contemporary work – oils, watercolours, mixed media, etchings, wood engravings and small sculpture – from artists, some well known, others beginning their careers, about a third from overseas. Gallery holds stock of work by about 30 artists with a price range of £20 to £1500. Talks by exhibiting artists. Sales a priority.

Cambridge Centre Library Exhibition Room and Area

Pa Ph Pr Cr Sc ✓ H 🗓

Gallery whose main purpose is to provide a good standard of exhibition space at a reasonable cost.
7 Lion Yard, Cambridge CB2 3QD, tel: 01223 65252, fax: 01223 62786
Contact: Ian Pryke, Operations Manager
Open: Mon-Sat 10-5
Space: 2 galleries with 38 lin m hanging space and 112 sq m floor space
Exhibitions: 30 a year all on a hire basis
Details: Self-contained room with kitchen and toilet facilities. Movable spotlights available to enhance the exhibits. Open-plan gallery surrounding a stair-well, with the emphasis on natural light. A hire fee is charged depending on the length of the exhibition plus a 10% commission on any sales.

Cambridge Darkroom Gallery

A centre for photography presenting programme of exhibitions alongside talks, courses and workshops.
Dales Brewery, Gwydir Street, Cambridge CB1 2LJ, tel: 01223 566725, fax: 01223 312188
Contact: Peter Ride, Director
Open: Tues-Sun 2-6
Space: 2 galleries with 77 lin m hanging space
Exhibitions: 7 a year of which 4 originated, 3 touring
Details: A centre for photography. Presents a varied and ambitious programme of exhibitions by local, national and international artists, alongside talks, discussions, courses and workshops for people of all ages and abilities. Sale of work not gallery's primary role.

CCA Galleries (Cambridge)

One of a network of commercial galleries in South of England specialising in original prints.
6 Trinity Street, Cambridge CB2 1SU, tel: 01223 324222, fax: 01223 315606
Contact: Denise Collins, Director
Open: Mon-Sat 9-5.30
Space: 3 galleries with 58 lin m hanging space and 78 sq m floor space
Exhibitions: 12 a year all originated
Details: CCA Galleries is a leading publisher of original limited edition prints with other galleries in London, Farnham, Bath and Oxford (see separate entries for these). Each gallery selects its own work. Primary aim is to promote handmade prints by CCA artists.

Conservatory Gallery

Commercial gallery showing and selling East Anglian contemporary art.
(Part of Business Arts), 6 Hills Avenue, Cambridge CB1 4XA, tel: 01223 211311, fax: 01223 214588
Contact: Pamela Barrell, Proprietor
Open: Sat 10-5; 1st Sun each month 10-5; by appointment any time
Space: 3 galleries with 70 sq m floor space
Exhibitions: 6 a year all originated
Details: Work by over 100 regular artists on display. 4-6 special exhibitions per year. Business Rental Service – East Anglian Art for East Anglian Companies. Framing service.

Eureka! The Float Place

Relaxed and informal small gallery.
45 Newnham Road, Cambridge CB3 9EY, tel: 01223 302502

Contact: Duncan Tait & Colleen Moore, Proprietors
Open: Mon-Sat 10-6
Space: 1 gallery with 9 lin m hanging space and 33 sq m floor space
Exhibitions: 12 a year all originated
Details: Paintings by local artists exhibited each month. Selection of pottery, ceramics, glassware, jewellery stocked. Sales from exhibition not considered primary role of gallery but all work taken on sale or return basis and 30% commission taken.

Fitzwilliam Museum

Two adjacent galleries in large University museum; one used for exhibitions and other for displays of museum's collections or exhibitions.
Trumpington Street, Cambridge CB2 1RB, tel: 01223 332900, fax: 01223 332923
Contact: Director
Open: Tues-Sat 10-5; Sun & BH 2.15-5; Closed 24 Dec – 1 Jan & Good Friday
Space: 2 galleries with 82 lin m hanging space and 212 sq m floor space
Exhibitions: 5 a year of which 3 originated, 2 touring
Details: Wide permanent collection. Aims to show as much as possible of permanent collection to public. Also shows Arts Council touring exhibitions and other temporary exhibitions. Sales not a priority.

Heffer Gallery

Commercial gallery presenting solo and group exhibitions by mainly local and East Anglian artists.
Heffers Stationers, 19 Sidney Street, Cambridge CB2 3HL, tel: 01223 568040, fax: 01223 568410
Contact: Christopher Witchall, Gallery Manager
Space: 1 gallery with 40 lin m hanging space and 72 sq m floor space
Exhibitions: 10 a year all originated
Details: Run by Heffers booksellers and stationers. Shows work in a variety of media and contemporary styles. Programme runs from January to September. Exhibitions run for two weeks.

Jock Colville Hall

Large hall offering facilities for temporary exhibitions during university term time.
Churchill College, Storeys Way, Cambridge CB3 0DS, tel: 01223 336138
Contact: Miss Mary Kendall
Open: At exhibitor's discretion
Space: 1 gallery with 13 lin m hanging space plus 44 lin m on screens and 104 sq m floor space
Exhibitions: 3 a year
Details: Exhibitions generally last 1-2

weeks. Young artists encouraged to show work. Sales not a priority. No commission on sales.

Junction (The)

Narrow gallery accessing bar and auditorium of arts and entertainments venue.
Clifton Road, Cambridge CB1 4GX, tel: 01223 410356, fax: 01223 412569
Contact: Jasmine Hendry
Open: Daily 12-6; evenings during performances
Space: 1 gallery with 20 lin m hanging space
Details: Long thin corridor with hanging on one wall venue dealing almost entirely with performing arts (particularly music). Large auditorium which has been used for installation. Open policy on exhibiting, although emphasis given to local artists. Audience includes those attending events who have not necessarily come to see the exhibition. Sales not a priority.

Kettle's Yard

A sequence of spaces of varying scale devoted to contemporary and C20th art.
Castle Street, Cambridge CB3 0AQ, tel: 01223 352124, fax: 01223 324377
Contact: Michael Harrison, Director
Open: Tues-Sat 12.30-5.30; Sun 2-5.30
Space: 5 galleries with 100 lin m hanging space
Exhibitions: 7 a year of which 5 originated, 2 touring
Details: The gallery presents a wide range of contemporary and C20th art. The exhibition and education programme encourages the exploration of art first from a visual point of view. Selling work is not a priority.

Pelican Gallery

Gallery on two floors where contemporary and traditional art may be exhibited for sale to the general public.
The Perse School, Hills Road, Cambridge CB2 2QF, tel: 01223 568267, fax: 01223 568293
Contact: Mark Judson, Director of Art
Open: Mon-Fri 11-3.30; Sat 10-1
Space: 2 galleries with 20 lin m hanging space plus 15 lin m on screens and 396 sq m floor space
Exhibitions: 5 a year all originated
Details: Breadth and variety of artistic input is desired over the course of a year in three large exhibitions. Gallery welcomes any artist group to apply. Sale of work not considered gallery's primary role but when work sold 25% commission taken. Gallery intends that work on display acts as an educational aid for younger art students

seeking influence of art 'in the flesh'. Gallery has natural and artificial lighting.

Primavera

Well-established commercial art and craft gallery on the Crafts Council's selected list.
10 Kings Parade, Cambridge CB2 1SJ, tel: 01223 357708
Contact: Ronald Pile, Exhibition Organiser
Space: 2 galleries with 25 lin m hanging space and 50 sq m floor space
Exhibitions: 5 a year all originated
Details: Shows two-week exhibitions of small-scale work in the gallery and changing displays from stock in the shop. Essentially an outlet for contemporary paintings and first-rate British craftwork. Exhibitions offer both gallery and artist the opportunity to focus on particular media, approaches, explorations. Audiences generally well-informed and interested.

Trumpington Gallery

Gallery in converted bakehouse showing work to give pleasure to visitors and provide an income for exhibiting artists.
18-20 Victoria Road, Mitcham's Corner, Cambridge CB4 3DU, tel: 01223 62292
Contact: Jonathan Miles
Open: Mon-Fri 10-6; Sat 10-1
Space: 2 galleries with 22 lin m hanging space and 33 sq m floor space
Details: Main hanging space has cast iron oven front and quarry tiled floor. Entrance from Victorian courtyard (where visitors can park their cars). Afternoon tea available during summer. Sale of work not primary role of gallery.

Wysing Arts

Multi-purpose space used for rehearsals, conferences and workshops as well as exhibitions.
Fox Road, Cambridge CB3 7TX, tel: 01954 718881, fax: 01954 718500
Contact: Annie Cargill, Curator Wysing Arts
Open: variable but closed Mon
Space: 1 gallery with 30 lin m hanging space and 90 sq m floor space
Exhibitions: 4 a year all originated
Details: Programme of commissioned and invited artists' exhibitions to improve education of the public in art and craft. Sales of work welcome (30% commission taken) but not a high priority. Occasional fund raising exhibitions for other charities when rent is charged and commission waived.

Camelford
CORNWALL SWA

North Cornwall Museum & Gallery

Permanent collection relating to North Cornwall and temporary exhibition programme.
The Clease, Camelford, tel: 01840 212954
Contact: Sally Holden, Exhibition Organiser
Open: (Apr – end Sep) Mon-Sat 10-5
Space: 1 gallery with 60 lin m hanging space
Exhibitions: 6 a year all originated
Details: Exhibitions held between April and September. Arts and crafts shown. Selling work is gallery's primary function.

Cannock
STAFFORDSHIRE WMA

Cannock Library

Run by Staffordshire Libraries the gallery is a dedicated exhibition space local artists.
Manor Avenue, Cannock WS11 1AA, tel: 01543 52019/71114
Contact: Christine Budworth, Cannock Group Librarian
Open: Mon & Thurs 9.30-7; Tues & Fri 9.30-5; Wed & Sat 9.30-1
Space: 1 gallery with 24 lin m hanging space and 42 sq m floor space
Exhibitions: 12 a year all originated
Details: Programme mostly local artists and societies, with exhibitions changing monthly. Sales not a priority.

Valley Heritage Centre & Museum

Space within museum for temporary/touring exhibitions of both local and national interest.
Valley Road, Hednesford, Cannock WS12 5QX, tel: 01543 877666, fax: 01543 462317
Contact: Adrienne Whitehouse, Curator
Open: (Easter – Oct 1) Mon-Sun 11-5; (Oct 1 – Easter) Mon-Fri 11-4
Space: 1 gallery with 22 lin m hanging space plus 10 lin m on screens and 38 sq m floor space
Exhibitions: 4 a year of which 3 originated, 1 on a hire basis
Details: Programme designed to provide a variety of exhibitions for a chiefly local audience. Substantial proportion comprises educational parties. Exhibitions are a small but important part of the overall programme. Additional facilities available including lecture room, café and outdoor areas. Sales not a priority.

Canterbury
KENT SEA

Drew Gallery

Privately-run commercial gallery.
16 Best Lane, Canterbury CT1 2JB, tel: 01227 458759
Contact: Sandra Drew, Owner/Director
Open: Mon-Sat 10-5
Space: 2 galleries with 25 lin m hanging space and 30 sq m floor space
Exhibitions: 11 a year all originated
Details: Continuous exhibition programme of contemporary art, particularly paintings but includes prints, sculpture, ceramics, textiles and jewellery. Ground floor Georgian building with courtyard garden in city centre. Changing stock of small works by gallery artists.

Gibbs Gallery Canterbury

Gallery exhibiting ceramics, sculpture and paintings with year-round display of crafts and jewellery.
53 Palace Street, Canterbury CT1 2DY, tel: 01227 763863
Contact: George Gibbs
Open: (Mar-Dec) Mon-Sat 10-5.30; (Jan-Feb) Tues-Sat 10-5.30
Space: 2 galleries with 10 lin m hanging space and 35 sq m floor space
Exhibitions: 4 a year all originated
Details: Sale of work is considered gallery's primary role. Visits from students at local colleges of art are welcomed. Gallery covers exhibition costs.

Graphics Gallery

Specialising in graphic arts with most exhibitions drawn from archive of cartoon artwork held at University but applications from artists welcomed.
Templeman Library, University of Kent at Canterbury, Canterbury CT2 7NU, tel: 01227 823127
Contact: Jame Newton, Assistant Director
Open: (Term-time), Mon-Fri 9-10; Sat 9-7; Sun 2-5; (Vacation time) Mon-Fri 9-7,
Space: 1 gallery with 12 lin m hanging space plus 15 lin m on screens and 52 sq m floor space
Exhibitions: 8 a year of which 4 originated, 4 on a hire basis
Details: A space on the third floor of the University Library overlooking large reading area, specialising in the graphic arts – drawings, cartoons, posters, photographs, prints and engravings. Audience predominantly library users, ie students. Archive of cartoon artwork held by Cartoon Research Centre at University. Sale of work not important.

Canterbury
KENT SEA

Herbert Read Gallery

Pa Ph Pr SC £ &

Public exhibitions held during academic year by Kent Institute of Art & Design, featuring contemporary works by national/ international artists.
Kent Institute of Art and Design, New Dover Road, Canterbury CT1 3AN, tel: 01227 769371, fax: 01227 451320
Contact: Christine Gist, Exhibitions Officer
Open: Mon-Fri 10-5
Space: 55 lin m hanging space and 104 sq m floor space
Exhibitions: 6 a year all originated
Details: All exhibitions are curated internally and frequently in collaboration with other galleries. Exhibitions programme reflects the Institute's strong links with mainland Europe, emphasising European-based group and solo shows. Lectures and artists' residencies often coordinated with the exhibitions. Foyer space adjacent to gallery can be used when appropriate. Sales not a priority.

Nevill Gallery

Pa Ph Pr ✓ &

Contemporary art gallery with established clientele and list of artists, but always willing to consider new work.
43 St Peters Street, Canterbury CT1 2BG, tel: 01227 765291
Contact: Mrs Ann Nevill
Open: Mon-Sat 10-5
Space: 2 galleries with 39 lin m hanging space and 44 sq m floor space
Exhibitions: 5 a year all originated
Details: Shows contemporary oils, prints and watercolours with regular exhibitions and mixed shows. Sales a priority.

Royal Museum & Art Gallery

Pa Ph Pr SC ✗

A local-authority run gallery mainly showing historical exhibitions, also occasional exhibitions by local artists.
High Street, Canterbury CT1 2JE, tel: 01227 452747
Contact: Brian Stewart, Exhibitions Officer
Open: Mon-Sat 10-5
Space: 1 gallery with 43 lin m hanging space and 42 sq m floor space
Exhibitions: 3 a year all originated
Details: Emphasis on historical and travelling shows and those internally originated. Average of eight temporary exhibitions, lasting 3-4 weeks, shown a year. Permanent collection relates to the Canterbury area, including work by contemporary artists, usually presented in group shows. Selling work not a priority.

Carlisle
CUMBRIA NA

Manor Photographic Gallery *

Ph ✓

Photographic gallery/darkroom/studio within a community centre.
Morton Community Centre, Wigton Road, Carlisle CA2 6JP, tel: 01228 28309
Contact: Mr Ken Fox, Community Liaison Officer
Space: 2 galleries with 22 lin m hanging space plus 8 lin m on screens and 30 sq m floor space
Exhibitions: 8 a year of which 1 originated, 7 touring
Details: Aims to provide an overview of both historic and contemporary photography and to encourage an understanding of how the medium reflects our society and lives and contributes to an understanding of our environment. Encourages expressive photography, ie the individual ideas and concerns of photographers.

Sark Gallery *

Pa Pr Cr SC ✓

Converted village chapel with open exhibition policy.
Hethersgill, Carlisle CA6 6EH, tel: 01228 75022
Contact: Sadie Allen, Director
Space: 2 galleries with 60 lin m hanging space and 160 sq m floor space
Exhibitions: 7 a year all originated
Details: Open from April to December. Visitors are, however, accepted anytime by appointment. Changing exhibitions in the Upper Gallery are supported by mixed shows of work by gallery artists on the ground floor. Establishing and maintaining a good standard has priority over commercial success. Adventurous work with limited sales appeal can be accommodated.

Tullie House

Pa Ph Pr Cr SC LA ✓ £ & Wc

Newly purpose-built space showing changing programme of contemporary art forms together with items from the permanent collection.
City Museum & Art Gallery, Castle Street, Carlisle CA3 8TP, tel: 01228 34781, fax: 01228 810249
Contact: Terry Bennett, Visual Art Officer
Open: Mon-Sat 10-5; Sun 12-5
Space: 1 gallery with 270 lin m hanging space and 370 sq m floor space
Exhibitions: 12 a year of which 7 originated, 5 touring
Details: Air conditioned, grade A standards of security, Lockwall screens, fully

adaptable lighting system. Aims to increase awareness, understanding and enjoyment of contemporary art. Programme includes artists working regionally, nationally and internationally. Collections and historical exhibitions occasionally shown. Local, regional and national audience. Sales not a priority.

Carnforth
LANCASHIRE NWA

Ingleborough Gallery

Pa Ph Pr SC ✓ £ &

Gallery exhibiting a broad range of visual arts and crafts with some touring exhibitions.
Ingleton, Carnforth LA6 3HG, tel: 01524 2 41701
Contact: Alan King, Hon Sec Ingleborough Arts, Ingleborough Community Centre, Ingleton, LA6 3HG
Open: Mon-Fri 10-4.30; Sat & Sun 1-4.30
Space: 1 gallery with 40 lin m hanging space and 10 sq m floor space
Exhibitions: 6 a year of which 4 originated, 2 touring
Details: Programme sometimes complementing music programme in adjacent hall.

Castlefield
GREATER MANCHESTER NWA

Dukes 92 Gallery

Pa Ph Pr Cr SC ✓ ✗ Wc

Gallery available free to artists for exhibitions.
Canalside Bar, 14 Castle Street, Castlefield M3 4LZ, tel: 0161 839 8646, fax: 0161 839 4706
Contact: Thomas Joyce
Space: 2 galleries with 291 sq m floor space
Exhibitions: 12 a year all originated
Details: First-floor gallery open to approaches from artists working in all media. Artists hang the show, organise publicity, preview, etc. No commission taken. Gallery is staffed. Wooden floors, white walls, spot lights.

Chagford
DEVON SWA

Stone Lane Gardens

Cr SC ✓ &

Birch and alder arboretum/ water garden (5.5 acres) providing varied settings for work by sculptors and designers under the titles 'The Mythic Garden'.
Stone Farm, Chagford TQ13 8JU, tel & fax: 01647 231311
Contact: K & J Ashburner
Exhibitions: 1 a year originated

Details: Work selected from sketches or photographs submitted by artists seeking to exhibit work in a mixed show. Work exhibited at artist's risk. Entry fee £2.

Chalford
GLOUCESTERSHIRE SWA

Gallery Pangolin

🄼 Ⓧ

Spacious gallery connected to a working foundry exhibiting wide range of contemporary works in bronze.
Unit 8b, Chalford Industrial Estate, Chalford GL6 8NT, tel: 01453 886527, fax: 01453 731499
Contact: Jane Buck, Gallery Manager
Open: By appointment.
Space: 1 gallery with 100 sq m floor space
Exhibitions: 6 a year of which 5 originated, 1 touring
Details: Sculpture always on display. Group, one-person and themes exhibitions held. Annual open day for viewing foundry and casting techniques; information on request.

Chatton
NORTHUMBERLAND NA

Chatton Gallery

🄿🄼 Ⓞ Ⓑ

Gallery opened Spring 1995 developing programme which aims to enable visitors to explore wide range of stimulating, high-quality work in a relaxed atmosphere.
Church House, Chatton Village, Chatton NE66 5PU, tel: 01668 215494
Contact: Robert Turnbull & John Fieldhouse
Open: Daily 10-7
Space: 4 galleries with 55 lin m hanging space and 3 sq m floor space
Details: Sale of work not considered gallery's primary role.

Chelmsford
ESSEX FA

Chelmsford Central Library

🄿🄱🄿🄼 Ⓞ🄷 Ⓑ🅆

Gallery is the only non-commercial dedicated exhibition space in Chelmsford, offering varied programme featuring work of local and national importance.
County Hall, Market Road, Chelmsford CM1 1LH, tel: 01245 492758, fax: 01245 492536
Contact: Roger Johnson or June Turner
Open: Mon-Fri 9-7; Sat 9-5
Space: 1 gallery with 5 lin m hanging space plus 66 lin m on screens and 84 sq m floor space

Exhibitions: 12 a year of which 1 originated, 2 touring, 9 on a hire basis
Details: Situated in a large public library run by Essex County Council Libraries. Over 20,000 visitors each week, all potential viewers of exhibitions. Purpose-built, with aspect onto internal public square. The programme is varied, with all arts covered.

Chelmsford & Essex Museum

🄿🄱🄲🄼 ⓄⒺ Ⓧ

Multi-disciplinary municipal museum with varied exhibitions in upstairs room.
Oaklands Park, Moulsham Street, Chelmsford CM2 9AQ, tel: 01245 353066/ 267299
Contact: A. Lutyens-Humfrey, Keeper of Art
Open: Mon-Sat 10-5; Sun & public holidays 2-5
Space: 1 gallery with 21 lin m hanging space and 41 sq m floor space
Exhibitions: 2 a year both originated
Details: Self-originated and outside exhibitions complement, or extend scope of, the museum's collections (historic & modern ceramic, glass, archeology, local history, militaria, natural history). Local links encouraged. Small contemporary craft display changes bimonthly. Selling work not a priority.

Essex Libraries *

🄿🄱🄿🄼 🄛🄐 Ⓞ

Although branch libraries are responsible for own programme, acts as originator for occasional touring shows.
County Library, Goldlay Gardens, Chelmsford CM2 0EW, tel: 01245 284981
Contact: Sheila Pengelly, Promotion & Development Assistant
Details: Various galleries and exhibition spaces around the county providing useful venues for both local and national exhibitions. Diverse range of exhibitions covering all areas of art, design, photography. (See entries for Witham, Wickford, Loughton, Harlow, Grays, Chelmsford, Colchester, Clacton on Sea, Brentwood and Berlesduna Gallery, Basildon. Also spaces at Saffron Walden, Harwich, South Woodham Ferrers, Maldon & Southend on Sea.)

Gallery (The)

🄿🄼 Ⓞ

Commercial gallery showing contemporary painting and sculpture by locally and nationally established artists.
43 Moulsham Street, Chelmsford CM2 0HY, tel: 01245 353825
Contact: Mike Adams
Open: Mon-Fri 9-5.30; Sat 9.30-5.30

Space: 2 galleries with 55 lin m hanging space and 142 sq m floor space
Exhibitions: 10 a year all originated
Details: 3 exhibitions a year in large main gallery and monthly programme of exhibitions in smaller upstairs gallery (no disabled access). Shows tend to be two-person with one mixed show every December.

Cheltenham
GLOUCESTERSHIRE SWA

Axiom Centre for the Arts

🄿🄱🄿🄲🄼🄛🄐 Ⓞ🄷 Ⓧ④

Community arts centre showing broad range of contemporary exhibitions and where education is an important part of the programme.
57-59 Winchcombe Street, Cheltenham GL52 2NE, tel: 01242 253183, fax: 01242 221549
Contact: Visual Arts Committee
Open: Mon-Sat 10-5.45
Space: 3 galleries
Exhibitions: 9 a year of which 3 originated, 3 touring, 3 on a hire basis
Details: Two galleries, one of them L-shaped plus smaller room available for installations and/or exhibitions. Aims to show high quality exhibitions across a broad range of work; often challenging avant garde. Aims to make these, and all shows, as accessible as possible through strong education programme of workshops, talks, etc. Tenure of building only till July 1995 and future of organisation under threat. Sale of work not a priority but helpful.

Cheltenham Art Gallery & Museum

🄿🄱🄿🄲🄼 ⓄⒺ Ⓑ🅆④

Local authority museum with collections of fine and applied arts, running a varied programme of exhibitions, both historical and contemporary.
Clarence Street, Cheltenham GL50 3JT, tel: 01242 237431, fax: 01242 262334
Contact: Jonathan Benington, Senior Exhibition Officer
Open: Mon-Sat 10-5.20
Space: 1 gallery with 20 lin m hanging space plus 33 lin m on screens and 51 sq m floor space
Exhibitions: 3 a year of which 2 originated, 1 touring
Details: Ground floor gallery adjacent to foyer in new (1989) extension. Exhibitions, both contemporary and historical, are selected with an emphasis on variety and quality of the material and its interpretation. Admission free. Mixed audience from Gloucestershire and beyond. Preference given to artists/craftspeople connected with the region. Sales not a priority.

Montpellier Gallery

Private gallery representing a variety of artists and craftspeople.
27 The Courtyard, Montpellier Street, Cheltenham GL50 1SR, tel: 01242 515165
Contact: Linda Burridge
Space: 1 gallery with 19 lin m hanging space and 58 sq m floor space
Exhibitions: 5 a year
Details: Both new and established artists/craftspeople represented. Painting, original etching, sculpture, studio ceramics, glass and designer jewellery, endorsed by the Crafts Council. Solo or thematic exhibitions with displays changing on a monthly basis.

Ogle Fine Arts *

Supplies art for working environment to small firms and major companies throughout UK.
1 Wellington Square, Cheltenham GL50 4JU, tel: 01242 231011, fax: 01242 522191
Contact: Douglas and Jenny Ogle, Directors
Space: 3 galleries with 60 lin m hanging space and 75 sq m floor space
Details: Large stock of limited edition prints. Wide range of painters', printmakers', sculptors' work included in in-house exhibitions from which businesses select work for purchase. Advice and assistance given in forming collections. Commission negotiable. Takes part in major UK contemporary art fairs. No regular exhibition programme, permanent rotating collection.

Pittville Gallery

College gallery showing both students'/staff work and similar exhibitions and bringing in touring shows from outside.
Cheltenham & Gloucester College of Higher Education, Pittville Campus, Albert Road, Cheltenham GL52 3JG, tel: 01242 532882, fax: 01242 532207
Contact: Kate Plume, GCAM
Open: (Term-time) Mon-Fri 9-6
Space: 1 gallery with 290 sq m floor space
Exhibitions: 18 a year of which 9 originated, 9 touring
Details: Single gallery space with upper balcony level which doubles hanging space. Student shows, also occasional international college exchange exhibitions and other projects initiated. Also shows touring exhibitions. Gallery available for hire. Workshop series can be organised as required. Sale of work not gallery's primary function.

Pittville Pump Room Museum

Exhibition programme of contemporary and historical costume and textiles in museum with collections in these areas.
Pittville Park, Cheltenham GL52 3JE, tel: 01242 523852, fax: 01242 526563
Contact: Sophia Wilson, Assistant Keeper Decorative Arts & Exhibitions Officer, Cheltenham Art Gallery & Museum, Clarence Street, Cheltenham, GL50 2JT, tel: 01242 237431, fax: 01242 262334
Open: (Oct – April) Mon & Wed-Sun 11-4; (May – Sept) Mon & Wed-Sun 11-4.30
Space: 1 gallery with plus 12 lin m on screens
Exhibitions: 2 a year both originated
Details: Oval room in grade 1 listed building which makes displays difficult. Programme tries to show a variety of costume and textiles both contemporary and historical, British, European or Asian emphasising areas not on show in the permanent displays – fashions from 1780 to present day of Cheltenham people. Sales not a priority. 25% commission taken on works sold.

Turtle Fine Art *

Commercial gallery dealing in oils, watercolours, etchings, lithos, wood engravings, etc C19th to contemporary.
30 Suffolk Parade, Cheltenham GL50 2AE, tel: 01242 241646
Contact: Pat Field, Exhibitions Organiser
Space: 20 lin m hanging space and 93 sq m floor space
Exhibitions: 3 a year all originated
Details: Exhibitions of contemporary work held 3-4 times annually. Invitations to private views mailed to a large file of regular customers, from a wide catchment area.

Chertsey
SURREY SEA

Chertsey Museum

Local authority museum with collections of local history and costume runing varied programme of temporary exhibitions, some historical and some contemporary.
33 Windsor Street, Chertsey KT16 8AT, tel: 01932 565764
Contact: Philip Sykas, Assistant Keeper
Open: Tues-Fri 12.30-4.30; Sat 11-4
Space: 1 gallery with 18 lin m hanging space and 32 sq m floor space
Exhibitions: 4 a year all originated
Details: Promotes artists from region and encourages appreciation of contemporary work through small high-quality displays with accompanying workshops or events. Work normally displayed in themes which

group several artists together. Screens and secure cases available. Sales not priority. Wheelchair access with assistance to ground floor but this does not include temporary exhibition gallery.

Chester
CHESHIRE NWA

Bishops' Gallery

Gallery in school aims to enable artists to exhibit without incurring cost, and to provide students with opportunity to show their work alongside professional artists.
Vaughans Lane, Great Boughton, Chester CH3 5XF, tel: 01244 313806
Contact: D J Wrigley, Head of Resources
Space: 1 gallery with 28 lin m hanging space plus 9 lin m on screens and 47 sq m floor space
Exhibitions: 3 a year all originated
Details: Committed to showing work of visiting artists, photographers, craftspeople and the work of pupils from the art, design and textiles departments. Gallery exists for benefit of the public and school students.

Chester Library

Three separate wall spaces in a busy central library available for one month to professional and amateur artists on a first-come-first-served basis.
Northgate Street, Chester CH1 2EF, tel: 01244 312935
Contact: Angus Madders, Librarian
Open: Mon & Thurs 9.30-7; Tues, Wed, Fri 9.30-5; Sat 9.30-1
Space: 3 galleries with 110 lin m hanging space plus 4 lin m on screens
Exhibitions: 24 a year all on a hire basis
Details: Participates in travelling exhibitions organised by Cheshire Libraries & Museums, showing work by professional artists from Cheshire and beyond, encompassing painting, drawing, prints, crafts and photography. Available for local amateurs. Attempts made to seek out the imaginative. Selling work not a primary aim.

Grosvenor Museum

Temporary exhibition space in museum where shows complement collections by expanding on topic or covering subjects not in collections.
27 Grosvenor Street, Chester CH1 2DD, tel: 01244 321616, fax: 01244 347587
Contact: S. Matthews, Museums Officer
Open: Mon-Sat 10.30-5; Sun 2-5
Space: 2 galleries with 50 lin m hanging space and 113 sq m floor space
Exhibitions: 11 a year of which 6 originated, 5 touring

Details: Galleries have no windows but variable lighting systems so watercolours or oils can be displayed. Small gallery used for watercolours/prints. Front gallery for more diverse topics (textiles, African art, etc). Each gallery has subject slots into which exhibitions must fall eg C20th contemporary art, craft/decorative arts with contemporary bias, design. Activities considered essential and are targeted at groups, schools, etc. Local bias to exhibitions preferred. Varied audience, schools, locals, tourists. Sales not a priority.

Chesterfield
DERBYSHIRE EMA

Peacock Heritage Centre

Space in C15th building for exhibitions of local interest or by local people.
Low Pavement, Chesterfield S40 1PB, tel: 01246 221016, fax: 01246 556726
Contact: Mrs Wainwright, Tourism Officer
Open: Mon-Sat 11-5
Space: plus 33 lin m on screens and 58 sq m floor space
Exhibitions: 13 a year all on a hire basis
Details: Exhibition space alongside gift shop, information centre and audio-visual presentation of history of Chesterfield. Sales not a priority.

Uno Gallery

Commercial gallery specialising in contemporary jewellery with space for small-scale contemporary crafts.
5 Falcon Yard, South Street, Chesterfield S40 1QX, tel: 01246 557145
Contact: Julie Benz, Gallery Manager
Open: Mon-Sat 10-5
Space: 1 gallery with 19 sq m floor space
Exhibitions: 3 a year all originated
Details: Exhibitions last two months and range from major display of one person's work to exhibitions on particular technique or style of jewellery. Exhibitions add variety and innovation to contemporary jewellery regularly stocked. Sale of exhibition work is a priority.

Chichester
WEST SUSSEX SEA

Chichester Centre for the Arts

Converted church housing two galleries and entrance hall, all used for changing 2D and 3D exhibitions.
St Andrews, East Street, Chichester PO19 1YH, tel: 01243 779103
Contact: Ann Smith, Programme Organiser

Open: Mon-Sat 10.30-4.30
Space: 2 galleries with 59 lin m hanging space plus 9 lin m on screens and 131 sq m floor space
Exhibitions: 10 a year of which 5 originated, 5 on a hire basis
Details: Opened in December 1993, centre aims to attract and welcome visitors and raise public awareness of art in general. Hopes to provide arts related activities especially for young people. Large gallery with monthly changing exhibitions where artists pay fee for space. Small gallery with both originated and hired exhibitions. Sales not a priority. If artist hires space no commission taken on sales; otherwise 30% commission taken.

Mitre Gallery

In higher education setting this dedicated exhibition space has varied programme featuring artists who usually have an association with the College.
Bishop Otter College, College Lane, Chichester PO19 4PE, tel: 01243 787911 ext 243, fax: 01243 536011
Contact: S. Robertson, Learning Resources Coordinator, Chichester Institute of Higher Education
Open: Mon-Fri 9-4.30
Space: 1 gallery with 66 lin m hanging space plus 15 lin m on screens and 150 sq m floor space
Exhibitions: 5 a year all originated
Details: Exhibitions include student shows and selection from College's own collection of C20th art. Exhibitions usually last 4 weeks. Sale of work is not a priority.

Pallant House

Shows of regional contemporary artists and craftspeople within exhibition programme largely comprising displays of permanent collections.
9 North Pallant, Chichester PO19 1TJ, tel: 01243 774557
Contact: David E. Coke, Curator
Open: Tues-Sat 10-5 15
Space: 2 galleries with 40 lin m hanging space plus 18 lin m on screens and 120 sq m floor space
Exhibitions: 5 a year of which 4 originated, 1 touring
Details: Varied programme of exhibitions and expanding educational programme for primary and secondary schools. Exhibitions relate to permanent collections of C20th art, C18th furniture, porcelain and glass, and silhouettes. Charity with grants from the district council aiming to attract all sections of the public. Gallery talks, workshops for schools, artist in residence programme organised. Much contemporary work displayed is for sale but not main purpose of gallery. Disabled access with assistance to Main Gallery only.

Chipping Norton
OXFORDSHIRE SA

Theatre (The) *

Theatre gallery promoting exhibitions by local professional artists and available for hire.
2 Spring Street, Chipping Norton OX7 5NL, tel: 01608 642349
Contact: Tamara Malcolm, Theatre Director
Space: 1 gallery with 100 sq m floor space
Exhibitions: 4 a year of which 2 originated, 2 on a hire basis

Chobham
SURREY SEA

Bank Gallery

Commercial gallery specialising in high quality British crafts.
73/75 High Street, Chobham GU24 8AF, tel: 01276 857369
Contact: Ros Hills
Open: Tues-Sat 10-5
Space: 1 gallery with 13 lin m hanging space and 50 sq m floor space
Exhibitions: 6 a year all originated
Details: Gallery opened March 1994. Gallery aims to provide a welcoming atmosphere, giving as much information as possible about crafts for sale. Plinths and shelf space as well as hanging space. Regular craft workshops proposed to "meet the maker". Gallery space is available for hire by craftspeople by selection.

Chorley
LANCASHIRE NWA

Chorley Central Library

Library corridors for display of 2D work and well-used library entrance for 3D work.
Union Street, Chorley PR7 1EB, tel: 01257 277223, fax: 01257 231730
Contact: Mr Heyes, Assistant Librarian, Lancashire County Library Service
Open: Mon, Wed, Fri 10-7; Tues, Thurs 10-5; Sat 10-4
Space: 2 galleries
Exhibitions: 17 a year of which 15 originated, 2 touring
Details: Busy high street library with exhibition space mostly devoted to exhibitions by locally-based artists who staff the exhibitions. Limited by restrictions of the space to small or light work. Sales not a priority. Applications welcomed from local artists.

Christchurch
DORSET SA

Red House Museum & Gardens

Pa Ph Pr Cr Sc LA ⊘✦ ⊕4

Local museum showing varied programme including contemporary and historical art and craft.
Quay Road, Christchurch BH23 1BU, tel: 01202 482860, fax: 01962 869836
Contact: Carol Littlefair, Exhibitions Officer, Hampshire County Council Museums Service, Chilcomb House, Chilcomb Lane, Winchester, SO23 8RD, tel: 01962 846315, fax: 01962 869836
Open: Tues-Sat 10-5; Sun 2-5
Space: 1 gallery with 30 lin m hanging space and 50 sq m floor space
Exhibitions: 8 a year of which 7 originated, 1 touring
Details: For policy see entry for Hampshire County Council Museums, Winchester.

Cirencester
GLOUCESTERSHIRE SWA

Brewery Arts

Pa Ph Pr Cr Sc ⊘✦ ⊕w4

Arts centre with particular emphasis in applied art and craft, comprising gallery, Crafts Council selected shop, theatre, resident craftworkers, coffee house.
Brewery Court, Cirencester GL7 1JH, tel: 01285 657181
Contact: Exhibition Officer
Open: Mon-Sat 10-5
Space: 2 galleries with 45 lin m hanging space and 76 sq m floor space
Exhibitions: 13 a year of which 10 originated, 3 touring
Details: Main gallery shows best in national contemporary craftwork, balanced by fine art and photography exhibitions. Theatre space shows predominantly regionally-based artists. Programme aims for balance of solo, in-depth shows and more general 'theme' group shows. Education programmes. Sales not a priority. Only theatre exhibition space accessible to wheelchair users.

Clacton on Sea
ESSEX EA

Clacton Library

Pa Ph Pr ⊘⊕

Exhibition space in library available for hire.
Station Road, Clacton on Sea CO15 1SF, tel: 01255 421207
Contact: Anne Tomkinson, Operations Manager
Space: 1 gallery with 6 lin m hanging space
Exhibitions: 10 a year all on a hire basis
Details: See Essex Libraries.

Clevedon
AVON SWA

Toll House Gallery

Pa Pr Sc ⊘⊕ ⊛

Run as a charitable trust presenting mixture of one-person and mixed shows of work by local, national & international artists.
Clevedon Pier, The Beach, Clevedon BS21 7QU, tel: 01275 878846
Contact: Ivor or Margaret Ashford
Open: Daily 9-5; closed Wed in winter
Space: 1 gallery with 23 lin m hanging space and 78 sq m floor space
Exhibitions: 12 a year all on a hire basis
Details: In toll house of Clevedon Pier. Aims to encourage new young artists. Applications to hire gallery welcomed. 25% commission charged on sales. All profits go towards pier restoration fund. Selling work is primary role of gallery.

Clitheroe
LANCASHIRE NWA

Platform Gallery

Pr Cr Sc ⊘ ⊕wc

Run by Ribble Valley Borough Council, this display centre offers varied programme of exhibitions mainly featuring contemporary craft work by North West based makers.
Station Road, Clitheroe BB7 2JT, tel: 01200 25111 ext 2556, fax: 01200 26339
Contact: Heather Fox, Arts Development Officer
Open: Mon-Sat 10-4.30
Space: 1 gallery with 22 lin m hanging space plus 5 lin m on screens and 70 sq m floor space
Exhibitions: 9 a year of which 6 originated, 3 touring
Details: Most exhibitions are group shows originated by gallery. Aims to increase awareness of craft and encourage audience feedback on all exhibitions. Is keen to collaborate with schools on exhibitions. In house publicity produced for all exhibitions. Sales welcome. 20% sales commission.

Cockermouth
CUMBRIA NA

Castlegate House

Pa Pr Cr Sc ⊘ ⊛

Three exhibition rooms and wide hall in Georgian house.
Cockermouth CA13 9HA, tel: 01900 822145
Contact: Chris Wadsworth, Director
Open: Mon-Tues & Fri-Sat 10.30-5; Wed 10.30-7

Space: 3 galleries with 55 lin m hanging space and 78 sq m floor space
Exhibitions: 9 a year all originated
Details: A beautiful Georgian house. Proportions of rooms mean modern work looks great. Looks for work of high standard and integrity. Walled Georgian garden shows for sculpture. Usually 5 solo shows and 4 group shows each year. Large mail list. Work hung on batons. Selling work is gallery's primary role.

Colchester
ESSEX EA

Chappel Galleries

Pa Pr Sc

Programmes of selling exhibitions centred around C20th East Anglian fine art.
15 Colchester Road, Chappel, Colchester CO6 2DE, tel: 01206 240326
Contact: Edna Mirecka, Co-Proprietor
Open: Wed-Sat 10-6
Space: 1 gallery with 58 lin m hanging space and 113 sq m floor space
Details: Exhibition programme presenting work by painters and sculptors who have already gained a regional/national/ international reputation, and those who are up and coming and of particular interest.

Colchester Institute, School of Art

Pa Ph Pr Cr ⊕ ⊛

Small gallery in foyer of School of Art.
Sheepen Road, Colchester CO3 3LL, tel: 01206 761660
Contact: Keith Albarn, Head of School of Art & Design
Open: Mon-Fri 10-5
Space: 1 gallery with 30 lin m hanging space plus 6 lin m on screens and 81 sq m floor space
Exhibitions: 8 a year of which 4 originated, 2 touring, 2 on a hire basis
Details: Exhibition space consists of 100 ft run of wall, 8 ft high. Exhibitions provide an educational aid for students and PR for School of Art within local community. Gallery is open to the public. Sale of work not a priority.

Colchester Library

Pa Ph Pr Cr Sc ⊘⊕ ⊛wc

Library gallery aims that exhibitions reach widest possible audience.
Trinity Square, Colchester CO1 1JB, tel: 01206 562243, fax: 01206 562413
Contact: Jo Lynch, Senior Librarian, Promotions
Open: Mon-Wed, Fri, 9-7.30; Thurs, Sat, 9-5
Space: 2 galleries with 10 lin m hanging space plus 17 lin m on screens and 100 sq m floor space

Exhibitions: 20 a year of which 2 originated, 4 touring, 14 on a hire basis
Details: Entrance landing leading into flexible space in main public area. Showcases and some plinths. Exhibitions last 3-4 weeks and have up to 60,000 people passing through, most of whom aren't gallery goers, but who encounter art naturally as they move through the building. Programme aims for balance of work from the locality of all styles and mediums (including computer generated art and video art), new and challenging work and some hired in from outside region. Sales not a main aim.

Craftsman (The) *

26 Trinity Street, Colchester CO1 1JN, tel: 01206 47097
Contact: Mr Dalton

Digby Gallery

Housed within Mercury Theatre complex gallery organises regular shows covering a wide range of art work.
Mercury Theatre, Balkerne Gate, Colchester CO1 1PT, tel: 01206 577006
Contact: Ray Stone, Exhibition Organiser
Space: 1 gallery with 27 lin m hanging space and 17 sq m floor space
Exhibitions: 10 a year all on a hire basis
Details: Aims to be as diverse as possible and encourages artists from the region. One main gallery area which can be extended down into the foyer area. No charge for hiring space. 25% commission. Exhibitions chosen by selection committee from artists' applications.

Firstsite at the Minories

Converted Georgian town house with garden, showing varied programme of temporary contemporary exhibitions.
74 High Street, Colchester CO1 1UE, tel: 01206 577067, fax: 01206 577161
Contact: Katherine Wood, Executive Director
Open: Tues-Sat 10-5; Sun 2-4
Space: 7 galleries with 133 lin m hanging space plus 17 lin m on screens and 320 sq m floor space
Exhibitions: 10 a year of which 2 originated, 8 touring
Details: Aims to present and promote new developments in contemporary visual and media arts. Education policy increases access, encourages participation and cultural debate. Sales not a priority. Access to upstairs galleries impossible for wheelchair users but wheelchair access with assistance to ground floor spaces, café and garden.

Hayletts Gallery

Small commercial gallery with shop front near town centre.
34 North Hill, Colchester CO1 1QR, tel: 01206 761837
Contact: Sally Patrick, Director
Open: Tues-Sat 10-5
Space: 1 gallery with 23 sq m floor space
Exhibitions: 12 a year
Details: Exhibitions primarily of work by East Anglian artists but would welcome others; working artists rather than amateurs. Work taken on sale or return basis. Space also available to rent. White walls.

Pam Schomberg Gallery

Crafts Council selected gallery promoting best in contemporary applied art.
12 St John's Street, Colchester CO2 7AN, tel: 01206 769458
Contact: Pam Schomberg, Proprietor
Open: Mon-Sat 10.30-5
Space: 1 gallery with 585 lin m hanging space and 720 sq m floor space
Exhibitions: 4 a year all originated
Details: Independent gallery promoting British contemporary applied art and craftsmanship featuring work by some of the country's leading craftspeople. Shop area in addition to gallery space. Sales a primary role of gallery.

Printworks

Small commercial gallery specialising in contemporary printmaking and works on paper.
45 Sir Isaacs Walk, Colchester CO1 1JJ, tel: 01206 562049
Contact: Elly Robinson
Open: Tues-Sat 10.30-5
Space: 1 gallery with 16 lin m hanging space and 29 sq m floor space
Exhibitions: 8 a year all originated
Details: Specialises in work of contemporary printmakers. Eight or nine one- or two-person shows per year. Mixed show of gallery artists between. Attempting to make art accessible to all. Printmakers only! Gallery takes 40% commission.

Trinity Street Studios

Artist-run gallery affiliated to Colchester Arts Forum showing work by emerging artists and community groups in Eastern region
6 Trinity Street, Colchester, tel: 01206 369188
Contact: Lin Broomfield, Gallery Team Coordinator
Space: 2 galleries with 32 lin m hanging space and 34 sq m floor space

Exhibitions: 12 a year all originated
Details: Programme selected by quality of work and artists are usually asked to give a talk. Community groups contribute towards exhibition costs.

University Gallery

University gallery showing a thematic series of exhibitions during the autumn and spring terms, with MA students devising their own projects during the summer term.
University of Essex, Wivenhoe Park, Colchester CO4 3SQ, tel: 01206 873260, fax: 01206 873598
Contact: Jessica Kenny, Exhibitions Curator
Open: (Term-time only) Mon-Fri 12-5; Sat 2-4.30
Space: 1 gallery with 50 lin m hanging space and 60 sq m floor space
Exhibitions: 6 a year of which 4 originated, 2 touring
Details: By reflecting the activities and composition of the campus community the gallery offers exhibitions that cannot be seen elsewhere in the region. Applications are therefore rigorously judged to provide a cohesive programme.

Colne
LANCASHIRE NWA

Barnoldswick Library

Exhibition space for work by local artists.
Fernlea Avenue, Barnoldswick, Colne BB8 5DW
Contact: Mrs E Gregson, Branch Librarian
Open: Mon & Wed 9.30-7; Thurs & Fri 9.30-5; Sat 9.30-4
Space: 2 galleries with 18 lin m hanging space
Exhibitions: 12 a year all originated
Details: Sales not a priority.

Colne Library

Display space mainly for contemporary artists and makers in library.
Market Street, Colne BB8 0HS, tel: 01282 871155
Contact: Mrs C. Bradley, Exhibition Organiser
Open: Mon & Fri 9.30-7; Tues 9.30-12; Wed & Thurs 9.30-5; Sat 9.30-4
Space: 2 galleries with 22 lin m hanging space
Exhibitions: 24 a year all on a hire basis
Details: Lockable display case with adjustable shelving in foyer and hanging space available on first floor. Shows usually last a month. Occasionally arranges live craft demonstrations. Sales not main function; 15% sales commission.

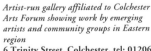

Trawden Library *

Wall-mounted exhibits around the walls of the library.
Church Street, Trawden, Colne BB8 8RU
Space: 1 gallery with 7 lin m hanging space
Exhibitions: 6 a year all originated
Details: One exhibition each month. Village audience.

Colyton
DEVON SWA

Dolphin House Gallery

Selling gallery showing small to medium scale work by professional artists.
Dolphin Street, Colyton EX13 6NA, tel: 01297 553805
Contact: R Laughton, Proprietor
Open: Tues-Sat 9.30-1 & 2-5.30; Wed early closing
Space: 1 gallery with 24 lin m hanging space and 33 sq m floor space
Exhibitions: 5 a year all originated
Details: Gallery aims to show and sell high-quality original works of art to people in East Devon and West Dorset. Owner is professional artist and temporary exhibitions by others alternate with those of his own work. Large north facing windows and white walls.

Congleton
CHESHIRE NWA

Carters Gallery *

Exhibition space fronting Carter House, a social education centre with conference room facilities and restaurant.
Lawton Street, Congleton CW12 1RS, tel: 01260 298 079, fax: 01606 83 5138
Contact: Mike Jackson, Centre Team Leader, PACE, 63a Wheelock Street, Middlewich, CW10 9AB, tel: 01606 83 5286
Space: 700 lin m hanging space and 450 sq m floor space
Exhibitions: 9 a year all originated

Corbridge
NORTHUMBERLAND NA

Corbridge Gallery

Small gallery programmed by Northumberland County Council situated within Corbridge Tourist Information Centre.
Hill Street, Corbridge, tel: 01434 632815
Contact: Visual Arts Officer, Northumberland County Council, County

---

Central Library, The Willows, Morpeth, NE61 1TA, tel: 01670 511156, fax: 01670 518012
Open: (April-Oct) Mon-Sat 10-1, 2-6; Sun 1-5
Space: 1 gallery with 9 lin m hanging space plus 2 lin m on screens and 30 sq m floor space
Exhibitions: 4 a year of which 3 originated, 1 touring
Details: Small gallery specialising in craft and original prints from invited artists/craftspeople. Of 3 exhibitions originated by gallery a year, 2 tour. Some plinths and 2 lockable showcases available. Aims to increase awareness of contemporary visual art and promote sales of work of both regional and national artists and craftspeople in thematic shows. Solo shows rare. Unsuitable for large work. Selling work is one of gallery's primary aims.

Corby
NORTHAMPTONSHIRE EMA

Corby Library

Shows work by local artists and craftspeople, with items of educational value or interest also shown.
9 The Links, Queens Square, Corby NN17 1PZ, tel: 01536 203304, fax: 01536 400954
Contact: Deanna Allan, Exhibitions Organiser
Open: Mon & Thurs 9.30-7; Tues,Wed, Fri 9.30-5; Sat 9.30-4
Space: 1 gallery with 10 lin m hanging space plus 13 lin m on screens and 50 sq m floor space
Exhibitions: 10 a year all on a hire basis
Details: Separate exhibition room and smaller clear area in library for use with freestanding Mahler/Haler boards. Exhibitions for one month. Promotion of literature-related displays in library area. Workshops, talks encouraged. Selling work not main aim of exhibiting work. Gallery booked well in advance. (See also entry for Northamptonshire Libraries.)

Cornhill
SUFFOLK EA

Bury St Edmunds Art Gallery *

Run by charity, situated on 1st floor of a distinguished Georgian building in the middle of town, with temporary exhibitions and musical performances.
Market Cross, Cornhill IP331BT, tel: 01284 762081
Contact: Sylvia Thomas, Curator, Manston Hall, Whepstead, Bury St Edmunds, tel: 01284 88229

Space: 1 gallery with 100 lin m hanging space plus 13 lin m on screens
Exhibitions: 12 a year of which 11 originated, 1 touring
Details: Integrates visual and performing arts, extending the significance of exhibitions. Artists' residencies, demonstrations and workshops.

Corpusty
NORFOLK EA

Old Workshop Art Gallery

Converted barn with separate shop/showroom, featuring exhibitions of modern regional art and craft.
The Street, Corpusty NR11 6QP, tel: 01263 587268
Contact: Margaret Melicharova, Exhibition Organiser, Stable Cottage, Creake Road, Burnham Thorpe, Kings Lynn, PE31 8HW, tel: 01328 738625
Open: (Summer) Tues-Sat 10-5, Sun 12-5; (Winter) Tues-Sat 10-4, Sun 12-4
Space: 2 galleries with 32 lin m hanging space plus 6 lin m on screens and 52 sq m floor space
Exhibitions: 6 a year all originated
Details: Specialises in new work by East Anglian artists and new young artists. Each exhibition features paintings and ceramics (and sculpture where possible). Continuous display of crafts and craftsman-made furniture in shop/showroom. Riverbank situation, sculpture garden, children's playground, tea/coffee all day. Always keen to hear from artists in all media.

Coventry
WEST MIDLANDS WMA

Bug Gallery

65 Lower Precinct, City Centre, Coventry

Herbert Art Gallery and Museum

Municipal museum with collections of fine and applied arts.
Jordan Well, Coventry CV1 5QP, tel: 01203 832381, fax: 01203 832410
Contact: Karen Belshaw, Exhibitions and Events Officer
Open: Mon-Sat 10-5.30; Sun 2-5
Space: 2 galleries with 86 lin m hanging space and 283 sq m floor space
Exhibitions: 12 a year of which 8 originated, 4 touring
Details: Aims to show balanced programme including all artforms. Quality, access, diversity, innovation, interpretation and education all considered important. Work by all age groups, disabled people and

people of non-western origin represented. Sales not a priority.

Lanchester Gallery

Pa Ph Pr Sc ● ⓔ

University gallery showing exciting and innovative work from artists, mainly in West Midlands area.
School of Art & Design, Coventry University, Gosford Street, Coventry CV1 5RZ, tel: 01203 631313, fax: 01203 838667
Contact: Professor Clive Richards, Associate Dean
Space: 2 galleries with 82 lin m hanging space and 217 lin m floor space
Exhibitions: 15 a year of which 12 originated, 3 touring
Details: Predominantly paintings, drawings and sculpture. Concourse Gallery shows photographs. Audience comprises both students and public, with large audience for the extensive workshop programme.

Mead Gallery

Pa Ph Pr Cr Sc ● ④

Part of Warwick University Arts Centre showing mostly established artists.
Warwick Arts Centre, University of Warwick, Coventry CV4 7AL, tel: 01203 523523 ext 2589, fax: 01203 523883
Contact: Sarah Shalgosky, Curator
Open: (Term-time only) Mon-Fri 12-8; Sat 10-8; BH 12-8pm; opening times may alter 1995/96
Space: 3 galleries with 86 lin m hanging space plus 139 lin m on screens and 600 sq m floor space
Exhibitions: 10 a year of which 3 originated, 7 touring
Details: Diverse range of contemporary and historical, solo and group exhibitions of C20th visual culture are shown in term time only. Collection of post-war paintings, prints and sculpture and the Rugby Collection of C20th British painting on loan. A range of talks, workshops and events are organised to complement the exhibition programme. Warwick Arts Centre contains a concert hall, theatre, studio theatre, film theatre, music centre, conference room, bookshop and restaurant. Exhibition space fully accessible for wheelchair users from summer 1995.

Cramlington
NORTHUMBERLAND NA

Forum Gallery

Pa Ph Pr Cr Sc ● ⓑ

Dedicated exhibition space featuring varied programme of small scale exhibitions within the library in Cramlington.
Cramlington Library, Forum Way, Civic Precinct, Cramlington NE23 6QE, tel: 01670 714371/733042

Contact: Helen Payne, Cultural Development Officer, Borough of Blyth Valley, Council Offices, Seaton Delaval, NE25 0DX, tel: 01670 542000, ex 348, fax: 01670 542323
Open: Mon-Wed & Fri 9.30-7.30; Sat 9-12
Space: 1 gallery with 16 lin m hanging space plus 8 lin m on screens and 64 sq m floor space
Exhibitions: 8 a year of which 6 originated, 2 touring
Details: A balanced programme of small-scale exhibitions of work by locally, regionally and nationally recognised artists, photographers and craftspeople.

Cranborne
DORSET SWA

Cranborne Gallery

Pa Pr Cr Sc ● ⓑ

Small commercial gallery showing contemporary art and craft.
14 The Square, Cranborne BH21 5PR, tel: 01725 517692
Contact: Ursula Leach, Owner/Director
Open: Fri & Sat 10-5; during exhibitions also Wed-Sat 10-5; or by appointment
Space: 2 galleries with 27 lin m hanging space
Exhibitions: 4 a year all originated
Details: Exhibitions are interspersed with changing display of contemporary art and craft. Gallery aims to encourage visitors to appreciate contemporary work in a semi-domestic setting. Sales important.

Cranleigh
SURREY SEA

Cranleigh Arts Centre

Pa Ph Pr Cr Sc ● ⓗ ⓑ ⓦ

Weekly exhibitions throughout year in welcoming gallery/coffee bar which can be hired with small commission taken.
High Street, Cranleigh GU6 8AS, tel: 01483 278001
Contact: Rosemary Dubois, Centre Manager
Open: Mon-Fri 10-3.30; Sat 10-12.30; (July & August) Mon-Sat 10-12.30
Space: 1 gallery with 18 lin m hanging space plus 6 lin m on screens and 60 sq m floor space
Exhibitions: 37 a year of which 15 originated, 22 on a hire basis
Details: Centre aims to foster the arts in the community principally through workshops, exhibitions and educational courses for all ages and abilities. Selling work is not the centre's main aim.

Crawley
WEST SUSSEX SEA

Hawth Theatre Foyer

Pa Ph Pr Cr lA ● ⓑ ⓦ

Aims to provide high quality visual art exhibitions which will engage the visitor in a stimulating and thought provoking manner.
Hawth Avenue, Crawley RH10 6YZ, tel: 01293 552941, fax: 01293 533362
Contact: Cathy Bailey, Arts Officer
Open: Mon-Sat 9.30-11 (when performances); 1 hour before show time on Sun
Space: 2 galleries with 27 lin m hanging space
Exhibitions: 6 a year of which 4 originated, 2 touring
Details: Busy exhibition space on two levels of theatre foyer. Programme of touring exhibitions, regional and national contemporary artists, local amateur artists. Large number of people attending theatre provides a good audience for works on show. Provision of related educational activities in form of talks/workshops for schools, colleges and general public by exhibiting artist will be prioritised 1995/6 Selling work not gallery's primary function.

Crook
CO DURHAM NA

Mall (The)

Pa Ph Pr Cr lA ● ⓔ ⓑ ⓦ ④

Exhibition space within council offices providing venue for local artists to show work.
Civic Centre, Crook, tel: 01388 765555
Contact: Jillian Aldred
Open: Mon 8.30-5; Fri 8.30-4.30
Space: 1 gallery with plus 22 lin m on screens
Exhibitions: 12 a year all originated
Details: Varied programme of exhibitions, one-person and group shows by amateur and professional local artists. Promotes local arts activities, provides stimulus for appreciation and production of visual arts in area and contributes to user friendly environment in Civic Centre. All hanging space is on 8'x4' screens. Sales of work important and 10% commission taken.

Cropredy
OXFORDSHIRE SA

Old Coal Wharf Arts at Cropredy

Pa Ph Pr Sc lA ● ⓗ ⓑ ⓦ ④

Gallery and arts club with varied programme of films, music, visual arts and workshops with canal-side café.

The Plantation, Cropredy OX17 1PW, tel: 01295 750878
Contact: John Foley, Proprietor/Artistic Director
Open: Mon-Fri 10.30-6; Sat, Sun, BH & other times as per programme.
Space: 1 gallery with 13 lin m hanging space plus 8 lin m on screens and 32 sq m floor space
Exhibitions: 7 a year
Details: Aims to encourage the public to meet and work with artists. Sales not considered a priority but 15% commission taken on sales made.

Crowborough
EAST SUSSEX SEA

Green Lane Gallery
Pa Ph Cr lA ✓ H
Gallery on a school site with varied programme of exhibitions, predominantly the work of living artists.
Beacon School, Green Lane, Crowborough TN6 2AS, tel: 01892 653451
Contact: Elizabeth Wood, Exhibition Organiser
Space: 1 gallery with 42 lin m hanging space plus 10 lin m on screens and 84 sq m floor space
Exhibitions: 3 a year of which 2 originated, 1 on a hire basis
Details: Aims to provide a focal point for a wide range of audiences and exhibitions. Accessible to as many people as possible and keeping costs, wherever possible, to a minimum. Anxious to involve exhibitors in seminars, workshops and residencies. Work used as a major learning resource by the school. Gallery space not available May to July.

Darlington
CO DURHAM NA

Bernhardt Gallery *
Pa Pr
A private gallery showing watercolours, etchings, lithographs and screenprints.
60 Coniscliffe Road, Darlington DL3 7RN, tel: 01325 356633
Contact: Margaret Reynolds, Exhibition Organiser
Space: 1 gallery with 25 lin m hanging space
Exhibitions: 3 a year all originated
Details: Professional and especially talented local artists. Periodic solo and group exhibitions.

Darlington Art Gallery
Pa Ph Pr SC ✓ ⊗
Small municipal gallery for touring and temporary exhibitions of work by local artists.

Crown Street, Darlington DL1 1ND, tel: 01325 462034, fax: 01325 381556
Contact: P White, Manager
Open: Mon-Fri 10-8; Sat 10-5.30
Space: 1 gallery with 44 lin m hanging space plus 12 lin m on screens and 154 sq m floor space
Exhibitions: 3 a year all originated
Details: Apart from gallery additional space available for local 'artist of the month' in entrance area. Sales not a priority.

Darlington Arts Centre
Pa Ph Pr Cr SC ✓ ⓔ ⊕ Wc
Arts centre with three exhibition spaces; Myles Meehan Gallery, Foyer and Craft Window.
Vane Terrace, Darlington DL3 7AX, tel: 01325 365794
Contact: Jocelyn Friel, Exhibition Officer
Open: Mon-Sat 10-6
Space: 2 galleries with 47 lin m hanging space and 117 sq m floor space
Exhibitions: 8 a year of which 3 originated, 5 touring
Details: Dimensions and number of exhibitions refer to Myles Meehan Gallery and Foyer spaces; Craft Window additionally has 8 exhibitions a year showing work by craftspeople in northern region. Activities and events programmed for most exhibitions. Sales not main function of arts centre's exhibition spaces.

Dartford
KENT SEA

Dartford Central Library Gallery
Pa Ph Pr SC lA ✓ ⓔ
Encourages local artists at all levels and presents work of more than local significance.
Central Park, Dartford DA1 1EU, tel: 01322 221133, fax: 01322 278271
Contact: Geoff Beetles, Media Services Officer
Open: Mon & Thurs-Fri 9-6; Tues 9-7; Wed 9-1; Sat 9-5
Space: 1 gallery with 11 lin m hanging space plus 10 lin m on screens and 45 sq m floor space
Exhibitions: 12 a year of which 10 originated, 2 touring
Details: Favours local artists and hopes to give them the opportunity to show and sell work to the public. Also aims to bring work in from outside the area and exhibit on a non-commercial basis. Publicises widely to attract more people to see exhibitions.

Dartmouth
DEVON SWA

Facets
Cr ✓ ⓖ
Specialist Crafts Council selected gallery showing large collection of contemporary jewellery.
14 Broadstone, Dartmouth TQ6 9NR, tel: 01803 833534
Contact: Jaqueline Dilley
Open: Mon-Sat 10-5; Wed 10-1; BH 10.30-4
Space: 1 gallery with 40 sq m floor space
Exhibitions: 2 a year both originated
Details: Pieces on show include precious and non-precious work from over 70 selected artists. Shows as innovative as possible, attracting a national audience. Gallery prefers to pay all exhibition costs, allowing complete control of private views and invitations. Walls have 30 alarmed eye level vertical display cases. Also 9 free standing alarmed glass topped cases with horizontal display. Sales a priority.

Higher Street Gallery
Pa Pr Cr ✓
Crafts Council selected gallery.
1 Higher Street, Dartmouth TQ6 9RB, tel: 01803 833157
Contact: Mark Goodwin, Exhibition Organiser
Space: 1 gallery with 40 lin m hanging space
Exhibitions: 3 a year all originated
Details: Speciality is contemporary watercolours, also shows ceramics, glass, textiles, wood and jewellery by leading British makers. Recently introduced limited edition prints. Purchases and sells mixed crafts. Maximum of four exhibitions a year.

Simon Drew Gallery *
Pa Pr Cr SC
Commercial gallery on Crafts Council selected list.
13 Foss Street, Dartmouth TQ6 9DR, tel: 01803 832832
Contact: Simon & Caroline Drew, Exhibition Organiser
Space: 3 galleries with 42 sq m floor space
Details: Changing display of work. Occasional exhibitions by specific artists and different potters. Buys work from stable of artists to add to permanent collection sold from premises.

Darwen
LANCASHIRE NWA

Sunnyhurst Wood Visitor Centre

Changing displays on history of Darwen also shows temporary exhibitions.
Sunnyhurst Wood, Off Earnsdale Road, Darwen BB3 0LA, tel: 01254 701545
Contact: Steve Morris, Exhibitions Officer, Blackburn Museum & Art Gallery, Museum Street, Blackburn, tel: 01254 667130
Open: Tues, Thurs, Sat, Sun & BH 2-4.30
Space: 1 gallery with 23 lin m hanging space and 41 sq m floor space
Exhibitions: 10 a year of which 4 originated, 6 on a hire basis
Details: Monthly solo or group exhibitions of mixed themes aiming to increase awareness of the arts. Where exhibition space is "hired" out, this is free. Selling work not gallery's main role. (See also entry for Blackburn Museum & Art Gallery.)

Daventry
NORTHAMPTONSHIRE EMA

Daventry Library *

Library exhibition space.
North Street, Daventry NN11 5PN, tel: 01327 703130
Details: See Northamptonshire Libraries, Northampton.

Moot Hall

Local history museum with temporary exhibition space devoted primarily to contemporary arts and crafts.
Market Square, Daventry NN11 4BH, tel: 01327 302418, fax: 01327 300011
Contact: Sonia Hawes, Arts Officer, Daventry District Council, Leisure Services Department, Lodge Road, Daventry, NN11 5AF, tel: 01327 302418
Open: (Oct-Mar) Tues-Sat 10-3.30; (Apr-Sept) Mon-Fri 10-5, Sats 10-4
Space: 1 gallery with 17 lin m hanging space plus 12 lin m on screens and 22 sq m floor space
Exhibitions: 10 a year of which 8 originated, 2 touring
Details: Exhibitions cover range of contemporary arts and crafts aimed at all ages and various interest. Workshops sometimes organised in conjunction with exhibitions. Sales not priority but encouraged; operates RAB interest free loan scheme for purchasers. 10% commission on sales.

Dawlish
DEVON SWA

Porch Galleries *

Small provincial gallery dedicated to the encouragement of new and young artists.
2a Iddesleigh Terrace, Dawlish EX7 9HS, tel: 01626 867080
Contact: A.M. Afifi, Director
Space: 2 galleries with 40 lin m hanging space and 60 sq m floor space
Exhibitions: 10 a year all originated
Details: Seeks to offer good contemporary art at affordable prices. Extensively involved in community projects. Not commercial. More interested in presenting good art and obtaining publicity for the artists.

Vivian Gallery

Small commercial gallery selling clothing, jewellery and accessories by designer/craftspeople from around the country.
2 Queen Street, Dawlish EX7 9HB, tel: 01626 867254
Contact: Peter Bunyan, Exhibition Organiser
Open: Mon-Sat 9-6
Space: 1 gallery with 3 lin m hanging space and 12 sq m floor space
Exhibitions: 4 a year all originated
Details: Occasional exhibitions of mainly small-scale items with emphasis on quality and value rather than avant garde extremes; demonstrating to the public that there are things worth buying outside chain stores.

Deal
KENT SEA

Deal Library Gallery

Varied programme focusing on the work of living artists in all media, particularly with connections to Kent.
Broad Street, Deal CT14 6ER, tel: 01304 372984
Contact: Arts & Heritage Officer
Space: 1 gallery with 11 lin m hanging space plus 11 lin m on screens and 41 sq m floor space
Exhibitions: 18 a year of which 1 originated, 17 on a hire basis
Details: Aims to promote artists' work, showing that which would not otherwise be seen in the area. Exhibitions run 3-4 weeks.

Derby
DERBYSHIRE EMA

Arbor Darkrooms & Gallery

Recently refurbished Grade II listed building housing nine darkrooms and a small gallery space.
Arboretum Lodge, Arboretum Square, Derby DE23 8FN, tel: 01332 299049
Contact: Project Co-ordinator
Open: (During exhibitions) Sat & Sun 11-3
Space: 1 gallery with 22 lin m hanging space and 48 sq m floor space
Exhibitions: 5 a year of which 4 originated, 1 touring
Details: One-person or group exhibitions presented. Workshops and short courses run. Darkrooms and studio facilities for hire. Operates equal opportunities policy. Sales not a priority.

Atrium Gallery

Shows contemporary work to attract business community and bringing together artists and potential patrons.
Derwent Business Centre, Clarke Street, Derby DE1 2BU, tel: 01332 298788, fax: 01332 298836
Contact: Stuart Mills, Art Locate, Derwent Business Centre, Clarke Street, Derby, DE1 2BU, tel: 01773 824690
Open: Mon-Fri 9-5; or by appointment
Space: 1 gallery with 77 lin m hanging space
Exhibitions: 10 a year all originated
Details: Provides exhibition space particularly for artists who have experienced difficulty in finding space because of scale of work, questionable commercial viability and progressive nature. As well as mounting major exhibitions gallery maintains collection of smaller drawings, paintings and prints as permanent changing display. Sales of work important but not primary function of gallery.

Derby City Council House

Space available for exhibitions in busy Payments Hall providing an extra venue for artists, craftspeople and photographers.
Corporation Street, Derby DE1 2FS, tel: 01332 293111, fax: 01332 255500
Contact: Frank Walters, Director of Art for All, Derby City General Hospital, Uttoxeter Road, Derby, DE22 3NE, tel: 01332 340131 ext 5910, fax: 01332 290559
Open: Mon-Fri 10-5
Space: 1 gallery with 20 lin m hanging space

Exhibitions: 8 a year of which 5 originated, 3 touring
Details: Space in the community charge hall with fluorescent and natural light, direct fixing onto wallboards. Work is for display only. For exhibition policy please see entry for Derby City General Hospital.

Derby City General Hospital

Pa Ph Pr Cr SC ● ⬤

Exhibitions held in admissions waiting area, seen by staff, patients & visitors, and organised by Art for All based here.
Uttoxeter Road, Derby DE22 3NE, tel: 01332 340131 ext 5910, fax: 01332 290559
Contact: Frank Walters, Director of Art for All
Open: Daily
Space: 1 gallery with 20 lin m hanging space
Exhibitions: 8 a year of which 3 originated, 5 touring
Details: Art for All arranges regular touring programmes in various venues (see separate entries for University of Derby (Concourse Gallery), Derby City Council House & Ilkeston Community Hospital). Loans exhibitions for touring and operates picture loan scheme. Exhibitions aim to increase audience for contemporary visual arts, and provide publicity and support for artists and makers. Sites used are carefully selected, equipped with blockboard-clad walls to provide a sympathetic environment for the exhibitions. Wide-ranging programme with emphasis on work by regional artists and makers. Supported by East Midlands Arts, Derby City Council, various health trusts & University of Derby. Sale of work is possible.

Derby Community Arts

Pa Ph Pr Cr SC LA ● ⬤ ⬤ ⬤ 4

Exhibition space situated in large shop front area of building, lit by natural light and shares space with informal vegetarian café.
31 Woods Lane, Derby DE3 3UA, tel: 01332 385601/2, fax: 01332 385602
Contact: Jose Mountford, Community Arts Worker
Open: Tues-Thurs 10-6
Space: 1 gallery with 29 lin m hanging space
Exhibitions: 7 a year of which 6 originated, 1 touring
Details: Aims to reflect and support creative work taking place in the centre and originated by the centre; to provide space for local artists to exhibit. Provides creative opportunities for people who often don't have access to the arts. Sales not a priority.

Derby Industrial Museum

Pa Ph SC ● ⬤ ⬤ 4

Small gallery mounting exhibitions on themes connected with science, technology, industry, transport and local history.
Silk Mill Lane, Off Full Street, Derby DE1 3AR, tel: 01332 255308, fax: 01332 255804
Contact: Jonathan Platt, Senior Keeper of Industry & Technology
Open: Mon 11-5 (except BH); Tues-Sat 10-5; Sun & BH Mon 2-5; closed Xmas Day & Boxing Day
Space: 1 gallery with 19 lin m hanging space plus 12 lin m on screens and 80 sq m floor space
Exhibitions: 6 a year of which 1 originated, 5 touring
Details: Where possible events and activities are organised in connection with exhibitions. Artists prepare work for the exhibition; museum assists with publicity and mounting.

Derby Museum & Art Gallery

Pa Ph Cr ● ⬤ ⬤ ⬤ 4

Municipal gallery housing Joseph Wright of Derby collection and Crown Derby porcelain with varied programme of temporary exhibitions and events.
The Strand, Derby DE1 1BS, tel: 01332 293111
Contact: Maggie Cullen, Keeper of Fine Art & Exhibitions
Open: Mon 11-5; Tues-Sat 10-5; Sun & BH 2-5
Space: 3 galleries with 116 lin m hanging space and 260 sq m floor space
Exhibitions: 12 a year of which 6 originated, 6 touring
Details: Three galleries for temporary exhibition programme and series of workshops. Exhibitions drawn from number of sources including national touring exhibitions and shows by established artists and makers in the region. Small crafts case in shop holds changing display of work for sale. Work also sold in gallery but this is not a priority.

Derby Playhouse

Pa Ph Pr Cr SC ● ⬤ ⬤ ⬤

Theatre foyer space aiming to show variety of work in informal atmosphere.
Theatre Walk, Eagle Centre, Derby DE1 2NF, tel: 01332 363271, fax: 01332 294412
Contact: Kirsty Doubleday, Deputy Sales & Marketing Manager
Open: Mon-Sat 9.30-6
Space: 1 gallery with 6 lin m hanging space
Exhibitions: 8 a year
Details: Exhibitions take theme of current production and try to develop into another art form. Exhibition space on staircase leading to entrance into the auditorium,

and is viewed by audience (530 capacity) and visitors to coffee bar and restaurant. Selling work not gallery's primary role.

Derby Tertiary College: Wilmorton

Pa Ph Pr Cr SC ● ⬤ ⬤

Main hall, reception area and canteen area in college available for exhibitions.
London Road, Derby DE24 8UG, tel: 01332 757570 ext 218, fax: 01332 573149
Contact: Anne Barker, Lettings Co-ordinator
Open: Mon-Fri 9-8
Space: 3 galleries
Exhibitions: 10 a year all on a hire basis
Details: Space available on hire basis. No policy; anything considered that is suitable for space. Often used by college's own students. Sales not a priority.

Gallery 93

Pa Pr SC ● ⬤ ⬤

Small gallery suitable for one-person exhibitions in context of domestic environment.
93 Belper Road, Derby DE1 3ER, tel: 01332 363574
Contact: Josephine Thomas, Gallery Owner
Open: Mon-Fri 2-7; Sat-Sun 10-4
Space: 1 gallery with 20 lin m hanging space and 42 sq m floor space
Exhibitions: 20 a year all originated
Details: Aims to encourage people too see art within domestic environment. Policy is to show work by local artists whose ability varies; some well known, others are beginners. Considers sales and making contemporary work available equally important functions of gallery.

Guildhall Theatre

Pa Ph LA ● ⬤ ⬤

Theatre foyer space for hire on weekly basis to amateur and professional artists.
Market Place, Derby DE1 3AH, tel: 01332 255447, fax: 01332 255788
Contact: Andy Falconer, Manager
Open: Mon-Sat 10-5
Space: 1 gallery
Exhibitions: 35 a year all originated
Details: Selling work is considered gallery space's primary role.

Metro Gallery

Ph SC ● ⬤ ⬤ ⬤ 4

Corridor gallery showing contemporary photography, housed in the University of Derby building and acting as a reception area and gallery for Metro Cinema.
Metro Cinema, Green Lane, Derby DE1 1SA, tel: 01332 295858
Contact: Elizabeth-Anne Williams, Galleries Officer, Montage Gallery, 35/36

Queen Street, Derby, DE1 3DS, tel: 01332 295858, fax: 01332 295859
Open: Mon 10-5; Tues-Fri 10-8; Sat & Sun 6-8 access with cinema
Space: 1 gallery with 31 lin m hanging space
Exhibitions: 9 a year of which 7 originated, 2 touring
Details: Programme closely linked to that at Montage Gallery. Where possible it also explores links with Metro Cinema film programme. Aims to promote and support photographers and artists at the start of their exhibiting career. Sales of work encouraged through interest free loan scheme for purchasers operated by RAB.

Montage Gallery

Independent photography gallery which challenges boundaries of photography.
35/36 Queen Street, Derby DE1 3DS, tel: 01332 295858, fax: 01332 295859
Contact: Elizabeth-Anne Williams, Galleries Officer
Open: Tues-Sat 10-5; Sun 2-5
Space: 1 gallery with 21 lin m hanging space 29 lin m on screens and 121 sq m floor space
Exhibitions: 9 a year of which 5 originated, 4 touring
Details: Exhibitions incorporating video and electronic imaging included in programme. Aims to promote photography as a medium of cultural significance and demonstrate its scope in a challenging and stimulating way. Education programme of lectures, workshops and events (including jazz and dance). Also a resource centre offering book shop, information and portfolio sessions. Sale of work not a primary role but sales encouraged and gallery is member of RAB Art Purchase interest free loan scheme. Co-ordinates biennial Derby Photography Festival.

Sinfin Library

Separate exhibition area visible from main library.
District Centre, Arleston Lane, Sinfin, Derby DE24 3DS, tel: 01332 773773
Contact: Mrs Glen Francis, Assistant in Charge
Open: Mon, Tues, Fri 10-5.30 ; Thurs 10-7; Sat 9.30-1
Space: 1 gallery with 8 lin m hanging space plus 11 lin m on screens and 26 sq m floor space
Exhibitions: 3 a year all originated
Details: Encourages visitors who might not normally visit galleries and local artists and craftspeople to exhibit their work. Wall space interrupted by windows/doors. Small lockable display case and video/TV. Demonstrations and workshops. If sales made 20% commission taken (10% for charities). Booking fee may be applicable.

St Michael's Gallery

Small commercial gallery attached to Cathedral Shop, suitable for individuals and small groups to hire.
St Michael's House, Queen Street, Derby DE1 3DT, tel: 01332 341201, fax: 01332 203991
Contact: Bill Dobson, Gallery Director
Open: Mon-Sat 9.30-4.30
Exhibitions: 12 a year all on a hire basis
Details: Run by Derby Cathedral, and forms part of the shop. Monthly exhibitions are mostly solo. Aims to encourage younger artists from the region and elsewhere, and show more established artists. Selling work not primary role.

University of Derby (Concourse Gallery)

Busy main concourse area leading to refectory, bookshop and teaching rooms.
Western Road, Mickleover, Derby DE3 5GX, tel: 01332 622222
Contact: Frank Walters, Director of Art for All, Derby City General Hospital, Uttoxeter Road, Derby, DE22 3NE, tel: 01332 340131 ext 5910, fax: 01332 290559
Open: Mon-Fri 9.30-6
Space: 1 gallery with 20 lin m hanging space
Exhibitions: 7 a year of which 3 originated, 4 touring
Details: Main concourse area with fluorescent and natural light, direct fixing on wallboards. A non-gallery venue initiated as a teaching and learning resource for the campus where Schools of Education & Social Sciences, Health and International Studies are based. (For Art for All exhibition policy see entry for Derby City General Hospital.) Sale of work is impossible.

Desford
LEICESTERSHIRE EMA

Bosworth College Gallery *

Part of community college which aims to encourage artists from all spheres of creative activity.
The Bosworth College, Leicester Lane, Desford LE9 9JL, tel: 01455 822841
Contact: Irene Landells, Exhibition Organiser

Dewsbury
WEST YORKSHIRE YHA

Art Gallery at Dewsbury Museum

Contemporary exhibition gallery within historical museum showing art, craft and print, and featuring local and regional artists.
Crow Nest Park, Heckmondwike Road, Dewsbury WF13 2SA, tel: 01924 468171, fax: 01924 464952
Contact: Helen Robinson, Galleries Officer
Open: Mon-Fri 11-5; Sat & Sun 12-5
Space: 1 gallery with 25 lin m hanging space plus 10 lin m on screens and 50 sq m floor space
Exhibitions: 9 a year of which 7 originated, 2 touring
Details: One-person and group shows in all media. Work by local societies and schools also shown. Education programme compliments displays. Gallery aims to make art, contemporary and historical, an important part of museum visit. Sales not priority.

Ditchling
EAST SUSSEX SEA

Craftsman Gallery

Wide range of work by makers living and working in Sussex shown in a changing display.
8 High Street, Ditchling BN6 8TA, tel: 01273 845246
Contact: Jill Pryke, Owner
Space: 1 gallery
Details: Crafts gallery and pottery workshop producing Jill Pryke's domestic thrown earthenware. Range of other work shown; wall hangings, weaving, pottery, wood, engravings, jewellery, etchings, paintings and prints.

Docking
NORFOLK EA

Unit 2 Gallery

Commercial gallery in North Norfolk holiday area specialising in sculpture, ceramics and collage by makers nationally.
The Rural workshops, Station Road, Docking PE31 8LT, tel: 01485 518817
Contact: Tony Eeles
Open: Tues-Sat 10-4; Sun 11-3
Space: 1 gallery with 25 lin m hanging space and 50 sq m floor space 4 a year all originated
Details: Exhibitions last one month and show work by one or more makers. Large exterior floodlit display area as well as

gallery. Between exhibitions changing displays of work by new and established artists and craftspeople. Aims to encourage visitors to appreciate contemporary sculpture and craftwork. Sales of work paramount and very good during summer visitor season.

Doncaster
SOUTH YORKSHIRE YHA

Church View Gallery

Pa Ph Pr Cr Sc ✓ ⬤

Small foyer gallery space used mainly to show work by new contemporary artists/ designers.
Metropolitan Institute of Higher Education, Church View, Doncaster DN1 1RE, tel: 01302 22122 ext 276
Contact: Rob Ward, Exhibition Organiser, Doncaster College, Church View, Doncaster, DN1 1RF, tel: 01302 553553, fax: 01302 553838
Open: Mon-Thurs 9-9; Fri 9-5
Space: 1 gallery with 40 lin m hanging space plus 4 lin m on screens and 104 sq m floor space
Exhibitions: 3 a year all originated
Details: Public gallery within Art & Design Education department of Doncaster College showing visual arts and crafts with emphasis on new work. Primarily an educational stimulus for students. Also shows work by artists and makers who have not exhibited before. Selling work is not a priority so commission on sales isn't charged. This may change in future. Looking for strong, unusual work which will stimulate the students and the general public.

Doncaster Museum & Art Gallery

Pa Ph Pr Cr Sc ✓ ⬤Vc

Seven galleries used to display temporary exhibitions as well as the permanent collection.
Chequer Road, Doncaster DN1 2AE, tel: 01302 734293, fax: 01302 735409
Contact: G Preece, Principal Museums Officer
Open: Mon-Sat 10-5; Sun 2-5
Space: 7 galleries with 231 lin m hanging space plus 115 lin m on screens and 886 sq m floor space
Exhibitions: 20 a year all originated
Details: Collections of British fine and decorative art. Large and varied temporary programme includes some contemporary work. Permanent displays of human history and archaeology, natural history, decorative art and fine art. Operates schools service and runs education programmes and activities. Sale of work not gallery's primary role.

Make Do and Mend Art Gallery and Exhibition Space

Pa Pr Cr Sc ✓ ⬤

Secondhand, old and unusual clothing shop with gallery above displaying and selling arts and crafts by local artists.
Roxy Fox (Upstairs at), 10 Thorne Road, Doncaster DN1 2HS
Contact: Marianne Shaw, Exhibitions Organiser
Open: Sat 10.30-5
Space: 2 galleries
Details: No policy as such: "a collection of artwork/junkabelia put together to create ambiances of Timeless Time. Just because its old and obsolete, doesn't have to mean it's useless." Two small galleries. Sales a priority. Interested to hear from local artists.

Museum of South Yorkshire Life

Pa Ph Cr LA ✓ H ⬤Wc

Family museum with programme of temporary exhibitions, events and activities.
Cusworth Hall, Doncaster DN5 7TU, tel: 01302 782342
Contact: Alison Devlin, Curator
Open: Mon-Fri 10-5; Sat 11-5; Sun 1-5
Space: 1 gallery with 30 lin m hanging space plus 38 lin m on screens and 63 sq m floor space
Exhibitions: 8 a year
Details: Collections illustrative of everyday life in South Yorkshire over last 200 years (costume, domestic life, childhood, occupations, transport etc) displayed in Georgian mansion. All exhibitions relate to South Yorkshire Life (includes local art and craft). Work scrutinised to ensure relevance to permanent collection.

South Yorkshire Art Gallery

Pa Pr ✓ ⬤

Small gallery in centre of Doncaster exhibiting work by both established artists and those at early stage in career.
52 Copley Road, Doncaster DN1 2QW, tel: 01302 329332
Contact: Colin Wedd, Gallery owner
Open: Tues & Wed, Fri & Sat 10-4; Thurs 10-1
Space: 4 galleries
Exhibitions: 7 a year all originated
Details: Gallery on two floors in former small terraced house. Wide range of media and subject matter is accepted; selection criterion is quality.

Dorchester
DORSET SWA

Dorchester Gallery *

Pa Pr Cr Sc ✓

Specialises in representational art, ceramics and sculpture.
10a High East Street, Dorchester DT1 1HS, tel: 01305 251144
Contact: Laura Wood Homer, Proprietor
Space: 1 gallery with 30 lin m hanging space and 45 sq m floor space
Exhibitions: 7 a year all originated
Details: Grade II listed building. Around seven two-week exhibitions a year, either solo or theme shows. Does not show abstract, nor commercial local art. Work is by professional artists. Clients tend to be art collectors and young couples, but not the 'county set'!

Gallery Gilbert

Pa Pr Cr Sc ✓ ⬤

Gallery exhibits and sells British and international modern and contemporary art by both well-known and promising artists.
48 High West Street, Dorchester DT1 1UT, tel: 01305 263740
Contact: ADF Gilbert, FM Gilbert & SA Gilbert, Partners
Open: Tues-Sat 10-5
Space: 3 galleries
Exhibitions: 6 a year
Details: Regular exhibitions of paintings, sculpture and fine studio pottery. Sales a priority.

Dorking
SURREY SEA

Gentle Gallery

Pa Pr

Shows contemporary work in a variety of media and offers a framing and restoration service.
268 High Street, Dorking RH4 1QT, tel: 01306 886088
Contact: Basil & Nicholas Gentle, Directors

Westcott Gallery

Pa ✓ ⬤4

Gallery exhibiting and selling 2D work by Surrey artists.
4 Guildford Road, Westcott, Dorking RH4 3NR, tel: 01306 876261, fax: 01306 740421
Contact: Mrs Barbara Wakefield
Open: (During exhibitions) Mon-Fri 11-3, Sat 10-5; otherwise by appointment
Space: 2 galleries with 12 lin m hanging space and 41 sq m floor space
Exhibitions: 2 a year both originated
Details: Gallery with policy of encouraging established and promising Surrey artists.

Dover
KENT SEA

Dover Museum
[Pa][Ph][Pr][Cr][SC] ✔ ♿[WC]

Gallery purpose-built as a community and tourism amenity.

Market Square, Dover CT16 1PB, tel: 01304 201066, fax: 01304 241186

Contact: Mark Frost, Assistant Curator
Space: 1 gallery with 54 lin m hanging space plus 26 lin m on screens and 162 sq m floor space
Exhibitions: 4 a year of which 3 originated, 1 touring
Details: Provides exhibitions of local and national interest on local history, national history, natural history, art history and decorative arts. A forum for exhibition and promotion of local and regional arts and crafts, both professional and amateur, as well as exhibitions of other themes where they would be of benefit and interest to the local community or promote the district to a wider audience. Sales not a priority.

Dover Town Hall
[Pa][Ph][Pr][Cr][SC] ✔[H] ♿

Multi-purpose very large function rooms available for hire.

Biggin Street, Dover CT16 1DL, tel: 01304 201200

Contact: Mr T Jones, General Manager
Open: Mon-Fri 9-5
Space: 2 galleries with 612 sq m floor space
Exhibitions: 20 a year all on a hire basis
Details: No active policy; responds to approaches from artists wishing to hire space.

Droitwich
HEREFORD & WORCESTER WMA

Droitwich Heritage Centre
[Pa][Ph][Pr][Cr][SC] ✔ ♿[WC]

Exhibition centre providing temporary exhibitions of local, national and educational interest.

St Richard's House, Victoria Square, Droitwich WR9 8DS, tel: 01905 774312, fax: 01905 794226

Contact: Serena Joule, Tourism Officer
Open: Mon-Fri 9.30-5; Sat 10-4
Space: 1 gallery with 22 lin m hanging space and 45 sq m floor space
Exhibitions: 8 a year of which 7 originated, 1 touring
Details: Changing exhibitions programme dealing with wide range of artistic media. Encourages public to view exhibitions and make more use of the centre. Talks, workshops and demonstrations arranged depending on exhibition. Programme mainly general interest and mixed exhibitions. Selling work is not gallery's main aim.

Droitwich Library
[Pa][Ph][Cr] ✔[H] ♿

First floor multi-purpose exhibition room in library.

Victoria Square, Droitwich WR9 8DQ, tel: 01905 773292/ 779970, fax: 01905 797401

Contact: Miss V Booler, Librarian
Open: Mon-Wed 9.30-5.30; Fri 9.30-8; Sat 9.30-4
Space: 1 gallery with 26 lin m hanging space and 73 sq m floor space
Exhibitions: 18 a year of which 4 touring, 14 on a hire basis
Details: Art/craft exhibitions as showcase for talents of local residents. Occasional touring exhibitions taken which bring to to town art/culture not otherwise experienced. Screens, cases, tables, etc available for display as well as wall space. Sale of work encouraged. (See also entry for Hereford & Worcester Libraries & Arts Department, Worcester.)

Dudley
WEST MIDLANDS WMA

Dudley Art Gallery
[Pa][Ph][Pr] ✔ ♿[4]

Municipal gallery with varied exhibition programme and occasional workshops and events.

St James's Road, Dudley DY1 1HU, tel: 01384 453571, fax: 01384 453576

Contact: Colin Reid, Museum Keeper
Open: Mon-Sat 10-5
Space: 3 galleries with 104 lin m hanging space and 221 sq m floor space
Exhibitions: 6 a year of which 3 originated, 3 touring
Details: Three large galleries for one major or three smaller exhibitions. Despite its small size the museum can accommodate national exhibitions and those requiring government indemnity. Exhibitions relevant to National Curriculum particularly welcome.

Dulverton
SOMERSET SWA

Dulverton Guildhall Heritage & Arts Centre
[Pa][Ph][Cr][SC] ✔[H] ♿

Gallery in a heritage information complex on Exmoor, for hire to individuals or groups of artists.

The Guildhall, Dulverton TA22, tel: 01398 24081

Contact: Jan Ross, Secretary, Civic Society
Open: Apr-Oct daily 10-4.30
Space: 1 gallery with 26 lin m hanging space
Exhibitions: 18 a year all on a hire basis
Details: Weekly to monthly bookings accepted. Used by professional and amateur artists and craftspeople. Good potential sales to Exmoor visitors and local people although sales not primary role of gallery. Weekly hire charge. A relaxed informal atmosphere.

Dunstable
BEDFORDSHIRE EA

Gallery (The)
[Pa][Ph][Pr][SC] ✔ ♿

Gallery situated in library entrance showing mix of national, regional and local artists' work.

Dunstable Library, Vernon Place, Dunstable LU5 4HA, tel: 01582 608441, fax: 01582 471290

Contact: Liz Lush, Arts Worker
Open: Mon, Tues, Wed & Fri 9.30-7; Thurs 9.30-5; Sat 9.30-4; closed BH
Spaces: 1 gallery with 14 lin m hanging space
Exhibitions: 15 a year of which 12 originated, 3 touring
Details: Aims to show 6 exhibitions a year of national/international importance (including for example South Bank touring shows). Aims to bring to the area work that would not otherwise be seen. Strong competition from local artists for remainder of the programme. Intention is to maintain high overall standard. Brief to promote photography. 20% commission taken on any sales made.

Queensway Hall *
[Pa][Ph][Pr][Cr][SC][LA] ✔

Exhibition space in civic centre.

Vernon Place, Dunstable LU5 4EU, tel: 01582 603326, fax: 01582 471190

Contact: Yvonne Mullins, General Manager
Details: All year round functions.

Durham
CO DURHAM NA

Almhouses Restaurant
Palace Green, Durham, tel: 0191 386 3553

Durham Art Gallery & DLI Museum
[Pa][Ph][Pr][Cr][SC] ✔ ♿[WC]

Two main galleries and adjacent Print Room providing major exhibitions plus workshops, concerts, lectures, films and other events.

Aykley Heads, Durham DH1 5TU, tel: 0191 384 2214, fax: 0191 386 1770

Contact: Dennis Hardingham, Exhibitions Organiser
Open: Tues-Sat 10-5; Sun 2-5; open BH except Xmas/New Year
Space: 2 galleries with 107 lin m hanging space plus 10 lin m on screens and 320 sq m floor space
Exhibitions: 5 a year of which 4 originated, 1 touring
Details: Varied programme of temporary exhibitions related to all aspects of the visual arts. Slides and CVs in first instance to Exhibition Organiser. Access: works must fit through a single door opening. Audience: families, tourists, general interest. Sales not primary role of gallery.

Easington Village
CLEVELAND NA

Long Gallery

Seaton Holme, Hall Walks, Easington Village, tel: 0191 527 3333

East Grinstead
WEST SUSSEX SEA

Autumn Art Show

Pa Pr Cr SS ✓ 🔴💧

Annual open exhibition held Aug/Sept.
Neale House Conference Centre, East Grinstead, tel: 01892 653873
Contact: Gillian Nassau
Space: 3 galleries
Details: Has grown in 5 years from local showcase to important regional event. Open to both professionals and amateurs, work judged purely on merit. Details of procedure published in advance, available to all artists who register for selection (cost £5). Traditional free-hand draughtsmanship forms core of the work on show. Artists expected to be available for help and comment on their work.

East Molesey
SURREY SEA

Molesey Gallery *

Pa Pr ✓

Gallery particularly oriented toward contemporary print in small editions.
46 Walton Rad, East Molesey KT8 0DQ, tel: 0181 941 2706
Contact: Michael Palmer
Space: 2 galleries with 61 sq m floor space
Exhibitions: 3 a year all originated
Details: Although it has a small frontage the available exhibition space is more substantial. As well as contemporary print also includes shows of painting, sculpture and ceramics. Changing display of prints from stock with approximately 4 solo shows a year.

Eastbourne
EAST SUSSEX SEA

Central Library Exhibition Room

Pa Ph Pr Cr SS ✓ 🚫

Run by East Sussex County Library Services, this exhibition space within the library building has a varied programme featuring local artists.
Central Library, Grove Road, Eastbourne BN21 4TL, tel: 01323 727899, fax: 01323 649174
Contact: Mr D W A Northey, Team Librarian, Arts & Music
Open: Mon, Tues, Thurs, Fri 9.30-7; Sat 9.30-5
Space: 1 gallery with 21 lin m hanging space plus 2 lin m on screens and 26 sq m floor space
Exhibitions: 12 a year of which 11 originated, 1 touring
Details: Preference given to local artists. All items are displayed at exhibitors' own risk and are not covered by County Council insurance. Sales welcomed, with 20% commission (plus VAT) charged. Sale of work not a priority.

Towner Art Gallery

Pa Ph Pr Cr SS ✓ 🔴🎫🅗 🔴💧

Local authority gallery set in a park committed to increasing the understanding, interest and enjoyment of the visual arts.
High Street, Old Town, Eastbourne BN21 8BB, tel: 01323 417961, fax: 01323 648182
Contact: Penny Johnson, Curator
Open: Wed-Sat 10-5; Sun & BH 2-5
Space: 8 galleries with 107 lin m hanging space and 301 sq m floor space
Exhibitions: 12 a year of which 9 originated, 2 touring, 1 on a hire basis
Details: Eight gallery divided into 3 specific areas. Gallery aims to provide high quality, wide ranging exhibition programme of both historical and contemporary art which informs current visual art practice and the context of the Gallery's permanent collection. Shows work of high quality that would otherwise be unseen in Eastbourne and the region. Encourages regular use of the gallery and runs an education programme which includes talks, workshops and drama led by specialists.

Eastleigh
HAMPSHIRE SA

Beatrice Royal Art Gallery

Pa Pr SS ✓ 🔴💧

Large gallery in converted church exhibiting work by over 100 contemporary artists.
Nightingdale Avenue, Eastleigh SO5 3JJ, tel: 01703 610592

Contact: Michael Gaca, Director
Open: Tues-Fri 11-8; Sat & Sun 11-5
Space: 12 galleries with 465 sq m floor space
Details: Opened 1994. Gallery runs series of quarterly thematic shows and one person shows in addition to continuous mixed exhibition. Main aims are to promote work of "living artists of talent and integrity", increase appreciation of art and sell work to benefit of artists. All exhibitions originated by gallery.

Eastleigh Museum

Pa Ph Pr Cr SS ✓🎫 🔴💧4

Local museum showing varied programme including contemporary and historical art and craft.
25 High Street, Eastleigh SO50 5LF, tel: 01703 643026
Contact: Carol Littlefair, Exhibitions Officer, Hampshire County Council Museums Service, Chilcomb House, Chilcomb Lane, Winchester, SO23 8RD, tel: 01962 846315, fax: 01962 869836
Open: Tues-Fri 10-5; Sat 10-4
Space: 1 gallery with 26 lin m hanging space and 51 sq m floor space
Exhibitions: 8 a year of which 6 originated, 2 touring
Details: (See entry for Hampshire County Council Museums, Winchester for policy.)

Egremont
CUMBRIA NA

Lowes Court Gallery

Pa Ph Pr Cr SS ✓ 🚫

Gallery aims to give both emerging and established local artists and craftspeople an opportunity to display their work.
12 Main Street, Egremont CA22 2DW, tel: 01946 820693
Contact: Jenni Payne, Exhibitions Organiser
Open: (Jan-Feb) Mon-Fri 10-1; Sat 10-5; (Mar-Dec) Mon & Tues 10-1, 2-5; Wed 10-1; Thurs, Fri & Sat 10-5
Space: 2 galleries with 260 lin m hanging space and 45 sq m floor space
Exhibitions: 11 a year all originated
Details: Gallery run by charitable association showing work by artists living locally or with Cumbrian connections. Also operates as a tourist information centre. Organises monthly solo, two-person and group shows of contemporary art by both emerging and established artists in all media and styles. Craft demonstrations related to exhibitions occasionally organised. Sale of work is gallery's primary role.

Ellesmere
SHROPSHIRE WMA

Ellesmere College Arts Centre *

Pa Ph Pr Gr Sf ⊘ ⊕

Foyer of college arts centre mainly used to show work of local artists/makers.
Ellesmere SY12 9AB, tel: 01691 622828, fax: 01691 623286
Contact: Sheila Breed
Space: 1 gallery
Exhibitions: 12 a year of which 10 originated, 2 on a hire basis
Details: Programme of music, dance, drama, poetry, workshops, and exhibitions. Booked until 1994 at time of going to press. The floor area is available for sculpture by arrangement.

Ellesmere Port
CHESHIRE NWA

Boat Museum

⊘ ⓖ ⓦ

Gallery within museum stimulating interest and awareness in & enjoyment of inland waterways and of themes connected with local environment & community as a whole.
South Pier Road, Ellesmere Port L65 4FW, tel: 0151 355 5017, fax: 0151 355 4079
Contact: Carol Bell
Details: Exhibitions using variety of media and approaches. Sales not priority.

Ely
CAMBRIDGESHIRE EA

Old Fire Engine House

Pa Ph Pr Sf ⊘ ⓖ

Galleries on ground and first floor exhibiting contemporary art in mixed media.
25 St Mary's Street, Ely CB7 4ER, tel: 01353 662582
Contact: Valerie Bent, Organiser
Open: Mon-Fri 10.30-10.30; Sat 10.30-5.30; Sun 12.30-5.30; closed BH
Space: 2 galleries with 76 lin m hanging space and 17 sq m floor space
Exhibitions: 10 a year all originated
Details: Sale of work is not gallery's primary concern. No access for wheelchair users to first floor gallery.

Epsom
SURREY SEA

Epsom Playhouse

Pa Ph Pr Gr Sf lA ⊘ ⊕ ⓖ ⓦ ④

Epsom Playhouse has an open foyer policy to attract non theatre goers to the venue.
Ashley Avenue, Epsom KT18 5AL, tel: 01372 742226/7
Contact: Trevor Mitchell, Playhouse Manager
Open: Mon-Sat 10am-10.30pm
Space: 1 gallery with 43 lin m hanging space
Exhibitions: 18 a year all on a hire basis
Details: Exhibition space in modern theatre foyer available to local amateur and professional artists. 20% commission charged on any sales made but sales not primary role of exhibition space.

Eton
BERKSHIRE SA

Contemporary Fine Art Gallery Eton

Pa Pr ⊘ ⓖ

Commercial gallery specialising in contemporary Scottish painters and major Zimbabwean stone sculpture.
31 High Street, Eton SL4 1HL, tel: 01753 854315, fax: 01753 620390
Contact: Nicholas Pritchard, Partner
Open: Daily 10-5.30
Space: 1 gallery with 49 lin m hanging space and 93 sq m floor space
Exhibitions: 4 a year all originated

CSK Gallery

54 High Street, Eton SL4 6BL, tel: 01753 840519, fax: 01753 868227

Evesham
HEREFORD & WORCESTER WMA

Evesham Library

Pa Ph Pr Gr ⊘ ⓖ ⓦ ④

Library gallery with exhibitions by local and national groups and individuals.
Oat Street, Evesham WR11 4PJ, tel: 01386 442291, fax: 01386 765855
Contact: Mrs C Evans, Librarian
Open: Mon, Tues & Fri 9.30-5.30; Thurs 9.30-8; Sat 9.30-4
Space: 1 gallery with 7 lin m hanging space plus 139 lin m on screens and 125 sq m floor space
Details: Exhibitions last about 3 weeks presenting work by local and national groups or individuals. Works for sale but not main purpose of gallery. (See also entry for Hereford & Worcester Libraries & Arts Department, Worcester.)

Ewell
SURREY SEA

Bourne Hall

Pa Pr Gr Sf ⊘ ⊕

Large foyer area in library and community centre.
Spring Street, Ewell KT17, tel: 0181 393 9573
Contact: Diane Ogle, Bourne Hall, Spring Street, Ewell, tel: 0181 393 9571
Exhibitions: 17 a year all on a hire basis
Details: Wide ranging programme of exhibitions by local artists.

Exeter
DEVON SWA

Exeter City Museums & Art Gallery

Pa Ph Pr Gr Sf lA ⊘ ⓔ ⓖ

Municipal museum interested in thematic shows and new ways of presenting contemporary art to the public.
Royal Albert Memorial Museum, Queen Street, Exeter EX4 3RX, tel: 01392 265858, fax: 01392 421252
Contact: Exhibitions Officer
Open: Mon-Sat 10-5
Space: 2 galleries with 88 lin m hanging space plus 50 lin m on screens and 255 sq m floor space
Exhibitions: 9 a year of which 5 originated, 4 touring
Details: Two main exhibition galleries with possible use of other spaces for small scale shows. Varied programme combining contemporary art with other subject areas. Full range of educational activities and events used to complement exhibitions. Small monthly 'Gallery Wall' exhibitions and 'Contemporary Crafts' showcase displays for artists from the region.

Exeter & Devon Arts Centre

Pa Ph Pr Sf ⊘ ⓔ ⓖ ⓦ

While reflecting the diversity of Exeter and Devon's visual arts work, main aim is to focus on new work.
Gandy Street, Exeter EX4 3LS, tel: 01392 219741, fax: 01392 499929
Contact: Andy Morley, Programme Manager
Open: Mon-Sat 9-8.30
Space: 4 galleries
Exhibitions: 15 a year all originated
Details: Centre with varied exhibition spaces; Studio One Gallery, Gallery Café, Upper Gallery and Reflection Photo-gallery. Photographic exhibitions regularly included in broad programme. Selling is not main function.

Exeter University (Library)

Pa Ph Pr Sc ●Ⓗ ●Wc

Exhibition space in library foyer used for bibliographic exhibitions as well as local artists' work and occasional touring exhibitions.
University Library, Stocker Road, Exeter EX4 4PT, tel: 01392 263880
Contact: Sue Guy, Exhibition Organiser
Open: Mon-Fri 9-5.30
Space: 1 gallery with plus 112 lin m on screens
Exhibitions: 4 a year all on a hire basis
Details: Exhibitions mounted on 8 double-sided 7'x4' display screens and 6 large lockable glass cases. Foyer shows local artists and travelling exhibitions. No policy as such; if approached by artists will generally accommodate them. Space 'hired out' at no charge to artists. Sales not a priority.

Spacex Gallery

Pa Ph Pr Sc LA ●ⓔⒽ Ⓖ

Carefully converted C19th warehouse dedicated to display of contemporary visual art.
45 Preston Street, Exeter EX1 1DF, tel: 01392 431786
Contact: Deborah Wood, Director
Open: Tues-Sat 10-5
Space: 3 galleries with 57 lin m hanging space and 90 sq m floor space
Exhibitions: 11 a year of which 10 originated, 1 on a hire basis
Details: Independent, non-profit making gallery, covering every aspect of contemporary visual art by showing work by lesser-known as well as established regional, national and international artists. Talks, educational workshops and school visits. Exhibitions usually booked one year ahead. Keen to collaborate with other galleries on exhibitions. Selling work not gallery's principal aim.

Vincent Gallery

Cr

Gallery devoted to showing ceramics and contemporary pottery.
15 Magdalen Road, Exeter EX2 4TA, tel: 01392 430082
Contact: Paul Vincent
Space: 1 gallery with 20 sq m floor space
Exhibitions: 4 a year all originated
Details: Programme gives good coverage to regional makers, but equally interested in work from further afield. 50% commission on sales.

Exmouth
DEVON SWA

Rolle Faculty Gallery (University of Plymouth) *

Pa Ph Pr Cr Sc LA ●

College gallery showing several exhibitions a year, some by local artists.
Rolle College, Douglas Avenue, Exmouth EX8 2AT, tel: 01395 255 326
Contact: Howard Jones, Exhibition Organiser

Eye
SUFFOLK EA

Wingfield College

Pa Ph Pr Cr Sc LA ●ⓔⒽ

Sculpture garden and gallery with programme featuring both young and established professionals.
Wingfield, Eye IP21 5RA, tel: 01379 384505, fax: 01379 384034
Contact: Administrator
Open: (Easter-Sept 30) Sat-Sun & BH Mon 2-6
Space: 1 gallery with 31 lin m hanging space and 12141 sq m floor space
Exhibitions: 4 a year of which 2 originated, 1 on a hire basis
Details: 3 acres of sculpture garden in the grounds of 700 year old College building. Completely devoted to exhibiting art. Houses permanent collection in addition to a temporary programme. 30% commission on sales.

Eynsford
KENT SEA

Lullingstone Visitors Centre

Pa Ph Pr Cr ●ⓔⒽ ⒼWc

Exhibition space on boards for local artists/craftspeople to exhibit their work.
Castle Road, Kingfisher Bridge, Eynsford DA4 0JF, tel: 01322 865995
Contact: Georgina White, Centre Supervisor
Open: Mon-Sun 11-5
Space: 1 gallery with 13 lin m hanging space and 35 sq m floor space
Exhibitions: 25 a year of which 9 originated, 16 on a hire basis
Details: At Lullingstone Park. Exhibition space on boards on open sided gallery. Sales a priority.

Eynsham
OXFORDSHIRE SA

Gundry Gallery

Pa Ph Cr ● Ⓖ

Commercial gallery holding mainly mixed exhibitions based on a changing theme.
62 Acre End Street, Eynsham OX8 1PD, tel: 01865 883120/64306
Contact: Harriet Mills, Partner
Open: Thurs-Sat 10-5; or by appointment; closed Jan, Feb & Aug
Space: 2 galleries
Exhibitions: 5 a year all originated
Details: Artists are invited to submit work on a theme. Crafts of all kinds are a priority. Welcomes new artists. Sales are a priority.

Falmouth
CORNWALL SWA

Beside the Wave

Pa Ph Cr ●

Shop floor area at street level with mixed exhibitions and first and second floor galleries opened for one-person shows.
10 Arwenack Street, Falmouth TR11 3JA, tel: 01326 211132, fax: 01326 212212
Contact: Lesley Dyer, Partner/Manageress
Open: Mon-Sat 9-5; other times by appointment
Space: 3 galleries with 100 lin m hanging space and 250 sq m floor space
Exhibitions: 5 a year all originated
Details: Two mixed exhibitions a year of established gallery artists and to introduce new artists. One-person shows organised of artists whose work sells well. These are continued on annual or biannual basis. Full colour invites with CVs always produced. Sales a priority. Ground floor accessible to wheelchair users with assistance. No lift to upper floors.

Falmouth Art Gallery

Pa Ph Pr Cr Sc ●ⓔ

Municipal art gallery with exhibitions from solo shows by contemporary artists to subjects of special local/historical interest.
The Moor, Falmouth TR11 2RT, tel: 01326 313863, fax: 03126 312662
Contact: Miss Catherine Wallace, Curator
Open: Mon-Fri 10-4.30; Sat10-1
Space: 2 galleries with 51 lin m hanging space plus 12 lin m on screens and 78 sq m floor space
Exhibitions: 8 a year of which 7 originated, 1 touring
Details: Includes regular interaction with Falmouth College of Arts, and some group shows. Gallery closed Nov 1995 – Spring 1996 for major refurbishment in the galleries and new extension to house lift for disabled access. Applications to exhibit

therefore temporarily suspended until May 1996.

Falmouth Arts Centre

Pa Ph Pr Cr Sc ◐ ⊕ ⓖ

Gallery exhibiting and selling range of work by local artists and those living further afield.
24 Church Street, Falmouth TR11 3EG, tel: 01326 314566, fax: 01326 211078
Contact: Mr M Carver, Administrator
Open: Daily 10-5
Space: 4 galleries with 76 lin m hanging space plus 46 lin m on screens and 363 sq m floor space
Exhibitions: 51 a year all originated
Details: Gallery aims to provide space for "culture in depth" for benefit of local residents and visitors in heart of popular tourist area. Sales considered gallery's primary role.

Falmouth College of Arts

Pa Ph Pr Cr Sc ◐ ⊕ ⓖⓊ

Purpose-built gallery split into two sections used for the exhibition of work by college students and visiting artists.
Woodlane, Falmouth TR11 4RA, tel: 01326 211077, fax: 01326 211205
Contact: Valerie Rooker, PR 8 Gallery Co-ordinator
Open: Mon-Fri 10-4.30; weekends by prior arrangement
Space: 2 galleries
Exhibitions: 8 a year of which 6 originated, 2 touring
Details: Continual programme of events in the gallery and encourages a diverse range of artistic practices which are aimed to widen the learning experiences of the students. Free usage to current Falmouth College of Arts students; other users by separate negotiation. Sales not a priority.

Fareham
HAMPSHIRE SA

Ashcroft Arts Centre

Pa Ph Pr Cr Sc ⊕ ⓖⓊ

Intimate exhibition/gallery space showing work by local/regional artists as well as some touring exhibitions.
Osborn Road, Fareham PO16 7DX, tel: 0329 235161
Contact: Steve Rowley, Director
Open: Mon-Fri 9-9; Sat 7-10
Space: 1 gallery with 14 lin m hanging space and 23 sq m floor space
Exhibitions: 9 a year of which 1 originated, 2 touring, 6 on a hire basis
Details: Centre aims to provide balanced programme of paintings, mixed media, sculpture, photography and craft. As well as gallery, 17.45 m of screens available as hanging space in other areas of the centre.

Sales not a priority. Exhibition fee sometimes paid.

Fareham Library

Pa Ph Pr Cr Sc ◐ ⊕ ⓖ

Run by Hampshire County Council, this is a dedicated exhibition space within a busy public library.
Osborn Road, Fareham PO16 7EN, tel: 01329 282715, fax: 01329 221 551
Contact: Miss A Muston, Senior Librarian
Open: Mon, Thur, Fri 9.30-7; Tues, Wed 9.30-5; Sat 9.30-4
Space: 1 gallery with 12 lin m hanging space and 21 sq m floor space
Exhibitions: 15 a year all on a hire basis
Details: Exhibition space hired out free of charge for displays of work by local groups and exhibitions of local arts and crafts. Majority of shows run 2-3 weeks. Sale of work is not a priority.

Westbury Manor Museum

Pa Ph Pr Cr Sc ◐ ⊕ ⓖⓦ

Local museum with L-shaped space designed for temporary exhibitions on a wide variety of themes, including contemporary art and craft.
84 West Street, Fareham PO16 0JJ, tel: 01329 824895, fax: 01962 869836
Contact: Carol LIttlefair, Exhibitions Officer, Hampshire County Council Museum Service, Chilcomb House, Chilcomb Lane, Winchester, SO23 8RD, tel: 01962 846315, fax: 01962 869836
Open: Mon-Fri 10-5; Sat 10-4
Space: 1 gallery with 24 lin m hanging space and 50 sq m floor space
Exhibitions: 7 a year of which 4 touring, 3 on a hire basis
Details: Aims to provide balanced programme of community, local artists and contemporary art and craft. Full education programme. Gives preference to artists who are willing to provide some educational input, eg lecture, workshops for public or schools. 20% commission on sales. Sale of work not a priority. Where space is 'hired out' there is no fee charged.

Farnham
SURREY SEA

Andrew Lloyd Gallery

Pa Pr Cr ◐

Converted cottage with two rooms and additional print bins for presenting selected mixed shows.
17 Castle Street, Farnham GU9 7JA, tel: 01252 724333
Contact: Andrew Lloyd
Open: Mon-Sat 10-5.30
Space: 2 galleries with 50 lin m hanging space and 44 sq m floor space
Exhibitions: 1 a year originated
Details: Shows work of contemporary

printmakers, part of business that also provides framing service and prints for offices scheme. Attracts wide audience of local, national and international visitors.

CCA Galleries (Farnham)

Pa Pr Sc ◐

One of a network of commercial galleries in the South of England specialising in limited edition prints.
13 Lion & Lamb Yard, West Street, Farnham GU9 7LL, tel: 01252 722231, fax: 01252 733336
Contact: Marian Orchard-Webb, Manager
Open: Mon-Sat 9-5.30
Space: 1 gallery
Exhibitions: 12 a year all originated
Details: CCA Galleries is a leading publisher of original, limited edition prints. Each gallery selects its own work. The primary aim is to promote hand-made prints by CCA artists. (See also CCA Galleries at Oxford, Bath, Cambridge & London.)

James Hockey Gallery

Pa Pr Cr Sc ⓕ

Contributes to the cultural life of the college and also serves as the major space in the region for showing contemporary art.
The Surrey Institute of Art & Design, Falkner Road, Farnham GU9 7DS, tel: 01252 732 241, fax: 01252 733 869
Contact: Julian Belmonte/Christine Barker, Gallery Supervisors
Space: 1 gallery with 65 lin m hanging space and 210 sq m floor space
Exhibitions: 6 a year all originated
Details: Purpose-built gallery. Programme of contemporary art of international significance. Exhibitions commissioned especially to offer artists the opportunity to produce large scale works. Hosts the annual Farnham Art Society Exhibition and part of the final year show by WSCAD students

New Ashgate Gallery

Pa Pr Cr Sc ◐

Commercial gallery showing young and established artists.
Wagon Yard, Farnham GU9 7PS, tel: 01252 713208
Contact: Elfriede Windsor, Director
Open: Tues-Sat 10-5
Space: 4 galleries with 60 lin m hanging space
Exhibitions: 10 a year all originated
Details: Also shows work by leading contemporary craftspeople in addition to the work featured in regular changing exhibitions. Established for more than 15 years, housed in a C17th building.

SC Johnson Gallery & Studio

Pd Ph Pr Sc LA ✓ ❶ ♿

Independent arts centre offering range of arts events, exhibitions and community activities.
Farnham Maltings, Bridge Square, Farnham GU9 7QR, tel: 01252 713637, fax: 01252 718177
Contact: Christine Kapteyn, Gallery Manager
Open: Mon-Fri 10-5; Sat 10-4; Sun closed
Space: 2 galleries with 53 lin m hanging space plus 2 lin m on screens and 100 sq m floor space
Exhibitions: 18 a year of which 4 originated, 2 touring, 12 on a hire basis
Details: Exhibitions last between 2 weeks and a month. Associated educational programme including workshops, slide talks and poetry readings. Exhibitions and activities programme reflect arts and community purpose which directs the Maltings as a whole.

Fleetwood
LANCASHIRE NWA

Fleetwood Library

Pd Ph Pr Cr Sc LA ❶

Shows mostly the work of local contemporary artists.
North Albert Street, Fleetwood FY7 6AJ, tel: 01253 778773
Contact: M. Ramsbottom, Librarian
Space: 1 gallery with 40 lin m hanging space and 400 sq m floor space
Exhibitions: 30 a year
Details: Programme for the benefit of local people and holiday visitors. Activities to accompany the exhibitions planned in the future.

Folkestone
KENT SEA

Platform Gallery *

Pd Pr Cr Sc ✓

Commercial gallery not exhibiting work for its saleability.
The Westcliff Centre, 136 Sandgate Road, Folkestone CT20 2BY, tel: 01303 220510
Contact: Visual Director
Space: 4 galleries with 60 lin m hanging space and 90 sq m floor space
Exhibitions: 5 a year all originated
Details: Eclectic exhibition calendar. Shows minimalist sculpture, abstracts, expressive, interpretive, hyper-real, primitive and naive works. Bias towards more abstracted and interpretive works. Constantly on the lookout for new exhibitors. Age is no barrier. Levies a hanging fee for large exhibitions.

Sassoon Gallery

Pd Ph Pr Cr Sc LA ✓ ⊗

Spacious gallery accentuated by high ceiling and skylights where works in almost any medium can be displayed.
Folkestone Library and Museum, 2 Grace Hill, Folkestone CT20 1HD, tel: 01303 850123, fax: 01303 242907
Contact: Simon Bolton, Arts Promotion Officer
Open: Mon-Sat 9.30-5
Space: 1 gallery with 38 lin m hanging space and 124 sq m floor space
Exhibitions: 12 a year of which 10 originated, 2 touring
Details: Walls 3M high with white hessian hanging surface. Plenty of floor space. Spotlights on tracking plus skylights. Work in any media is considered for exhibition. Applications judged on suitability of work as part of year-long programme, as well as on their quality. Selling work not gallery's main function.

Fowey
CORNWALL SWA

Cry of the Gulls Gallery

Pd Ph Pr Cr Sc ✓ ♿

Small commercial gallery exhibiting range of arts and crafts with special interest in contemporary jewellery.
No 4 Fore Street, Fowey PL23 1AQ, tel: 01726 833838
Contact: Tony Jones
Open: Mon-Sun 9.30-6; Winter hours best checked
Space: 2 galleries with 28 lin m hanging space and 48 sq m floor space
Exhibitions: 3 a year all originated
Details: Gallery has double shop frontage and two exhibition areas; one modern white space, the other walled with old Cornish stone. Tries to include as many disciplines and media as possible. Contemporary jewellery flourishes. Works from new artists accepted. Flexible about number of pieces held in stock at any one time. Also more defined solo and theme exhibitions. Artists predominantly from South West.

Framlingham
SUFFOLK EA

Boundary Gallery

Pd ✓ ♿

Selling gallery in converted stable block showing work by East Anglian contemporary artists.
Boundary House, Cransford, Framlingham IP13 9NU, tel: 01728 723862
Contact: Nicole Harris, Owner
Open: Thurs-Sun 10.30-4.30; Wed-Sun 10.30-4.30 (July & Aug)

Space: 1 gallery with 93 sq m floor space
Exhibitions: 3 a year all originated
Details: Exhibitions of paintings by mainly Suffolk-based artists. Workshops by exhibiting artists held in summer. Commission taken on sales made. Artist owner has studio on site.

Martin Gallery *

Pd Ph Pr Cr Sc ✓

Reputation for showing textiles.
11 Market Hill, Framlingham IP13 9AN, fax: 01728 724253
Contact: Martin Humphreys
Space: 2 galleries with 25 sq m floor space
Exhibitions: 6 a year all originated
Details: Mixed programme of solo and small group shows. Wide audience and large mailing list.

Freshwater
ISLE OF WIGHT SA

Freshwater Gallery

Pd Ph Pr ✓ ❶

Small gallery off library.
School Green Road, Freshwater PO40 9AP, tel: 01983 752377
Contact: A D Payne, Head of Libraries & Arts, Cultutural & Leisure Services Directorate, I.W. County Council, The Guilhall, High Street, Newport, PO30 1ty, tel: 01983 823822, fax: 01983 823841**
Open: Mon-Wed, Fri & Sat library opening hours
Space: 1 gallery with 11 lin m hanging space and 7 sq m floor space
Exhibitions: 12 a year all on a hire basis
Details: Professional and amateur individual artists and groups. Island population and seasonal visitors. No hanging or commission fee. Payment by picture donation or 10% of sales discretion.

Fressingfield
SUFFOLK EA

Martha Stevns Gallery

Pd Ph Pr Sc LA ✓ ♿

Commercial gallery showing international and local contemporary art concentrating on abstract art but not excluding photography or installation.
Willow House, Harleston Road, Fressingfield IP21 5PE, tel: 01379 586455, fax: 01379 586799
Contact: Martha Stevns, Director
Space: 2 galleries with 44 lin m hanging space and 56 sq m floor space
Exhibitions: 6 a year all originated
Details: Has a view to Europe by bringing in 1-2 artists a year from the continent. Solo and group exhibitions. Wheelchair user access to only part of exhibition space.

Frodsham
CHESHIRE NWA

Castle Park Arts Centre

[Pa] [Ph] [Pr] [Cr] [Sc] ✔ ♿ [Wc]

Victorian outbuilding serving as centre for arts with exhibition programme, workshops and arts and crafts classes.

Off Fountain Lane, Frodsham

Contact: Nancy Harris, Exhibitions Organiser, Greystones, Beech Avenue, Frodsham, WA6 6PS, tel: 01928 733395

Open: Tues-Sat 10-12.30 & 2-4; Sun 2-4

Space: 3 galleries with 114 sq m floor space

Exhibitions: 15 a year of which 12 originated, 3 touring

Details: Centre aims to stimulate interest, knowledge and understanding of arts in broadest sense by local community and young people in particular. Aims to hold exhibitions of national, regional and local significance. Craftspeople have own workshops on premises. 3 galleries plus foyer and arcade space for exhibitions. Galleries are multi-purpose and floor space not usually vacant for whole of exhibition period. Sales not a priority. Exhibition fee sometimes paid.

Frome
SOMERSET SWA

Black Swan Guild

[Pa] [Ph] [Pr] [Cr] [Sc] ✔ [H] ♿

Complex of galleries, shop and studios set up for the promotion of fine art and craft.

2 Bridge Street, Frome BA11 1BB, tel: 01373 473980

Contact: Ann O'Dwyer, Exhibition Organiser

Open: Mon-Sat 10-5

Space: 2 galleries with 40 lin m hanging space plus 10 lin m on screens

Exhibitions: 32 a year

Details: Arts centre with large first-floor gallery showing work by local and national artists. Year's programme includes mixed media, themed exhibitions, and those particular to a craft form. Occasional talks, evening and weekend events. 8 major exhibitions a year in gallery. Remainder are one-person exhibitions in spaces throughout building; café, shop and Round Tower. Programme usually fixed 12 months in advance. Wheelchair access with assistance to ground floor only.

Craft Movement (The)

[Pa] [Ph] [Pr] [Cr] [Sc] ✔ [H]

Craft Movement promotes high-quality crafts through events where craftworkers/artists can present and sell their work to public and trade buyers.

PO Box 1641, Frome BA11 1YY, tel: 01373 453153

Exhibitions: 8 a year all on a hire basis

Details: Makers are selected by an independent panel. Venues around the country are chosen for their cultural heritage and in areas of known affluence. Each event lasts 2-3 days with private view. Full-colour promotional material, local and national advertising and direct mail campaign. Three types/sizes of stands available to selected makers/artists and price includes screens, lighting, name plate, catalogue entry and invitation cards. Disabled access varies depending on venue. Sales a priority.

Merlin Theatre *

[Pa] [Ph] [Pr] [Cr] [Sc] [LA] ✔ [£] [H]

Programme of exhibitions in theatre foyer.

Bath Road, Frome BA11 2HG, tel: 01373 461360

Contact: Simon Jutton, Director

Space: 1 gallery

Exhibitions: 9 a year of which 3 originated, 3 touring, 3 on a hire basis

Details: Venue for professional and amateur performances of music, dance, theatre. In foyer exhibitions aims to show a varied selection of work, predominantly professional artists from the South West region. Also aims to encourage local amateurs. Programme selected to complement theatre activities.

Gainsborough
LINCOLNSHIRE EA

Art in the Bar

[Pa] [Ph] [Cr] [Sc] ✔ ♿

Small exhibition space in bar area of cinema and theatre at present showing only 2D work.

Trinity Centre, Trinity Street, Gainsborough DN21 2AL, tel: 01427 810298, fax: 01427 811198

Contact: Kate Sanderson, Sales & Customer Services

Open: Mon-Fri 10-late; Sat

Space: 1 gallery with 8 lin m hanging space

Exhibitions: 6 a year of which 5 originated, 1 touring

Details: Centre started holding exhibitions in the bar in 1994. So far only 2D work considered, from photography to contemporary art. Also touring crafts show once a year generated by Eastern Arts Board. Sale of work not primary role but sales possible and minimum commission taken.

Kirton Pottery

[Pa] [Pr] [Cr] ✔ ♿

Pottery showroom with wall space to exhibit 2D work.

36 High Street, Kirton in Lindsey, Gainsborough DN21 4LX, tel: 01652 648867

Contact: Christine & Peter Hawes

Open: Mon-Sat 9.30-5.30; Sun 2.30-5

Space: 2 galleries with 18 lin m hanging space and 26 sq m floor space

Exhibitions: 2 a year both originated

Details: Wall space available to artists and craftspeople to show work that complements pottery produced on site. Main purpose of pottery showroom is to sell. 10% commission taken on sales of other artists' work.

Lindsey Gallery

[Pa] [Ph] [Pr] [Cr] [Sc] ✔ ♿ [Wc]

Lindsey Gallery complements extensive range of craft products & craft workshops within centre by presenting work which is challenging and exciting.

Hemswell Craft Centre, Lindsey House, Hemswell Cliff, Gainsborough DN21 5TH, tel: 01427 667066, fax: 01427 668178

Contact: Mrs Ann Wallis, Exhibition Organiser

Open: Daily 10-5

Space: 1 gallery with 22 lin m hanging space and 77 sq m floor space

Exhibitions: 16 a year all originated

Details: Exhibitions, 2 & 3D, by professional artists, crafts guilds and amateur groups. Aim to challenge and, through example, educate. Gallery opened early summer 1994. Exhibitions change every 6 weeks. Sales a priority. Occasionally pays exhibition fee to artists exhibiting.

Garstang
LANCASHIRE NWA

Old Grammar School Arts Centre

[Pa] [Ph] [Pr] [Cr] ✔ ♿ [Wc]

Most exhibitors are local amateur artists.

Croston Road, Garstang PR3 1EB

Contact: Dorothy Bicknell/Marion Probyn, Exhibition Organisers, Garstang & District Arts Society

Open: Tues 10-12.30, 2-4; Thurs 10-4; Sat 10-12.30

Space: 1 gallery with 55 lin m hanging space and 60 sq m floor space

Exhibitions: 11 a year all originated

Details: Open exhibition in Jan/Feb each year. No charge to exhibit. 20% commission on sales. Number of regular visitors and summer tourists. The Arts Society is a registered charity and apart from paid curator all work is voluntary.

Gateshead
TYNE & WEAR NA

Design Works
[Pa][Ph][Pr][Cr][SC] ✔

Promotes design in the north of England, hosting many conferences and exhibitions as well as 23 design orientated businesses.

William Street, Felling, Gateshead NE10 0JP, tel: 0191 495 0066, fax: 0191 495 3207

Contact: Robert Walker, Event Co-ordinator

Open: Mon-Fri 8.30-6

Space: 2 galleries with 97 lin m hanging space plus 39 lin m on screens and 552 sq m floor space

Details: Combination of white walls and Canadian maple flooring. Lighting is both natural and artificial. Extensive floor area and 2 levels allows full and varied viewing of the work. Exhibitions booked on four-week blocks. Visitors are numerous: tenants, conference and exhibition delegates, general visitors.

Gateshead Library Gallery
[Pa][Ph][Pr][Cr][SC] ✔ £ ♿ [WC] [4]

A local authority run gallery showing work by contemporary artists, favouring regional painting, printmaking and photography, with some touring and national shows.

Prince Consort Road, Gateshead NE8 4LN, tel: 0191 477 3478, fax: 0191 477 7454

Contact: Visual Arts Manager, Gateshead Libraries/Arts

Open: Mon-Tues & Thurs-Fri 9-7; Wed 9-5; Sat 9-1

Space: 1 gallery with 29 lin m hanging space and 60 sq m floor space

Exhibitions: 10 a year of which 7 originated, 3 touring

Details: Within the main Central Library complex. Exhibitions are seen by a wide audience. White block-board and track lighting with movable spots and floods. One fixed glass showcase but other showcases and plinths available. Programme is varied but focuses on regional artists and exhibitions linked to the overall arts programme. Sales not a priority.

Portcullis Crafts Gallery
[Cr] ♿ [WC] [4]

Crafts Council listed retail gallery, specialising in ceramics, glass, jewellery and wood, organising major annual exhibition on specialist theme.

7 The Arcade, Metrocentre, Gateshead NE11 9YL, tel: 0191 460 6345, fax: 0191 460 4285

Open: Mon-Fri 10-8; Thurs 10-9; Sat 9-7

Space: 1 gallery

Exhibitions: 1 a year originated

Details: Housed in Europe's largest indoor shopping centre Portcullis offers quality crafts showing the work of regional and national craftspeople. Pieces chosen are provided on sale or return basis. Catalogue provided. Customer mailout and invitations to preview night. Space for exhibition varies depending on size of exhibition and amount of retail work left on display.

Shipley Art Gallery
[Pa][Ph][Pr][Cr][SC] £ ♿ [WC]

Local gallery and museum specialising in contemporary craft with temporary exhibitions and activities including crafts, fine art and local history.

Prince Consort Road, Gateshead NE8 4JB, tel: 0191 477 1495

Contact: Andrew Greg, Curator

Open: Tues-Fri 10-5.30; Sat 10-4.30; Sun 2-5

Space: 2 galleries with 76 lin m hanging space and 225 sq m floor space

Exhibitions: 7 a year of which 5 originated, 2 touring

Details: Most exhibitions are group or theme shows, hired in where possible. Educational and participatory activities essential. Audiences are a regional craft audience and a more general local one. Particularly welcomes advance notice of touring exhibitions at the planning stage. Fine art and local history exhibitions also held. Sales not gallery's primary role.

Gillingham
KENT SEA

Gillingham Library Gallery
[Pa][Ph][Pr][Cr][SC] ✔ [H] ♿

A dedicated exhibition space within the library building with a varied programme featuring artists who have a particular relevance to the area.

High Street, Gillingham ME7 1BG, tel: 01634 281066, fax: 01634 855814

Contact: Valerie Mawhinney, Group Manager

Open: Mon & Tues 9.30-7; Wed 9.30-1, 2-5; Thurs & Fri 9.30-6; Sat 9.30-5

Space: 1 gallery with 90 lin m hanging space and 500 sq m floor space

Exhibitions: 10 a year of which 1 touring, 9 on a hire basis

Details: Aims to promote work of locally-based artists and to show exhibitions that may not otherwise be seen in the area. Touring shows and occasional museum archive exhibitions. Lectures and slide shows organised when appropriate. Shows normally run three to four weeks. Sale of work not seen as gallery's primary function.

Space Frame Gallery
[Pa][Ph][Pr][Cr][SC][LA] ✔

Regularly changing programme of exhibitions by well-known and unknown artists, professional and amateur.

Gillingham Adult Education Centre, Green Street, Gillingham ME7 1XA, tel: 01634 856439 or 850235, fax: 01634 570297

Contact: Nicholette Goff, Director

Open: Mon-Fri 9-4, 6.30-8.30

Space: 3 galleries with 38 lin m hanging space and 89 sq m floor space

Exhibitions: 20 a year all originated

Details: Work selected by a gallery committee composed of students and tutors from the centre. Looks favourably on work which addresses issues of equal opportunity and which seeks to explore or extend the use of materials and images.

Spiral Arts
[Pa][Ph][Pr][Cr][SC][LA] ✔ [H] ♿ [WC]

One room for exhibitions in community centre that holds performances, workshops and has darkroom facilities.

Marlborough Road, Gillingham ME7 5HB, tel: 01634 576830

Contact: Moira Tugwell

Open: Tues-Fri 9.30-3.30; usually closed weekends

Space: 1 gallery with 10 lin m hanging space and 55 sq m floor space

Exhibitions: 2 a year both originated

Details: Large room with windows to three walls, opening onto lawns which can be used for summer openings. Parquet flooring. Space for standing units/ sculptures. Limited wall space due to number of windows. Exhibitions of work by local artists and photographers. Can be hired. Audience of centre users and local residents. Sales not a priority.

Glastonbury
SOMERSET SWA

Somerset Rural Life Museum
[Pa][Ph][Pr][Cr][SC][LA] ✔ [H] ♿ [WC]

Supports wide range of exhibitions of interest to local community, schools and tourists.

Abbey Farm, Chilkwell Street, Glastonbury BA6 8DB, tel: 01458 831197

Contact: Mary C. Gryspeerdt, Keeper – Extension Services

Open: (Easter-Oct) Mon-Fri 10-5, Sat-Sun 2-6; (Nov-Easter) Mon-Fri 10-5, Sat 11-4

Space: 1 gallery with 19 lin m hanging space plus 6 lin m on screens and 43 sq m floor space

Exhibitions: 10 a year of which 1 originated, 1 touring, 8 on a hire basis

Details: Attractive exhibition room in

Victorian farmhouse. Spotlights on tracking, polished wood floor, hessian-covered chipboard on walls for easy hanging. Special emphasis on Somerset arts and crafts. Strong local community support and tourists in season. 20% commission on sales which are encouraged but not essential.

Gloucester
AVON SWA

Glassbarn (The)

Combined shop and temporary exhibition space specially designed for showing glass.
31 Culver Street, Newent, Gloucester GL18 1DB, tel: 01531 821173
Contact: Harry Cowdy
Open: Tues-Fri 10-12.30, 1.30-5; Sat 10-12.30; Jan-Mar times vary; closed 24 Dec-1 Jan
Space: 1 gallery with 74 sq m floor space
Exhibitions: 3 a year all originated
Details: A gallery selling studio glass by designer-makers. Exhibitions reflect current developments in art glass. Glass shelving units, cases and plinths specially designed for showing glass and three large windows for hanging stained glass. Sales of work a priority.

Gloucester City Museum & Art Gallery

Purpose-built exhibition gallery within the city councils principal museum, showing mainly group exhibitions all year round.
Brunswick Road, Gloucester GL1 1HP, tel: 01452 524131, fax: 01452 410898
Contact: Amanda Wadsley, Head of Museums & Cultural Services
Open: Mon-Sat 10-5; Sun (July-Sept) 10-4
Space: 1 gallery with 42 lin m hanging space plus 6 lin m on screens and 108 sq m floor space
Exhibitions: 8 a year of which 2 touring, 6 on a hire basis
Details: Modern gallery appended to a fine museum of archaeology, natural history, decorative art and C18th landscape painting. Main space shows exhibitions by societies and ad hoc groups of artists; one-person shows are held in the foyer. Visitors both local people and tourists, about 40,000 annually.

Guildhall Arts Centre

Arts centre exhibiting artists working in all artforms.
23 Eastgate Street, Gloucester GL1 1NS, tel: 01452 505089
Contact: Mel Rann, Administrative Officer
Open: Tues-Sat 10-8; Sun 4.30-8
Space: 2 galleries

Exhibitions: 15 a year all originated
Details: Varied exhibition programme presented, including installation work. Centre currently expanding education programme and exhibitors may be asked to participate. Sales not gallery's primary consideration.

Godalming
SURREY SEA

Godalming Museum

Well-lit airy gallery with mixture of group and solo shows organised on the basis of hiring out the space to artists.
109a High Street, Godalming GU7 1AQ, tel: 01483 42 6510
Contact: Adela Goodall, Curator
Open: (Summer) Tues-Sat 10-5; (Winter) Tues-Sat 10-4
Space: 2 galleries
Exhibitions: 20 a year all on a hire basis
Details: Gallery run by the Godalming Museum Trust. Aims to encourage local or national organisations and individuals. Small shop on the premises and gallery is used as a meeting room for various activities. Exhibitions are a mixture of group and solo shows, normally lasting two or three weeks. Hire of the gallery in summer can include use of adjoining Jekyll garden, for open evening or meeting place. Sale of work is not gallery's primary concern.

Gomshall
SURREY SEA

Gomshall Gallery

Gallery/shop with permanent shows of English crafts in wood, glass, metal and ceramics.
Station Road, Gomshall GU5 9LB, tel: 01483 203795, fax: 01483 203282
Contact: Mrs Julia von Bertele
Open: Mon-Sat 10-6; closed BH
Space: 1 gallery with 30 lin m hanging space and 60 sq m floor space
Details: Some work is purchased; some taken on a sale or return basis. New artists constantly sought. Furniture shown amongst other work.

Goodwood
WEST SUSSEX SA

Sculpture at Goodwood

Changing collection of contemporary British sculpture set in grounds of Hat Hill Copse.
Hat Hill Copse, Goodwood PO18 0QP, tel: 01243 538449, fax: 01243 531852

Contact: Ann Elliott, Head of Sculpture
Space: 1 gallery with 18 lin m hanging space and 99 sq m floor space
Exhibitions: 3 a year all originated
Details: Hat Hill Copse consists of 30 acres of woodland walks providing an unrivalled setting for works of art by major artists. Exhibitions in the gallery are small and are related to study days "Sculpture on Saturdays."

Goole
HUMBERSIDE YHA

Snaith Arts & Crafts

Selling gallery on ground floor of refurbished Georgian building.
3 High Street, Snaith, Goole DN14 9HF, tel: 01405 860423
Contact: Audrey Vincent, Gallery Organiser
Open: Wed 12-5; Thurs & Sat 9.30-5; Fri 9.30-8; open BH except Christmas.
Space: 1 gallery with 15 lin m hanging space and 25 sq m floor space
Exhibitions: 3 a year of which 1 originated, 2 on a hire basis
Details: Aims to introduce the general public to the arts and crafts through exhibitions. 80% of exhibition material must be saleable.

South Farm Craft Gallery

Gallery selling art, craft and other work by local and national makers.
Blacktoft, Via Gilberdyke, Goole DN14 7XT, tel: 01430 441082
Contact: Jerry Harper
Open: Wed-Sat 10-5; Sun 11-5
Space: 1 gallery with 15 lin m hanging space
Details: A craft gallery with permanent hanging space for paintings etc. Licensed tearoom on site. Craft studios available for designer/makers. Permanent home of the Jerry Harper Pottery and Dolls House Shop. Prepared to mount exhibitions if approached. We have a large paved courtyard suitable for a number of live arts/ sculptures etc.

Goring on Thames
OXFORDSHIRE SA

Goring Mill Gallery

Selling gallery in old watermill building showing art and crafts by selected regional artists and makers, specialising in painting and ceramics.
Lock Approach, Goring on Thames RG8 9AD, tel: 01491 875030, fax: 01491 872519
Contact: Lesley Bridle or Diana Davies

Open: Tues-Sun 10-4 (later in summer)
Space: 4 galleries with 37 lin m hanging space plus 10 lin m on screens and 36 sq m floor space
Exhibitions: 4 a year all originated
Details: Gallery opened 1994. Popular picturesque riverside location. Plans to hold 3-4 one person and group selling exhibitions a year. Also "continuous exhibition" facilities for selected artists and craftspeople on sale or return basis. Priority given to local and regional artists but others considered. Enquiries welcomed.

Gorleston-on-Sea
NORFOLK EA

Hardies Gallery

Pa Ph Pr ● ⊗

Small commercial gallery, much of which is visible from the street, displaying work of contemporary East Anglian artists.
205/6 High Street, Gorleston-on-Sea NR31 6RR, tel: 01493 668003
Contact: Michael Wide, Proprietor
Open: Mon-Sat 10-6
Space: 2 galleries with 22 lin m hanging space plus 3 lin m on screens and 29 sq m floor space
Exhibitions: 2 a year both originated
Details: Slowly- changing general collection of paintings punctuated with occasional 2-week exhibitions by particular artists, especially those trying to make their way. Audience is typically families looking for something to go over the fireplace. Ground floor gallery but entrance from street too narrow to be fully wheelchair accessible.

Gosport
HAMPSHIRE SA

Gosport Museum

Pa Ph Pr Cr Sc A ●⟨£⟩

Exhibition space opened May 1995 with emphasis on contemporary art & craft with national and regional perspective.
Walpole Road, Gosport PO12 1NS, tel: 01705 588035, fax: 01962 869836
Contact: Carol Littlefair, Exhibitions Officer, Hampshire County Council Museums Service, Chilcomb House, Chilcomb Lane, Winchester, SO23 8RD, tel: 01962 846315, fax: 01962 869836
Open: Tues-Sat 10-5; (May-Oct) Sun 1-5
Space: 1 gallery
Exhibitions: 8 a year of which 5 originated, 3 touring
Details: One of 8 museums run by Hampshire County Council Museums Service. As well as national & regional quality contemporary art and craft, new gallery to be opened May 1995 will also show HCC collections and touring exhibitions. Similarly access facilities.

Grantham
LINCOLNSHIRE EA

Grantham Guildhall Centre

Pa Ph Pr Cr A ●⟨£⟩ ● wc ④

Small gallery in arts centre for exhibitions by regional, national and international artists.
St Peters Hill, Grantham NG31 6PZ, tel: 01476 593341, fax: 01476 591810
Contact: Iona Sadler, Centre Manager
Open: Mon-Sat 9.30-5
Space: 1 gallery with 20 lin m hanging space plus 16 lin m on screens and 91 sq m floor space
Exhibitions: 8 a year of which 5 originated, 3 touring
Details: Workshops and lectures to support exhibitions are being developed. Sale of work is not gallery's primary role.

Grantham Museum

Pa ● ●

Permanent collections and temporary exhibition gallery with occasional exhibitions of contemporary art, mainly by local artists.
St Peter's Hill, Grantham NG31 6PY, tel: 01476 68783, fax: 01476 592457
Contact: Mr John F Smith, Curator Manager, Stamford & Grantham Museums, Stamford Museum, Broad Street, Stamford, PE9 1PJ, tel: 01780 66317, fax: 01780 480363
Open: Mon-Sat 10-5
Space: 1 gallery with 25 lin m hanging space plus 12 lin m on screens and 80 sq m floor space
Exhibitions: 1 a year originated
Details: Permanent collection including archaeology, natural history, and material relating to Sir Isaac Newton. Balanced by much wider range of displays in temporary exhibition programme covering all subjects. Hanging onto boarded walls with movable boards and display cases available. Caters for local audience, plus large tourist element. Sales not a priority but 20% commission taken on any sales made.

Willoughby Memorial Trust Gallery

Pa Ph Pr Cr Sc ● ⊗

Small gallery on top floor of restored C17th Grammar School encourages first-time exhibitors and brings art to the area.
Moreley's Lane, Corby Glen, Grantham NG33 4HB
Contact: Elizabeth Grenfell
Open: (During exhibitions) Wed-Sun 12-5; Tues 12-5; open BH
Space: 1 gallery with plus 38 lin m on screens and 62 sq m floor space
Exhibitions: 3 a year all originated
Details: Showing mainly work of artists and craftspeople with Lincolnshire connections. Nearly all hanging space on screens due to angle of walls. Annual art competition and local schools exhibition. Sale of work not gallery's primary function.

Gravesend
KENT SEA

Gravesend Central Library Gallery

Pa Ph Pr Sc ● ●

Corner of the library used for exhibiting, by national artists and local amateurs.
Windmill Street, Gravesend DA12 1AQ, tel: 01474 365600, fax: 01474 320284
Contact: Anne Atkinson, Arts & Heritage Officer
Open: Mon-Tues & Thurs-Fri 9.30-6; Wed 9.30-1.30; Sat 9.30-5
Space: 1 gallery with 7 lin m hanging space plus 10 lin m on screens and 24 sq m floor space
Exhibitions: 12 a year of which 10 originated, 2 touring
Details: Programme booked up a year in advance. Always plenty of library users and occasional special exhibition previews. 20% commission.

Grays
ESSEX EA

Grays Library

Pa Ph Pr Cr Sc ● ●

Small area of public library available for variety of temporary exhibitions and displays alongside collection of fine art available for loan.
Orsett Road, Grays RM17 5DX, tel: 01375 383611, fax: 01375 37806
Contact: Robert Worcester, Operations Manager, Grays
Open: Mon, Tues, Thurs & Fri 9-7.30; Wed & Sat 9-5
Space: 1 gallery with plus 7 lin m on screens and 28 sq m floor space
Exhibitions: 12 a year
Details: Exhibition space in library, available for hire covering wide variety of subject areas, art being one of most important. Shows touring exhibitions as well as being available for individuals and groups. Sales can be made but this is not a priority.

Thameside Theatre Foyer

Pa Ph Pr Cr ●⟨H⟩ ● wc

Large open area in foyer of Thurrock's busiest public building with theatre, library and museum
Orsett Road, Grays RM17 5DX, tel: 01375 382555
Contact: Mark Allinson, Assistant Leisure Manager

Space: 1 gallery with 10 lin m hanging space plus 8 lin m on screens and 20 sq m floor space
Exhibitions: 32 a year of which 2 touring, 30 on a hire basis
Details: Policy allows space to be booked for one-week periods. Non-commercial organisations given free access, otherwise hire fee of £17.35 a day for those 'making financial gain'. Commission-only basis for Thurrock residents.

Great Bookham
SURREY SEA

Kingsmead Gallery
[Pa] [Ph] [Pr] ✔ ♿

Commercial gallery promoting and selling representational work by living artists.
40 Church Road, Great Bookham KT23 3PW, tel: 01372 459579, fax: 01372 454894
Contact: Edwin Pollard, Gallery Director
Open: Mon-Sat 10-5
Space: 1 gallery with 24 lin m hanging space
Exhibitions: 10 a year all originated
Details: One-person and group shows by professional artists, mainly painters. Workshops and demonstrations can be arranged with one-person shows, depends on artist.

Great Malvern
HEREFORD & WORCESTER WMA

Malvern Arts Workshop
[Pa] [Ph] [Pr] [Cr] [Sc] ✔ ♿ [Wc]

Main gallery and hanging space in café area provide lively and informal atmosphere appealing to wide variety of people.
90 Worcester Road, Link Top, Great Malvern WR14 1NY, tel: 01684 568993
Contact: Su Barber, Exhibitions Organiser
Open: Wed-Sat 10-5; Sun 10.30-5
Space: 2 galleries with 51 lin m hanging space and 65 sq m floor space
Exhibitions: 10 a year all originated
Details: Particularly welcomes work from young artists nationwide. Main gallery for 2D and 3D work and a café area with wall space for 2D work. Exhibitions change monthly. Applications in writing accompanied by CV and slides. Classes include special sessions for those with acute learning disabilities. Welcomes offers from professional artists to join the expanding team of art workers. Sales not a priority. Café fully accessible to wheelchair users; lower level main gallery only with assistance.

Malvern Festival Theatre
[Pa] [Ph] [Pr] [Cr] [Sc] ✔ ♿ [Wc]

3 galleries showing small-scale mixed exhibitions, each lasting 8 weeks, to enhance theatre and afford artists exhibitions and possible sales.
Winter Gardens Complex, Grange Road, Great Malvern WR14 3HB, tel: 01684 892277
Contact: Mrs S K Bishop, Hon Exhibitions Organiser, Festival Artists Group, 96 Old Road, Bromyard, Herefordshire, HR7 4AT, tel: 01885 483381
Open: Mon-Sat 10-6 and during performances
Space: 3 galleries with 34 lin m hanging space
Exhibitions: 5 a year all originated
Details: Three gallery spaces used in theatre to show wide range of professional work from invited artists and makers. "Resident" Festival Artists Group. Annual Malvern Festival exhibition mounted May/June of theatre related work. Selling work is not primary function of gallery. Independent access for wheelchair users to one gallery only.

Malvern Library Art Gallery
[Pa] [Ph] [Pr] [Cr] [Sc] ✔ [H] ♿

Small self-contained and largely unsupervised gallery space providing as wide a range of exhibitions as possible for interest of local community.
Graham Road, Great Malvern WR14 2HU, tel: 01684 561223, fax: 01684 892999
Contact: Keith Barber, Malvern Librarian and Group Coordinator
Open: Mon & Thurs-Fri 9.30-5.30; Tues 9.30-8; Sat 9.30-1
Space: 1 gallery with 35 lin m hanging space plus 15 lin m on screens and 100 sq m floor space
Exhibitions: 10 a year of which 2 touring, 8 on a hire basis
Details: Gallery on two levels separated by short flight of steps. As well as hanging space, 4 glass-topped display cases and 11 plinths for 3D objects. Decor is slate blue and light grey. 20% + VAT commission on sales though sales not given high priority. Dimmable and tracked lighting which is ultraviolet free. Overnight burglar alarm protection. See also entry for Hereford & Worcester Libraries & Arts Department, Worcester.

Winter Gardens Complex
[Pa] [Ph] [Pr] [Sc] ♿ [Wc]

Work by local artists, mixed exhibitions and special exhibitions for the Malvern Festival in May and June.
Winter Gardens Complex, Grange Road, Great Malvern WR14 3HB, tel: 01684 569256
Contact: Nic LLoyd, Chief Executive
Space: 2 galleries
Exhibitions: 5 a year all originated
Details: Run by Festival Theatre Trust Limited. Exhibitions held in two separate galleries normally run for 8 weeks. Audience of local population and tourists.

Works of Art Gallery
[Pa] [Sc] ✔ £ [H]

Commercial gallery on first floor of C15th barn.
Lower Nupend, Cradley, Great Malvern WR13 5NP, tel: 01886 880500, fax: 01886 880848
Contact: Jane or Peter Wynne-James
Space: 4 galleries with 123 lin m hanging space and 180 sq m floor space
Exhibitions: 3 a year all originated
Details: Set in Herefordshire in an area of outstanding beauty 5 miles from Malvern. Mixed and one-person exhibitions. Policy to show diverse range of art in each exhibition, contemporary landscapes, abstract organic painting, natural life paintings, etc. Commission on sliding scale from 30%-50%.

Great Yarmouth
NORFOLK EA

Great Yarmouth Museums' Galleries
[Pa] [Ph] [Pr] [Cr] [Sc] ✔ [H] ♿

Three galleries plus mezzanine in central library run by Great Yarmouth Museums to take exhibitions generated by the Museums & touring exhibitions.
Central Library, Tolhouse Street, Great Yarmouth NR30 2SH, tel: 01493 858900
Contact: Damian Eaton, Assistant Museums Officer (Collections)
Open: Mon-Fri 10-1, 2-5; Sat 9-12.30, 1.30-5
Space: 4 galleries with 100 lin m hanging space and 312 sq m floor space
Exhibitions: 8 a year
Details: Permanent collection of C19th and C20th art. Exhibitions include local groups, individual artists & travelling shows. Annual winter open exhibition. Exhibitions catering for schools' curriculum needs only Jan-June each year. Hire fee payable by contemporary exhibitors. Talks & other activities arranged for some exhibitions. Selling work not a main aim of gallery.

Grimsby
HUMBERSIDE YHA

Central Library *
[Pa] [Ph] [Pr] [Cr] [Sc] ✔ [H]

At present no planned programme, but library accepts any good local work.

Town Hall Square, Grimsby DN31 1HG,
tel: **01472 240410**
Contact: Kath Baker, Entertainments
Manager
Space: 2 galleries with 114 lin m hanging
space plus 20 lin m on screens and 1723 sq
m floor space
Exhibitions: 5 a year all on a hire basis

Grimsby College of Technology (Gallery One Hundred) *

Pa Ph Pr Cr SC ✓

*Within a college showing occasional
external work.*
Eleanor Road, Grimsby DN32 9DU, tel:
01472 361613, fax: 01472 79924
Contact: Gallery Co-ordinator, School of
Art & Design

Guildford
SURREY SEA

Forest Contemporary Art

85 High Street, Guildford GU1 4AU, tel:
01483 5066222

Guildford House Gallery

Pa Ph Pr Cr SC ✓ (&)

*C17th house with shop and tearoom,
showing exhibitions and selections from the
Borough's art collection.*
Guildford House, 155 High Street,
Guildford GU1 3AJ, tel: **01483 444740,
fax: 01483 444742**
Contact: Miss I C Rhodes, Curator
Open: Tues-Sat 10-4.45
Space: 4 galleries with 43 lin m hanging
space and 121 sq m floor space
Exhibitions: 6 a year of which 4
originated, 2 touring
Details: A varied exhibition programme
includes historical and modern paintings,
drawings, photography and craftwork, some
in house others on hire or loan. Rooms may
be hired for a minimum of 3 weeks.
Educational programme includes lunchtime
lectures, workshops and guided tours of the
house on request. Sales not a priority.

Harvey Gallery

Pa Ph Pr Cr SC ✓ (H)

*Supports busy visual arts department
within adult education centre where
exhibitions of students' work are given
priority.*
Harvey Road, Guildford GU1 3RX, tel:
01483 60978, fax: 01483 440379
Contact: Carol Orwin, Gallery Organiser,
Surrey Adult & Continuing Education,
Sydenham Road, Guildford, GU1 3RX, tel:
01483 60978, fax: 01483 440379
Space: 1 gallery with 61 lin m hanging
space plus 3 lin m on screens and 150 sq m
floor space

Exhibitions: 15 a year of which 10
originated, 5 on a hire basis
Details: Gallery is rectangular in shape,
with good high light and hessian walls to
height of 3m. Programme very varied –
crafts as well as arts. Fortnightly exhibitions
throughout term times.

Jonleigh Gallery

Pa SC

*Rural gallery showing work by artists of
quality and international reputation.*
Wonersh, Guildford GU5 0PF, tel:
01483 893177
Contact: John Hudson-Lyons, Director
Open: (During exhibitions) Wed, Fri, Sat
11-12.30; Thurs 2-5; otherwise by special
appointment.
Exhibitions: 3 a year
Details: Selection and hanging committee:
Sir Roger de Grey PPRA, Carel Weight,
CBE RA, Leslie Worth PRWS. Exhibitions
include work by approximately 20 RA's and
many top contemporary artists. Sales a
priority.

Library Gallery *

Pa Ph Pr Cr SC ✓

*Most exhibitions are for the benefit of
university students, staff and the local
community.*
University of Surrey, Guildford GU2
5XH, tel: **01483 300800, fax: 01483
300803**
Contact: Mrs Patricia Grayburn, Arts
Administrator
Space: 1 gallery with 26 lin m hanging
space and 48 sq m floor space
Exhibitions: 12 a year all originated
Details: Shows mainly the work of
contemporary artists, some internationally
and nationally known, some local. Also art
schools and occasional touring shows.

Guisborough
CLEVELAND NA

Walton Galleries

Pa Ph ✓ (H)

*Small commercial gallery showing
landscapes, watercolours, etc, though
approaches welcomed from artists working
in more adventurous subjects and media.*
Walton Terrace, Guisborough TS14
6QG, tel: **01287 610191**
Contact: T.O.L. Wealleans, Director
Open: Mon-Sat 8.15-5.30
Space: 1 gallery with 10 lin m hanging
space plus 4 lin m on screens and 9 sq m
floor space
Exhibitions: 12 a year all on a hire basis
Details: Main business is picture-framing
so discounts offered to artists exhibiting in
gallery. Downstairs, up to 12 artists have a
small area – usually for work to be
permanently displayed, offered for sale.

Hailsham
EAST SUSSEX SEA

Michelham Priory

Pa Ph Pr Cr SC LA ✓ (&) (Wc)

*Historic house exhibiting local works in
unique setting as an added visitor
attraction.*
Upper Dicker, Hailsham BN27 3QS, tel:
01323 844224, fax: 01323 844030
Contact: Allex Jenkinson, Director
Open: (25 Mar – 31 Oct) Mon-Sun 11-5;
(Nov– Mar) Sun only 11-4
Space: 3 galleries with 317 sq m floor space
Exhibitions: 8 a year all originated
Details: Great Tudor Barn holds
exhibitions by local artists Mar-Oct; C14th
gatehouse holds sculpture exhibitions and
Picture Gallery exhibits annual themed
exhibition from Sussex Archaeological
Society which includes education
workshops. Sales not a priority.
Independent access for wheelchair users to
Barn and Picture Gallery; access not
possible to Gatehouse.

Halesworth
SUFFOLK EA

Halesworth Gallery

Pa Ph Pr SC ✓

*Non-profit making gallery in Elizabethan
building with exhibitions of contemporary
work.*
Steeple End, Halesworth IP19, tel:
01986 873064
Contact: Jan Martin, Exhibition Organiser
Space: 3 galleries
Exhibitions: 6 a year
Details: Building formerly an alms house.
Library and museum on ground floor,
gallery on first floor. Aims to show work of
highest standard and exhibitions generally
last 3 weeks. One exhibition a year is an
open exhibition. Artists usually have East
Anglian connection. A fee of £50 covers
artists' publicity and private view. 25%
commission.

Halifax
WEST YORKSHIRE YHA

Bankfield Museum and Art Gallery

Pa Ph Pr Cr SC ✓ (£) (&)

*Former textile mill owner's mansion, now a
museum with permanent galleries and
temporary exhibitions focussing on textiles,
crafts and decorative art.*
Boothtown Road, Halifax HX3 6HG, tel:
01422 354823, fax: 01422 349020
Contact: Hazel McHugh, Exhibitions
Officer, Calderdale Museums and Arts,
Piece Hall, Halifax, HX1 1RE, tel: 01422
358087, fax: 01422 349020

Open: Tues-Sat 10-5; Sun 2-5; Open BH Mons only.
Space: 1 gallery with 152 lin m hanging space
Exhibitions: 8 a year of which 6 originated, 2 touring
Details: Museum houses permanent collection of textiles, a toy gallery, and the Duke of Wellington Regimental Museum. Temporary programme usually features work by regional artists, often with a textile theme. Yorkshire and Humberside EPR is available for single- or two-person shows. Sales not a high priority.

David Holmes Ceramics *

Pd Cr ⊘

Private gallery showing contemporary ceramics, also exhibits paintings or wall hangings.
Back Chantry House, Paradise Lane, Warley, Halifax HX2 7SA, tel: 01422 833864
Contact: David Holmes
Space: 2 galleries with 130 sq m floor space
Exhibitions: 8 a year all originated
Details: During summer months pottery workshops run from 1-5 days. Accommodation available.

Dean Clough Galleries

Pd Ph Pr Cr Sc LA ⊘

Emphasis on showing regional artists.
Dean Clough Industrial Park, Halifax HX3 5AX, tel: 01422 344555, fax: 01422 361032
Contact: Douglas Binder, Gallery Director
Open: Daily 10-5
Space: 6 galleries with 80 lin m hanging space and 300 sq m floor space
Exhibitions: 19 a year of which 16 originated, 3 touring
Details: Shows work by artists from further afield from time to time. Aims to show a balanced programme covering a variety of media and approaches including fine art to crafts and design-based areas.

Henry Moore Sculpture Trust Studio

Sc ⓑ

Major sculpture studio which becomes exhibition galleries when appropriate with projects developed through invitation only.
Dean Clough, Halifax HX7 7AA, tel: 01422 320250, fax: 01422 344191
Contact: Robert Hopper, Director
Open: Varies due to the nature of individual artist's projects
Space: 2 galleries with 1023 sq m floor space
Exhibitions: 2 a year
Details: Two large rooms in industrial complex, suitable for large scale or ambitious installations by invited artists. Projects are developed through invitation only. Artists who have worked with us to

date: Giuseppe Penone, Richard Long, Ulrich Ruckriem, Bruce McLean, John Newling, Jannis Kounellis, Alison Wilding, Magdalena Jetelova, Mario Merz, Conrad Atkinson, Lawrence Weiner, James Turrell, Jaume Plensa, Wolfgang Laib, Sir Anthony Caro.

Piece Hall Art Gallery

Pd Ph Pr Cr Sc LA ⊘⊕ ⊕④

Gallery developing a challenging programme of exhibitions and related events which show high-quality contemporary art, crafts and photography.
The Piece Hall, Halifax HX1 1RE, tel: 01422 358087, fax: 01422 349310
Contact: Hazel McHugh, Exhibitions Officer, Calderdale Museums/Arts Division of Leisure Services
Open: Tues-Sun 10-5; open BH
Space: 1 gallery with 200 lin m hanging space and 640 sq m floor space
Exhibitions: 8 a year of which 6 originated, 2 touring
Details: Municipal gallery with exhibitions of both contemporary and historical art and crafts. Emphasis on making contemporary art more accessible, often in an historical context. Organises series of exhibitions exploring different aspects of one theme. Commitment to improving accessibility to the arts for sections of the community who may be alienated by particular social, economic or educational factors. Sales not a priority.

Square Chapel Centre for the Arts *

Pd Ph Pr Cr Sc ⊘
10 Square Road, Halifax HX1 1QG

Throstle Nest Gallery

Pd Pr Cr Sc ⊘ ⓑ

Converted 250 year old barn, providing space for artists and craftspeople to both show and sell their work; speciality ceramics.
Old Lindley, Holywell Green, Halifax HX4 9DF, tel: 01422 374388
Contact: Pat Kaye, Owner
Open: Mon-Sun 10-5
Space: 2 galleries with 18 lin m hanging space plus 12 lin m on screens and 96 sq m floor space
Exhibitions: 5 a year all originated
Details: Gallery in rural setting between two major W. Riding industrial towns. Supplies contemporary craft and paintings to this particular market, aiming to keep standards as high as possible. Domestic ware, glass, sculpture, patchwork, baskets and selected cards also stocked.

Haltwhistle
NORTHUMBERLAND NA

Haltwhistle Library

Pd Ph Pr ⊘

Established library exhibition wall.
Mechanics Institute, West Gate, Haltwhistle NE49 0AX, tel: 01434 320462
Contact: Joyce Stonehouse, Administrator, Queens Hall Arts Centre, Beaumont Street, Hexham, NE46 3LS, tel: 01434 606787/606788, fax: 01434 606043
Open: Mon & Fri 9.30-12.30, 2-5, 5.30-7; Tues & Thurs 9.30-12.30, 2-5; Sat 9.30-12.30
Space: 1 gallery with 11 lin m hanging space
Exhibitions: 8 a year all originated
Details: A long, well-lit wall suitable for medium- scale 2D works, usually one person shows. Interested exhibitors should send slides/photos, background information & CV to Queens Hall Arts Centre.

Harleston
NORFOLK EA

Halo Frames *

Pd Pr ⊘ⓗ

Gallery in old warehouse building in small market town.
Old Mineral Works, Redenhall Road, Harleston IT20 9EN, tel: 01379 853609
Contact: Jack Crampton
Space: 2 galleries with 76 sq m floor space
Exhibitions: 6 a year of which 5 originated, 1 on a hire basis
Details: Main gallery and smaller subsidiary space are clean, uncluttered areas ideally suited to exhibiting high quality contemporary and abstract painting. Artists can either hire gallery space or pay commission on sales.

Harlow
ESSEX EA

Harlow Library

Pd Ph Pr ⊘ⓗ ⓑ

Gallery situated between quiet study area and newspaper/magazine tables in main body of library.
The High, Harlow CM20 1HA, tel: 01279 413772, fax: 01279 424612
Contact: Freda Staines, Exhibitions Organiser
Open: Mon, Tues, Thurs, Fri 9-7.30; Wed, Sat 9-5
Space: 1 gallery with 37 lin m hanging space and 58 sq m floor space
Exhibitions: 14 a year of which 3 touring, 11 on a hire basis
Details: Aims to provide varied and interesting display for artwork of high

standard, by both individual artists and societies/organisations. Exhibits work by Essex artists of all levels of experience and by societies local to Harlow. Approx 54,000 visitors per month. Sales not a priority.

Harlow Study Centre

Pa Ph Pr Cr SC ✓ & Wc

Exhibition space in mediaeval tithe barn for display of art or other material with an educational purpose.
Netteswellbury Farm, Harlow CM18 6BW, tel: 01279 446745, **fax:** 01279 421945
Contact: Sandra Farrington, Manager
Open: Mon-Fri 9.30-4.30
Space: 1 gallery with 15 lin m hanging space
Exhibitions: 5 a year of which 3 originated, 2 touring
Details: Exhibition space consists of 4 separate bays each 12ft x 8ft. Sale of work not gallery's primary consideration.

Playhouse Gallery

Pa Ph ✓ & Wc

A gallery situated at the top of a theatre to provide varied exhibitions for the public.
The Playhouse, The High, Harlow CM20 1LS, tel: 01279 424391, **fax:** 01279 451192
Contact: Anthea Whitworth/Ken Shilingford, Gallery Assistants
Open: Daily 11am-11pm
Space: 25 lin m hanging space
Exhibitions: 12 a year all originated
Details: Selling work is not gallery's primary function. White painted canvas covered walls, 11 ft high.

Harrogate
NORTH YORKSHIRE YHA

Godfrey & Twatt

Ph Cr ✓ &

Gallery showing and selling contemporary British craft.
7 Westminster Arcade, Harrogate HG1 2RN, tel: 01423 525300
Contact: Alex Twatt
Open: Mon-Sat 10-5.30
Space: 1 gallery with 14 lin m hanging space plus 6 lin m on screens and 24 sq m floor space
Exhibitions: 5 a year all originated
Details: Continually changing stock of contemporary crafts and original prints. Generally focus on one or two individual makers. Four or five shows a year, each lasting four weeks. Sale of work is gallery's primary concern.

Masai Mara

Pa Ph Pr Cr ✓ &

Retail of African art and images of Africa.

32 Cheltenham Parade, Harrogate HG1 1DB, tel: 01423 527862
Contact: Al Jackson, Director, Retail Operations
Open: Daily 9-5.30
Space: 2 galleries with 18 lin m hanging space and 46 sq m floor space
Exhibitions: 1 a year originated

Mercer Art Gallery

Pa Ph Pr Cr SC ✓ £ & Wc 4

Housed in Harrogate's oldest spa building, the Mercer Art Gallery is a new venue for art exhibitions and Harrogate's fine art collection.
Harrogate Museums Service, 31 Swan Road, Harrogate HG1 2SA, tel: 01423 503340, **fax:** 01423 840026
Contact: Karen Southworth, Visual Arts Officer
Open: Tues-Sat 10-5, Sun 2-5
Space: 1 gallery with 15 lin m hanging space plus 60 lin m on screens and 136 sq m floor space
Exhibitions: 10 a year of which 7 originated, 3 touring
Details: Varied programme of exhibitions and related activities. Sales not a priority.

Hartlepool
CLEVELAND NA

Hartlepool Art Gallery

Pa Ph Pr Cr SC LA ✓ £ & Wc 4

Hartlepool's new purpose-designed Art Gallery exhibiting contemporary and other art in a series of over 20 separate exhibitions per year.
Church Square, Hartlepool, tel: 01429 266522 ext 2609, **fax:** 01429 869625
Contact: Frank Caldwell, Curator, Hartlepool Museum Service, Gray Art Gallery, Clarence Road, Hartlepool, TS24 8BT
Open: Tues-Sun 12-5
Space: 5 galleries with 65 lin m hanging space plus 50 lin m on screens and 290 sq m floor space
Exhibitions: 13 a year of which 9 originated, 4 touring
Details: Converted church opening September 1995. 5 exhibition galleries which can be used individually or in any combination. Exhibitions of local, regional and nationally important works, including sculpture, installation and the 'avant-garde'. Plain light walls, daylight excluded. Sales not a priority.

Hartley Wintney
HAMPSHIRE SA

Century Galleries *

Ph Pr Cr SC LA

A fine art consultancy service.

The High Street, Hartley Wintney RG27, tel: 01252 842747
Contact: Carolyn Patterson, Manager
Details: (See also Century Galleries, Henley-on-Thames.)

Harwich
ESSEX EA

Bodgeners

Pa Ph Pr Cr SC &

A small gallery shop in old Harwich run as a co-op to show work of about 20 local artists.
52 Church Street, Harwich
Contact: Exhibitions Organiser, Harwich Arts Workshop, c/o 86 Fronks Road, Dovercourt, CO12 3RS, tel:** 01255 502563
Open: Tues-Sun 1-4; and by appointment.
Space: 1 gallery with 20 lin m hanging space and 22 sq m floor space
Exhibitions: 6 a year all originated
Details: A gallery run by co-op of 20 artists living locally providing exhibition space to show their work. All members have free hand to show what they like, pay share of outgoings and take turns to sit in shop. Occasional vacancies for new members. Some members run workshops in gallery with local children. Selling work is not gallery's main aim.

Haslemere
SURREY SEA

Haslemere Museum

Pa Ph Pr Cr SC ✓ H &

Natural history museum with lecture room and exhibition room available on hire basis.
High Street, Haslemere GU27 2LA, tel: 01428 642112
Contact: Diana Hawkes, Curator
Open: Tues-Sat 10-5
Space: 2 galleries with 80 lin m hanging space plus 10 lin m on screens and 152 sq m floor space
Exhibitions: 15 a year of which 2 originated, 3 on a hire basis
Details: Houses collections of natural history, archaeology, local history and European arts and crafts. Exhibition programme aims to forward and advance the study of science, literature and fine arts. Founded in 1888, a private society governed by trustees with a large active membership. Keen to encourage increased use of the exhibition space and to hold lectures and workshops in conjunction with exhibitions.

Hastings
EAST SUSSEX SEA

Hastings Exhibitions
[Pa] [Ph] [Pr] [Cr] [SC] [LA] ✔ [H] ♿ [WC] [4]

Commercial exhibition centre available for hire with extensive main hall, bar and facilities.

The Bourne, Old Town, Hastings TN34 3AY, tel: 01424 424848

Contact: Tony Smith, Proprietor/ Exhibition Organiser, Brownbread Horse Rescue, Ashburnham, Battle, TN33 9NX, tel: 01424 892381

Open: Daily 9-5; evenings by arrangement

Space: 3 galleries with 82 lin m hanging space plus 37 lin m on screens and 195 sq m floor space

Exhibitions: 2 a year of which 1 originated, 1 on a hire basis

Details: Embraces all the arts and endeavours to maintain its multi-purpose facilities and role providing special consideration to disabled people and children in any proposals received from them.

Hastings Museum & Art Gallery
[Pa] [Ph] [Pr] [Cr] [SC] ✔ ♿

Two rooms within museum mixing current art with historical and other types of exhibition.

Johns Place, Cambridge Road, Hastings TN34 1ET, tel: 01424 721202

Contact: Lesley Cornish, Exhibitions Officer

Open: Mon-Fri 10-5; Sat 10-1, 2-5; Sun 3-5

Space: 2 galleries with 53 lin m hanging space

Exhibitions: 5 a year of which 4 originated, 1 touring

Details: Specially converted with no daylight. Very adaptable but not suited to very large paintings owing to size. Priority tends to be given to artists living in region but no strict policy. Sales not a priority.

Old Town Art Gallery
[Pa] [Ph] [Pr] [Cr] ✔ [H]

Commercial gallery on two floors available for rent to artists for exhibitions.

3 Courthouse Street, Old Town, Hastings TN34 3JE, tel: 01424 213599

Contact: Peter Lindsay-Vail, Owner, 1 South Cliff, Bexhill on Sea, TN39 3EJ, tel: 01424 213599

Open: To suit exhibitors

Space: 1 gallery with 54 sq m floor space

Exhibitions: 6 a year all on a hire basis

Details: Gallery opened early 1994. Timber-beamed ceilings, old brick walls, with modern amenities. Sales are gallery's main purpose. Wheelchair users can reach ground-floor gallery only.

Riviera (The)
[Pa] [Ph] [Pr] [Cr] [SC] [LA] ✔ [H] ♿

Public gallery run by volunteers with varied monthly programme of exhibitions.

6 Pelham Arcade, Hastings TN34 3AE, tel: 01424 427088

Contact: Christine Warrington, Gallery Administrator

Open: (Apr-Sept) Tues-Sun 10-6; (Oct-Mar) Tues-Sun 11-5

Space: 1 gallery with 46 lin m hanging space and 140 sq m floor space

Exhibitions: 15 a year of which 11 originated, 4 on a hire basis

Details: Ground-floor level on the sea front, large open-plan exhibition space. Regular programmes of exhibitions, group, individual, professional and amateur, national and local. Also holds art auctions, craft fairs, launches, public meetings. Visitors include members, locals, school children, OAPs, local and international students, tourists. Sales not a priority.

Stables Theatre Gallery
[Pa] [Ph] [Pr] [Cr] [SC] [LA] ✔ [H]

Two exhibition spaces available for hire by professional artists or 'good amateurs'.

High Street, Hastings TN34 3EY, tel: 01424 423221

Contact: Hon Secretary

Open: Daily 10.30-1; evenings of performances 6.30-9

Space: 2 galleries with 40 lin m hanging space and 27 sq m floor space

Exhibitions: 9 a year all on a hire basis

Details: Mainly shows work of professional artists with occasional exhibitions by 'good amateurs'. Usually booked two years in advance. One of spaces is a purpose built gallery. Fees for exhibitions discussed with the venue.

Hatfield
HERTFORDSHIRE EA

Mill Green Museum & Mill
[Pa] [Ph] [Pr] [Cr] ✔ [£] ♿

Provides a variety of temporary exhibitions on different themes with a local audience primarily in mind.

Welwyn Hatfield Museum Service, Mill Green, Hatfield AL9 5PD, tel: 01707 271362, fax: 01707 272511

Contact: Ms Sue Kirby, Curator

Open: Tues-Fri 10-5; Sat, Sun 2-5; BH 2-5

Space: 1 gallery with 11 lin m hanging space plus 4 lin m on screens and 16 sq m floor space

Details: Museum collections figure strongly but others welcome, especially local craft workers. Exhibitions last between eight and ten weeks with craft demonstrations to tie in with exhibitions. Five showcases available plus garden and small summerhouse.

Havant
HAMPSHIRE SA

Havant Arts Active
[Pa] [Ph] [Pr] [Cr] [SC] ✔ [£] [H] ♿ [WC]

Arts centre gallery showing a broad range of exhibitions from local to international.

O.T.H., East Street, Havant PO9 1BS, tel: 01705 472700

Contact: Nigel Draycott, Gallery Administrator

Open: Mon-Fri 10-6.30; Sat 10-4.30; evenings 5-10.30 when there is a performance

Space: 1 gallery with 28 lin m hanging space and 156 sq m floor space

Exhibitions: 14 a year of which 7 originated, 7 on a hire basis

Details: L-shaped gallery situated at the front of the arts centre. Attracts not only those specifically interested in the exhibitions but also those using the building for other interests, over 45,000 each year. As many diverse forms of contemporary art are programmed as possible. Sales not a priority.

Havant Museum
[Pa] [Ph] [Pr] [Cr] [SC] ✔ [£] ♿ [4]

Local museum showing varied programme including contemporary and historical art and craft.

East Street, Havant PO9 1BS, tel: 01705 451155, fax: 01962 869836

Contact: Carol Littlefair, Exhibitions Officer, Hampshire County Council Museums Service, Chilcomb House, Chilcomb Lane, Winchester, SO23 8RD, tel: 01962 846315

Open: Tues-Sat 10-5

Space: 1 gallery with 32 lin m hanging space and 41 sq m floor space

Exhibitions: 8 a year of which 6 originated, 2 touring

Details: See entry for Hampshire County Council Museums, Winchester for policy.

Heckington
LINCOLNSHIRE EA

Pearoom Centre for Contemporary Craft
[Cr] ✔ [H] ♿ [WC]

Top floor of a converted pea sorting warehouse specialising in contemporary craft from new and established makers with a regional emphasis.

Station Road, Heckington NG34 9JJ, tel: 01529 460765

Contact: Clare Bryan/Ann Wallis, Exhibition Officer, North Kesteven District Council, Kesteven Street, Sleaford, NG34 7EK, tel: 01529 414155 ext 482

Open: Mon-Sat 10-5; Sun 12-5

Space: 2 galleries with 51 lin m hanging

space plus 7 lin m on screens and 317 sq m floor space
Exhibitions: 11 a year of which 4 originated, 2 touring, 5 on a hire basis
Details: Offers opportunity for visitors who might never enter formal gallery to see innovative work from new and established makers working in wood, metal, textiles, glass, ceramics and jewellery. Occasionally shows fine art, printmaking and photographs. Information provided with exhibitions to promote better understanding of artists' work and techniques. Demonstrations, short courses and artist in residence scheme. Sales not a priority.

Helmsley
NORTH YORKSHIRE YHA

Look Gallery

`Pa` `Cr` `SC` ✓

Shows a wide range of contemporary painting in all media. Some sculpture, ceramics and glass.
20 Castlegate, Helmsley YO6 5AB, tel: 01439 70545
Contact: Nicholas Coombes, Manager
Open: Mon-Sat 10.30-5; Sun 2-5
Details: Maintains throughout the year a mixed show of work by gallery artists which is ever changing.

Sissons William Gallery *

`Pa` `Pr` ✓

Commercial gallery organising occasional exhibitions usually on a rural theme.
23 Market Place, Helmsley YO6 5BJ, tel: 01439 71385
Contact: Mrs D Sissons, Exhibition Organiser
Space: 2 galleries with 279 sq m floor space
Exhibitions: 4 a year all originated
Details: Always interested to see work by new artists. Stock is constantly changing.

Helston
CORNWALL SWA

Cornwall Crafts Association at Trelowarren *

`Cr`

Crafts shop and exhibitions housed in Georgian stable-block of the Trelowarren estate.
Trelowarren, Mawgan-in-Meneage, Helston TR12 6AF, tel: 01326 22567
Contact: Jenny Welch, Secretary
Space: 3 galleries
Exhibitions: 4 a year all originated
Details: Licensed bistro and coffee bar. (See also Cornwall Crafts Association at Pencarrow Bodmin and Trelissick Gallery, Truro).

Mullion Gallery

`Pa` `Cr` `SC` ✓ ✻ ⬤

Gallery showing contemporary art and crafts with strong connections with the Lizard Peninsula and with exhibition room available for hire.
Nansmellyon Road, Mullion, Helston TR12 7DQ, tel: 01326 241170
Contact: Agnes Lewis
Open: (Summer) Daily 10-1, 2.30-5.30; (Winter) Wed-Sat 10-1, 2.30-5.30
Space: 18 lin m hanging space and 22 sq m floor space
Exhibitions: 4 a year of which 1 originated, 3 on a hire basis
Details: Gallery offers permanent exhibition space to local artists and craftspeople in an informal setting which aims to be inviting to art lovers and casual visitors. Separate room available for special exhibitions of contemporary art and craft. Sales a priority.

Hemel Hempstead
HERTFORDSHIRE EA

Old Town Hall Arts Centre

`Pa` `Ph` `Pr` `Cr` `IA` ✓ ✻

Gallery in restaurant of arts centre.
High Street, Hemel Hempstead HP1 3AE, tel: 01442 241789
Contact: VAC
Space: 1 gallery with 50 sq m floor space
Exhibitions: 14 a year of which 1 touring, 13 on a hire basis
Details: Art work is seen by customers of the restaurant as well as those coming to the exhibitions. Well-lit and all artwork is clearly visible from all angles. Most exhibitions run for 3 weeks. No hiring charge, but 20% commission on sales.

Henley in Arden
WARWICKSHIRE WMA

Gallery Upstairs

`Pa` `Pr` `Cr` `SC` ✓ ⊘

Commercial gallery in Elizabethan building with exhibitions designed to encourage high-quality work from new and established craftspeople.
Torquil, 81 High Street, Henley in Arden B95 5AT, tel: 01564 792174
Contact: Mr Reg Moon
Open: Mon-Sat 10-6
Space: 1 gallery with 29 lin m hanging space plus 9 lin m on screens and 75 sq m floor space
Exhibitions: 3 a year all originated
Details: Gallery has natural northern light and overlooks cobbled courtyard and large walled garden. Private views are particularly well attended with a growing mailing list of over 1500. Sale of work is gallery's primary role.

Henley on Thames
OXFORDSHIRE SA

Barn Galleries

`Pa` `Cr` `SC` ✓ ✻ ⬤ `4`

C18th barns and gardens offer sympathetic space, friendly to artists and visitors.
Middle Culham Farm, Aston, Henley on Thames RG9 3DX, tel: 01491 577786
Contact: Bridget Fraser, Director
Open: During exhibitions and for workshops.
Space: 2 galleries with 134 lin m hanging space and 257 sq m floor space
Exhibitions: 2 a year of which 1 originated, 1 on a hire basis
Details: Annual "Artspace" exhibition showing accessible work by 40 invited professional artists, aimed at new collectors buying for their homes. Galleries hired to groups for exhibition in September each year. Sales priority.

Bohun Gallery *

`Pa` `Pr` `Cr` `SC`

Commercial gallery showing contemporary British work by established and up & coming young artists.
15 Reading Road, Henley on Thames RG9 1AB, tel: 01491 576 228
Contact: Patricia Speirs, Managing Partner
Space: 1 gallery
Exhibitions: 10 a year all originated
Details: Handles the estate of Julian Trevelyan etchings.

Century Galleries *

`Pa` `Pr` `Cr` `SC`

Fine art consultancy service.
Thames Side, Henley on Thames RG9 2LJ, tel: 01491 575 499, fax: 01491 410 273
Contact: Michael Shemilt, Director
Space: 2 galleries
Exhibitions: 30 a year all originated
Details: Exhibitions of mostly nationally- and internationally-known artists working in a wide range of styles and media. Work of about 100 artists is held in stock. Framing and restoration work is undertaken and a range of services offered to businesses, including leasing, advice on office decoration etc. (See separate entry for Century Galleries, Hartley Wintney.)

Luxters Fine Art

`Pa` `Ph` `Pr` ✓ ✻ ⬤ `vc`

Converted C17th barn in a farm location featuring both 2D and 3D C20th works.
Old Luxters Gallery, Hambleden, Henley on Thames RG9 6JW, tel: 01491 638816, fax: 01491 638645
Contact: Julie Nicholson, Gallery Manager
Open: (Summer) daily 10-6; (Winter) daily 10-5

Space: 1 gallery with 58 lin m hanging space and 111 sq m floor space
Exhibitions: 8 a year of which 1 touring, 7 on a hire basis
Details: Aim is to create harmony between art displayed and regular classical concerts held in the gallery which adjoins a working winery & brewery. Visitors are encouraged to enjoy a total experience and relaxed atmosphere. Artists are invited to give a talk or demonstration in conjunction with their exhibition. Exhibitions run 1-2 months. Sales a priority.

Hereford
HEREFORD & WORCESTER WMA

Gallery at 89

Small gallery in café providing opportunities for local artists and craftspeople.
89 East Street, Hereford HR1 2LU, tel: 01432 278226
Contact: Mike Gell, Jeweller
Open: Mon-Sat 10-5
Space: 1 gallery with 9 lin m hanging space
Exhibitions: 6 a year all originated
Details: Opened March 1994. Hanging space interrupted by windows. Commitment to equality of opportunity. Exhibitions include work by those who would not generally exhibit their work in public. Reflects special events, eg Hereford Summer Festival. Sales not primary role. 15% commission taken on sales. Mike Gell also has jewellery workshop and gallery at same address, where he sells his own and other jewellers' work.

Hatton Art Gallery

Purpose-built gallery houses work of Brian Hatton, a Herefordshire artist killed in the First World War and showing some temporary exhibitions of contemporary work.
Churchill House Museum, Venns Lane, Hereford, tel: 01432 267409, fax: 01432 342662
Contact: Anne Sandford, Curator, Hereford City Museum & Art Gallery, Broad Street, Hereford, HR4 9AU, tel: 01432 268121 ext 207
Space: 1 gallery
Exhibitions: 4 a year of which 2 originated, 2 touring
Details: See entry for Hereford City Art Gallery, Hereford.

Hereford City Art Gallery

Municipal gallery with selling shows.
Broad Street, Hereford HR4 9AU, tel: 01432 368761, fax: 01432 354764

Contact: Miss A.E. Sandford, Curator
Open: Tues-Wed & Fri 10-6; Thurs 10-5; Sat (Winter) 10-4, (Summer) 10-5; Sun (Summer) 10-5
Space: 1 gallery
Exhibitions: 12 a year of which 9 originated, 3 touring
Details: Used mainly for temporary exhibitions, usually of three-week duration. Lockwall spaceframe system gives considerable flexibility. There are also eight Click cases available for display. Exhibitions booked 18 months to two years in advance, of local and national interest. Shows a wide variety of exhibitions of fine and applied art, and caters for a cross-section of local population. Sale of work is primary role of gallery. Also programmes Hatton Art Gallery, Hereford (see separate entry).

John McKellar Designer Jewellery

Commercial gallery showing contemporary jewellery.
23 Church Street, Hereford HR1 2LR, tel: 01432 354460
Contact: Julie Thomas
Open: Mon-Sat 9.30-5.30
Space: 1 gallery with 225 sq m floor space
Exhibitions: 10 a year all originated
Details: Stocks and exhibits only contemporary jewellery in all materials. Exhibit two designers each calendar month, with occasional larger group exhibitions.

Hertford
HERTFORDSHIRE EA

Hertford Museum

Gallery in museum showing variety of exhibitions, mainly art and local history, as complementary interest to permanent displays.
18 Bull Plain, Hertford SG14 1DT, tel: 01992 582686
Contact: Andrea George, Senior Curator
Open: Tues-Sat 10-5
Space: 1 gallery with 15 lin m hanging space plus 4 lin m on screens and 25 sq m floor space
Exhibitions: 6 a year of which 3 originated, 3 touring
Details: Ground-floor exhibition space in a museum which displays mainly local and social history collections. Audience mainly local. Sales not a priority. Museum also organises exhibitions at Mill Bridge Rooms, Hertford (see separate entry).

Mill Bridge Rooms

Independent room suitable for display of many kinds of art and sculpture.

Seed Warehouse, The Wash, Hertford SG14, tel: 01992 587979
Contact: Sheila Every, Museum Administrator, Hertford Museum, 18 Bull Plain, Hertford, SG14 1DT, tel: 01992 582686
Open: Mon-Sat 9-10
Space: 1 gallery with 28 lin m hanging space plus 12 lin m on screens and 60 sq m floor space
Exhibitions: 6 a year all on a hire basis
Details: Multi-purpose hall for community use. Can be booked for meetings, coffee mornings, sales of work, or for art and craft exhibitions. Self-catering facilities available. Bookings of the Mill Bridge Rooms administered by Hertford Museum (see separate entry) on a first-come, first served basis. Sales not seen as primary role by Museum.

Heswall
MERSEYSIDE NWA

Dee Fine Arts

Simple open-plan area for the sale of original wall-hung work.
182 Telegraph Road, Heswall L60 0AJ, tel: 0151 342 6657
Contact: Deirdre Waite, Partner
Open: Mon-Sat 9.30-5
Space: 1 gallery with 25 lin m hanging space and 33 sq m floor space
Exhibitions: 9 a year all originated
Details: Promotes original art and contact between artists and the public in the form of painting demonstrations. Glass etching and engraving has been shown. Sale of work is gallery's primary role. Part of the gallery is fully accessible and part impossible for wheelchair users.

Hexham
NORTHUMBERLAND NA

Abbey Prints

Retail gallery showing original prints and paintings mostly by artists who live and work in the area.
22 Hallgate, Hexham NE46 1XD, tel: 01434 607550
Contact: Mrs Anne Biggs, Owner
Open: Mon-Sat 9.30-5
Space: 1 gallery with 23 lin m hanging space and 25 sq m floor space
Exhibitions: 1 a year originated
Details: As space is limited gallery organises annual exhibition in Hexham Moot Hall and combines this with special exhibition of original prints in permanent gallery.

Moothall Gallery

[Pa][Ph][Pr][Cr][Sc] ✔[H] ♿

Gallery available for hire – shows are primarily of work by local groups.
Market Place, Hexham NE46 3NH, tel: 01434 652351, fax: 01434 652423
Contact: Flora Fairbairn, Museums Development Assistant, Leisure, Tourism & Economic Development Department, Tynedale District Council, Prospect House, Hexham, NE46 3NH
Exhibitions: 28 a year all on a hire basis
Details: Part of a hall hired out for meetings, classes and social functions.

Queens Hall Arts Centre

[Pa][Ph][Pr][Cr][Sc] ✔[£][H] ♿[Wc]

Local authority run arts centre with gallery showing work by local and national, amateur and professional artists and photographers.
Beaumont Street, Hexham NE46 3IS, tel: 01434 606787, fax: 01434 606043
Contact: Joyce Stonehouse, Administrator
Open: Mon-Sat 9.30-5.30
Space: 1 gallery with 27 lin m hanging space and 70 sq m floor space
Exhibitions: 11 a year of which 8 originated, 2 touring, 1 on a hire basis
Details: Centre also houses library, theatre, studio darkroom and restaurant.

High Wycombe
BUCKINGHAMSHIRE SA

Spring Gardens Arts Centre

[Pa][Ph][Pr][Cr][Sc][LA] ✔[£][H] ♿[Wc]

Gallery in old Victorian school building.
Pinions Road, High Wycombe HP13 7AG, tel: 01494 464800, fax: 01494 530476
Contact: Charlie Dearden, Director
Space: 2 galleries with 54 lin m hanging space plus 43 lin m on screens and 42 sq m floor space
Exhibitions: 9 a year
Details: Large, square white space with good natural and track lighting. Centre's café also available but can only cater for 2D work. Programme has a mixture of established and young local artists in both solo and mixed shows. 7 exhibitions from local sources and 2 national touring.

Hinckley
LEICESTERSHIRE EMA

Hinckley College of Further Education

[Pa][Ph][Sc] ✔

Space in college foyer showing small exhibitions of students' work and work from County Collection.
London Road, Hinckley LE10 1HQ, tel: 01455 251222
Contact: G Wilson, Division of Textiles & Design
Space: 6 lin m hanging space plus 10 lin m on screens and 25 sq m floor space

Hitchin
HERTFORDSHIRE EA

Rikki Harcourt Gallery at Phillips of Hitchin

[Pa][Pr][Sc] ✔[H] ♿

Contemporary art, mainly paintings and small sculptures, in a period domestic setting, alongside Georgian furniture .
The Manor House, 26 Bancroft, Hitchin SG5 1JW, tel: 01462 432067, fax: 01462 441368
Contact: Rikki Harcourt, The Clock House, Gosmore, Hitchin, SG4 7QR, tel: 01462 450393
Space: 5 galleries with 70 lin m hanging space and 164 sq m floor space
Exhibitions: 4 a year all originated
Details: Keen to promote the work of contemporary artists from London, Hertfordshire and adjoining counties, and artists from elsewhere who wish to reach a Hertfordshire audience. Space hired (5 or more works per artist) at a charge based on linear size of works. Access for wheelchair users only possible on first floor.

Hitchin Museum & Art Gallery

[Pa][Ph][Pr][Cr][Sc] ✔[H] ♿

Space within small local history museum, mainly displaying work by local artists to a general audience.
Paynes Park, Hitchin SG5 1EQ, tel: 01462 434476
Contact: Alison Taylor, Curator
Open: Mon-Sat 10-5; Sun 2-4.30
Space: 2 galleries with 30 lin m hanging space plus 4 lin m on screens and 54 sq m floor space
Exhibitions: 10 a year of which 8 originated, 2 on a hire basis
Details: Two rooms within small local history museum, showing variety of media. Preference given to local artists, both professional and amateur. Audience mainly local and with conservative tastes, so representational work preferred. Exhibitions last for 3 or 4 weeks. Selling work not gallery's primary function.

Hoddesdon
HERTFORDSHIRE EA

Hoddesdon Library

[Pa][Ph][Pr][Cr][Sc] ✔[H] ♿[Wc]

Five small exhibition spaces within public library showing work predominantly by local artists.
98a High Street, Hoddesdon EN11 8HD, tel: 01992 462296
Contact: Jean Holmes, Librarian
Open: Mon, Tues, Wed, Fri 9.30-8; Sat 9.30-4
Space: 5 lin m hanging space
Details: Two walls in foyer and 2 areas within library using plinths and additional display boards. Wide variety of work by local artists shown. Hanging by mirror plates and picture hooks. Lighting by fluorescent tubes and adjustable spots. Hire periods variable but need to book at least 6 months in advance. 5% +VAT commission on sales if exhibitor handles sales; 20% + VAT if library handles sales. Marketing is exhibitor's responsibility.

Holt
NORFOLK EA

Ben Nicholson Gallery

[Pa][Ph][Pr][Cr][Sc] ✔ ♿[Wc]

Non-commercial exhibition space showing a diverse range of work that has an educational value.
Greshams School, Holt NR25 6EA, tel: 01263 711480, fax: 01263 712028
Contact: Simon Poppy, Head of Art
Open: (During school term-time) Mon Wed Fri 9-1, 2-5.30; Tues, Thurs, Sat 9-1, 2-4
Space: 1 gallery with 26 lin m hanging space and 66 sq m floor space
Exhibitions: 10 a year of which 9 originated, 1 touring
Details: Space for a diverse range of art forms. Situated within a school but exhibitions are open to the public and widely supported by the local community. Preference is given to local artists, and work that will stimulate a young adult audience. Artists organise their own publicity.

Made in Cley

[Pa][Cr][Sc] 🚫

Crafts co-operative with workshops and gallery selling own work.
High Street, Cley next the Sea, Holt NR25 7RF, tel: 01263 740134
Contact: Exhibition Organiser
Open: (July-Sept) Mon-Sat 10-6, Sun 11-5; (Oct-June) Mon, Tues, Thurs-Sat 10-5, Sun 11-5
Exhibitions: 1 a year
Details: Shows pottery, jewellery and sculpture. Profit-sharing cooperative with

workshop and gallery space to show own work. Sale of work is gallery's primary concern.

Picturecraft of Holt

Large, naturally-lit gallery exhibits work by 19 artists on a three-weekly rental system with no commission deducted from sales.
North Norfolk's Art Centre, 23 Lees Courtyard, off Bull Street, Holt NR25 6HP, tel: 01263 711040, fax: 01263 711151
Contact: Michael Hill and Teresa Hill, Partners
Open: Mon-Sat 9-5; Thurs 9-1
Space: 19 galleries with 36 lin m hanging space and 128 sq m floor space
Exhibitions: 16 a year
Details: Commercial art gallery operating on a unique three-weekly rental display bay system. Nineteen artists exhibit each week in the display bays. Major solo shows are held during July-Sept for one week each. Regular demonstrations of calligraphy, oriental brushwork, video presentations, etc.

Hornchurch
ESSEX EA

Queens Theatre

Theatre with exhibitions linking with theatre events.
Billet Lane, Hornchurch RM11 1QT, tel: 01708 456118, fax: 01708 452348
Contact: Mary Sweeney
Space: 1 gallery with 10 lin m hanging space and 80 sq m floor space
Exhibitions: 10 a year all originated
Details: All exhibitions well publicised in theatre programme. 10% commission on sales.

Horsham
EAST SUSSEX SEA

Christ's Hospital Theatre

Theatre foyer for small-scale wide-ranging exhibitions.
Christ's Hospital, Horsham RH13 7LE, tel: 01403 252709/267005, fax: 01403 211580
Contact: Duncan Noel-Paton, Director of Drama
Open: When theatre open for teaching, rehearsals, performances.
Space: 1 gallery with 57 lin m hanging space and 80 sq m floor space
Exhibitions: 7 a year
Details: Arts complex in grounds of Christ's Hospital School including 500-seat theatre. Programme of professional and

school events throughout school year, covering all performing and visual arts. Most exhibitions originated in-house. Audience comprises school pupils, parents friends, general public. Occasional exhibitions of historic material. Sales not a priority. No commission on sales.

Horsham Arts Centre Gallery

Presents wide range of art works and encourages young contemporary artists and established artists, both local and national.
Horsham Arts Centre, North Street, Horsham RH11 1RL, tel: 01403 259708, fax: 01403 262985
Contact: David Tebbs, Visual Art Coordinator
Space: 2 galleries with 43 lin m hanging space
Exhibitions: 30 a year of which 29 originated, 1 touring
Details: Two spaces for contemporary exhibitions in main foyer areas of an original 1930s building.

Hove
EAST SUSSEX SEA

Hove Museum & Art Gallery

Situated in converted Victorian house, gallery provides varied programme of exhibitions.
19 New Church Road, Hove BN3 4AB, tel: 01273 779410, fax: 01273 202275
Contact: Timothy Wilcox, Curator
Open: Tues-Fri 10-5; Sat 10-4.30; Sun 2-5
Space: 60 lin m hanging space and 176 sq m floor space
Exhibitions: 6 a year of which 2 originated, 2 touring, 2 on a hire basis
Details: Mixed audience, including large sectors of children and old people. Wide variety of interests, most with some previous knowledge of fine & decorative art. Relatively inexperienced in contemporary art. Sales not a priority.

Huddersfield
WEST YORKSHIRE YHA

Booth House Gallery & Pottery (Robison Ceramics)

Converted C19th barn incorporating gallery and artist's ceramics studio.
3 Booth House, Holmfirth, Huddersfield HD7 1QA, tel: 01484 685270
Contact: Jim Robison

Open: Sat, Sun 2-5; evenings & other days by appointment
Space: 1 gallery with 15 lin m hanging space and 60 sq m floor space
Exhibitions: 2 a year both originated
Details: Visitors may see the artist/owner's workshop and kiln areas. Exhibitions include speciality features of contemporary studio pottery, and ceramic sculpture. In addition continuous changing display. Some screens available. Sales of work important to gallery.

Bryam Galleries

Occasional exhibitions organised in shop section.
5 Station Street, Huddersfield HD1 1LS, tel: 01484 25747
Contact: D. Hooley, Proprietor
Space: 1 gallery with 40 lin m hanging space and 50 sq m floor space
Details: Original watercolours and oils by local and national artists in group and solo shows.

Huddersfield Art Gallery

Local authority gallery housing collection of C20th art plus exciting visual arts programme throughout the year.
Princess Alexandra Walk, Huddersfield HD1 2SU, tel: 01484 513808 x216, fax: 01484 531983
Contact: Jane Speller, Galleries Officer
Open: Mon-Fri 10-6; Sat 10-4
Space: 6 galleries with 161 lin m hanging space plus 30 lin m on screens and 525 sq m floor space
Exhibitions: 12 a year of which 8 originated, 4 touring
Details: Broad cultural visual Art programme features exhibitions by artists working in all media from Britain and abroad. Diverse range of educational activities organised to complement programme. Admission free. Sales of work not main function of gallery.

Hull
HUMBERSIDE YHA

Ferens Art Gallery

Municipal gallery with extensive collection and major temporary exhibition and live art spaces created by extension to original building.
Queen Victoria Square, Hull HU1 3RA, tel: 01482 593912, fax: 01482 595062
Contact: Art Exhibitions Officer
Open: Mon-Sat 10-5; Sun 1.30-4.30
Space: 5 galleries
Exhibitions: 15 a year
Details: Ferens has total of 12 gallery spaces, of which about half are used to

display permanent collections. Temporary exhibition spaces comprise 3 galleries (2 of these octagonal), sculpture court and dedicated live art space. The 3 main galleries have movable screen system using ceiling track. Programme presents cross-over of historic works and contemporary installation, sculpture, photographic work, painting and artworks. Major purpose of Live Art Space is to support development of new works created in Hull and tour them including video, film, dance, music, performance etc.

Spring Street Theatre

Pa Ph Pr Cr SC LA ✓ H

Exhibition boards are mounted in the foyer and bar area of the theatre and exhibitions vary on a monthly basis.
Spring Street, Hull HU2 8RW, tel: 01482 224800, fax: 01482 228546
Contact: Angela Marshall, Publicity & Marketing Officer
Open: Mon-Fri 9.30-11.30; Sat 9.30-11.30; Sun 7-10.30
Space: 1 gallery with 49 lin m hanging space and 116 sq m floor space
Exhibitions: 12 a year all on a hire basis
Details: Programme always representative of different styles of art and includes paintings, drawings, photographs and sculpture, in a variety of media. Artists usually local. Space booked 18 months ahead.

University of Hull Art Collection

Pa Pr

Specialises in British art 1890-1940 but occasional contemporary art exhibitions held.
University of Hull, Cottingham Road, Hull HU6 7RX, tel: 01482 465035, fax: 01482 440541
Contact: John G. Bernasconi, Hon. Curator
Space: 3 galleries with 80 lin m hanging space plus 20 lin m on screens and 350 sq m floor space
Exhibitions: 3 a year of which 1 originated, 2 touring
Details: Contemporary art exhibitions occasionally held in the circulation area of the Middleton Hall. Exhibitions arranged in term time for University staff and students and the general public.

Hunstanton

NORFOLK EA

Ringstead Gallery

Pa SC ✓

Commercial gallery specialising in wildlife and countryside pictures.
Ringstead, Hunstanton PE36 5JZ
Contact: D.S. Greer, Proprietor

Space: 1 gallery with 30 lin m hanging space and 40 sq m floor space
Exhibitions: 12 a year all originated
Details: The gallery is a converted stable dating from the C17th, adjacent to the village inn. As well as wildlife and countryside subjects also show still lifes, sporting cartoons and bronze sculpture.

Huntingdon

CAMBRIDGESHIRE EA

Cottage Gallery

Pa Ph Pr Cr SC ✓ H ♿

Selling gallery displaying work by local artists.
143 High Street, Huntingdon PE18 6TF, tel: 01480 411521
Contact: Emma Scutt, Art Co-ordinator
Open: Daily 9-5.30
Space: 1 gallery with 21 lin m hanging space and 33 sq m floor space
Exhibitions: 10 a year of which 8 originated, 2 on a hire basis
Details: Gallery aims to give as many artists as possible the opportunity to exhibit their work, however unusual.

Huyton

MERSEYSIDE NWA

Knowsley Libraries

Pa Pr Cr SC ✓ ♿ 4

Several of Knowsley Libraries have exhibition space or display facilities.
Knowsley Borough Council, Stockbridge Lane, Huyton, tel: 0151 443 3744
Contact: Mrs Evelyn Craig, Promotions Librarian
Open: Various
Details: Arts Sub-Committee revising arts provisions. Huyton Library has 10 display screens and is Knowsley's main display library; Kirkby has spaces in foyer, inside library and on mezzanine floor (this last space coordinated by local art/photography groups); Whiston, 2 display screens; Page Moss, 2 display screens; Stockbridge Lane, 2 display screens; Halewood, 2 display screens. Enquiries about exhibitions in any of above branches can be directed through Mrs Craig. Selling work is not a priority throughout libraries. Hire fee not charged for space but commission taken on sales.

Ilkeston

DERBYSHIRE EMA

Erewash Museum

Pa Pr Cr SC ✓ ♿

Gallery, complementary to the museum, offering opportunities for local artists and craftspeople and providing variety for

regular visitors and attracting new audiences.
High Street, Ilkeston DE7 5JA, tel: 0115 944 0440 ext 331
Contact: Nigel Overton, Curator
Open: Tues & Thurs-Sat 10-4; BH (not Xmas or New Year) 10-4; closed January
Space: 2 galleries with 37 lin m hanging space plus 7 lin m on screens and 84 sq m floor space
Exhibitions: 9 a year all originated
Details: Small local museum/gallery. Priority given to Erewash-based artists, otherwise Derbyshire/Nottingham (East Midlands). Gallery 1: permanent screens in painted ply; good natural light & spotlighting. Gallery 2: permanent screens with hessian finish; spotlighting. Sales not a priority.

Ilkeston Community Hospital

Pa Ph Pr Cr SC ♿ ♿

Exhibition space along main corridor initiated to provide interest for patients, staff and visitors by showing work by artists, craftspeople and photographers.
Heanor Road, Ilkeston DE7 8LN, tel: 0115 9305522
Contact: Frank Walters, Director of Art for All, Derby City General Hosptial, Uttoxeter Road, Derby, DE22 3NE, tel: 01332 340131 ext 5910, fax: 01332 290559
Open: Daily
Space: 1 gallery with 40 lin m hanging space
Exhibitions: 8 a year of which 3 originated, 5 touring
Details: Corridor and waiting room area. Fluorescent and natural light, direct fixing onto walls and 1 show case on stand. Sale of work is a possible. For policy please see entry for Derby City General Hospital.

Ilkley

WEST YORKSHIRE YHA

Lauron Gallery

Pa Pr Cr

Small shop and gallery stocking watercolours, pastels and limited edition prints.
122 Bolling Road, Ben Rhydding, Ilkley LS29 8PN, tel: 01943 600725
Contact: Margaret Walton
Space: 2 galleries with 85 sq m floor space
Exhibitions: 3 a year all originated
Details: Sells gifts & greetings cards that are a little bit different and tries to be individual. 3 temporary exhibitions staged a year by Yorkshire artists including members of the Yorkshire Watercolours Society.

Manor House Art Gallery & Museum

 ✓ ⓘ ✗

Municipal gallery with collection of fine and decorative art with two adjoining galleries showing contemporary art and archeological/historical exhibitions.
Castle Yard, Ilkley LS29 9DT, tel: 01943 600066, fax: 01943 817079
Contact: Caroline Krzesinska, Senior Keeper, Arts & Exhibitions, Cartwright Hall, Lister Park, Bradford, BD9 4NS, tel: 01274 493313
Space: 2 galleries with 40 lin m hanging space
Exhibitions: 6 a year all originated
Details: Emphasis on the promotion of contemporary art from the region. Policy to involve Ilkley and surrounding areas in a programme of mainstream contemporary art and craft: exhibitions, accompanying lectures, residencies and workshops. Gallery particularly welcomes applications from young artists from the region although work from further afield also considered. Exhibitions last 6-8 weeks. Gallery especially favours two-person shows. Selling work not gallery's primary function.

Instow

DEVON SWA

Waterside Gallery

 ✓ ⓐ

Commercial gallery specialising in contemporary paintings and crafts by local artists plus some imported craft objects.
2 Marin Terrace, Instow EX39 4HZ, tel: 01271 860786
Contact: Judith James, Owner
Open: Tues-Sat 10-1, 2-5
Space: 1 gallery with 17 lin m hanging space and 42 sq m floor space
Exhibitions: 5 a year all originated
Details: One-person exhibitions held. Rest of time has changing stock of paintings and crafts, mainly by local artists as well as stock of unusual crafts and gifts from abroad. Scenic location by estuary. Paintings shown tend towards marine and landscape subjects. Selling is gallery's primary function.

Ipswich

SUFFOLK EA

Haste Gallery

⯐⯐ ✓ ✗

Selling gallery that concentrates on showing artists with regional significance, both historical and contemporary.
3 Great Coleman Street, Ipswich IP4 2AD, tel: 01473 258429
Contact: J D Haste, Exhibition Organiser
Open: Mon-Sat 9-5

Space: 1 gallery with 18 lin m hanging space plus 10 lin m on screens and 74 sq m floor space
Exhibitions: 10 a year all originated
Details: An outlet for art materials and framing with exhibition facility. Organises four group shows a year and six solo shows which last 3-4 weeks. As well as a collection of East Anglian oils and watercolours, there is a regularly changing display of work. Exhibitions occasionally supported by demonstrations. Would like to encourage more touring shows.

John Russell Gallery

⯐⯐⯐ ✓ ⓐ

Selling gallery in 1750 building on Docklands wharf next to floating restaurant and marina showing monthly exhibitions of East Anglian artists.
4-6 Wherry Lane, Ipswich IP4 1LG, tel: 01473 212051
Contact: Anthony Russell Coe, Gallery Director
Open: Mon-Sat 9.30-5
Space: 1 gallery with 259 lin m hanging space and 116 sq m floor space
Exhibitions: 10 a year all originated
Details: Leading and longest established contemporary art gallery in Ipswich with gallery opened Sept 1994 on Docklands. Programmes exhibitions two years ahead. 8 solo and 2 mixed shows per year. Specialises in East Anglia contemporary art and sculpture.

Number Eight Gallery *

⯐⯐⯐⯐

Gallery spaces within C15th studio/home; more interested in ideas than representation, but shows a diversity of styles.
10 The Street, Bramford, Ipswich IP8 4EA, tel: 01473 240622
Contact: Richard Pinkney, Proprietor
Details: Four mixed and three one-person shows each year. Two spaces one with 18m, artificial lighting, and the other 9m with daylight. Linear hanging space, though individual works larger than 0.6m x 1m difficult to show well. Exhibitions by invitation, artists may introduce themselves on visiting gallery if interested.

Suffolk County Council Libraries & Heritage *

⯐⯐⯐⯐⯐ ✓

Initial contact for exhibitions within Suffolk Libraries.
St Andrew House, County Hall, Ipswich IP4 2JS, tel: 01473 264565
Contact: Jayne Knight, Arts Officer
Space: 2 galleries with 760 sq m floor space
Details: On of the service's aims is to introduce best of new photography into public spaces by commissioning photographers to make work to tour to the

small spaces available. Also craft showcases. Also administers the SCILS gallery picture loan scheme.

Wolsey Art Gallery

⯐⯐⯐ ✓ ⓐ④

Purpose-built gallery: to encourage the interest in contemporary arts and highlight the museums collections.
Christchurch Mansion, Christchurch Park, Ipswich IP4 2BE, tel: 01473 253246, fax: 01473 210328
Contact: Rebecca Weaver, Exhibitions Officer, Ipswich Museums & Galleries, Ipswich Museum, High Street, Ipswich, IP1 3QH, tel: 01473 213761, fax: 01473 281274
Open: Tues-Sat 10-5; Sun 2.30-4.30; park closes at dusk in winter
Space: 1 gallery with 32 lin m hanging space
Exhibitions: 14 a year of which 10 originated, 4 touring
Detail: Administered by Ipswich Borough Council the programme has included Arts Council exhibitions as well as those promoting younger and less exposed artists, particularly those with a regional connection. Exhibitions are supported by a range of talks, schools workshops and artists residencies.

Jarrow

TYNE & WEAR NA

Bede Gallery

⯐⯐⯐⯐ ✓ⓘ ✗

The gallery presents mainly one-person exhibitions by contemporary artists.
Springwell Park, Butchersbridge Road, Jarrow NE32 5QA, tel: 0191 489 1807
Contact: Vince Rea, Gallery Director
Open: Tues-Fri 10-4.30; Sun 2-4.30
Space: 2 galleries with 76 lin m hanging space and 200 sq m floor space
Exhibitions: 11 a year of which 9 originated, 2 touring
Details: Permanent collection and regular programme of contemporary art exhibitions. Shows established British and international, and young experimental artists. Outlet for work of North East artists. Encourages public appreciation of visual arts. Art video library available.

Bede's World

 ✓ ✗Ⓦ

Two temporary exhibition rooms and a café gallery which display work by artists and craftspeople as well as exhibitions relevant to Anglo-Saxon world.
Jarrow Hall, Church Bank, Jarrow NE32 3DY, tel: 0191 489 2106, fax: 0191 428 2361
Contact: Miss Susan A. Mills, Curator
Open: (Apr-Oct) Mon-Sat 10-5.30, Sun

2.30-5.30; (Nov-Mar) Mon-Sat 11-4.30, Sun 2.30-5.30; open BH, closed between Christmas and New Year.
Space: 3 galleries with 38 lin m hanging space plus 4 lin m on screens and 84 sq m floor space
Exhibitions: 10 a year of which 6 originated, 4 touring
Details: Permanent displays tell story of Anglo-Saxon/mediaeval monastery of St Paul, and history of museum (built c.1800). Temporary exhibition programme includes local and regional artists and craftspeople, in-house and touring archaeological and historical exhibitions. Audience is a good regional cross-section. Museum has a friendly atmosphere. Workshops and activities organised to coincide with temporary exhibitions. New museum and recreated Anglo-Saxon farm opened 1995. Sales not a priority.

Keele
STAFFORDSHIRE WMA

Keele University Art Exhibitions

University gallery showing current work by artists in the region and elsewhere.
Chancellor's Building, Keele University, Keele ST5 5BG, tel: 01782 583433, fax: 01782 584165
Contact: Janet Flynn, Exhibitions Organiser, RDBA, Keele University, Keele, ST5 5BG, tel: 01782 583433, fax: 01782 584165
Open: 10-8 in term-time
Space: 2 galleries with 75 lin m hanging space plus 8 lin m on screens and 150 sq m floor space
Exhibitions: 10 a year all originated
Details: Purpose-built space in the Chancellor's Building. Also hanging space in Concourse (main thoroughfare). Aims to promote local talent and show current work of artists in the region and elsewhere. Varied programme of art, craft, sculpture, photography, plus informative/educational exhibitions of a more general nature. Sales not a priority.

Keighley
WEST YORKSHIRE YHA

Cliffe Castle

Two exhibition galleries showing a mixture of natural history, history and local art exhibitions.
Spring Gardens, Keighley BD20 6LH, tel: 01274 758230, fax: 01535 610536
Contact: Caroline Krzesinska, Senior Keeper, Arts & Exhibitions, Cartwright

Hall, Lister Park, Bradford, BD9 4NS, tel: 01274 493313
Open: (Apr-Sept) Tues-Sun 10-6; (Oct-Mar) Tues-Sun 10-5; closed Mon, except BH
Space: 2 galleries with 140 lin m hanging space and 300 sq m floor space
Exhibitions: 3 a year of which 2 originated, 1 touring
Details: Municipal gallery with permanent collection of Victorian fine and decorative art. Lively programme of temporary exhibitions relating to Cliffe Castle's collections; art, history, natural sciences. Sales not a priority.

Kendal
CUMBRIA NA

Abbot Hall Art Gallery

Three domestic-scale rooms on upper floor of Georgian town house used for temporary exhibitions.
Kendal LA9 5AL, tel: 01539 722464
Contact: J.C.S. Barnes, Exhibitions Officer
Open: Varies
Space: 3 galleries
Exhibitions: 4 a year of which 2 originated, 2 touring
Details: Concentration on British painting and sculpture from C18th to contemporary. Exhibitions by invitation only. The gallery welcomes information from artists and exhibition organisers. Sales not a priority.

Brewery Arts Centre Photographic Gallery

Aims to encourage photography as an art form and to promote its understanding as a vital and influential medium in contemporary culture.
Brewery Arts Centre, Highgate, Kendal LA9 4HE, tel: 01539 725133, fax: 01539 730257
Contact: Photography Officer
Open: Mon-Sat 10am-11pm
Space: 2 galleries with 38 lin m hanging space and 80 sq m floor space
Exhibitions: 10 a year all originated
Details: The gallery doubles as a first-floor foyer leading to other spaces in the building. As well as traffic passing through to other rooms there is a significant regular audience for exhibitions, talks and workshops. Courses in photography (both lecture and darkroom-based) augment the programme of exhibitions.

Warehouse Gallery

Part of a rts centre, the Warehouse Gallery specialises in contemporary work from young professional artists in the first few years of their careers.
Brewery Arts Centre, Highgate, Kendal LA9 4HE, tel: 01539 725133, fax: 01539 730257
Contact: Lene Bragger, Visual Arts Officer
Open: Mon-Sat 10-5
Space: 1 gallery with 40 lin m hanging space and 125 sq m floor space
Exhibitions: 9 a year of which 8 originated, 1 touring
Details: Open, light space, converted from a warehouse. Spotlighting on tracks and direct fixing to 7ft high boards. Sales not gallery's main function but Art Purchase Plan encourages sales.

Keswick
CUMBRIA NA

Keswick Museum & Art Gallery

Shows temporary exhibitions, mainly contemporary 2D work, some historical from museum's permanent collections.
Fitz Park, Station Road, Keswick CA12 4NF, tel: 017687 73263
Contact: Hazel Davison, Curator
Open: (Easter–Oct) 31 daily 10-4; open BH
Space: 1 gallery with 33 lin m hanging space and 78 sq m floor space
Exhibitions: 7 a year
Details: Exhibitions from local artists/craftspeople or of related interest. One per month. Access to gallery via museum. Visitors mainly tourists. No hanging fee. Commission on sales. Gallery size to increase 1996. Occasional solely education orientated exhibitions taken with full education officer backup. Sale of work not a priority. Adapted toilets planned 1996.

Kettering
NORTHAMPTONSHIRE EMA

Alfred East Art Gallery

Municipal gallery with temporary exhibitions.
Sheep Street, Kettering, tel: 01536 410333 ext 4381, fax: 01536 410795
Contact: Su Davies, Heritage Manager, Kettering Borough Council, Bowling Green Road, Kettering, NN15 7QX, tel: 01536 410333 ext 4394, fax: 01536 410795
Open: Mon-Sat 9.30-5; closed BH
Space: 3 galleries with 76 lin m hanging space and 130 sq m floor space

Exhibitions: 30 a year of which 28 originated, 2 touring
Details: Exhibits works from its own collection, in particular Alfred East and Thomas Cooper Gotch. A the same time runs a temporary exhibitions programme showing new works of local artists and a selection of touring exhibitions.

Kettering Library

Pa Ph Cr ⊙ Ⓗ ❸ Ⓐ

Exhibition space used primarily by local artists and craftspeople to display their work.
Sheep Street, Kettering NN16 0AN, tel: 01536 512315, fax: 01536 411349
Contact: Donna Gillett, Exhibitions Co-ordinator
Open: Mon & Tues 9.30-8; Wed, Thurs & Fri 9.30-5; Sat 9.30-4
Space: 1 gallery with 17 lin m hanging space
Exhibitions: 12 a year all on a hire basis
Details: Administered by Northamptonshire Libraries and Information Service (see Northamptonshire Libraries, Northampton). Concentrates mainly on local artists and craftspeople giving them a forum to sell work (15% commission). Publicity and insurance provided. Selling work not a main aim.

Rothwell Library

Pa Ph Pr Cr Sc ⊙ ❸ Wc

Library exhibition space.
Market Hill, Rothwell, Kettering NN14 2EP, tel: 01536 711880
Contact: Deanna Allan, Exhibitions Organiser, Corby Library, 9 The Links, Queens Square, Corby, NN17 1PZ, tel: 01536 203304, fax: 01536 400954
Space: 1 gallery with 20 lin m hanging space and 54 sq m floor space
Exhibitions: 10 a year
Details: Wall of glass display cases and screening in room equipped with track lighting, power points in floor and built-in case 4' x 4' x 1'. Audience mainly library users. (See entry for Northamptonshire Libraries, Northampton)

Kidderminster
HEREFORD & WORCESTER WMA

Hartlebury County Museum

Pa Ph Pr Cr ⊙ ❸

Two small galleries exhibiting work of local relevance within the museum's C17th building.
Hartlebury Castle, Hartlebury, Kidderminster DY11 7XZ, tel: 01299 250416
Contact: Robin Hill, County Museums Officer

Open: (31 Mar – 30 Nov) Mon-Thurs 10-5; Fri & Sun 2-5
Space: 2 galleries with 26 lin m hanging space plus 13 lin m on screens and 62 sq m floor space
Exhibitions: 5 a year all originated
Details: Varied programme of temporary exhibitions, reflecting both the historical nature of the collections as well as contemporary crafts. Aim of exhibitions is to bring the work of locally based workers to the attention of visiting public. Integration of educational activities and practical work and demonstrations are encouraged . Exhibitions usually last 3-6 weeks. Selling work is not of primary importance. See also entry for Hereford & Worcester Libraries & Arts Department, Worcester.

Kielder
NORTHUMBERLAND NA

Duchess Gallery

Pa Ph Pr Cr Sc ⊙ ❸ Wc

Gallery in Kielder Castle, Forest Enterprise's Visitor Centre for Kielder Forest.
Kielder Castle, Kielder NE48 1ER, tel: 01434 250209
Contact: Penny Knock, Recreation Head Ranger
Open: (Easter-July, Sept & Oct) daily 10-5; (Aug) daily 10-6; (Nov-Easter) Sat & Sun 11-4
Space: 1 gallery with 30 lin m hanging space
Exhibitions: 6 a year all originated
Details: Mixture of contemporary art and natural history exhibitions shows. Art exhibitions of work by amateur & professional North East artists usually have natural elements in there theme, subject or materials used. Artists hang and take down exhibitions, produce posters if required or arrange previews if wished. Forest Enterprise includes notice of forthcoming exhibitions in own promotional leaflets, etc. Considered a good selling space and sales important but not gallery's primary role. Space not hired out to artists but 20% commission taken on sales made.

King's Lynn
NORFOLK EA

Bircham Art Gallery

Pa Pr Cr Sc ⊙ ⊗

Commercial gallery specialising in contemporary paintings, prints, ceramics, sculpture and craft.
Church Lane, Bircham, King's Lynn PE31 6QW, tel: 01485 578604
Contact: Christopher Harrison, Director
Open: (Feb-Oct) Wed-Sat 10-5.30; (Nov-Jan) Wed-Sat 10-4.30

Space: 3 galleries with 34 lin m hanging space and 48 sq m floor space
Exhibitions: 10 a year all originated
Details: Three exhibition rooms on ground floor of traditional brick, flint and pantile cottage. Garden area displays outdoor work.

King's Lynn Arts Centre

Pa Ph Pr Cr Sc ⊙ ⊙ Ⓗ ❸

Mainly contemporary art and craft exhibitions in gallery within arts centre complex.
27-29 King Street, King's Lynn PE30 1HA, tel: 01553 774725, fax: 01553 770591
Contact: Liz Falconbridge, Gallery Organiser
Open: (Apr-Oct) Tues-Sat 10-5; (Nov-March) Tues-Sat 11-4
Space: 2 galleries with 58 lin m hanging space and 105 sq m floor space
Exhibitions: 12 a year of which 4 originated
Details: Galleries with workshop space and foyer for crafts showcases. Theatre, cinema, coffee shop, restaurant. Centre for large rural area. Solo and mixed shows with regular residencies, workshops, art classes and artists' talks. Annual Eastern Open competition.

Lynn Museum

Pa Pr Cr ⊙ ❸ Wc Ⓐ

Local museum showing temporary exhibitions related to West Norfolk.
Old Market Street, King's Lynn PE30 1NL, tel: 0553 775001
Contact: Michael Johnson, Assistant Curator
Open: Mon-Sat 10-5
Space: 1 gallery with 14 lin m hanging space plus 10 lin m on screens and 20 sq m floor space
Exhibitions: 5 a year all originated
Details: Audience includes school groups and general public. Rectangular gallery/temporary exhibition area. Sales not a priority.

Kingswinford
WEST MIDLANDS WMA

Broadfield House Glass Museum

Cr ⊙

Specialist museum of the British glass industry.
Compton Drive, Kingswinford DY6 9NS, tel: 01384 273011, fax: 01384 273952
Contact: Charles Hajdamach or Roger Dodsworth
Exhibitions: 5 a year of which 3 originated, 2 touring
Details: Run by Dudley Art Gallery.

Exhibits a collection of English glass from the C18th to present day. Emphasis on C19th Stourbridge glass. Large selection of studio, Scandinavian and Dartington glass for sale. Glass-making studio at rear of museum. Wheelchair access to ground floor including glass studio.

Kington
HEREFORD & WORCESTER WMA

Penrhos Art Gallery *

Pa Ph Pr Cr Sc LA ✓

Private gallery promoting local artists.
Penrhos Art, Penrhos Court, Kington HR5 3LH, tel: 01544 230720, fax: 01544 230754
Contact: Martin Griffiths
Space: 2 galleries with 45 lin m hanging space plus 20 lin m on screens and 85 sq m floor space
Exhibitions: 4 a year all originated
Details: Eight mixed exhibitions covering general art movement have been held – these now followed by six solo exhibitions of well-known local artists. Has a database of around 5000 art buyers and dealers. 15% commission for sales. Organise promotions on behalf of artists.

Knaresborough
NORTH YORKSHIRE YHA

Courthouse Museum (Little Gallery)

Pa Ph Pr Cr Sc ✓ 🖼4

Temporary exhibition gallery showing three shows over summer season including Knaresborough Art Society and local themed shows.
Castle Grounds, Knaresborough HG5
Contact: Mary Kershaw, Curator, Royal Pump Room Museum, Royal Parade, Harrogate, HG1 2RY, tel: 01423 503340, fax: 01423 840026
Open: (May-Sept) daily 10.30-5
Space: 1 gallery with 15 lin m hanging space
Exhibitions: 3 a year
Details: Municipal local history museum. Selling work is considered primary role of gallery.

European Ceramics Gallery

Pr Cr Sc ✓ 🖼

Contemporary European ceramics shown in informal setting.
The Warehouse, Breakers Yard, Finkle Street, Knaresborough HG5 8AA, tel: 01423 867401
Contact: Maggie Barnes, Owner/Manager, Maggie Barnes Ceramics/European Ceramics, 18 Finkle Street, Knaresborough

Open: Mon-Sat 11-5; Sun 2-5
Space: 1 gallery with 12 lin m hanging space and 60 sq m floor space
Exhibitions: 4 a year all originated
Details: Shows contemporary ceramics from Europe. Retail sales plus selling exhibitions. Applications from artists to exhibit only by appointment. Selection of books on ceramics and other subjects and casual clothing from Thailand also sold.

Gordon Reece Gallery

Pa Pr Cr Sc

Commercial gallery promoting arts of non-European societies through changing exhibitions.
Finkle Street, Knaresborough HG5 8AA, tel: 01423 866219, fax: 01432 866219
Contact: Gordon Reece or Jane Munro
Open: Mon-Wed, Fri & Sat 10.30-5; Sun 2-5; closed between exhibitions
Space: 3 galleries
Exhibitions: 9 a year
Details: Provides opportunity for visitors to 'handle and see rare and exciting artifacts and textiles and for them to purchase and cherish such items', aims to increase awareness, understanding and appreciation of non-European cultures. Changing exhibitions complement collection of furniture and non-European decorative arts and costume.

Lacock
WILTSHIRE SA

Fox Talbot Museum *

Ph ✓

Three exhibitions per year: at least one is normally C19th work. Strong emphasis on international links.
Museum upper gallery, Lacock SN15 2LG, tel: 01249 730 459, fax: 01873 830 474
Contact: Michael Grey, Curator
Open: (March-Oct) Mon-Sun 11-5, except Good Friday
Space: 16 galleries with 30 sq m floor space
Exhibitions: 3 a year all originated
Details: Visitors: general public/holiday makers June/August, and Germans, French, Dutch, Japanese with specific photographic interest. Space consists of 17 bays, fibre optic lighting 40-150 lux and environmentally controlled 'click' display cases.

Lamport
NORTHAMPTONSHIRE EMA

Lamport Hall

Pa Pr Cr Sc ✓ 🅷 🅱 🆆

Exhibitions usually of work by local artists or societies in historic house run by Lamport Trust.

Lamport NN6 9HB, tel: 01604 686272, fax: 01604 686224
Contact: G P S Drye, Administrator
Open: (Easter – end Sept) Sun & BH; (Aug) daily
Space: 2 galleries with 30 lin m hanging space and 58 sq m floor space
Exhibitions: 6 a year all originated
Details: Two rooms used for exhibitions in former home of Sir Charles Isham inventor of the garden gnome, run by the Lamport Trust. Occasional exhibitions of regional scope are mounted. The trust also runs series of musical events at the hall. Sales not a priority.

Lancaster
LANCASHIRE NWA

Lancaster City Museum

Pa Ph Pr Cr Sc ✓ 🅱

Museum provides varied programme that generally reflects the local community in some way.
Market Square, Lancaster LA11HT, tel: 01524 64637, fax: 01524 847663
Contact: Paul Thompson, Exhibitions Officer
Open: Mon-Sat 10-5; closed Sun
Space: 2 galleries with 30 lin m hanging space plus 31 lin m on screens and 98 sq m floor space
Exhibitions: 8 a year of which 7 originated, 1 touring
Details: Exhibitions usually last 4-6 weeks with programme balanced between informative and aesthetic. Artists usually have a local connection. Major summer exhibition is themed topic with historical, educational and local relevance. Sale of work not a priority but 20% handling charge taken on sales. Artists welcome to apply but large number of artists awaiting consideration.

Lancaster Maritime Museum

Pa Ph Pr ✓ 🖼

Gallery providing series of temporary exhibitions loosely based on maritime history/the sea.
St George's Quay, Lancaster LA1, tel: 01524 64637
Contact: Dr Nigel Dalziel/Paul Thompson, Exhibitions Organisers
Open: (Easter-Oct) daily 11-5; (Nov-Easter) daily 2-5
Space: 1 gallery with 26 lin m hanging space plus 9 lin m on screens and 23 sq m floor space
Exhibitions: 4 a year of which 3 originated, 1 touring
Details: Aims to inform and educate about maritime issues, particularly in relation to Lancaster/Morecambe Bay area. Where possible exhibitions are adapted or chosen

to fit in to needs of National Curriculum. Aims to develop artistic awareness and appreciation. Sales not priority.

Ludus 2D Gallery

[Pa] [Ph] [Pr] [Sc] ✔ ♿ [Wc]

Unattended entrance hall of busy dance centre providing space for new/unknown local artists to promote their work.

Assembly Rooms, King Street, Lancaster LA1 1RE, tel: 01524 35936
Contact: J. Dowthwaite, Administrator
Open: Mon-Thurs 9.30am-9.30pm; Fri 9.30-5.30; Sat 9.30-12.30
Space: 1 gallery with 16 lin m hanging space and 24 sq m floor space
Exhibitions: 6 a year all originated
Details: Visited by a wide cross section of the public as well as those using the centre. Well-lit by artificial light. Mounting and presentation responsibility of the artist. Sales not a priority.

Peter Scott Gallery

[Pa] [Ph] [Pr] [Cr] [Sc] ✔ ♿ [Wc]

University gallery running temporary exhibitions of contemporary art, and also housing university's collection of C20th art.

Lancaster University, Lancaster LA1 4YW, tel: 01524 593057, fax: 01524 592603
Contact: Mary Gavagan, Director
Open: Mon-Wed, Fri 12-5; Thurs 12-5, 6-8.30
Space: 1 gallery with 83 lin m hanging space and 306 sq m floor space
Exhibitions: 5 a year of which 3 originated, 2 touring
Details: Part of arts centre at the University. Collection of 400 paintings, original prints and sculpture. Policy is to stage exhibitions of significance, especially work that cannot be seen elsewhere in the region, and to promote innovative ideas in the visual arts. Educational programme to help develop and foster understanding of contemporary arts. Sales not a priority.

Storey Institute Art Gallery

[Pa] [Ph] [Pr] [Cr] [Sc] [LA] ✔ ♿ [Wc]

A large purpose-built Victorian gallery and adjoining dedicated space providing a varied programme of contemporary exhibitions.

Storey Institute, Meeting House Lane, Lancaster LA1 1TH
Contact: Exhibitions Organiser
Open: Mon-Sat 10-4
Space: 2 galleries with 78 lin m hanging space and 317 sq m floor space
Exhibitions: 8 a year of which 6 originated, 2 touring
Details: To provide exhibition space for a broad range of cultural events and activities by contemporary practitioners. Typical exhibitions last 3-5 weeks Half are group exhibitions. Sale of work is encouraged and 20% commission is taken.

Lavenham
SUFFOLK EA

Reclamations Gallery

[Cr] ✔ 🚫

Changing exhibitions of contemporary crafts and applied art in gallery-style shop occupying three floors of mediaeval building.

73 Water Street, Lavenham CO10 9RW, tel: 01787 248542
Contact: Sarah Conwell
Space: 1 gallery with 9 lin m hanging space and 50 sq m floor space
Exhibitions: 3 a year all originated
Details: Outlet for commercial contemporary crafts and applied arts, especially jewellery, papier-mâché and ceramics. Specialises in new-comers and students.

Wildlife Art Gallery

[Pa] [Pr] [Sc] ✔

Commercial gallery showing and selling contemporary wildlife and East Anglian paintings and sculptures.

Phoenix House, 97 High Street, Lavenham CO10 9PZ, tel: 01787 248562
Contact: Andrew Haslen, Director
Open: Mon-Sat 10-5; Sun 2-5
Space: 76 lin m hanging space and 93 sq m floor space
Exhibitions: 6 a year all originated

Leamington Spa
WARWICKSHIRE WMA

Earl of Smith Gallery

7 The Parade, Leamington Spa CV32 4DG, tel: 01926 338666
Contact: William Sander

Griffin Gallery

[Pa] [Ph] ✔ ♿

Commercial gallery specialising in C20th prints with work by mostly established artists.

118 Regent Street, Leamington Spa CV32 4NR, tel: 01926 499777
Contact: Suzie Goldmark, Exhibitions Organiser
Open: Tues-Sat 9.30-5.30
Space: 3 galleries with 29 lin m hanging space and 84 sq m floor space
Exhibitions: 6 a year all originated
Details: Three interlinked rooms in gallery off main street. About half exhibitions are 'very' contemporary. Would consider applications from artists seeking exhibitions but must include cost of return post and would prefer it if an application was preceded by a phone call.

Leamington Spa Art Gallery & Museum

[Pa] [Ph] [Pr] [Cr] [Sc] ✔ [H] ♿ [Wc]

Museum with local history gallery, two galleries devoted to permanent collections of paintings, ceramics and glass and two temporary exhibition galleries.

Avenue Road, Leamington Spa CV31 3PP, tel: 01926 426559, fax: 01926 887260
Contact: Alison Plumridge, Acting Manager
Open: Mon-Tues & Fri-Sat 10-1, 2-5; Thurs 6-8
Space: 2 galleries with 40 lin m hanging space plus 16 lin m on screens and 108 sq m floor space
Exhibitions: 9 a year of which 8 originated, 1 touring
Details: Aims to increase public awareness of rich history and strong artistic community of area and appreciation of art in general and to make gallery an educational and entertaining place to visit for all. Exhibitions last 3-7 weeks. Programme includes historical and contemporary art & craft, social history and local interest subjects. Mainly shows work by local artists and makers but artists from outside Warwick District welcome to apply. Exhibitions are complemented by series of arts activities for all ages and abilities. 10% + VAT commission on any sales made but this not a priority.

North Lodge

[Pa] [Ph] [Cr] [Sc] ✔ ♿

Lodge at entrance to Jephson Gardens available for temporary exhibitions.

Jephson Gardens, Leamington Spa
Contact: Nigel Bishop, Parks Manager, Warwick District Council, Amenities Department, Regent Square, Regent Street, Leamington, CV32 4VJ, tel: 01926 450000 ext 2053
Open: By arrangement with Parks Manager.
Space: 1 gallery with 7 lin m hanging space plus 3 lin m on screens and 18 sq m floor space
Exhibitions: 5 a year
Details: Small building with no specialist staff attached. Sales not gallery's primary role.

Royal Spa Centre

[Pa] [Pr] [Sc] ✔ 🚫

Multi-purpose arts and entertainment venue offering a limited amount of exhibition space to local artists and organisations.

Newbold Terrace, Leamington Spa CV32 4HN, tel: 01926 334418, fax: 01926 832054
Contact: Peter F Cresswell, General Manager & Licensee

Open: Mon-Sat 10-5; evenings when events are taking place
Space: 14 lin m hanging space
Details: Programme exclusively work by local artists. Large and wide audience, and exhibitions have ranged from experienced artists to beginners. Sale of work not gallery's primary concern but commission taken on any sales made.

South Town Gallery

GAIA, 7 Regent Place, Leamington Spa, tel: 01926 338805
Contact: Ali Gouedard

Leatherhead
SURREY SEA

Fire and Iron Gallery

Cr SG ✚ H ⟳

Converted workshop in 10 acre grounds of 1450 building that specialises in decorative metalwork.
Rowhurst Forge, Oxshott Road, Leatherhead KT22 0EN, tel: 01372 375148, fax: 01372 386516
Contact: Lucy Quinnell, Managing Director
Open: Mon-Sat 10-5
Space: 4 galleries with 300 sq m floor space
Exhibitions: 7 a year
Details: Main aim is to further the standards and appreciation of decorative metal work. One large brick room and three painted rooms with permanent display and varied programme of events and exhibitions which challenge metal workers and attract and inform all sectors of the general public. Exhibitions sometimes organised on basis of hiring out gallery.

Thorndike Theatre Gallery

Pa Ph Pr Cr ✚ H ⟳ Wc

One bright wall in theatre bar.
Thorndike Theatre, Church Street, Leatherhead KT22 8DF, tel: 01372 376211, fax: 01372 362595
Contact: Mike Power/Nikki Hopkins, Theatre Managers
Space: 1 gallery with 15 lin m hanging space
Exhibitions: 16 a year all on a hire basis
Details: Well lit. 3000+ patrons per week. Usual programming consists of local artists and occasional national artists. Now seeking to expand parameters and take in national tours. Willing to discuss any ideas.

Ledbury
HEREFORD & WORCESTER WMA

Collection Gallery

Cr ✔ ⟳

Crafts Council selected gallery displaying broad selection of contemporary crafts.
13 The Southend, Ledbury HR8 2EY, tel: 01531 634641, fax: 01531 631555
Contact: Gallery Director
Open: Mon-Sat 9.30-5.30
Space: 1 gallery with 750 sq m floor space
Exhibitions: 4 a year all originated
Details: Crafts displayed include ceramics, glass, jewellery, wood, metal and basketry. Welcomes approaches by mail if the sender is able to include good photos or slides, CV and price guide. Often approaches makers through shows like Creative Eye, Chelsea Crafts Fair, and Top Drawer. Selling work is gallery's primary role.

Heritage Gallery

Ledbury HR8 1NP, tel: 01531 640353
Contact: Jean Ashley, c/o Forge Cottage, Staplow

Leeds
WEST YORKSHIRE YHA

Art & Design Movement

Pa Pr Cr SG ✔ ⟳

Commercial gallery below established shop in central Leeds mainly showing work by Northern-based artists/craftspeople.
4 New Station Street, Leeds LS1 5DL, tel: 0113 234 0436
Contact: Jane Darnley
Open: (Jan-Oct) Wed-Sat 10.30-5.30; (Nov-Dec) Wed-Sat 10.30-5.30, Sun 12-5
Space: 1 gallery with 29 lin m hanging space and 60 sq m floor space
Exhibitions: 7 a year all originated
Details: Innovative work by less-established practitioners/recent graduates encourages although sale of work must be a priority (40% commission taken). Scope for larger 3D work/furniture. Some publicity and some insurance cover provided. Aim of gallery to promote artistic interest within the context of a busy city/shopping centre.

Benjamin Gott

Armley Mills Museum, Canal Road, Leeds LS12 2QF, tel: 0113 263 7861
Contact: Samantha Flavin

BRAHM Gallery

Pa Ph Pr SG ✔ ⟳ Wc

Gallery aims to provide an accessible environment for the display of exciting and challenging work by visual artists from throughout Britain.

The BRAHM Building, 9a Alma Road, Headingly, Leeds LS6 2AH, tel: 0113 230 4000, fax: 0113 230 4443
Contact: Chris Taylor, Exhibitions Director
Open: Mon-Fri 9.30-5
Space: 1 gallery with 37 lin m hanging space and 142 sq m floor space
Exhibitions: 6 a year all originated
Details: In the headquarters of the Brahm Agency, a busy gallery which supports and encourages both regional and national painters, printmakers, photographers and sculptors. Provides bridge between the arts and business community. Programme is diverse, aiming to get a good mixture of art forms, and particular favour shown to artists who have not had a solo exhibition. Occasionally provides sponsorship for other art projects. Small commission on sales. Sale of work is considered one of the gallery's primary roles.

Cookridge Street Gallery *

Pa Pr Cr SG LA ✔

Run by Jacob Kramer College of Further Education shows work by students and staff, occasionally by artists and makers from outside institution.
Jacob Kramer College, Vernon Street, Leeds LS2, tel: 0113 243 9931
Contact: Gary Barker, Exhibitions Organiser
Details: Aims to provide students with opportunity to experience putting together and promoting shows and enrich visual experience of those working in the college. Wishes to promote plural view of visual arts so no house-style. 18 exhibitions a year equally divided between group and mixed shows.

Craft Centre & Design Gallery

Ph Pr Cr ✔ ⟳

Craft centre displays contemporary work by local and national designers.
City Art Gallery, The Headrow, Leeds LS1 3AB, tel: 0113 247 8241
Contact: Hayley Walker, Manager
Open: Mon-Fri 10-5; Sat 10-4
Space: 1 gallery
Exhibitions: 3 a year
Details: On the lower ground floor of Leeds City Art Gallery promoting, selling and exhibiting an eclectic mix of contemporary applied arts. In addition to 2-3 exhibitions a year also monthly showcases for jewellers. Emphasis on the work of leading jewellers and craftspeople, but encompassing semi-industrial design and fine print-making. Sale of work not gallery's primary role.

Gilbert Scott Gallery

Pa Ph SC ● ① ● Wc

Exhibition space in Gilbert Scott designed building (1868) showing contemporary work appropriate for healing environment.
General Infirmary at Leeds, Great George Street, Leeds LS2 9N, tel: 0113 292 6568, fax: 0113 292 6463
Contact: Gail Bolland, Arts Co-ordinator, Healthcare Arts, 10 Clarendon Road, Leeds, LS2 9NS, tel: 0113 292 6668, fax: 0113 292 6463
Open: Daily 8.30-8.30
Space: 1 gallery with 23 lin m hanging space
Exhibitions: 5 a year all originated
Details: Aims to show examples of good contemporary practice appropriate to healing environment. Sales not a priority.

Henry Moore Institute

SC ① Wc

Ground floor devoted to temporary exhibitions within centre for the study of sculpture.
74 The Headrow, Leeds LS1 3AA, tel: 0113 246 7467/ 234 3158, fax: 0113 246 1481
Contact: Robert Hopper, Director
Open: Mon, Tues-Sat 10-5.30; Wed 10-9
Space: 4 galleries with 330 sq m floor space
Exhibitions: 4 a year of which 2 originated, 2 touring
Details: Headquarters of the Henry Moore Sculpture Trust. Aims to increase public awareness of sculpture and sculptural issues. Exhibits all aspects of sculpture from ancient to modern within centre providing specialist library and archive, audio visual room with video and slides to support lectures and seminars.

Leeds City Art Gallery

Pa Ph Pr SC LA ● ① ● Wc

Municipal gallery with modern collection and exhibition programme to match.
The Headrow, Leeds LS1 3AA, tel: 0113 247 8248
Contact: Nigel Walsh, Senior Assistant Keeper (Exhibitions)
Open: Mon-Tues & Thurs-Fri 10-5.30; Sat 10-4; Wed 10-9
Space: 2 galleries with 127 lin m hanging space and 300 sq m floor space
Exhibitions: 14 a year of which 7 originated, 7 touring
Details: Houses collections of C20th British art as well as French C19th and Victorian paintings, and large collection of English watercolours. Emphasis of the temporary exhibition programme is on the modern and contemporary; the education service seeks to create access to all sectors of the community through an interactive programme of workshops, talks and seminars.

Leeds Design Innovation Centre

Pa Ph Pr SC ● ● Wc 4

Foyer space for varied programme of two- and three-dimensional work featuring artists that have a particular relevance to the area.
46 The Calls, Leeds LS2, tel: 0113 243 6077
Contact: Louisa Ferguson, Design Centre Manager
Open: Mon-Fri 8.45-5.15
Space: 1 gallery with 47 lin m hanging space and 56 sq m floor space
Exhibitions: 15 a year all originated
Details: A venue for local artists. Relaxed and informal atmosphere. Gallery aims to increase public awareness and appreciation of art in general. Work sold is not a priority.

Leeds Metropolitan University Gallery

Pa Ph Pr Cr SC LA ● ① ● Wc

Contemporary art gallery showing new work by professional artists.
City Campus, Woodhouse Lane, Leeds LS1 3HE, tel: 0113 283 3130, fax: 0113 283 3112
Contact: Claire Slattery, Gallery Development Officer
Open: Mon-Fri 10-5; Sat 10-3
Space: 1 gallery with 74 lin m hanging space and 203 sq m floor space
Exhibitions: 7 a year of which 4 originated, 3 touring
Details: Annual programme of temporary exhibitions. Originates shows and hosts national touring exhibitions. Exhibitions are accompanied by educational events, seminars and workshops. Members of the public are offered the opportunity to meet with artists, gain practical skills and explore exhibitions critically. Sales not gallery's main function.

Lotherton Hall

Pa Ph ● ● Wc 4

Room in historic house suitable for display of contemporary prints, drawings and paintings, particularly of Yorkshire subjects.
Aberford, Leeds LS25 3EB, tel: 0113 281 3259, fax: 0113 260 2285
Contact: Adam White, Keeper
Open: Tues-Sat 10.30-12, 1-5.45 (or dusk if earlier)
Space: 1 gallery with 11 lin m hanging space
Exhibitions: 7 a year all originated
Details: Sales not a priority.

Newlyn Gallery

Pa Ph Pr SC ● ● Wc

Young artists and community groups from the region and exhibitions linked to the theatre season given priority.
West Yorkshire Playhouse, Playhouse Square, Quarry Hill, Leeds LS2 7UP, tel: 0113 244 2141
Contact: Rachel Murphy, House Manager
Space: 1 gallery with 25 lin m hanging space plus 7 lin m on screens
Exhibitions: 12 a year all originated
Details: Aims to establish links with the community. Part of a public space in Front of House also seen by theatregoers entering the Courtyard Theatre. Suitable for smaller 2D works especially intricate worked pictures, as standing room is either from 5ft to 15ft away from pictures. two cabinets for pottery, jewellery, etc also available.

Site (Architecture) Gallery

Pa Ph Pr Cr SC ● ①

Gallery on two floors of Georgian terraced house promoting architecture and related artforms.
RIBA, 8 Woodhouse Square, Leeds LS3 1AD, tel: 0113 245 6250, fax: 0113 2426 791
Contact: Robert MacBurney, Exhibitions Organiser, Longfellow Fine Art
Open: Mon-Fri 9-5; Sat 10-4
Space: 3 galleries
Exhibitions: 8 a year of which 7 originated, 1 touring
Details: Gallery will consider showing anything related to architecture, either with obvious connection (planning, interior design, etc) or less obvious. This encompasses almost everything except performance. Shows international architecture as well as local/national work. Sales not a priority. Exhibition spaces in hall, basement and ground floor.

Space (The)

Pa Ph Pr Cr SC LA ● ⊕ ● Wc

Unused space with potential made available to emerging artists as free venue for exhibitions, music & dance workshops.
Granary Wharf, Canal Basin, Leeds, tel: 0113 244 6570, fax: 0113 245 0153
Contact: Rachel Anstis, Exhibitions Organiser
Open: Daily 10-5
Space: 1 gallery with 60 lin m hanging space
Exhibitions: 20 a year all on a hire basis
Details: Anyone may apply to use "The Space"; usually groups of young artists launching first show after college. Exhibitions usually last 2-3 weeks. This policy to continue as long as space available. Sales not primary function of gallery.

Terrace Gallery

Pa Ph Pr Cr SC ●

Gallery extends full length of central corridor, out onto the C18th terrace of Harewood House.

c/o Estate Office, Harewood House, Leeds LS17 9LQ, tel: 0113 288 6296, fax: 0113 288 6467
Contact: Alison Sherlock
Space: 1 gallery with 106 lin m hanging space and 61 sq m floor space
Exhibitions: 3 a year of which 2 originated, 1 touring
Details: Programme is diverse, including for example the Australian season of Aboriginal art in 1992 and Scottish season including Craigie Aitchison retrospective 1994.

University Gallery Leeds

Pa Ph Pr Cr Sc ✓ ⓔ ⓖ

Gallery with exhibitions of University's collection and some from outside sources.
Parkinson Building, Woodhouse Lane, Leeds LS2 9JT, tel: 0113 233 2777
Contact: Hilary Diaper, Keeper of University Art Collection
Open: (Term-time) Mon-Fri 10-5; closed during exhibition changeover
Space: 3 galleries with 70 lin m hanging space and 133 sq m floor space
Exhibitions: 4 a year of which 3 originated, 1 touring
Details: Opened in 1970 to show university's permanent collection of British drawings, paintings and prints and provide a space within the university for contemporary exhibitions. About half devoted to display of university collection through regular changing exhibitions. Originate a number of exhibitions from outside sources,will consider touring exhibitions. Each show lasts up to ten weeks.

Yorkshire Dance Centre

Pa Ph Pr LA ✓ ⓖ ⓦ

Small exhibition space within the centre which is used for exhibitions by local artists.
3 St Peter's Buildings, St Peter's Square, Leeds LS9 8AH, tel: 0113 242 6066
Contact: Simon Dove, Director
Space: 1 gallery
Exhibitions: 3 a year all originated
Details: Criteria for the exhibitions is that they must all be wall-mountable, by artists predominantly from the Yorkshire & Humberside region. Exhibitions have included various work by local artists, an installation performance piece, photography and video and work by children.

Leicester
LEICESTERSHIRE EMA

27A Access Artspace *

Pa Ph Pr Cr Sc

Independent building-based arts workshop and gallery area.

27a Belvoir Street, Leicester LE1 6SL, tel: 0116 254 4981
Contact: Steve Morris, Project Coordinator
Space: 1 gallery with 23 lin m hanging space and 50 sq m floor space
Exhibitions: 3 a year all originated
Details: Works mainly with disabled people in all aspects of the arts. Funded by Leicester City Council, Leicestershire County Council and East Midlands Arts.

City Gallery

Pa Ph Pr Cr Sc ✓ ⓔ ⓗ ⓖ ⓦ

Aims to promote best in local, regional, national and international fine art & craft through dynamic programme of accessible but challenging exhibitions and events.
90 Granby Street, Leicester LE1 1DJ, tel: 0116 254 0595, fax: 0116 254 0593
Contact: Sylvia Wright, Manager, City Gallery
Open: Tues-Fri 11-6; Sat 10-5; closed BH
Space: 3 galleries with 64 lin m hanging space plus 31 lin m on screens and 802 sq m floor space
Exhibitions: 52 a year of which 18 originated, 5 touring, 29 on a hire basis
Details: Platform for contemporary art and craft. One gallery hired to local artists and can be booked on a weekly basis. Touring exhibitions organised on local and national level for both gallery and non-gallery venues (15 exhibitions organised to tour to non gallery venues extra to 58 per year exhibitions held in gallery.) Educational programme to accompany exhibitions being developed. Shop frontage attracts a wide audience from people passing by, as well as people paying specific visits. Managed by Leicester City Council, grant-funded by East Midlands Arts. Sales not a priority.

Craft Gallery *

Cr ✓

Commercial craft gallery and shop.
54 London Road, Leicester LE2 0QD, tel: 0116 255 0773
Contact: Aldona Grodecka, Exhibition Organiser
Details: Wide range of work by different makers, occasional exhibitions by individual makers. The changing display includes pottery, wood, jewellery and glass.

Gadsby Gallery

Pa Pr Sc ✓

Shows gallery and internationally-known artists, and work by local artists.
22 Market Place, Leicester LE1 5GF, tel: 0116 262 2410/ 251 7792
Contact: Peter Gadsby, Manager
Space: 1 gallery with 50 lin m hanging space
Exhibitions: 2 a year both originated
Details: Artists materials on sale. Framing and restoration service.

Haymarket Theatre

Pa Ph Pr Cr Sc LA ✓ ⓖ ⓦ

Presents work thematically linked to theatre productions, and work reflecting multicultural ideas.
Belgrave Gate, Leicester LE1 3YQ, tel: 0116 253 0021, fax: 0116 251 3310
Contact: Samantha Stevens, Theatre Manager
Open: Mon-Sat 10-11
Space: 35 galleries with 50 lin m hanging space and 18 sq m floor space
Details: Shows work by local up-and-coming artists and national touring exhibitions. High walls and a vaulted ceiling. Work shown in foyer areas upstairs and down. Policy is to stimulate, inform and entertain as well as introducing new artists to a public who do not visit art galleries regularly. Selling work not main function of gallery. Fully accessible 10am-6pm; access for wheelchair users with assistance 6pm-11pm.

Leicester Print Workshop

Pr

Use made of City Gallery Touring Exhibition spaces for shows organised mainly of members' work.
68 Knighton Lane, Leicester LE2 8BR, tel: 0116 283 0587
Contact: Sarah Kirby, Exhibition Organiser
Exhibitions: 4 a year all originated
Details: Members encouraged to exhibit. Members Exhibition organised annually. Workshops run with exhibitions. Touring Exhibition available for hire. Always looking for artists to run printmaking workshops. Set up to provide facilities and instruction for etching and relief printing.

Leicester Royal Infirmary

Pa Ph Pr

Exhibition space in reception area of major general hospital runs programme of solo exhibitions by professional regional artists.
Infirmary Square, Leicester LE1 5WW, tel: 0116 254 1414
Contact: Louise O'Reilly, Projects Officer, ArtPoint Trust, North Pavilion, Parklands, Great Linford, Milton Keynes, MK14 5DZ
Space: 1 gallery with 30 lin m hanging space
Exhibitions: 4 a year of which 2 originated
Details: Policy of purchasing and commissioning works of art. Aims to introduce contemporary arts to a new audience. Exhibitions form part of hospital art programme organised by Works of Art Steering Committee.

Leicestershire Museum & Art Gallery

Regional museum & art gallery, representing new developments in art locally, nationally and internationally in addition to historical exhibitions.
New Walk, Leicester LE1 6TD, tel: 0116 255 4100, fax: 0116 247 3005
Contact: Keeper of Fine Art, Leicestershire Museums, Arts and Records Service, The Rowans, College Street, Leicester, LE2 0JJ, tel: 0116 255 4100, fax: 0116 247 3005
Open: Mon-Sat 10-5.30; Sun 2-5.30
Space: 3 galleries with 107 lin m hanging space and 316 sq m floor space
Exhibitions: 5 a year of which 3 originated
Details: Extensive collections of fine art, both historical and contemporary. Temporary exhibitions tend to be large shows originated in-house of national significance, some touring exhibitions from other organisations. Smaller solo and group shows featuring contemporary artists also mounted, with some emphasis on regional artists. Programme includes multi-cultural events and educational activities. Sales not a priority.

Phoenix Art Centre

11 Newarke Street, Leicester LE1 5FS, tel: 0116 255 4854
Contact: Exhibitions Organiser

Picture House

Ph ○①①ⓗ ⓗ⽊

Gallery in Victorian house dedicated to photography exhibitions.
113 Princess Road East, Leicester LE1 7LA, tel: 0116 255 1310, fax: 0116 255 0132
Contact: Roger Bradley or Anna Smalley, Exhibition Organiser
Open: Mon, Tues, Thurs-Sat 9-5; Wed 9-9; 1st Sat of the month 10-1
Space: 2 galleries with 63 lin m hanging space
Exhibitions: 18 a year of which 5 originated, 6 touring, 7 on a hire basis
Details: The gallery enhances a comprehensive practical facility including darkrooms, studio and electronic imaging. Exhibitions feature local , national and international work on diverse subjects. Picture House directors are both teachers and photographers offering a definite 'educational' base to all activities. Sale of work not gallery's primary concern. Exhibition hanging space comprises standing boards plus walls and staircase. Where space is 'hired out' there is no charge.

Vaughan College

Pa Pr Sc ○ ⓗ

Space within adult education centre aiming to provide high quality context for exhibitions and to give energy and interest to the college.
St Nicholas Circle, Leicester LE1 4LB, tel: 0116 251 7368
Contact: Alan Caine, Organising Tutor for Art
Open: Mon-Fri 9-9
Space: 1 gallery with 40 lin m hanging space
Exhibitions: 5 a year all originated
Details: Exhibition committee looks for work of high standard with some sort of personal identity. Exhibitions last 4-6 weeks. No charge but 10% of sales taken. Constant flow of students as audience. Exhibition facilities above average for its context, but not a gallery. Publicity, insurance and hanging responsibility of the artist. Sales of work not a main aim.

Woods Gallery

Pa Ph Pr Sc ○

Gallery on three floors presenting predominantly solo exhibitions.
17 King Street, Leicester, tel: 0116 2471067, fax: 0116 254 5684
Contact: Jeff Woods
Space: 2 galleries
Exhibitions: 7 a year all originated
Details: In addition to exhibition space shop on ground floor sells original works, prints, cards, etc.

Leigh
GREATER MANCHESTER NWA

Turnpike Gallery

One large gallery space which aims to encourage visitors to appreciate innovative contemporary art and craft by professional artists.
Leigh Library, Civic Square, Leigh WN7 1EB, tel: 01942 404558, fax: 01942 262451
Contact: Vicky Charnock, Assistant Gallery Officer
Open: Mon-Fri 10-5.30; Wed 10-5; Sat 10-3
Space: 1 gallery with 67 lin m hanging space and 279 sq m floor space
Exhibitions: 6 a year of which 4 originated, 2 touring
Details: Continuous programme of contemporary exhibitions,from painting, sculpture and prints to ceramics and textiles, accompanied by a full programme of educational workshops. Conceives and formulates virtually all the exhibitions through its own resources. Gallery based

artist-in-residence. Artist-led public workshops when appropriate funding is available. Admission free. Sale of work not gallery's primary role although artists may choose to sell work through exhibiting.

Leighton Buzzard
BEDFORDSHIRE EA

Leighton Buzzard Library Gallery

Pa Ph Pr Cr ○ ⓗ⽊④

Dedicated exhibition space on ground floor of library.
Lake Street, Leighton Buzzard LU7 8RX, tel: 01525 371788
Contact: Stephanie Record, County Arts Officer, South and Luton, Bedfordshire County Council Leisure Services, Luton Central Library, St Georges Square, Luton, LU1 2NG, tel: 01582 30161, fax: 01582 24638
Open: Mon-Fri 9.30-7; Sat 9.30-4
Space: 1 gallery with 15 lin m hanging space and 40 sq m floor space
Exhibitions: 11 a year of which 9 originated, 2 touring
Details: Gallery in public library which attracts 33,000 visitors monthly. Exhibitions, mostly by invitation. National, regional and local professional artists. Two-dimensional work with occasional craft exhibitions and photography. Associated one-off workshops and talks arranged. Interpretive material displayed.

Leiston
SUFFOLK EA

Aldringham Craft Market Gallery

Pa Cr ○ ⓗ

Family-owned complex incorporating three galleries and coffee shop where exhibitions are only offered to artists and craftspeople whose work is handled on an on-going basis.
Aldringham, Leiston IP16 4PY, tel: 01728 830397
Contact: Mr Godfrey Huddle
Open: Mon-Sat 10-5.30; Sun 10-12, 2-5.30; Sun opening hours may vary in winter months.
Space: 1 gallery with 11 lin m hanging space and 15 sq m floor space
Exhibitions: 4 a year all originated
Details: Dedicated to retailing of art, craft and supporting products. Exhibitions held in Gallery 3 where all normal retailing functions suspended during exhibitions. No publicity charges

Leominster
HEREFORD &
WORCESTER WMA

Farmers Gallery
Pa Pr ⊘ ⊕

Commercial gallery in centre of Leominster showing broad range of exhibitions and with 3 rooms for hire.
28 Broad Street, Leominster HR6 8BS, tel: 01568 611413, fax: 01568 611492
Contact: David Hanmer
Open: Mon-Sat 10.30-4.30 during exhibitions
Space: 3 galleries with 130 lin m hanging space
Exhibitions: 6 a year all originated

Leominster Library
Pa Ph SC ⊘ ⊕ ⊕ ⊛

Exhibition space in library for work considered suitable by any artists in any medium.
8 Buttercross, Leominster HR6 8BN, tel: 01568 612384, fax: 01568 616025
Contact: Peter Holliday, Librarian
Open: Tues, Wed, Fri 9.30-5.30; Thurs 9.30-8; Sat 9.30-4
Space: 1 gallery with 22 lin m hanging space plus 28 lin m on screens and 71 sq m floor space
Exhibitions: 10 a year of which 3 originated, 1 touring, 6 on a hire basis
Details: As public library operates on as wide a brief as possible accepting work by both professional and amateur artists, groups and individuals. Sales not primary function. Gallery well-lit with natural light and spots. See also entry for Hereford & Worcester Libraries & Arts Department, Worcester.

Letchworth
HERTFORDSHIRE EA

Letchworth Central Library
Pa Ph Pr SC ⊘

Exhibition space in library lecture hall on first floor showing mainly public information and occasional painting or sculpture exhibitions.
Broadway, Letchworth SG6 3PF, tel: 01462 685646
Contact: Ms Myra Campbell, Librarian
Open: Mon, Tues, Fri 9.30-7.30; Thurs 9.30-8; Sat 9.30-1
Space: 2 galleries
Details: Library lecture hall approx 18'x27' (mixed use) plus garden space for sculpture. Lecture room day-lit. Variable hire period and hire fee negotiable. Venue promoted by library by local leaflet distribution. Sales possible by negotiation.

Letchworth Museum
Pa Ph Pr Cr SC ⊘ ⊕ ⊕ ⊛ ▣

First-floor gallery in general local museum aiming to provide a varied programme of art and craft exhibitions, giving priority to local artists, for a mainly local audience.
Broadway, Letchworth SG6 3PF, tel: 01462 685647
Contact: Curator
Open: Mon-Sat 10-5
Space: 1 gallery with 30 lin m hanging space plus 20 lin m on screens and 72 sq m floor space
Exhibitions: 7 a year of which 1 touring, 6 on a hire basis
Details: Flexible lighting/layout. Most exhibitions generated by local artists, both amateur and professional and exhibition space provided free of charge; just commission on sales taken. Interprets 'local' very broadly – considers artists from outside the immediate area. Exhibitions last three to four weeks. Occasional workshops for schools and the public. Regular 'Artist in Residence' days organised. Sale of work not gallery's primary role.

Lewes
EAST SUSSEX SEA

Charleston Gallery
Pa Ph Pr Cr SC ⊘ ⊕ ⊛

Simple showing space alongside Charleston Farmhouse, former home of Duncan Grant and Vanessa Bell.
Near Firle, Lewes BN8 6LL, tel: 01323 811626
Contact: James Beechey, Exhibitions Organiser
Open: (Apr-Oct) Wed-Sun 2-6
Space: 1 gallery with 15 lin m hanging space and 30 sq m floor space
Exhibitions: 7 a year all originated
Details: Primarily one-person shows of one month's duration for contemporary artists and craftspeople, both young and established; and at least one historical show per year; and a mixed show at Christmas.

Hesketh Gallery
Pa Cr SC ⊘ ⊕

Contemporary craft gallery with emphasis on local artists/makers.
4 Lansdown Place, Lewes BN7 2JT, tel: 01273 487150
Contact: Christine Vinall, Proprietor
Open: Mon, Tues, Thurs-Sat 9.15-5
Space: 1 gallery with 22 sq m floor space
Exhibitions: 10 a year all originated
Details: Gallery aims to give local craftspeople an opportunity to exhibit, whilst at the same time providing one-off exhibitions for more well-known artists/craftspeople. Sales a priority.

Leyburn
NORTH YORKSHIRE YHA

Chandler Gallery
Pa Pr Cr SC ⊘ ⊛

Exhibition programme and permanent stock offering shop-front for mainly local professional artists.
Commercial Square, Leyburn DL8 5BP, tel: 01969 623676
Contact: Charles Chandler, Exhibitions Organiser
Open: Mon, Tues, Thurs & Fri 9.30-5; closed Feb
Space: 1 gallery with 13 lin m hanging space and 27 sq m floor space
Exhibitions: 8 a year all originated
Details: Offers public variety of work by professional artists. Sales not gallery's main purpose.

Old School Arts Workshop
Pa Ph Pr SC ⊘ ⊕

Exhibition area shared with bookshop, providing additional attraction for visitors to Middleham.
Middleham, Leyburn DL8 4QG, tel: 01969 23056
Contact: Peter Hibbard, Exhibition Organiser
Open: (Summer) daily 10-5; (Winter) Mon, Wed-Sun 10-5
Space: 1 gallery with 14 lin m hanging space and 36 sq m floor space
Exhibitions: 9 a year all originated
Details: Artist-run with exhibitions changing every 5 weeks. Aim is to show widest possible range of professional work in visual arts. Also functions as a residential study centre for sculpture and other visual arts. Has an outdoor area for display of sculpture made on the premises. Sale of work important but probability of sales not deciding factor in selecting work for exhibition.

Leyland
LANCASHIRE NWA

South Ribble Museum and Exhibition Centre
Pa ⊘

The Old Grammar School, Church Road, Leyland PR5 1EJ, tel: 01772 422041
Contact: David Hunt, Museum Custodian
Open: Tues & Fri 10-4; Thurs 1-4; Sat 10-1
Space: 1 gallery with 10 lin m hanging space
Exhibitions: 1 a year originated
Details: Restored Tudor grammar school. Caters for work by local artists, for a local audience.

Lichfield
STAFFORDSHIRE WMA

Lichfield Arts Centre
[Pa] [Ph] [Pr] ✓ [H] ♿

Small gallery in arts centre to encourage displays by local artists.

Bird Street, Lichfield WS13 6PR, tel: 01543 262223

Contact: Brian Pretty, Administrator
Open: Mon-Sat 10-4
Space: 1 gallery with 10 lin m hanging space and 32 sq m floor space
Exhibitions: 8 a year all on a hire basis
Details: Small arts centre run by Lichfield District Arts Association for professional and amateur productions, events and exhibitions. Exhibitions drawn from local and regional sources. Half are of professional work. Occasional workshops and events arranged. Hopes to encourage higher standards by exhibiting work from outside the immediate area and increase public involvement and awareness of visual arts. Sales not seen as priority.

Lincoln
LINCOLNSHIRE EA

Branston Comprehensive School & Community College *
[Pa] [Ph] [Pr] [Cr] [Sc] [LA] ✓ [H]

Space in concert hall of a school with exhibitions of work by local artists, students and school pupils.

Station Road, Branston, Lincoln LN4 1LH, tel: 01522 791 279

Contact: Mr L Brown, Exhibition Organiser
Space: 1 gallery with 126 sq m floor space
Exhibitions: 5 a year of which 4 originated, 1 touring
Details: Runs evening adult education classes and has an active Friends organisation. Weekend, one-week and one month exhibitions. Would like to develop gallery space further. Possibility of hiring it out, and encouraging artists from outside the region to apply.

Gallery in the Garden
[Pa] [Pr] [Cr] [Sc] ✓ ♿

Two galleries and studio have work by artist/owner on show together with occasional exhibitions of work by other artists.

East Road, Navenby, Lincoln LN5 0EP, tel: 01522 811064

Contact: Dennis Valentine
Open: Wed-Sat 10-1, 2-5; or by appointment.
Space: 2 galleries with 44 lin m hanging space plus 7 lin m on screens and 78 sq m floor space
Exhibitions: 2 a year both originated
Details: Two gallery spaces in a limestone and pantiled barn in the garden of the owner's house. One has Dennis Valentine's studio space on a mezzanine floor. Shows local and national contemporary art and craft work. The galleries can be used together for larger exhibitions. Draws interest from a wider audience as well as having a local following. Selling work is gallery's primary function.

Greestone Gallery
[Pa] [Ph] [Pr] [Cr] [Sc] [LA] ✓ [£] ♿ [WC]

Varied exhibition programme of contemporary artworks and events both in the gallery and in non-gallery venues in the region.

The School of Applied Arts and Design, De Montfort University Lincoln, Lindum Road, Lincoln LN2 1PF, tel: 01522 512912, fax: 01522 542167

Contact: Dawn Walters, Exhibitions Organiser
Open: Mon-Fri 8.30-6; opening hours change – please check with gallery beforehand
Space: 1 gallery with 25 lin m hanging space plus 54 lin m on screens and 122 sq m floor space
Exhibitions: 7 a year of which 2 originated, 5 touring
Details: All visual arts, crafts, lens based work, performance and design shown. Workshops and lectures. Audience for all shows include School of Applied Arts & Design students and staff, other colleges, schools and members of the general public. Sale of work not gallery's primary function.

Lincolnshire County Council, Recreational Services, Libraries *
[Pa] ✓

Initial contact point regarding exhibitions in area's libraries.

Brayford House, Lucy Tower Street, Lincoln LN1 1XN, tel: 01522 552866

Contact: K. Jefferson, Library Service Manager
Details: Exhibition spaces at Lincoln, Stamford, Grantham, Louth, Boston, Spalding, Gainsborough and Sleaford libraries.

Museum of Lincolnshire Life
[Pa] [Cr] [Sc] ✓ ♿ [WC]

Museum with displays and exhibitions showing wide range of social history mainly with local relevance.

The Old Barracks, Burton Road, Lincoln LN1 3LY, tel: 01522 528448, fax: 01522 521264

Contact: Rodney Cousins, Curator/Manager
Open: (May-Sept) daily 10-5.30; (Oct-Apr) Mon-Sat 10-5.30, Sun 2-5.30
Space: 1 gallery with 40 lin m hanging space and 90 sq m floor space
Exhibitions: 3 a year all originated
Details: Exhibition space interrupted by 3 cast iron columns. Glass display cases available. From time to time will accept national or international material. Sales not a priority.

Usher Gallery
[Pa] [Ph] [Pr] [Cr] [Sc] ✓ [£]

Municipal gallery promoting the work of both established and less well-known artists with regional, national and international reputations.

Lindum Road, Lincoln LN2 1NN, tel: 01522 527980, fax: 01522 560165

Contact: Mrs J. Elton, Exhibitions Officer
Open: Mon-Sat 10-5.30; Sun 2.30-5
Space: 3 galleries with 110 lin m hanging space and 248 sq m floor space
Exhibitions: 10 a year of which 3 originated, 7 touring
Details: Encourages public awareness and understanding of visual arts, crafts and design through historical and contemporary exhibitions and collections. Runs educational and interpretative events and reaches new audiences through outreach projects and touring exhibitions. Collection Peter de Wint; topographical paintings; C19th sculpture and C20th paintings; James Ward Usher Bequest.

Liphook
HAMPSHIRE SA

Working Tree
[Cr] ✓ ♿

Upstairs gallery space part of an environmentally concerned timber company.

Milland, Liphook GU30 7JS, tel: 01428 741672, fax: 01428 741679

Contact: Don Dennis, Director/Owner
Open: Mon-Fri 9-5.30; Sat 9-5
Space: 1 gallery with 37 sq m floor space
Details: Gallery has continuous changing display of timber crafts and furniture which fits the company's principles of providing alternative timber from sustainable 'sensible' forestry practices. Sales a priority.

Liverpool
MERSEYSIDE NWA

Acorn Gallery
[Pa] [Pr] [Sc] ✓ [H] ♿

Open-plan large attic gallery and café in Victorian listed building.

Newington Buildings, 16-18 Newington, Liverpool L1 4ED, tel: 0151 707 2755

Contact: Peter Daniels, Exhibitions Organiser
Open: Mon-Sat 10-5.30
Space: 39 lin m hanging space and 54 sq m floor space
Exhibitions: 12 a year
Details: Main Gallery and Café Gallery both available for hire either singly or together. Facilities are available to run workshops and fairs. Although the gallery is run commercially it makes every effort to be of practical assistance to artists.

Ainscough Gallery

Two shop units with large purpose-built gallery at back and access from adjacent restaurant throughout day and evening.
11 Falkner Street, Liverpool L8 7PU, tel: 0151 709 9963
Contact: Martin Ainscough, Director
Open: Mon-Fri 8-6; Sat & Sun 10-4
Space: 3 galleries with 100 lin m hanging space and 140 sq m floor space
Exhibitions: 10 a year all originated
Details: Privately funded commercial gallery showing work by local, foreign and national artists, ranging from the figurative to abstract, with a concentration on texture and colour.

Art Cellar

Gallery available to artists working in the North West with emphasis on artists who have not previously exhibited.
Off Stage, Cornwallis Hall, 4 Cornwallis Street, Liverpool L1 5DQ, tel: 0151 708 5542
Contact: Rita Johnson, Visual Arts Coordinator
Space: 2 galleries with 40 lin m hanging space and 209 sq m floor space
Exhibitions: 10 a year
Details: Brick-vaulted cellar with bays suitable for installations and sculpture, other space suitable for 2d work. Aims to encourage local community to visit and appreciate contemporary art. A number of workshops for schools organised. Charges £100 to cover publicity, etc.

Artreach

Artreach creates exhibitions for libraries, schools, art centres and the workplace, and can design an interactive education programme to meet the needs of each venue.
Unit B61, Brunswick Small Business Centre, Brunswick Bus Park, Liverpool L3 4BD, tel: 0151 708 7620, fax: 0151 709 2684
Contact: Carolyn Murray, Exhibitions Director
Open: Mon-Fri 10-5
Details: Artreach takes exhibitions directly to people wherever they already meet, work

and learn. Exhibitions introduce the work of new and established artists in order to promote awareness and enjoyment, providing a stepping-stone towards greater involvement with the visual arts. Selling work is not a main aim of Artreach. Access, facilities etc will vary according to venue.

Blackie Gallery

Cultural arts project based in a historic building in Liverpool City Centre, providing exhibitions space and performance area for contemporary, multi-cultural work.
Great Georges Project, Great George Street, Liverpool L1 5EW, tel: 0151 709 5109, fax: 0151 709 4822
Contact: Liz Robson/Kirstine Tillotson, Exhibition Organiser and Assistant
Open: Mon-Sat 10am-midnight; Sun 12 noon-midnight
Space: 1 gallery with 20 lin m hanging space and 130 sq m floor space
Exhibitions: 8 a year of which 7 originated, 1 touring
Details: Space is provided for those not usually catered for in conventional galleries of the region – so priority is given to women, crafts (especially textiles), artists from non-white cultures. Visitors: mix of local kids, parents, passers by, tourists and people with specific interests (eg textiles, 'green' issues, Chinese painting, women's artwork etc). Workshops held in gallery sat 11-5. Sales not a priority.

Bluecoat Display Centre

Craft Council selected craft gallery showing and selling British craft work.
School Lane, Liverpool L1 3BX, tel: 0151 709 4014, fax: 0151 707 0048
Contact: Maureen Bampton, Director
Open: Mon-Sat 10.30-5.30
Space: 1 gallery with 100 lin m hanging space
Exhibitions: 7 a year all originated
Details: Comprises two interconnecting rooms one of which is the exhibition area. Policy is to promote the work of regional and national crafts makers through exhibitions, workshops, informal talks and formal lectures and exhibitions are mixed media. Exhibitions publicised widely. Catalogues and information sheets produced to accompany exhibitions. Selling work is considered gallery's primary role. Non-profit making organisation.

Bluecoat Gallery

Four interconnecting galleries for changing exhibition programme.
School Lane, Liverpool L1 3BX, tel: 0151 709 5689, fax: 0151 707 0048
Contact: Janice Webster, Gallery Officer

Open: Tues-Sat 10.30-5
Space: 4 galleries with 79 lin m hanging space and 153 sq m floor space
Exhibitions: 9 a year of which 7 originated, 2 touring
Details: Policy is to promote the work of regional, national and international artists through exhibitions (including video/electronic media), live art, workshops and site-specific projects reflecting critical practice in contemporary art. Besides visual arts there is a varied programme of music, dance and performance. Sales not primary role of gallery.

Bridewell Studios *

Run by ArtSpace Merseyside Ltd showing work by both Bridewell-based artists and outsiders.
Prescot Street, Liverpool L7 8UE, tel: 0151 260 6333
Contact: Laird Downie, Director
Space: 1 gallery
Exhibitions: 6 a year of which 3 originated, 3 on a hire basis
Details: Provides free exhibition space for artists, outsiders are charged a nominal fee, part of which goes towards publicity. Idea is to give young, unknown artists chance to experience what organising an exhibition entails.

Concord Gallery

Exhibition space in main architectural studio available during vacations.
Liverpool University, School of Architecture, PO Box 147, Liverpool L69 3BX, tel: 0151 794 2604, fax: 0151 794 2605
Contact: John Hardie, Administrator
Open: Mon-Fri 9-5
Space: 1 gallery with 80 lin m hanging space plus 40 lin m on screens and 391 sq m floor space
Exhibitions: 5 a year all originated
Details: Space also occasionally available in coffee bar and foyer. Mainly local and regional artists who exhibit but welcome applications from other areas; will consider anything that's not immoral or illegal so long as the space is free. Selling work not main purpose of showing work. No commission charged on any sales made.

Hanover Galleries

Two spacious galleries exhibiting contemporary art available for hire; the works being for sale.
11/13 Hanover Street, Liverpool L1 3DN, tel: 0151 709 3073
Contact: E. Patricia Austin, Administrator
Open: Tues-Sat 10.30-5
Space: 2 galleries with 49 lin m hanging space and 1340 sq m floor space

Exhibitions: 25 a year all on a hire basis
Details: Two spacious galleries on ground and first floors. Connected by a spiral staircase. Wall runs 85ft and 81ft respectively. Good natural light, 30 fully adjustable track spots per gallery. Available for rent. Contemporary art exhibitions change fortnightly. Installation of exhibitions is the responsibility of the artist. Sales a priority.

Harold House Jewish Youth & Community Centre

Pa Ph Pr IA ✪ & ᴡ

Three exhibition areas in well-used Jewish community centre.
Dunbabin Road, Liverpool L15 6XL, tel: 0151 475 5671, fax: 0151 475 2202
Contact: Esmond Rosen, Director
Open: Mon-Thurs 9-5; Fri 9-11
Space: 2 galleries with plus 5 lin m on screens and 20 sq m floor space
Details: Exhibition spaces in foyer, restaurant/bar and studio showing work related to centre activities, local artists and shows from Merseyside Exhibitions. Will show almost anything of professional standard, particularly work relating to young people. Sales not a priority.

Liverpool Central Library

Pa Ph Pr Sc IA ✪ ᴴ

Permanent display of historical watercolours and drawings and programme of temporary exhibitions of work by local artists, makers and groups.
William Brown Street, Liverpool L3 8EW, tel: 0151 225 5418/5458, fax: 0151 207 1342
Contact: Margo Storey/Howard Pate, Marketing Officer/Extra-mural Officer
Space: 2 galleries
Exhibitions: 12 a year all on a hire basis
Details: In addition to 2 exhibition areas, café displays paintings in relaxed atmosphere. As well as exhibitions also shows work from Merseyside Exhibitions and Visionfest. Initial contact for enquiries about exhibitions at Liverpool City Libraries branches at Allerton, Childwall, Edge Hill, Everton, Fazakerley, Garston, Great Homer Street, Kensington, Kirkdale, Knotty Ash, Larkhill, Lister Drive, Netherley, Norris Green, Speke, Spellow, Toxteth, Walton and Wavertree.

Methodist Centre

Pa Ph Pr ✪ ᴴ & ᴡ

Exhibition hall with wall space.
Beaconsfield Street, Liverpool L8 2UD, tel: 0151 727 2035
Contact: George Eleady-Cole, Centre Manager
Open: Mon 9-5; Tues-Fri 9-5.30
Space: 2 galleries with 6 lin m hanging space plus 11 lin m on screens

Exhibitions: 6 a year all on a hire basis
Details: Aims to educate and empower local community through visual images and creative work. Sales not a priority.

Open Eye Gallery

Ph ✪✪ & ᴡ

Gallery in centre of Liverpool aims to exhibit the best in contemporary photography.
110 Bold Street, Liverpool OL1 4HY, tel: 0151 709 9460, fax: 0151 709 3059
Contact: Catriona Henderson, Exhibitions Co-ordinator
Open: Tues-Sat 10-5.30
Space: 1 gallery with 40 lin m hanging space plus 12 lin m on screens and 144 sq m floor space
Exhibitions: 10 a year of which 8 originated, 2 touring
Details: Exhibits work of local, national and international photographers, both historical and contemporary. Situated in city centre on the edge of China Town. Audience ranges from casual 'drop in' shopper to art students from nearby Universities. Sales not a priority.

Tate Gallery Liverpool

Pa Ph Sc & ᴡ

A converted Victorian warehouse, Tate Gallery Liverpool shows the best of the national collection of C20th art as well as special loan exhibitions.
Albert Dock, Liverpool L3 4BB, tel: 0151 709 3223, fax: 0151 709 3122
Contact: Lewis Biggs, Curator
Open: Tues-Sun 10-6; open BH
Space: 9 galleries with 330 lin m hanging space and 2600 sq m floor space
Exhibitions: 4 a year of which 3 originated, 1 touring
Details: Opened in May 1988 to house the national collection of modern art in the north of England. Programme of changing displays, 9 months to 3 years from the collection. Temporary loan exhibitions of internationally recognised C20th artists. Active education department, Momart artist in residence scheme. Bookshop and café.

Unity Theatre

Pa Ph IA ✪ &ᴡ④

Exhibition space in large foyer area and corridor within theatre aiming to exhibit and sell work by local, national and international artists.
Hope Place, Liverpool L1 9BG, tel: 0151 709 4988, fax: 0151 709 7182
Contact: Chris Hennessey, House Manager
Open: Vary, depending on show times & programme.
Space: 2 galleries with 31 lin m hanging space
Exhibitions: 9 a year all originated
Details: Exhibitions originated in

collaboration with Innovative Arts Network (tel: 0151 726 1587). Sales encouraged but not primary role. 20% commission taken on sales made.

University of Liverpool Senate House Exhibition Hall

Pa Ph Pr Cr Sc ✪ ᴴ & ᴡ

Gallery on access route to university offices.
Senate House, Abercromby Square, Liverpool L69 3BX, tel: 0151 794 2347/8, fax: 0151 708 6502
Contact: Janice Carpenter, Curator, Art Collections, University of Liverpool, PO Box 147, Liverpool, L69 3BX, tel: 0151 794 2347/8, fax: 0151 708 6502
Open: Mon-Fri 9-5; closed BH
Space: 1 gallery with 40 lin m hanging space plus 73 lin m on screens and 176 sq m floor space
Exhibitions: 4 a year all on a hire basis
Details: Most exhibitions by local artists and aimed at students and the public. No fee charged for use of exhibition space. Artists pay for transport and drinks at private view. University covers cost of publicity including posters and invitations to press, insurance and arrangement for sales. 10% commission taken. Selling work not main function of gallery.

Walker Art Gallery

Pa Ph Pr Cr Sc IA & ᴡ④

Nineteenth century traditional gallery used for wide variety of exhibitions.
William Brown Street, Liverpool L3 8EL, tel: 0151 207 0001, fax: 0151 298 1816
Contact: Julian Treuherz, Keeper of Art Galleries
Open: Mon-Sat 10-5; Sun 12-5; closed Christmas & New Year
Space: 2 galleries with 86 lin m hanging space and 257 sq m floor space
Exhibitions: 4 a year
Details: Houses a collection of paintings and sculpture dating from C14th to C20th. Especially rich in European Old Masters, Victorian and Pre-Raphaelite work and modern British art. Regular temporary exhibitions held on a variety of subjects. Mixture of originated and touring shows. Runs a full programme of exhibition-related activities. Sale of work not a priority

London
GREATER LONDON LA

152(c) Brick Lane

Pa Ph Sc ✪ & ᴡ

Commercial gallery showing innovative contemporary work.
152c Brick Lane, London E1 6RU, tel: 0171 247 2047/01956 398611, fax: 0171 247 2047

numbers don't exist

Contact: Christine Anstice, Director, Studio & Education Access, 37 Elliots Road, London, SE11 4SZ, tel: 0171 247 2047/01956 398611, fax: 0171 247 2047
Open: Thurs & Fri 12-6; Sun 12-4; or by appointment
Space: 2 galleries with 53 lin m hanging space and 118 sq m floor space
Exhibitions: 4 a year all originated
Details: Mixture of group and one-person exhibitions. Gallery's curatorial policy aims to underline ideas content behind work shown. Sales a priority.

198 Gallery

Pa Ph Pr SE ✓ & We

Contemporary art by Black Artists.
198 Railton Road, Herne Hill, London SE24 0LU, tel: 0171 978 8309, fax: 0171 652 1418
Contact: Zoe Linsley-Thomas, Administrator
Open: Mon-Sat 11-7
Space: 2 galleries with 78 lin m hanging space and 100 sq m floor space
Exhibitions: 8 a year all originated
Details: Black Arts gallery founded 1988. Exhibition space, shop & education resource offering access to culturally diverse visual arts and artists. Education & Training Resource Centre works with schools providing experience of working with culturally diverse artists. Creative arts & media training for young unemployed people. Policy to positively promote aesthetic arts and crafts of contemporary Black artists to as wide an audience as possible. Gives exhibition space to artists of Africa, Afro-Caribbean & Asian descent as priority. Enables those not having previously exhibited to do so, thereby beginning to redress imbalance. Showcases young artists. Welcomes innovative proposals from young curators. All shows available for tour and enquiries welcomed. Sales not a priority.

5 Dryden Street Gallery

Pa Pr SE ✓ ⓗ ⊘   NO SHOP

Small gallery in office building suitable for 2D work.
5 Dryden Street, Covent Garden, London WC2E 9NW, tel: 0171 240 2430, fax: 0171 240 5600
Contact: Jenny Coleman, Exhibition Organiser
Open: Mon-Thurs 10-6; Fri 10-5.30
Space: 1 gallery with 244 lin m hanging space and 46 sq m floor space
Exhibitions: 20 a year
Details: Provides opportunities for lesser-known artists to show work, run on non-profit-making basis. Exhibitions organised on self-help basis and change fortnightly. Wide variety of work shown, mostly small in size. Selling work not gallery's primary role.

A.D. Fine Art   LEFT MSSGE. 21/10

Pa Pr SE ✓ ⓗ

Commercial gallery showing a wide range of contemporary original prints and paintings.
65 Sheen Lane, Sheen, London SW14 8AD, tel: 0181 878 8800
Contact: Brian Stiles or Roger Kenney, Partners
Space: 1 gallery with 50 lin m hanging space and 60 sq m floor space
Exhibitions: 5 a year all on a hire basis
Details: Well-equipped town centre gallery (which also specialises in framing) with work presented in room with layout similar to typical home. Friendly informal approach. Partners have 40 collective years' experience of working with artists. Artists are encouraged to get in touch. Exhibitions on a hire basis (rental only – no commission).

Abbey Mills Gallery & Tea House *

Pa Pr Cf SE ✓ ⓗ

Craft village beside River Wandle with exhibition space available for hire.
Merton Abbey Mills, Riverside Craft Village, Merantum Way, Wimbledon, London SW19 2RD, tel: 0181 542 5035
Contact: Jane Harris
Space: 2 galleries with 156 sq m floor space
Exhibitions: 2 a year both originated

Academia Italiana   ✓ 28/4

Pa Pr SE £ & We 4

Converted C19th warehouse used to exhibit and promote Italian art and culture to a wide British audience.
Smiths Galleries, 56 Earlham Street, London WC2H 9PY, tel: 0171 235 0303, fax: 0171 235 0404
Contact: Rosa Maria Letts
Open: Daily 11-8
Space: 3 galleries with 300 lin m hanging space and 800 sq m floor space
Exhibitions: 8 a year all originated

Adam Butler Fine Art

Pa Ph SE ⊘

Gallery dedicated to exhibiting Scottish non-abstract contemporary painting and sculpture.
31a New Cavendish Street, London W1M 7RL, tel: 0171 487 3730
Contact: Adam Butler
Open: By appointment
Space: 2 galleries with 30 lin m hanging space and 45 sq m floor space
Exhibitions: 3 a year all originated
Details: Gallery shows only 'high quality' work; some by English artists but all figurative. Gallery covers exhibition costs. Sales a priority.

Addison Ross Gallery *

Pa Ph Pr ✓ ⓗ

40 Eaton Terrace, London SW1 W8TS, tel: 0171 730 1536, fax: 0171 823 5081
Contact: David Ross
Space: 50 sq m floor space
Exhibitions: 8 a year of which 4 originated, 4 on a hire basis

Agency (The)

Pa Ph SE ✓ &   NO SHOP

Commercial gallery with its own agenda in recent contemporary art; representing artists and works on a national and international level.
35-40 Charlotte Road, London EC2, tel: 0171 613 2080, fax: 0171 613 2080
Contact: Bea de Souza, Gallery Director
Space: 90 sq m floor space
Exhibitions: 7 a year all originated
Details: Exhibitions selected from international current artists and represent part new works, part agency commissions and part works previously never featured in Britain. The direction is loosely conceptual. Exhibitions also arranged in other locations.

Agnew's

43 Old Bond Street & 3 Albermarle Street, London W1X4BA, tel: 0171 629 6176, fax: 0171 629 4359

Africa Centre Gallery

Pa Ph Pr ✓ ⓗ

Established 1961 as a charity to be a "flagship for African arts, culture and opinion" holding regular exhibitions from Africa and Europe about African culture.
38 King Street, Covent Garden, London WC2E 8JT, tel: 0171 836 1973, fax: 0171 836 1975
Contact: Exhibition Organiser
Space: 1 gallery with 150 lin m hanging space and 1250 sq m floor space
Exhibitions: 8 a year all originated
Details: Aims to support the social and cultural activities of African communities in Britain and Europe and provide high-quality spaces for visitors, tenants and hirers. ✓ 4/10 (Judy Morell)

Alexandra Gallery   Palace

Pa Ph Cf SE & We

Gallery holding exhibitions, art and craft workshops and also selling cards, posters and providing picture framing service.
Alexandra Garden Centre, London N22 4BB, tel: 0181 444 2674
Contact: Judy Morell, Director
Open: Tues-Sat 10-5 or 6 in summer; Sun 10.30-5
Space: 1 gallery
Exhibitions: 1 a year originated
Details: Exhibitors share costs and get trade prices for framing. Sales a priority.

Alternative Arts

[Pa][Ph][Pr][Cr][Sc][LA] ✔

Publicly-funded arts organisation that negotiates temporarily empty shop spaces, clears, cleans and paints them white to exhibit contemporary art.

c/o 47a Brushfield Street, Spitalfields, London E1 6AA, tel: 0171 375 0441, fax: 0171 375 0484

Contact: Maggie Pinhorn, Director
Open: Tues-Sat 11-5
Exhibitions: 100 a year all originated
Details: Publicly-funded arts organisation and non-commercial galleries based in temporarily empty shops in West End of London. May have anything from 4-8 spaces available at any time. All kinds of artists welcome. Alternative Arts curates the exhibitions. Artists run their own gallery and relate directly to the public. Sales not a main aim of organisation and no commission taken. Shows run for one month and are highly accessible to the public. Submit CV and slides or photos for selection. Spaces constantly changing and vary in size and in accessibility and facilities. Available free to artists.

Amalgam Gallery

[Pa][Ph][Cr] ✔ ♿

Two exhibition rooms and shop selling ceramics, prints, drawings/watercolours.

3 Barnes High Street, London SW13 9LB, tel: 0181 878 1279

Contact: T.A.M. Boon
Open: Tues-Sat 10-6
Space: 2 galleries with 27 lin m hanging space
Exhibitions: 6 a year all originated
Details: Strong emphasis on studio ceramics and original prints. Half exhibiting gallery, half shop.

Andrew Usiskin Contemporary Art 21/10 mssge

[Pa][Pr][Cr][Sc] ✔ ♿

Commercial gallery specialising in fine art and crafts.

9-11 Flask Walk, London NW3 1HJ, tel: 0171 431 4484, fax: 0171 435 5520

Contact: Mary-Alice Stack, Administrative Assistant
Open: Tues-Sat 10-6; Sun 12-6
Space: 3 galleries
Exhibitions: 12 a year
Details: Contemporary art with a broad range of prices. Exhibitions include one-person and mixed shows. Interested in encouraging young British artists. Crafts Council selected with strong bias towards ceramics.

Anna Bornholt Gallery 21/10 Mssge

[Pa][Ph][Pr][Cr][Sc] ✔

Exhibits the work of contemporary artists together with the work of C20th masters.

3-5 Weighhouse Street, London W1Y 1YL, tel: 0171 499 6114

Contact: Tiffany Lacey, Exhibitions Organiser
Open: Mon-Fri 9.30-6
Space: 2 galleries
Exhibitions: 6 a year all originated

Anna-Mei Chadwick

[Pa][Ph][Pr][Sc] ✔ ♿ not interested

Gallery specialising in affordable original works by living British artists presenting exhibitions by established and talented new artists.

64 New Kings Road, London SW6 4LT, tel: 0171 736 1928

Contact: Anna-Mei Chadwick, Director
Open: Mon-Fri 10-6; Sat 10-5.30
Space: 3 galleries
Exhibitions: 17 a year all originated
Details: Shows contemporary oils, watercolours, prints, sculpture. Presents theme shows, mixed and solo exhibitions. Exhibition space on two floors and in small print room.

Anne Faggionato

[Pa][Ph][Pr][Cr][Sc][LA] not interested

Modern and contemporary work shown.

Fourth Floor, 20 Dering Street, London W1R 9AA, tel: 0171 493 6732, fax: 0171 493 9693

Exhibitions: 3 a year all originated
Details: Space was designed by Arata Isozaki and has natural lighting. Small flight of stairs up to the lift which provides access to the fourth floor.

Annely Juda Fine Art

[Pa][Pr][Sc] ♿ no shop

Gallery showing mostly contemporary exhibitions but also specialising in early C20th Russian art.

23 Dering Street, off New Bond Street, London W1R 9AA, tel: 0171 629 7578, fax: 0171 491 2139

Contact: Annely Juda, David Juda, Directors
Open: Mon-Fri 10-6; Sat 10-1
Space: 23 galleries
Exhibitions: 6 a year all originated
Details: Shows work by established C20th artists from Britain and abroad. Sale of work considered gallery's primary concern.

Anthony d'Offay X 28/4

[Pa][Pr][Sc] ♿

Shows and deals in work by living artists in variety of media.

9, 21 & 23 Dering Street, London W1R 9AA, tel: 0171 499 4100, fax: 0171 493 4443

Contact: Anthony d'Offay, Director
Open: Mon-Fri 10-5; Sat 10-1
Space: 4 galleries
Exhibitions: 8 a year all originated
Details: Exhibitions include post war painting, drawing, sculpture and installation by British and international artists. Most shows solo, lasting one month.

Anthony Reynolds Gallery

[Pa][Ph][Pr][Sc][LA] ♿ not interested

Exhibitions of work by gallery artists, both British and international, with occasional thematic and group exhibitions.

5 Dering Street, London W1R 9AB, tel: 0171 491 0621, fax: 0171 495 2374

Contact: Anthony Reynolds, Director
Open: Tues-Sat 10-6
Space: 1 gallery with 49 lin m hanging space and 88 sq m floor space
Exhibitions: 10 a year all originated
Details: Exhibition space on two floors. Independent access for wheelchair users to ground floor only. Sales important.

Architectural Association

36 Bedford Square, London WC1 B3EG, tel: 0171 636 0974

Contact: Linda Brown/Jane McGrath, Exhibitions Organiser
Open: Mon-Fri 10-7, Sat 10-3
Space: 2 galleries with 200 sq m floor space
Exhibitions: 9 a year of which 8 originated, 1 touring
Details: Frequent exhibitions of historical and contemporary architecture.

Argenta *

[Cr] not interested.

Commercial gallery on Crafts Council selected list specialising in jewellery.

82 Fulham Road, London SW3, tel: 0171 584 1841, fax: 0171 584 3119

Contact: Exhibition Organiser
Space: 2 galleries with 65 sq m floor space
Details: Shows jewellery by about 80-90 younger designers and makers specialises in individual handmade jewellery. Permanent exhibition content representing Argenta's stable of artists.

Argile Gallery & Café

[Pa][Pr] ✔ Call ~~Wed 22/10~~ pm – Ask Mai Sab

Specialises in contemporary British and international work by established artists and new talents. .

7 Blenheim Crescent, London W11 2EE, tel: 0171 792 0888, fax: 0181 241 8876

Contact: Marie Saba, Exhibition Organiser
Open: Tues-Sat 11-6
Space: 90 sq m floor space
Exhibitions: 8 a year

Aria / Pushpa Bulhane

[Pa][Ph][Cr] ✔ ♿ 7046222

Gallery selling variety of contemporary craftwork with continuous changing display of work by number of artists/craftspeople.

133 Upper Street, Islington, London N1 1QP, tel: 0171 226 1021, fax: 0171 433 1763
Contact: Pushpa Gulhane
Open: Mon-Fri 10-7; Sat 10-6.30
Space: 1 gallery with 30 lin m hanging space and 60 sq m floor space
Details: Gallery specialises in ceramics and glass but also shows and sells furniture, jewellery, textiles and prints. Most display space on shelves. New pieces/artists always considered and paintings/prints especially welcome.

Ark (the)

Pa Ph Pr Cr Sc ✓ 🖼 🌐

Galleries mainly showing exhibition relating to gardening, heritage and environment.
Museum of Garden History, 220 Lambeth Road, London SE1 7JY, tel: 0171 633 9701, fax: 0171 401 8869
Contact: Mrs Rosemary Nicholson, Chairperson, Museum of Garden History, Lambeth Palace Road, London, SE1 7LB, tel: 0171 261 1891, fax: 0171 401 8869
Open: Daily 9.30-4; or as per users' wishes; Evenings when required
Space: 4 galleries with 118 lin m hanging space plus 5 lin m on screens and 212 sq m floor space
Exhibitions: 6 a year all originated
Details: Broad selection policy but preference given to exhibitions relating to gardening, heritage and environment. Exhibitions generally educational.

Art after Hours

Pa Pr Sc LA 🅗

5 floors, 5 bars, 2 dance-floor galleries, ideal for exhibitions, shows, receptions, parties.
Limelight, 136 Shaftesbury Avenue, London WC2H, tel: 0171 287 1426
Contact: Jane Vernol, Functions Manager
Space: 800 sq m floor space
Exhibitions: 14 a year all on a hire basis

Art East

Pa Ph Pr Cr Sc ✓ 🅗 🅐

Two floors dedicated to exhibiting mixed work from new and emerging artists and available for hire.
Old Spitalfield's Market, 7 Lamb Street, London E1 6EA, tel: 0171 375 3472
Contact: Mark Herring, Gallery Director
Open: Mon-Fri 11-4; Sun 11-5
Space: 2 galleries with 20 lin m hanging space and 40 sq m floor space
Details: Upper gallery shows mixed work (sculpture, furniture, painting, etc with artists paying small monthly rent. Lower gallery available for one-person or group hire. Rates negotiable. Sales considered important function of gallery. No access for wheelchair users to lower gallery.

Art First *not interested*

Pa Pr ✓ 🚫

Contemporary selling gallery showing British and international artists, and also focusses on new work from South Africa.
9 Cork Street, London, tel: 0171 734 0386, fax: 0171 734 3964
Contact: Exhibitions Organiser
Open: Mon-Wed, Fri 10-6; Thurs 10-8; Sat 11-2
Space: 2 galleries with 46 lin m hanging space and 74 sq m floor space
Exhibitions: 10 a year all originated

Art for London

19/20 Grosvenor Street, London W1, tel: 0171 408 0007
Contact: Mr Mogens Hauschildt

Art for Offices

Pa Ph Pr Cr Sc ✓ 🅗 🚫

Viewing and presentation space for in-house artists, space for hire for external artists interested in corporate/city venue.
15 Dock Street, London E1 8JL, tel: 0171 481 1337, fax: 0171 481 3425
Contact: Peter Harris & Andrew Hutchison, Directors
Open: Mon-Fri 9.30-5.30 by appointment
Space: 1 gallery with 38 lin m hanging space plus 6 lin m on screens and 140 sq m floor space
Exhibitions: 5 a year of which 3 originated, 2 on a hire basis
Details: Contemporary visual arts for architects, interior designers, corporate sector. Full consultancy service for exhibitions and commissions to clients using contemporary artists work. 3 spaces for contemporary art; the Print Gallery; Main Gallery houses rotating exhibition of stable of artists and Collectors Gallery for hire for temporary shows (dimensions above refer to this last space). Application by slide. Viewing of space for hire by appointment. Sale of work is primary role of Art for Offices.

Art Now

Pa Pr

Gallery featuring former London arts graduates.
17 Halsmere Road, London SE5 9LN, tel: 0171 582 5785
Contact: Eirlys Tynan, Owner
Open: By appointment
Space: 5 galleries
Details: Aims to interest a suburban clientele in the work and careers over time of a group of artists selected from the final degree shows of the London art colleges during the period 1982-6. Among these Nicholas Hamper and Dick French are prizewinners of the John Moores biennial competition. Exhibitions from permanent stock.

Art of Change, Community Insight Billboards

Pa Ph Pr Sc LA ✓

The Art of Change, Level 3, Building 3, Lion Court, 435 The Highway, London E1 9HT, tel: 0171 702 8802, fax: 0171 702 8803
Contact: Bob Harris, Coordinator
Open: Sites are publicly accessible at all times
Details: Promotes billboard images concerned with issues of change and have relationship with locality. Environment of sites typical inner city. Part of programme involves participation with communities of interest local to billboard site. Audience is public local to billboard. With some sites large travelling public included. Welcomes contact with artists outside London as is developing regional and national links.

Art Space Gallery

Pa Ph Pr ✓ 🚫

Commercial gallery specialising in contemporary painting, print and sculpture.
Michael Richardson Contemporary Art, 84 St Peter's Street, London N1 8JS, tel: 0171 359 7002
Contact: Michael Richardson, Director
Open: Tues-Sat 2-7; or by appointment.
Space: 1 gallery with 40 lin m hanging space and 60 sq m floor space
Exhibitions: 8 a year all originated
Details: Contemporary figurative art of distinction. Annual programme comprises 8-10 exhibitions by invitation, mainly by artists whom the gallery represents. Continues to look for new artists but applications should be made with slides initially.

Artelier *

Pa Ph Pr Cr Sc ✓ *N℈ ʋɔɒɣ*

231 Kentish Town Road, London NW5 2JT, tel: ~~0171 485 8128~~
Contact: Michael or Amanda Dimant
Space: 1 gallery with 15 lin m hanging space
Exhibitions: 2 a year both originated
Details: Open, flexible attitude, willing to show almost anything that will interest local community. Space itself behind high street frontage selling fine art prints and frames. Applications from local London artists welcomed.

Artemidorus & Gallery ✓ *22/10*

Pa Pr Cr Sc ✓ 🅗 🚫

Small gallery and shop exhibiting and selling fine, decorative and applied works by British contemporary makers and artists.
27b Half Moon Lane, Herne Hill, London SE24 9JU, tel: 0171 737 7747
Contact: Amanda Walbank

Open: Tues-Fri 10.30-7; Sat 10.30-6
Space: 1 gallery with 32 lin m hanging space and 30 sq m floor space
Exhibitions: 6 a year all originated
Details: First-floor gallery. Individual or mixed shows lasting 5-8 weeks. Gallery is narrow and suits wall hung rather than free standing work. Shelves and plinths available but limited. Gallery aims to encourage appreciation of high quality art and craft. Shop follows same principle stocking selection of smaller, more affordable ceramics, jewellery, wood textiles and metal pieces. Sales a priority. Commissioning of work by customers is encouraged where possible.

Artichoke Art

56 Highbury Hill, London N5 1AP, tel: 0171 226 8809
Contact: Laura and Kate Hare

Association Gallery

Contemporary photography gallery featuring work by members of Association of Photographers in addition to outside photographers.
9-10 Domingo Street, London EC1Y 0TA, tel: 0171 608 1445/1441, fax: 0171 253 3007
Contact: Alex Steele-Mortimer, Gallery Administrator
Open: Mon-Fri 9.30-6
Space: 1 gallery with 24 lin m hanging space and 50 sq m floor space
Exhibitions: 23 a year of which 19 originated, 4 on a hire basis
Details: Gallery on two floors. Shows work of professional photographers working within fields of advertising and editorial photography. Aims to promote work of its members to advertising agencies, magazines, etc. Also seeks to promote awareness of high standard and quality of professional photography to general public. Available for private hire for photographic shows of high standard. Sales not gallery's main role.

Atelier One *

Exhibition area on ground floor of Atelier One Design Engineer's office with occasional shows that relate to design and fashion.
4 Googe Place, London W1P 1FL, tel: 0171 323 3350, fax: 0171 636 5282
Contact: Neil Thomas
Space: 1 gallery
Exhibitions: 1 a year originated

Atlantis Galleries

 no shop

Large East End contemporary exhibition space opened October 1993.

Atlantis European Ltd, 146 Brick Lane, London E1 6RU, tel: 0171 377 8855
Contact: Vernita Zimri
Open: Mon-Sat 10-5; Sun 10-4.30
Space: 3 galleries with 3660 sq m floor space
Details: Venue for shows of C20th British and international art which will show a wide range of contemporary exhibits, from abstract paintings through to installation pieces, figurative work and sculpture. Sales not priority.

Austin/Desmond *

no shop

Commercial gallery showing modern and contemporary British paintings, prints, books and sculpture.
Pied Bull Yard, 68/69 Great Russell Street, London WC1B 3BN, tel: 0171 242 4443, fax: 0171 404 4480
Contact: Exhibition Organiser
Space: 2 galleries
Exhibitions: 4 a year all originated

BAC Steve Mannix 22/10

Photographic gallery with additional site-specific work based within thriving arts venue.
Old Town Hall, Lavender Hill, London SW11 5TF, tel: 0171 223 6557, fax: 0171 978 5207
Contact: Geraldine Collinge, Assistant to the Director
Open: Tues-Sun 12-9; Mon 12-6
Space: 2 galleries with 53 lin m hanging space and 89 sq m floor space
Exhibitions: 6 a year of which 2 originated, 4 touring
Details: Gallery space within arts centre presenting contemporary commissioned/invited work. Sale of work not gallery's primary concern.

Baik Gallery MSSge 22/10

Small but versatile gallery available for hire and suitable for one-person or group shows.
115 Tanners Hill, London SE8 4QD, tel: 0181 691 5860
Contact: Andrew Hinton
Open: Tues-Sat 11-6; Sun 1-6
Space: 1 gallery with 13 lin m hanging space plus 9 lin m on screens and 24 sq m floor space
Exhibitions: 8 a year of which 5 originated, 3 on a hire basis
Details: Gallery seeks to exhibit wide range of contemporary work of high quality. Always open to proposals to use the space. Sales not gallery's main role. Grey wood panelled walls and variety of screens available.

Bankside Gallery Richard Ru

22/10

Small friendly space mainly devoted to exhibitions by members of Royal Watercolour Society and Royal Society of Painter-Printmakers.
48 Hopton Street, Blackfriars, London SE1 9JH, tel: 0171 928 7521, fax: 0171 928 2820
Contact: Judy Dixey, Director
Open: (During exhibitions) Tues 10-8; Wed-Sat; 10-5, Sun 1-5
Space: 1 gallery with 84 lin m hanging space and 200 sq m floor space
Exhibitions: 10 a year of which 9 originated, 1 touring
Details: Annual exhibitions of work by members of RWS and RE. Watercolour open exhibition. Occasional historical loan exhibitions and external exhibitions. Societies run comprehensive educational programme including demonstration days, teaching courses, guided tours, lectures, studio visits, etc; aim being to encourage an appreciation of watercolour & print both in theory and practice.

Barbican Art Gallery

Run by the Corporation of London, this large gallery on 2 levels of the Barbican Centre, holds major exhibitions of photography, painting and sculpture of C19th and C20th.
Barbican Centre, Silk Street, London EC2Y 8DS, tel: 0171 638 4141 ext 7632, fax: 0171 628 0364
Contact: Lynne Overend, Publicity Officer
Open: Mon, Wed & Sat 10-6.45; Tues 10-5.45; Sun & BH 12-6.45
Space: 369 lin m hanging space and 1348 sq m floor space
Exhibitions: 3 a year of which 2 originated, 1 touring
Details: To develop national and international reputation of Barbican Art Gallery through the mounting of exhibitions of highest quality for the enjoyment, education and enlightenment of the public. Sales of work not a high priority.

Barking Central Library

Exhibition space within library.
Axe Street, Barking, London IG11 7NB, tel: 0181 517 8666, fax: 0181 594 1156
Contact: Miss S Currie, Central Library Manager
Open: Mon, Tues, Thurs, Fri 9.30-7; Wed, Sat 9.30-5
Space: 1 gallery with 37 lin m hanging space and 80 sq m floor space
Exhibitions: 10 a year all originated
Details: Programme features work by local artists, craft workers and societies chosen

on relevance to area and community. Sales not priority.

Barnes Gallery

 Pa Ph Pr ♿

Commercial gallery specialising in contemporary figurative work.
51 Church Road, Barnes, London SW13 9HH, tel: 0181 741 1277
Contact: Roseline Harvie Watt & Catherine Harrisson, Partners/directors
Open: Tues-Sat 10-5
Space: 1 gallery
Exhibitions: 11 a year all originated
Details: Figurative paintings, watercolours and pastels. Also figurative and animal sculptures. Exhibitions vary from one person to mixed or theme shows.

Barnet Libraries Arts & Museums

Pa Ph Pr Cr Se LA

Exhibition space for hire in branch libraries.
Arts Office and Service Development, Educational Services, (formerly Friern Barnet Town Hall), Friern Barnet Lane, London N11 3DL, tel: 0181 359 2000
Contact: Arts and Service Development
Details: Main spaces being at Hendon and North Finchley. Initial contact for enquiries about exhibitions within Barnet's Libraries and at Church Farmhouse Museum. Temporary exhibition programme at Church Farmhouse Museum coordinated from Barnet Educational Services Department.

Bartley Drey Gallery

Pa Pr Cr Se ✓ ⓗ ●

Selling gallery in converted old stable in heart of Chelsea suitable for one person exhibitions by British figurative painters and sculptors.
62 Old Church Street, London SW3 6DP, tel: 0171 352 8686
Contact: Stephen Bartley & Gill Drey, Director
Open: Tues-Sat 10-6
Space: 1 gallery with 28 lin m hanging space and 68 sq m floor space
Exhibitions: 15 a year of which 11 originated, 4 on a hire basis
Details: Shows contemporary work in changing exhibitions and from gallery artists. Most gallery originated, occasionally agents hire space for artists. Available for individual artists to hire subject to submission of slides & CV.

Battersea Library Gallery

Pa Ph Pr Cr Se ✓ ⓗ ⊘

Established library exhibition space with varied programme.
265 Lavender Hill, London SW11 1JB, tel: 0181 871 7037

Contact: Charlie Catling, Senior Arts Officer, Wandsworth Arts Office, Room 224A, Town Hall, Wandsworth High Street, London, SW18, tel: 0181 871 7037
Open: Mon-Wed & Fri-Sat 10-5
Space: 1 gallery with 46 lin m hanging space and 116 sq m floor space
Exhibitions: 15 a year all on a hire basis
Details: On 1st floor of main library. Dedicated room with gallery feel. Emphasis on local individual artists, local arts groups and organisations. Space is run by Wandsworth Borough Council Arts Section. Also used for visual arts talks, poetry readings and small scale plays. Arts Section help with local publicity. 20% commission taken on sales but selling work not a priority.

Battlebridge Centre

Pa Ph Pr Cr Se LA ✓ ● ⓦ

Disused warehouse, converted to Ecology Centre.
2-6 Battlebridge Road, London NW1 8XB, tel: 0171 278 7172
Contact: Clare Barrett
Open: Mon-Fri 10-6; weekends by arrangement
Space: 1 gallery with 180 lin m hanging space and 2511 sq m floor space
Exhibitions: 2 a year
Details: Exhibits work by local artists whose work reflects ecological aims and objectives of the Trust, including installation/performance work. Space is huge, industrial with high ceiling. Sales not a priority.

Beaconsfield

Ⓐ

Newport Street, London SE11, tel: 0171 852 6465

Beardsmore Gallery *

Pa Ph Pr Cr Se ✓ no shop
22-24 Prince of Wales Road, Kentish Town, London NW5 3LG, tel: 0171 485 0923, fax: 0171 267 0824
Contact: Amanda and Brian Beardsmore
Space: 2 galleries with 85 sq m floor space
Exhibitions: 10 a year all originated
Details: Monthly programme of quality contemporary art, mainly solo shows. Shop frontage makes work easily viewable from street and attracts good passing audience. Already popular with designers, architects and local residents. Available for evening hire by arrangement.

Beau Monde

Pa Pr Se ✓ ♿

Deliberately reserved areas within women's fashion retail outlet, allowing art to be seen by the public
43 Lexington Street, London W1, tel: 0171 734 6563

Contact: Sylvia Young
Open: Mon-Sat 10.30-6.30
Space: 1 gallery with 5 lin m hanging space and 1 sq m floor space
Exhibitions: 9 a year all originated
Details: Owner hopes that in displaying art in this space it will be perceived as much an everyday factor of life as designs for clothing. Sales not considered a primary role of gallery space.

Beaux Arts London

Pa Se ✓ ● no shop

Ground-floor and basement exhibition space with window onto street showing and selling work by painters and sculptors.
22 Cork Street, London W1X 1HB, tel: 0171 437 5799, fax: 0171 437 5798
Contact: The Directors
Open: Mon-Fri 10-6; Sat 10-5
Space: 80 lin m hanging space and 300 sq m floor space
Exhibitions: 10 a year all originated
Details: Gallery invites artists to exhibit. Happy to help educationally and welcome people to look and ask questions. Sales a priority.

Bedales Gallery

Pa Ph Pr Cr Se ✓ ●

Gallery on ground floor of converted Victorian fruit warehouse.
4 Bedale Street, London SE1 9AL, tel: 0171 357 0665, fax: 0171 357 0747
Contact: J C Carlton-Smith
Open: Mon-Fri 10-6
Space: 1 gallery with 30 lin m hanging space plus 45 lin m on screens and 700 sq m floor space
Exhibitions: 10 a year of which 9 originated, 1 touring
Details: Ground floor gallery in elegant Victorian fruit warehouse with three sizable floor to ceiling windows. Plenty of natural light from skylights. Also 20 halogen wall washers and spotlights. £200-£300 per week

Belgrave Gallery

Pa Se ✓ no shop

Commercial gallery specialising in C20th British art.
53 England's Lane, London NW3 4YD, tel: 0171 722 5150
Contact: Director
Space: 2 galleries with 1600 sq m floor space
Exhibitions: 8 a year

Ben Uri Gallery

Pa Pr Se ✓ ⓗ ● ④

Well-established gallery showing work by Jewish artists or of Jewish interest.
21 Dean Street, London W1V 6NE, tel: 0171 437 2852
Contact: Julia Weiner, Curator

Open: Mon-Thurs 10-5; Sun 2-5
Space: 1 gallery with 37 lin m hanging space and 88 sq m floor space
Exhibitions: 8 a year of which 6 originated, 1 touring, 1 on a hire basis
Details: Founded in 1915 to promote Anglo-Jewish cultural life with a special emphasis on visual arts. Interested to view work by Jewish artists. Not suitable for heavy installations or performance art. Work of explicitly sexual nature not suitable (synagogue in same building). Open exhibition in September. Low (for London) commission rate taken on sales. Selling work not main purpose of gallery.

Bernard Becker Gallery

Purpose-designed gallery for exhibiting and promoting contemporary glass work.
1a Jerusalem Passage, Clerkenwell, London EC1V 4JP, tel: 0171 250 3042, fax: 0171 250 3046
Contact: Mark Ibbotson
Open: Mon-Fri 9.30-6
Space: 1 gallery with 37 sq m floor space
Details: All aspects of glass work shown, but primarily stained glass. Gallery may be hired for single or group shows. Contracts are worked out individually with the artists. Gallery takes between 30-50% commission on sales and 15% on commissions. Gallery wishes to become centre for glass artists. At present selling work is primary role out of necessity of income.

Bernard Jacobson Gallery

Gallery exhibiting work by C20th British artists.
14a Clifford Street, London W1X 1RF, tel: 0171 495 8575, fax: 0171 495 6210
Contact: Bernard Jacobson, Director
Open: Mon-Fri 10-6; Sat 10-1
Space: 1 gallery with 88 sq m floor space
Exhibitions: 8 a year all originated
Details: Specialises in modern British masters, including Stanley Spencer, Ben Nicholson, William Scott. Contemporary artists include Glynn Williams, Ivor Abrahams, Maggi Hambling, Maurice Cockrill, William Tillyer, Ian McKeever and Wendy Connelly.

Bhownagree & Today Galleries

Promotes young unknown and established artists from the Commonwealth and of Commonwealth origin resident in the UK.
Commonwealth Institute, Kensington High Street, London W8 6NQ, tel: 0171 603 4535, fax: 0171 602 7374
Contact: Nicola Harold, Projects Co-ordinator
Open: Mon-Sat 10-5; Sun 2-5

Space: 2 galleries with 55 lin m hanging space and 50 sq m floor space
Exhibitions: 12 a year
Details: Exhibitions reflect Commonwealth cultures which are further emphasised with supportive educational programmes. A variety of media is shown.

Billboard Gallery

Contemporary art exhibited in restaurant area.
222 Kilburn High Road, London NW6, tel: 0171 328 1374, fax: 0171 625 1550
Contact: Jeremy Cole, Exhibitions Organiser, 173a Mount View Road, Crouch Hill, London, N4 4JT, tel: 0181 341 0706
Open: evenings
Space: 1 gallery with 25 lin m hanging space plus 10 lin m on screens
Exhibitions: 7 a year all originated
Details: Exhibitions concentrating on contemporary painting, print and drawing. Based within high profile restaurant. Shows sometimes linked with Tricycle Gallery, Tricycle Theatre. 30% commission on sales.

Bishopsgate Institute Gallery

Main corridor in busy City of London library used to raise awareness of public to local groups and artists.
Bishopsgate Institute, 230 Bishopsgate, London EC2M 4QH, tel: 0171 247 6844, fax: 0171 375 1794
Contact: William Doyle, Clerk to the Governors
Open: Mon-Fri 9.30-5.30
Space: 1 gallery with 63 lin m hanging space and 42 sq m floor space
Exhibitions: 12 a year all on a hire basis
Details: 2D work by artists/groups living usually within 10 mile radius. Work by disabled people and disadvantaged particularly encouraged. Open-access public building housing libraries, concert halls, meeting rooms, etc used intensively during the day by the local working population. Aims to mix art with general activities. Sales not a priority.

Blackheath Gallery 22/10

 ● *Mrs Corless*

Busy, light and airy gallery that displays contemporary paintings, sculpture, fine glass and ceramics up to 'life size' scale.
34A Tranquil Vale, Blackheath, London SE3 0AX, tel: 0181 852 1802
Contact: Claire Askin, Exhibition Organiser
Open: Mon & Tues 10-6; Wed, Fri, Sat 10-6
Space: 1 gallery with 83 lin m hanging space and 142 sq m floor space

Exhibitions: 6 a year all originated
Details: Exhibitions run for six weeks. Work shown is selected from gallery artists plus artists new to the gallery. Gallery space is divided by two floors with more modern and abstract work shown in lower gallery. Blackheath has good percentage of art buyers. Sales considered gallery's primary role; commission taken. Applications for space with photographs or slides and SAE.

Blond Fine Art *

Commercial gallery showing C20th British painting, drawing, sculpture and graphics.
Unit 10, Canal Side Studios, 2-4 Orsman Road, London W1, tel: ~~0171 739 4383~~ 0118 9260880
Contact: Director
Space: 1 gallery with 31 lin m hanging space and 65 sq m floor space
Exhibitions: 4 a year all originated

Bloomsbury Theatre

Informal theatre foyer for mix of exhibitions during spring and autumn seasons.
15 Gordon Street, London WC1H 0AH, tel: 0171 383 5976, fax: 0171 383 4080
Contact: Kath Abrahams, General Manager
Open: Mon-Fri 9.30-5; or during performance times
Space: 1 gallery with 30 lin m hanging space
Exhibitions: 6 a year all originated
Details: Offers an all-year-round programme of events, encompassing music, dance, opera and alternative cabaret. Exhibitions are hung in the foyer area and are mainly seen by the theatre's audiences. Foyer is "L" shaped and hanging space is interrupted. Sales not exhibition space's primary role.

Bloomsbury Workshop

Small gallery focussed on the Bloomsbury artists and their successors.
12 Galen Place, Off Bury Place, London WC1A 2JR, tel: 0171 405 0632
Contact: Tony Bradshaw
Open: Mon-Fri 10-5.30
Space: 1 gallery
Exhibitions: 12 a year all originated
Details: Specialises in art and literature of the Bloomsbury Group. Continuous and changing stock of paintings and drawings by Duncan Grant, Vanessa Bell and other Bloomsbury artists. Occasional contemporary shows by other artists. The Bloomsbury Workshop also stocks extensive range of Bloomsbury literature. Selling work is considered gallery's primary role.

Blue Gallery

Pa Ph Sc ✓ ♿

Commercial gallery specialising in contemporary art and sculpture.
93 Walton Street, London SW3 2HP, tel: 0171 589 4690
Contact: Susannah Baker-Smith, Director
Open: Mon-Sat 10-6.30
Space: 1 gallery with 32 lin m hanging space and 60 sq m floor space
Exhibitions: 15 a year all originated
Details: Exhibitions include one-person or a group of artists, plus one sculptor or ceramicist. Gallery aims to show strong work, both figurative and abstract. Sales a priority. Gallery takes 50% commission on all sales.

Bolivar Hall *

Pa Ph Sc

Part of the cultural centre of the Venezuelan Embassy in London.
52-54 Grafton Way, London W1P 5LB, tel: 0171 387 6727, fax: 0171 383 3253
Contact: Yolanda Reyna, Director
Space: 1 gallery with 30 lin m hanging space
Exhibitions: 10 a year all originated
Details: Has become a Latin American centre because it is open for all Latin artists sponsored by their respective embassies. The only Latin American country which has a space with this characteristic. Exhibition programme is then centred on Latin American contemporary art.

Book Works

Ph Cr Sc LA

No longer a gallery, Book Works publishes artists' books and curates exhibitions in a variety of venues.
19 Holywell Row, London EC2A 4JB, tel: 0171 247 2536, fax: 0171 247 2540
Contact: Jane Rolo, Exhibition Organiser
Exhibitions: 2 a year both originated
Details: Aims to bring together as many disparate elements of the field as possible. Although no longer have space of their own, still follow these aims through programme of events in other venues. Writers, artists, printers and bookbinders given a chance to exhibit and collaborate on projects.

Boundary Gallery Mssge 22/10

Pa Pr ✓

Commercial gallery exhibiting mostly well-established artists.
98 Boundary Road, London NW8 0RH, tel: 0171 624 1126
Contact: Agi Katz, Director
Open: Wed-Sat 11-6
Space: 1 gallery
Exhibitions: 10 a year all originated
Details: Exhibits modern British artists such as Bomberg, Epstein, Wolmark. Also

exhibits contemporary artists – Phillippa Clayden, Albert Louden, Neil McPherson, Sonia Lawson, etc.

Bow House Gallery

Pa Sc ✓ ⊗ WRONG №.

Small commercial gallery specialising in sculpture and paintings.
35 Wood Street, Barnet, Hertfordshire, London EN5 4BE, tel: 0181 440 4672
Contact: Pauline and John Brown, Directors
Open: Thurs-Sat 10-5; Sun during exhibitions 2-5; at other times by appointment
Space: 1 gallery with 37 lin m hanging space and 85 sq m floor space
Exhibitions: 7 a year all originated
Details: Aims to present a wide range of work by professional artists – painting and sculpture – and provide affordable art for home or work place through a programme of seven exhibitions a year. Also an annual Sculpture in the Garden exhibition. Applications for exhibiting welcome. Send slides or photographs.

Bridge Lane Theatre

Pa Ph Pr Cr LA ♻

Large 200-seater theatre space suitable for performance art with small bar gallery – generally used for photographic work and illustration.
Bridge Lane, Battersea, London SW11 3AD, tel: 0171 228 5185/8828
Contact: Administration Section
Open: By arrangement
Space: 1 gallery
Exhibitions: 4 a year all on a hire basis
Details: Gallery exhibition often relates to current show in theatre. Theatre auditorium available when no show running – floor space approx 63 sq m.

Brixton Art Gallery

Pa Ph Pr Cr Sc LA ♻ ♿

Promotion of artwork produced by members of Brixton Artists' Collective through exhibitions, sales and community education programme.
35 Brixton Station Road, London SW9 8PB, tel: 0171 733 6957
Contact: Exhibition Committee, Brixton Artists' Collective Ltd
Open: Mon-Sat 10-6; Sun 12-6
Space: 1 gallery with 21 lin m hanging space and 70 sq m floor space
Exhibitions: 8 a year
Details: Gallery forms dynamic focus for the numerous and diverse artists living in and around Brixton. Run by the Brixton Artists' Collective, the gallery aims to give the people of Brixton and beyond an insight into the cultural diversity, talent and thriving community interest that exist within the area. Positive contribution that Black people have made to British society is

recognised and 50% of Collective's activities and exhibitions are set aside for the promotion of artists of African/Asian descent. Exhibition priority given to Collective members represented in its Equal Opportunity Policy and supports broad range of artforms; all areas of work are positively represented and welcomed.

Browse & Darby Limited *

Pa Sc

Commercial gallery specialising in C19th and C20th British and French painting and sculpture.
19 Cork Street, London W1, tel: 0171 734 7984, fax: 0171 437 0750
Contact: W Darby, Director
Space: 1 gallery with 17 lin m hanging space
Exhibitions: 7 a year all originated
Details: Exhibitions of contemporary English painting also shown.

Brunel Gallery

Pa Ph Pr Cr Sc ✓

University gallery featuring new artists.
Brunel University Library, Cleveland Road, Uxbridge, London UB8 3PH, tel: 01895 274000, fax: 01895 232806
Contact: Alan Bennett, Exhibitions Organiser, Brunel University Arts Centre
Open: Mon-Thurs 10-9; Fri 10-7; Sat 10-1; Sun 2-7; (during vacations) Mon-Fri 10-5; closed BH
Space: 1 gallery with 9 lin m hanging space plus 31 lin m on screens and 112 sq m floor space
Exhibitions: 6 a year of which 5 originated, 1 touring
Details: Provides exhibitions of interest to those who work in the university, and the general public. Presents shows displaying work of committed and newly emerging artists who deserve attention.

Bruton Street Gallery

Pa Pr ✓ ♻ ♿

Gallery featuring contemporary art from Europe with bias towards figurative work.
28 Bruton Street, London W1X 7DB, tel: 0171 499 9747, fax: 0171 409 7867
Contact: Patricia Herrod
Open: Mon-Fri 10-6; Sat 12-4
Space: 3 galleries with 160 lin m hanging space and 284 sq m floor space
Exhibitions: 12 a year of which 10 originated, 2 on a hire basis
Details: One large open space divided into 3 exhibition areas, each with good natural light. Exhibitions monthly, alternating between solo and mixed shows. Audience of metropolitan and international collectors. Sale of work considered gallery's primary concern.

Building Centre

Pa Ph Pr Cr Sc ✓ H 🖾 Wc

Exhibitions of work of architects, designers, artists and photographers whose subjects are closely related to the construction industry.
26 Store Street, London WC1E 7BT, tel: 0171 637 1022, fax: 071 580 9641
Contact: Richard Price, General Manager
Open: Mon-Fri 10-5; Sat 10-1
Space: 1 gallery with 20 lin m hanging space plus 11 lin m on screens and 78 sq m floor space
Exhibitions: 8 a year of which 4 originated, 2 touring, 2 on a hire basis
Details: As well as exhibitions gallery also provides a flexible setting for the staging of product launches and conferences. Selling work is not considered primary function of gallery.

Burgh House

Pa Ph Pr Cr Sc ✓ H 🖾 Wc

Ground-floor gallery in local arts centre and Hampstead Museum showing mainly local artist's work.
New End Square, Hampstead, London NW3 1LT, tel: 0171 431 0144
Contact: Pauline Pleasance, Administrator/Custodian
Open: Wed-Sun 12-5; BH Mons 2-5; closed Xmas, Good Friday and New Year
Space: 1 gallery with 16 lin m hanging space and 27 sq m floor space
Exhibitions: 24 a year all on a hire basis
Details: Queen Anne house (museum), panelled gallery. 20,000 visitors per year. Separate exhibition space in Hampstead Museum upstairs for mixed shows on local themes. Sales not a priority of gallery.

Business Design Centre

Pa Ph Pr Sc ✓ 🖾 Wc

Exhibition, trade and conference centre holding art fairs as well as other events.
52 Upper Street, Islington Green, London N1 0QH, tel: 0171 359 3535, fax: 0171 226 0590
Contact: Lucy Sicks, Director of Art
Details: Venue for annual London Contemporary Art Fair which has 24,000 visitors from UK and abroad. Applications welcomed from galleries throughout the UK.

Cabinet *

Pa Ph Sc LA

8 Clifton Mansions, 429 Coldharbour Lane, London SW9 8LL, tel: 0171 274 4252
Contact: Martin McGeown
Space: 2 galleries
Exhibitions: 6 a year all originated
Details: Presents contemporary art 'of a serious nature' in varied programme of well-established and younger artists from Britain, mainland Europe and US. 6 solo shows planned, each lasting four weeks. Audience those involved in visual arts – critics, collectors, other artists.

Cadogan Contemporary

Pa Pr Sc 🖾

Commercial gallery specialising in British contemporary art with new exhibitions each fortnight.
108 Draycott Avenue, London SW3 3AE, tel: 0171 581 5451, fax: 071 589 9120
Contact: Penny Light or Chirstopher Burness
Open: Mon-Thurs 10-7; Fri & Sat 10-6
Space: 1 gallery with 42 lin m hanging space and 370 sq m floor space
Exhibitions: 22 a year all originated
Details: Specialises in contemporary British figurative painters, predominantly young artists. Artists include Brian Ballard, Nicola Bealing, Joy Girvin, Dick Lee, Peter Lloyd-Jones, Sargy Mann, Kate Montgomery, Bridget Leaman, Emma McClure & Charles Baird.

Café Casbar *

Pa Ph Pr ✓

Monthly solo exhibitions of prints, illustration and photography by young talented artists who have not exhibited before.
52 Earlham Street, Covent Garden, London WC2H 9HT, tel: 0171 379 7768, fax: 0171 836 8395
Contact: Frances McKellar, Exhibition Organiser, 7 Neal Street, London, WC2H 9PU, tel: 0171 836 6252
Space: 1 gallery with 46 lin m hanging space and 112 sq m floor space
Exhibitions: 12 a year all originated
Details: Commission charged on sales. (See entry for Smith's Galleries). Artists encouraged to play upon café environment as theme for exhibitions, including designing menu cover and poster to be used for duration of show. Prices reasonably low.

Café Gallery

A Pa Ph Pr Cr Sc LA

Aims to provide exhibition space for artists and other groups, and to encourage active involvement in visual arts.
By the Pool, Southwark Park, Bermondsey, London SE16, tel: 0171 237 2170
Contact: Ron Henocq, Exhibition Organiser
Exhibitions: 9 a year all originated
Open: Wed-Sun 11-5
Details: Administered by Bermondsey Artists Group. Innovative new work. Shows normally run for three weeks.

Café Gallery Masbro Centre *

Pa Ph Pr Cr ✓ H

Cheerful managed space for exhibitions of 2-D work on a smaller scale.
87 Masbro Road, London W14 0LR, tel: 0171 603 1293
Contact: Nancy Crozier, Arts Coordinator
Space: 1 gallery with 14 lin m hanging space
Exhibitions: 10 a year of which 5 originated, 5 on a hire basis
Details: The multi-cultural programme includes work of local artists, centre tutors and students. Priority is to give positive representation to Black and Asian people, gays and lesbians, women, disabled people, single parents, and senior citizens. These people make up local audience as well.

Camden Arts Centre

Pa Ph Sc LA 🖾 ✗

Emphasis on new work from Britain and abroad as well as providing an opportunity to reappraise artists from the earlier part of the century.
Arkwright Road, London NW3 6DG, tel: 0171 435 2643, fax: 0171 794 3371
Contact: Jenni Lomax, Director
Open: Tues-Thurs 12-8; Fri-Sun 12-6
Space: 3 galleries
Exhibitions: 5 a year of which 4 originated, 1 touring
Details: Artists and their work are the focus for activities which aim to give people access to contemporary art and current ideas. Opportunites for schools, colleges, community groups and individuals to participate in courses and workshops linked to the exhibiitors; an active artist-in-residence scheme.

Camerawork

Ph Pr LA ✓ 🖾 Wc 4

Broad range of lens-based media work which addresses contemporary photographic and artistic debates as well as issues of social importance.
121 Roman Road, Bethnal Green, London E2 0QN, tel: 0181 980 6256, fax: 0181 983 4714
Contact: Helen Sloan, Exhibition Organiser
Open: Tues-Sat 1-6
Space: 1 gallery with 30 lin m hanging space plus 8 lin m on screens
Exhibitions: 8 a year of which 7 originated, 1 touring
Details: British and international artists.Theme based group shows, many self generated, of new, often commissioned work. Installation work and video and electronic art shown. Touring shows also taken. Audience local, national and international. Darkroom facilities and

practical courses and workshops in photography. Sales not a priority.

Canada House Gallery *

Holds exhibitions of contemporary Canadian art.
Canada House, Trafalgar Square, London SW1, tel: 0171 629 9492 ext 246
Contact: Michael Regan, Visual Arts Officer
Space: 2 galleries with 170 lin m hanging space and 1500 sq m floor space
Exhibitions: 3 a year all originated
Details: Work shown includes painting, sculpture, drawings, prints, crafts, photography and live art. Number and length of exhibitions varied. Also runs an education programme of talks, seminars and cultural events generated by the Cultural Affairs Department. Many of these relate to the exhibitions being held.

Candid Gallery Café

Exhibition space in café and gallery to promote and sell work of artists and designers.
3 Torrens Street, London EC1V 1NQ, tel: 0171 278 9368
Contact: Duncan, Exhibitions Organiser
Open: Daily 12-6
Space: 2 galleries with 87 lin m hanging space plus 24 lin m on screens and 242 sq m floor space
Exhibitions: 12 a year of which 6 originated, 6 on a hire basis
Details: Gallery aims to promote and sell work of artists and designers in all disciplines, from furniture to fashion, fine art to film. Sales a priority. Access for disabled people being reviewed.

Cartoon Gallery *

Shows work of established and up-and-coming cartoonists in mixture of group and solo shows.
83 Lambs Conduit Street, London WC1A 3NA, tel: 0171 242 5335
Contact: Pat Huntley, Mel Calman, Exhibition Organiser, 44 Museum Street, London, WC1A 1LY
Details: Aims to appeal to people that would not normally visit galleries. Atmosphere informal. Many customers are young and buying for the first time. Graphic works (prints, watercolours and illustrations) also shown. Exhibitions normally run two to three weeks.

Cassian de Vere Cole

50 Elgin Crescent, London W11, tel: 0171 221 9161, fax: 0171 221 1082

Castlebar Gallery *

Gallery owned by print publishing business will show work suitable for offices and business world only
17 Castlebar Road, Ealing, London W5 2DL, tel: 0181 997 6060, fax: 0181 998 2592
Contact: Pamela Ellner
Space: 2 galleries with 24 sq m floor space
Exhibitions: 1 a year originated
Details: Rare exhibitions of contemporary artists by invitation. Only one public show every 2/3 years.

Catto Gallery

Selling gallery showing work by contemporary painters.
100 Heath Street, Hampstead, London NW3 1DP, tel: 0171 435 6660, fax: 0171 431 5620
Contact: Mrs Catto, Exhibition Organiser
Open: Mon-Sat 10-6; Sun 2.30-6
Exhibitions: 12 a year all originated
Details: Specialises in contemporary oils and watercolours.

CCA Galleries (London)

One of a network of commercial galleries in the South of England specialising in original prints.
8 Dover Street, London W1X 3PJ, tel: 0171 499 6701, fax: 0171 409 3555
Contact: Julian Lonergan, Director
Open: Mon-Fri 9.30-5.30; Sat 10-4
Space: 1 gallery
Exhibitions: 10 a year all originated
Details: CCA Galleries is a leading publisher of original, limited edition prints with galleries also in Cambridge, Farnham, Oxford and Bath (see separate entries for each). Each gallery selects its own work. The primary aim is to promote hand-made prints by CCA artists.

Centaur Gallery

Private gallery with sculpture garden.
82 Highgate High Street, Highgate Village, London N65HE, tel: 0181 340 0087
Contact: Dinah Wieliczko & Jan Wieliczko
Open: Mon-Fri 11-6; Sun 12-6
Space: 3 galleries with 300 lin m hanging space
Exhibitions: 4 a year all originated
Details: Unique gallery with special character and ambience. Access to sculpture garden on terraces. Policy to combine various aspects of art – spatial as well as pictorial, with accent on ethnic and primitive as well as sophisticated contemporary art.

Centerprise Coffee Bar

Exhibition space in local community centre coffee bar aiming to promote local and 'new' artists and exhibit to a non-gallery going audience.
136-138 Kingsland High Street, London E8 2NS, tel: 0171 254 9632 ext 23
Contact: Zahid Dar, Acting Arts Co-ordinator, Centerprise Trust Ltd
Open: Mon-Sat 10.30-5
Space: 1 gallery with 11 lin m hanging space and 60 sq m floor space
Exhibitions: 12 a year all originated
Details: Exhibition space in local community centre coffee bar. Work mostly from the Hackney community but also some national artists. Ensures an equal opportunity policy on the work displayed and hopes that it represents the community. Sometimes exhibitions can coincide with book launches or readings. Sale of work is important.

Central Saint Martins College of Art & Design

Primarily exhibits student work but also occasional group exhibitions other artists and design organisations.
Southampton Row, London WC1B 4AP, tel: 0171 753 9090, fax: 0171 242 0240
Contact: Exhibition Organiser
Space: 3 galleries
Details: Gallery's function is to display the work of current students. However exhibition proposals will be considered if the work to be shown is of the highest visual standard and will contribute by its presence to the education of students.

Central Space

In studio complex, run by Association for Cultural Advancement through Visual Art (ACAVA).
23-29 Faroe Road, London W14 0EL, tel: 0171 603 3039, fax: 0171 603 3278
Contact: Duncan Smith, Artistic Director
Space: 1 gallery with 44 lin m hanging space and 105 sq m floor space
Exhibitions: 9 a year all originated
Details: Shows wide range of innovative work relevant to contemporary artistic, cultural and social concerns, including painting, sculpture, drawing, prints, photography and live art, with emphasis on installation work. Most shows solo, with occasional two-person or mixed exhibition.

Centre Gallery

Gallery with sculpture court shows and promotes 'green' and environmental arts with emphasis on London/local issues.

21 Endell Street, Covent Garden, The London Ecology Centre, London WC2Y 9HJ, tel: 0171 379 4324
Contact: Michael Waller, Gallery Administrator
Open: Mon-Sat 10-6
Space: 1 gallery with 30 lin m hanging space and 150 sq m floor space
Exhibitions: 25 a year of which 5 originated, 20 on a hire basis
Details: Gallery shows work in sympathy with the aims of London Ecology Centre: to raise awareness of environmental issues. Sculpture court in addition to gallery space. Sales a priority.

Centre Space

[Pa][Ph][Pr][Cr][Sc] ✔ [H] ♿ [WC]

Lively and regular arts input to arts and library centre intended for general use.
24 Treaty Centre, High Street, Hounslow, London TW3 1ES, tel: 0181 570 0622, fax: 0181 569 4330
Contact: Pam Cole
Details: Potential audience is wide-ranging as centre is situated in a shopping centre, parts of which may also be used for exhibitions. Programme of workshops, seminars and culturally-related council exhibitions planned.variety of small exhibition spaces available.

Chalk Farm Gallery

[Pa][Pr][Cr][Sc] ✔

Commercial gallery open to all, with artists from all over the world.
20 Chalk Farm Road, London NW1 8AG, tel: 0171 267 3300
Contact: Su-Ellen Shorter, Art Director
Open: Daily 10-6
Details: Exhibition space; two floors and conservatory with constantly changing exhibitions. No schedule. Not suitable for installations. Prices from £10-£1000. Established 15 years. Large range of printmakers represented plus paintings, ceramics, glass, sculpture and jewellery. Commission on sales. Applications in writing with CV and slides or photographs

Changing Room Gallery

[Pa][Ph][Pr][Cr][Sc] ✔ ♿ [WC]

Situated in a public park, the gallery provides opportunity for artists to present their work to an audience that might not normally visit a gallery.
Lloyd Park, Forest Road, London E17 4PP
Contact: Jean Oxenham, Arts & Tourism Assistant, London Borough of Waltham Forest, Arts & Leisure Department, Arts Section, Willima Morris Gallery, Lloyd Park, Forest Road, London, E17 4PP, tel: 0181 527 7070
Open: (Apr-Sept) Mon-Fri 1-6
Space: 1 gallery with 20 lin m hanging space and 54 sq m floor space
Exhibitions: 16 a year
Details: Principally shows work by North East London-based artists and craftspeople. Occasionally includes exhibitions by local groups and students from local colleges. Gallery has natural light. Sales not important.

Chat Noir Gallery (Le)

35 Albemarle Street, Mayfair, London W1X 3FB, tel: 071 495 6710
Contact: Nicole Tinero

Chats Palace *

[Ph] ✔

Bar wall within community centre
42/44 Brooksbys Walk, Homerton, London E96D, tel: 0181 986 6714
Contact: Programme Organiser
Space: 2 lin m hanging space
Exhibitions: 12 a year of which 11 originated, 1 touring
Details: Exhibits work of various groups from ethnically and socially mixed local population, especially those with disabilities, women artists and photographers. Programme of six two to three week exhibitions. Varied programme of workshops held, and work produced forms part of exhibition programme.

Cherry Orchard Veg Restaurant

[Pa][Ph][Pr][Cr] ✔ ♿

Vegetarian Buddhist-run restaurant with monthly exhibitions of 2D, small scale artwork, including textiles.
241 Globe Road, London E2 0JD, tel: 0181 980 6678
Contact: Liz Tarr, Exhibition Organiser
Open: Mon, Thurs & Fri 11-4; Tues, Wed 11-7
Space: 2 galleries with 16 lin m hanging space
Exhibitions: 12 a year
Details: Weekday lunchtime vegetarian restaurant run in conjunction with the London Buddhist Centre. Only small works can be accommodated as walls impeded by light fixtures – average 2'x 3'. New colour scheme demands barrier (mounts) between orange walls and pictures or black and white pictures. Audience – professionals who work locally in schools and social services, local Buddhist community, colleges and East End businesses. Selling work not primary function of exhibiting work.

Chisenhale Gallery

[Pa][Sc] [£] ♿ [WC]

Public gallery presenting innovative contemporary art.
64 Chisenhale Road, London E3 5QZ, tel: 0181 981 4518, fax: 0181 980 7169
Contact: Jonathan Watkins, Director
Open: Wed-Sun 1-6
Space: 1 gallery
Exhibitions: 7 a year all originated
Details: Non-profit making gallery. New work often commissioned. Educational programme targets local primary schools. Sales not priority.

Chris Beetles Gallery *

[Pa] ✔

Shows C19th and C20th watercolours, drawings and illustrations.
10 Ryder Street, London SW1, tel: 0171 839 7551, fax: 0171 839 1603
Contact: Director
Space: 2 galleries with 62 lin m hanging space and 59 sq m floor space
Exhibitions: 5 a year all originated
Details: Six contemporary gallery artists, yearly open exhibition and watercolour competition.

Christopher Hull Gallery

[Pa][Pr][Sc] ✔ ♿

17 Motcomb Street, London SW1X 8LB, tel: 0171 235 0500
Contact: Christopher Hull
Open: Mon-Fri 10-6; Sat 10-1
Space: 3 galleries with 62 lin m hanging space and 156 sq m floor space
Exhibitions: 12 a year all originated
Details: Our reputation is based upon our finding young artists of promise. We also concentrate on British artists born in the C20th, most often in the years 1918-1930.

Churzee Studio Gallery

[Pa] ♿

Small commercial gallery specialising in contemporary and Russian work.
17 Bellevue Road, Wandsworth Common, London SW17 7EG, tel: 0181 767 8113
Contact: Cheryl Howeld, Director
Open: Thurs-Sat 10-6
Space: 1 gallery with 23 lin m hanging space
Exhibitions: 10 a year
Details: Specialises in contemporary Russian painting, mainly figurative work in watercolours and oils. A range of young and established artists. The gallery considers applications but majority of new artists come through introductions.

Citizens Gallery

[Pa][Ph][Sc][LA] ✔ [H]

Exhibition space showing local displays in conjunction with community groups.
Powis Street, London SE18, tel: 0181 855 3240
Contact: B Gillow
Space: 1 gallery with 37 lin m hanging space plus 8 lin m on screens and 130 sq m floor space
Exhibitions: 8 a year

City Racing

Gallery run by a group of 5 artists with programme which iconcentrating on contemporary art by young and/or unstablished artists.
60 Oval Mansions, Vauxhall Street, Kennington, London SE11 5SH, tel: 0171 582 3940
Contact: John Burgess, Keith Coventry, Matt Hale, Paul Noble, Peter Owen
Space: 3 galleries with 43 lin m hanging space and 47 sq m floor space
Exhibitions: 6 a year
Details: Two ground-floor and one first-floor spaces. Appeals to mixed audience: students, artists, dealers and collectors. 25% commission on sales goes towards running costs.

Claremont Fine Art

New art gallery in busy and prominent position in centre of Surbiton specialising in contemporary painting, prints and photography.
15 Claremont Road, Surbiton, London KT6 4QR, tel: 0181 399 9902, fax: 0181 390 7446
Contact: V Philbin, Owner
Open: Mon-Sat 10-5.30
Space: 31 lin m hanging space and 57 sq m floor space
Details: Prominent window frontage and halogen spots. One large and one small exhibition per month. Applications welcomed from local artists; Surrey and South West London preferred. 33% commission on sales. 15 miles from central London (2 minutes from Surbiton BR station).

Collection Gallery *

264 Brompton Road, London SW3 2AS, tel: 0171 581 2716, fax: 0171 584 7829
Contact: James Ghani
Space: 1 gallery with 6 lin m hanging space and 493 sq m floor space
Exhibitions: 21 a year of which 3 originated, 18 on a hire basis
Details: Norman Foster-designed gallery. Large white single-storey site ideal for sculpture and 3D work. Wide ranging programme presents established artists, degree shows, solo shows, fashion shows, and trade exhibitions.

Commercial Gallery

Gallery on two floors curated by two artists showing mainly one-person shows of international contemporary work.
109 Commercial Street, London E1 6BG, tel: 0171 377 9868
Contact: Keith Ball & Shaheen Merali

Open: Tues-Fri 12-6; Sun 12-5
Space: 2 galleries with 61 lin m hanging space and 143 sq m floor space
Exhibitions: 9 a year all originated
Details: The gallery is run on a non-commercial basis and shows work by unknown and established artists. A programme of talks and lectures is also scheduled. Artists are requested to visit the gallery before submitting proposals. The gallery forms part of a wider cultural centre which includes a restaurant and arts/performance club under the umbrella of the Spitalfields Arts Project which also provides 70 artists' studios.

Coningsby Gallery

Multi-artform private gallery.
30 Tottenham Street, London W1 9PN, tel: 0171 636 1064, fax: 0171 388 6491
Contact: Andrew Coningsby/Nicky Marks
Open: Mon-Fri 12-6
Space: 1 gallery
Exhibitions: 10 a year of which 4 originated, 6 on a hire basis
Details: Contemporary art works that embrace a broad spectrum of media; commercial, 3D illustration, photography, painting and sculpture.

Connaught Brown

Gallery exhibiting and selling post impressionist, modern and contemporary painting, drawing, sculpture and graphics.
2 Albermarle Street, London W1X 3HF, tel: 0171 408 0362, fax: 071 495 3137
Contact: Anthony Brown, Director
Open: Mon-Fri 10-6; Sat 10-12.30
Space: 23 lin m hanging space and 28 sq m floor space
Exhibitions: 8 a year all originated
Details: Selection of work from gallery's stock available in addition to exhibitions. Sales a priority.

Contemporary Applied Arts

Retail gallery aims to stimulate excellence and make the best contemporary craftwork available to the public and collectors.
43 Earlham Street, Covent Garden, London WC2H 9LD, tel: 0171 836 6993
Contact: Mary La Trobe Bateman, Director
Open: Mon-Sat 10-6; Thurs 10-7
Space: 1 gallery
Exhibitions: 8 a year all originated
Details: Gallery specialising in craft holds several exhibitions a year ranging from solo and small group shows to large mixed exhibitions. The basement shop has a constantly changing display of high quality crafts. Established 1948. An association of

selected professional craftspeople. Sale of work is gallery's primary role.

Contemporary Ceramics

Crafts Council selected gallery showing group exhibitions of ceramics of a domestic nature, with emphasis on sculptural and figurative works.
Crafts Potters Shop, William Blake House, 7 Marshall Street, London W1V 1LP, tel: 0171 437 7605, fax: 0171 287 9954
Contact: Marta Donaghey, Exhibition Organiser
Space: 1 gallery with 40 sq m floor space
Exhibitions: 10 a year all originated
Details: Fosters interest in studio ceramics and shares technical information with students, makers and collectors. Promotes work of members of Crafts Potters Association of Great Britain. Visitors include all levels of the general public, specialist collectors and overseas visitors. Talks, slide shows and workshops organised.

Contemporary Textile Gallery

Vigo Galleries, 6a Vigo Street, London W1X 1AH, tel: 0171 439 6971, fax: 0171 439 2353
Open: Mon-Thurs 9-5.30, Fri 9-5

Conway Hall *

Hall used as public meeting place with space suitable for up and coming artists.
25 Red Lion Square, London WC1R 4RL, tel: 0171 242 8032/3
Contact: Steve Norley, Exhibition Organiser
Space: 3 galleries with 33 lin m hanging space and 169 sq m floor space
Exhibitions: 10 a year all on a hire basis
Details: Owned by Humanist Society. Three areas available, a large hall, an entrance hall (3D only) and small adjacent passage way.

Cool Tan Arts Centre

Main purpose is to provide open access to all artists without censorship. At time of going to press Cool Tan was seeking new premises.
Contact: Michelle Baharier, Arts Co-ordinator, tel: 0171 701 9608

Corbally Stourton Contemporary Art *

Contemporary Aboriginal art from Australia and occasional contemporary Australiana.

2a Cork Street, London W1X 1PA, tel: 0171 734 8903, fax: 0171 734 8906
Space: 1 gallery with plus 50 lin m on screens and 140 sq m floor space
Exhibitions: 5 a year all originated

Cotman Gallery *

[Pa][Ph][Pr] ✔

Kings College School, Southside, Wimbledon Common, London SW19 4TT, tel: 0181 947 9311, fax: 0181 944 6526
Contact: Mr Barnes
Space: 2 galleries with 7 lin m hanging space plus 14 lin m on screens and 139 sq m floor space
Exhibitions: 6 a year all originated
Details: 2 floor gallery space within school, open to public. Temporary programme concentrates on 2D work, mostly painting, drawing, and print, by young artists from London and further afield. Audience from all over South London area.

Courtyard Gallery

[Pa][Ph][Pr][Cr][Sc] ✔ [H] ♿

Converted from old stables and coach house, gallery doubles as theatre foyer showing mainly work by new and innovative artists.
10 York Way, Kings Cross, London N1 9AA, tel: 0171 833 0870
Contact: Fatima Malagueira, Manager
Open: Mon, Tues, Thurs-Sun 12-7
Space: 1 gallery with 25 lin m hanging space and 45 sq m floor space
Exhibitions: 12 a year all on a hire basis
Details: Converted gallery with original features. Visitors are general public and theatre goers. Priority given to new and innovative artists who have not been given a chance to exhibit elsewhere. Sales welcome (20% commission taken) but not essential. Minimal rental charge for the space.

Coventry Gallery

[Pa][Ph][Pr][Sc][LA] ✔ ♿

Lower-ground-floor gallery between City and West End exhibiting work by young emerging artists particularly installation and performance work.
7 Corsham Street, London N1 6DR, tel: 0171 336 7034
Contact: Paul Woods, Gallery Owner
Open: Ring for details
Space: 1 gallery with 11 lin m hanging space and 74 sq m floor space
Exhibitions: 12 a year all originated
Details: Exhibitions mainly selected themed group shows of emerging artists, especially 'difficult' work. Aims to provide a platform for work to be seen. Workshops, life drawing classes, lecture evenings. Position ensures passing trade. Sales not considered gallery's primary role.

Crafts Council

[Cr] ✔ £ ♿ [Wc] [4]

Major temporary exhibition gallery for presentation of contemporary craft in ground floor of converted chapel, with adjacent gallery shop.
44a Pentonville Road, London N1 9BY, tel: 0171 278 7700, fax: 0171 837 6891
Contact: Head of Exhibitions
Open: Tues-Sat 11-6; Sun 2-6
Space: 2 galleries with 93 lin m hanging space plus 166 lin m on screens and 269 sq m floor space
Exhibitions: 6 a year of which 5 originated, 1 touring
Details: Gallery policy is to present a changing programme of high-quality contemporary craftwork in such a way as to encourage understanding and appreciation of craft nationally, aided by an associated touring service. Sales not primary role of gallery.

Crafts Council Shop at the V&A

[Cr] ♿ [Wc]

Wide selection of objects in all media, with monthly exhibitions of new work.
Victoria & Albert Museum, South Kensington, London SW7 2RL, tel: 0171 589 5070
Contact: Clare Beck, Shop Manager
Space: 1 gallery with 14 lin m hanging space and 5 sq m floor space
Exhibitions: 10 a year all originated
Details: Monthly showcase exhibitions arranged in the shop, promoting work of one maker with occasional group exhibitions based on a theme. Work selected from makers on Crafts Council Index. Shows a wide variety of work by well-established and lesser-known makers. Arranges commissions and special orders to a customer's particular requirement, provides a packing and postal service. Exhibitions often linked with activities at the Crafts Council Gallery or events in the Victoria & Albert Museum. Sales a priority.

Crane Gallery *

[Pa][Pr]

Deals in naive art 1750-1900, contemporary paintings and international modern masters.
171A Sloane Street (First Floor), Knightsbridge, London SW1, tel: 0171 235 2464, fax: 0171 235 7718
Contact: Andras Kalman, Director
Space: 3 galleries
Exhibitions: 6 a year all originated

Crane Kalman Gallery *

[Pa][Sc]

Gallery shows and deals in British and European C20th paintings and sculpture.
178 Brompton Road, London SW3, tel: 0171 584 7566/3843, fax: 0171 584 3843
Contact: Andras Kalman, Director
Details: Some contemporary, Ben Nicholson, Graham Sutherland, Winifred Nicholson, Henry Moore, Lowry, Rusking Spear and others. Exhibitions about 6 weeks, all gallery originated.

Crocodile Gallery

[Pa] ✔ 🚫♿

Exhibition space on two floors (upstairs space combined with café); both showing and selling contemporary wall hung work.
122 Muswell Hill, Broadway, London N10 3RU, tel: 0181 444 0273, fax: 0181 444 0223
Contact: Joanna Kelly
Open: Mon-Sat 9.30-7; Sun 11-6
Space: 2 galleries
Exhibitions: 12 a year all originated
Details: Downstairs: mixed continually changing display of mainly watercolours, pastels, life drawings, etc shown alongside gifts, glassware. Upstairs: shows one-person exhibitions of 2D work usually bold, often figurative work hung on walls of café area with exhibitions changing every three weeks. Gallery selects work and either accepts it on sale or return basis or commission taken. Independent access for wheelchair users to downstairs gallery; not possible for upstairs space. Sale of work is considered a priority.

Crouch End Art School

[Pa][Ph][Cr][Sc] ✔ [H] ♿

Exhibition space with glass front to street in art school providing wide range of art and craft classes for adults and children.
10 Middle Lane, London N8 8PL, tel: 0181 341 3565
Contact: Paul Garratt
Open: Any time according to need.
Space: 2 galleries with 34 lin m hanging space plus 7 lin m on screens and 88 sq m floor space
Exhibitions: 7 a year of which 3 originated, 4 on a hire basis
Details: Provide service for local community through classes and exhibitions. Sale of work not a priority. Artists exhibiting sometimes contribute to costs, depending on their financial position.

Croydon Central Library

[Pa][Ph][Pr][Cr][Sc][LA] ✔ ♿

Library exhibition space shows work of local artists and societies in mixture of group and solo shows.
Katharine Street, Croydon, London CR9 1ET, tel: 0181 760 5400, fax: 0181 760 5632
Contact: Karen Mann, Exhibitions Officer
Space: 2 galleries with 75 lin m hanging space

Details: Policy is to provide dynamic exhibitions on variety of topics with focus on innovative use of interactive technology. Occasionally work of those living and working outside area shown. Exhibitions targeted towards local residents and international community.

Cubitt Gallery

Exhibitions and events held including music, live art, film & video and talks.
2-4 Caledonia Street, London N1 9DZ, tel: 0171 278 8226
Contact: Gallery committee
Open: Thurs-Sat 10-6
Space: 2 galleries with 75 lin m hanging space and 250 sq m floor space
Exhibitions: 8 a year

Curtain Road Arts

96a Curtain Road, London, tel: 0171 613 53

Curwen Gallery

Commercial gallery featuring contemporary, international & modern British painting, sculpture and limited edition graphics.
4 Windmill Street, off Charlotte Street, London W1P 1HF, tel: 0171 636 1459, fax: 0171 436 3059
Contact: Karol Pawsey, Director
Open: Mon-Fri 10-5.30; Sat 10.30-1
Space: 2 galleries with 33 lin m hanging space and 35 sq m floor space
Exhibitions: 10 a year all originated
Details: Gallery and print publishers shows monthly exhibitions of contemporary British art. Promotes contemporary artists working with specific group and organises mixed exhibitions. Exhibitions of international graphics and solo exhibitions of gallery artists.

Cut Gallery

Central London gallery specialises in collaborating with artists to mount exciting contemporary exhibitions.
82 The Cut, Waterloo, London SE1 8LW, tel: 0171 207 8388, fax: 0171 207 8390
Contact: Mark Segal
Open: Mon-Sat 10-6
Space: 1 gallery with 23 lin m hanging space and 39 sq m floor space
Exhibitions: 20 a year all originated
Details: New exhibition venue in Central London. Gallery shows and promotes a variety of contemporary artforms. Artists are encouraged to give talks/workshops etc during the course of the exhibition. Sale of work is important to the gallery. Any artists

applying to the gallery should include slides, CV and stamped addressed envelope. No SAE, no return.

Cynthia Bourne Gallery

International modern and contemporary paintings, etchings and sculpture.
16 Clifford Street, London W1X 1RG, tel: 0171 439 0007, fax: 0171 439 2181

Dance Attic

Exhibition space in large studio complex designed to give artists chance of their own show in London setting and available for hire.
368 North End Road, Fulham, London SW6 1LY, tel: 0171 610 2055
Contact: Andrew Corbet Burcher, Gallery Administrator
Open: Mon-Sat 9.30-10; Sun 9.30-5.30
Space: 1 gallery with 10 lin m hanging space
Exhibitions: 20 a year all on a hire basis
Details: Large rehearsal studio complex. There are studios upstairs and down, about 6 very large ones at the back plus a gymnasium. Around 8000 members. Sales not primary role.

Danielle Arnaud Contemporary Arts

123 Kennington Road, London SE11 6SF, tel: 0171 735 8292

Dash Gallery

Ground-floor gallery in Dockland Neighbourhood Centre.
Jack Dash House, 2 Lawn Close, Marsh Wall, Isle of Dogs, London E14 9YQ, tel: 0171 987 7925, fax: 0171 538 3314
Contact: Denise Terry-Roberts, The Tiller Centre, Tiller Road, London, E14 8PX, tel: 071 987 7925
Space: 1 gallery with 177 sq m floor space
Details: Circular exhibition space, direct access from street. Policy of showing work by artists from Isle of Dogs area of East London, or work relevant to area undergoing urban regeneration/multi-cultural diversity etc.

David Curzon Gallery

Commercial gallery promoting representational art.
35 Church Road, Wimbledon Village, London SW19 5DQ, tel: 0181 944 6098
Contact: Mr D. Curzon
Open: Tues-Sat 10-6; Sun by appointment
Space: 1 gallery with 55 lin m hanging space and 130 sq m floor space
Exhibitions: 9 a year all originated
Details: Presents continually changing

exhibitions of professional artists working in a traditional manner, including landscape, marine, still life and depiction of the figure. "We make it our responsibility to look after the interests of the artists thus establishing a good relationship between us."

David Mellor

Craftsman made collections of pottery, glass, woodware and basketware displayed on two floors and in two shop windows interspersed with mass produced ranges of household goods.
4 Sloane Square, London SW1, tel: 0171 730 4259, fax: 0171 730 7240
Contact: David Mellor, Director, David Mellor Design Ltd, The Round Building, Gundleford Road, Hathersage, S30 1BA, tel: 01433 650220, fax: 01433 650944
Open: Mon-Sat 9.30-5.30
Details: Kitchen and tableware shop sells equipment by various makers; pottery, woodware, baskets, David Mellor cutlery (on Crafts Councils selected list). Promotes best of British craftsmanship using work from stable of artists. Sales a priority. Independent access for wheelchair users to ground floor only.

David Messum Fine Paintings *

One of main dealers in UK of C18th and C19th British painting and contemporary painting.
34 St George Street, London W1R 9FA, tel: 0171 408 0243, fax: 0171 491 3162
Contact: Michael Roosen, 1 Aylesbury End, Beaconsfield, Bucks, tel: 0494 680 880
Space: 2 galleries
Exhibitions: 5 a year all originated
Details: Prices range from £1000 to £10,000 for contemporary work.

Delfina Studios Trust

Artists' studios centre with two galleries and café.
50 Bermondsey Street, Southwark, London SE1 3UD, tel: 0171 357 6600, fax: 0171 357 7944
Contact: Bridget Ashley-Miller, Adminstrator
Space: 2 galleries with 115 lin m hanging space plus 22 lin m on screens and 604 sq m floor space
Details: Gallery opened December 1994. Plans annual exhibitions of Trust artists. Exhibitions selected by panel. Programme of workshops incorporating art, music and theatre held for local school pupils and community.

Design Museum

Pa Ph Pr C SC H 🖰 🖰🖰 4

World's first museum of mass produced consumer objects.
Butlers Wharf, London SE1 2YD, tel: 0171 403 6933, fax: 071 378 6540
Contact: Dr Paul Thompson, Curatorial Director
Open: Mon-Fri 11.30-6; Sat-Sun 12-6
Space: 2 galleries
Exhibitions: 4 a year of which 1 originated, 1 touring, 2 on a hire basis
Details: Aims to offer fascinating and accessible introduction to C20th design, technology and consumer culture. Examines role of design in everyday lives and asks how and why mass produced consumer products work and look the way they do. Regular changing programme of exhibitions and displays including: cars, furniture, domestic appliances, cameras, graphics and ceramics.

Diorama

Pa Ph Pr SC LA 🖰🖰 H 🖰🖰

Aims to provide an exciting programme of contemporary art, within a national and international context.
34 Osnaburgh Street, London NW1 3ND, tel: 0171 916 5467
Contact: Julia Davis, Exhibition Organiser
Open: Mon-Fri 11-6
Space: 1 gallery with 72 sq m floor space
Exhibitions: 15 a year all originated
Details: Situated within the Diorama Arts Centre, a charitable, non-profit making organisation. Exhibitions include work by emerging local and regional artists, artists with disabilities and international exhibitors. Wide variety of art shown.

Dover Street Gallery

13 Dover street, London W1X, tel: 0171 409 1504

Dragonfly

Pa Pr C SC

Specialist glass gallery.
69 White Hart Lane, Barnes, London SW13 0PP, tel: 0181 878 7892
Contact: Milena Oak, Exhibition Organiser
Open: Thurs, Fri, Sat 10-1, 2-5; and by appointment
Space: 1 gallery with 26 lin m hanging space and 40 sq m floor space
Exhibitions: 9 a year of which 5 originated, 4 touring
Details: Long-term display by a dozen artists. Concentrates on one-off and unusual glass pieces with intention of interesting collectors, particularly from abroad. Occasionally shows paintings and sculpture. Semi-permanent display of stained and blown glass with changing display of specialist and fine art work.

Drian Galleries *

Pa Pr Cr SC LA

Shows 'modern masters'.
7 Porchester Place, London W2, tel: 0171 723 9473
Contact: Halima Halecz, Director
Exhibitions: 12 a year all originated

Drill Hall Arts Centre

Pa Ph Pr SC 🖰 🖰🖰

New work exhibited in theatre bar area.
16 Chenies Street, London WC1 7EX, tel: 0171 631 5107, fax: 0171 631 4468
Contact: Gail Veasey, Courses & Exhibitions Director
Open: Tues-Sat 6-11; Women only: Mon 6-11
Space: 1 gallery with 14 lin m hanging space
Exhibitions: 9 a year all originated
Details: Exhibits work that has never been shown before in London, usually in the form of solo shows, only occasionally group shows. Theatre reserves one night each week for women only. Space hired free to artists. 10% commission taken on sales made. Selling work not primary role of gallery.

Dulwich Picture Gallery

Pa 🖰

Regular temporary exhibitions relating to an aspect of the permanent collection or of international interest.
College Road, London SE21 7AD, tel: 0181 693 5254, fax: 0181 693 0923
Contact: Giles Waterfield, Director
Details: First public art gallery in England; built by Sir John Soane. Permanent collection of works by artists such as Rembrandt, Rubens, Claude, Poussin and Watteau. Public guided tours Saturday and Sunday.

Duncan Campbell Contemporary Art

Pa Pr SC 🖰 🖰

Compact, well-lit commercial gallery with good natural light dedicated to talented young and established artists alike.
15 Thackeray Street, Kensington Square, London W8 5ET, tel: 0171 937 8665
Contact: Duncan Stewart Campbell, Exhibition Organiser
Open: Mon-Fri 11-6; Sat 10-5
Space: 1 gallery with 24 lin m hanging space and 456 sq m floor space
Exhibitions: 15 a year all originated
Details: Talented graduate level young artists encouraged. Supported by a fairly conservative representational and abstract group of established painters, watercolourists and wood engravers. Applications from artists seeking exhibitions only on a long-term continuing basis.

Eagle Gallery

Pa Ph Pr SC 🖰

Gallery with a particular interest in installation work and also shows and publishes bookworks.
159 Farringdon Road, London EC1, tel: 0171 833 2674
Contact: Emma Hill
Open: Thurs & Fri 11-6; Sat & Sun 11-4
Space: 1 gallery
Exhibitions: 10 a year all originated
Details: 3 book shows planned each year. Artists on show include young contemporary artists as well as more established names. Those wishing to apply should first telephone for details.

Earlsfield Library Exhibition Room

Pa Ph Pr Cr SC 🖰🖰 H 🖰

Run by Wandsworth Libraries, this multi-purpose exhibition space features mainly local artists and occasional information displays.
Magdalen Road, Earlsfield, London SW18 3NY, tel: 0181 871 6389
Contact: Roger Coton, Branch Librarian
Open: Mon, Tues, Thurs 9.30-7; Fri 9.30-5; Sat 9-5
Space: 1 gallery with 28 lin m hanging space plus 15 lin m on screens and 117 sq m floor space
Exhibitions: 15 a year all on a hire basis
Details: A general purpose room also used as a study room and hired out for meetings etc. Audience is library users and hirers of room. Spotlit. Mainly, but not exclusively, used for exhibitions by local artists. £20 charge for 3 week exhibition + 20% commission on any sales made though this is not main function of exhibition space.

East West

Pa Ph SC 🖰 🖰

Commercial gallery showing British and international artists.
8 Blenheim Crescent, London W11 1NN, tel: 0171 229 7981, fax: 0171 2210741
Contact: David Solomon, Co-Director
Open: Tues-Sat 11-6; or by appointment
Space: 1 gallery with 38 lin m hanging space plus 8 lin m on screens and 50 sq m floor space
Exhibitions: 10 a year all originated
Details: Programme comprises mostly one-person exhibitions. Work shown has figurative bias with emphasis on strong drawing. Most artists selected are graduates with 10 or more years spent developing their individuality. Gallery represents and exhibits approx 100 artists of 25 nationalities and promotes them in UK and abroad.

East-West Restaurant *

Display area in restaurant eating space.
188 Old Street, London EC1V 9FR, tel: 0171 608 0300
Contact: Mr Royston Day, Manager/Head Chef
Space: 1 gallery with 30 lin m hanging space
Exhibitions: 12 a year all on a hire basis
Details: No charge for exhibitors. Anybody welcome to exhibit if we deem the artwork suitable. Artwork displayed for 1 month.

Economist

Office complex with exhibition space, inside and outside, to show interesting contemporary art.
25 St James's Street, London SW1A 1HG, tel: 0171 830 7000, fax: 0171 839 2968
Contact: Helen Mann, Arts Committee
Open: Mon-Sun 10-7
Space: 1 gallery with 68 lin m hanging space and 225 sq m floor space
Exhibitions: 17 a year all originated
Details: The Economist newspaper has space available, both inside and out, which can be used for a changing programme of exhibitions. Outdoor courtyard space for sculpture and inside for paintings etc by artists who have no dealer or whose dealer is based outside the West End of London. Approx 10 exhibitions a year inside and 7 exhibitions outside. Sale of work not a primary concern but 20% commission taken on any sales made.

Edith Grove

Gallery overlooking garden with good natural light exhibiting and selling a variety of contemporary art.
10a Edith Grove, London SW10 0NW, tel: 0171 376 3127
Contact: Catherine Tappenden, Owner
Open: Mon-Fri 2-6; other times by appointment
Space: 1 gallery with 6 lin m hanging space and 42 sq m floor space
Exhibitions: 15 a year of which 13 originated, 2 on a hire basis
Details: Small, friendly and informal gallery with good lighting and daytime light in conservatory area. Aims to always have on view an interesting selection of contemporary paintings and sculpture to a high standard. Small group shows and new artists encouraged. Mailing list encompasses all age groups, main preferences being for work which is realistic rather than abstract. Sale of work is gallery's primary role.

Edward Totah *

Shows and deals in figurative and abstract art from Britain and abroad.
13 Old Burlington Street, London W1, tel: 0171 734 0343, fax: 0171 287 2186
Contact: Edward Totah, Director
Space: 2 galleries with 64 lin m hanging space and 120 sq m floor space
Exhibitions: 8 a year all originated
Details: Work by new and established names every two months. 2 rooms available on ground and lower ground floors, both with natural light.

Electrum Gallery *

Exhibits and sells contemporary modern jewellery.
21 South Molton Street, London W1, tel: 0171 629 6325
Contact: Barbara Cartlidge, Director
Space: 3 galleries
Exhibitions: 10 a year all originated
Details: Shows over 85 different jewellers' work.

Elms Lesters Painting Rooms

Large gallery between Soho and Covent Garden with varied programme of exhibitions; also available for hire.
1-5 Flitcroft Street, Soho, London WC2H 8DH, tel: 0171 836 6747, fax: 071 379 0789
Contact: Fiona McKinnon
Open: Mon-Fri 12-6; Sat by appointment
Space: 1 gallery with 190 sq m floor space
Exhibitions: 6 a year of which 5 originated, 1 on a hire basis
Details: Presents contemporary and tribal art in one very large space. Aims to bring new and established artists from Britain, Europe, Africa and Oceania, to a wide cross-section of public. Solo and mixed shows. Selling work one of main aims of gallery.

Entwhistle

Smart new small commercial gallery showing young international artists: painting, sculpture, multi-media.
37 Old Bond Street, London W1X 3AE, tel: 0171 409 3484, fax: 0171 499 5795
Contact: Helen St Clyr, Administrator
Open: Mon-Fri 10-5.30; Sat 11-2
Space: 1 gallery with 21 lin m hanging space
Exhibitions: 8 a year of which 6 originated, 2 touring
Details: Privately funded gallery with wide ranging programme showing innovative work. Aims to educate Old Bond Street with the contemporary.

Europa Gallery

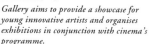

Headquarters for the London Borough of Sutton's Library Service, suitable for arts, crafts and many commercial displays and promotions.
Central Library, St Nicholas Way, Sutton, London SM1 1EA, tel: 0181 770 4700, fax: 0181 770 4777
Contact: Lesley Vye, Support Services
Space: 2 galleries with plus 802 lin m on screens and 833 sq m floor space
Exhibitions: 35 a year all on a hire basis

Everyman Cinema Foyer Gallery *

Gallery aims to provide a showcase for young innovative artists and organises exhibitions in conjunction with cinema's programme.
Everyman Cinema, Hollybush Vale, Off Heath Street, Hampstead, London NW3, tel: 0171 435 1525/431 2240
Contact: Exhibition Organiser, 9 Denning Road, London, NW3
Space: 1 gallery with 8 sq m floor space
Exhibitions: 12 a year all originated
Details: Foyer space within world's oldest repertory cinema showing work by living artists. Exhibitions attract the attention of large cinema-going public passing through the space. Work shown includes drawings, prints, photography, textiles and paintings. All shows are solo, most are the work of young first-time exhibitors. Cinema also keeps a collection of posters dating back 50 years.

Factual Nonsense (FN)

Business with policy to produce idealist exchange mechanism between art, advertising and commerce.
44a Charlotte Road, London EC2 3PD, tel: 0171 613 5048, fax: 0171 613 5780
Contact: Joshua Compston, Director
Open: Wed-Sat 12-6; or by appointment
Space: 1 gallery with 37 lin m hanging space and 74 sq m floor space
Exhibitions: 6 a year all originated
Details: Aims to present itself on a mass produced scale as a cultural and critical example within commerce, thus producing political leverage within late capitalism.

Fieldborne Galleries

Commercial gallery exhibiting the work of British artists and sculptors only.
63 Queens Grove, St John's Wood, London NW8 6ER, tel: 0171 586 3600
Contact: Bernard & Victoria Stemfield, Director
Open: Mon-Fri 10-5.30; all times by appointment

Space: 2 galleries with 70 lin m hanging space and 100 sq m floor space
Exhibitions: 3 a year all originated
Details: Two areas, on ground and lower ground floors. Access for wheelchair users to ground floor only.

Filef

96-98 Central Street, Islington, London EC1 YAJ, tel: 0171 6080125, fax: 0171 4900938
Contact: Francesca
Open: Mon-Fri 10-1, 2-6
Space: 3 galleries
Exhibitions: 6 a year all originated
Details: Space within Italian community centre. Only Italian artists or artists with Italian origins need apply. Upstairs room and two downstairs rooms available to artists who organise own publicity and private views.

Finchley Fine Art Galleries *

983 High Road, North Finchley, London N12 8QR, tel: 0181 446 4848
Contact: Exhibition Manager
Details: Four galleries currently used for retailing of C18th-C20th watercolours, painting and prints, sculpture, bronzes, ceramics, etc. Possible future exhibitions currently under consideration.

Flowers East

Commercial gallery whose main aim is to promote artists' careers.
199-205 Richmond Road, London E8, tel: 0181 985 3333, fax: 0181 985 0067
Contact: Angela Flowers
Open: Tues-Sun 10-6
Space: 2 galleries
Exhibitions: 24 a year all originated
Details: Expansion of the Angela Flowers Gallery, opened in 1988. 2 gallery areas one of which is a graphics gallery.

Flowers East at London Fields

Gallery works in conjunction with Flowers East with shows primarily by gallery artists.
282 Richmond Road, London E8, tel: 0181 985 3333, fax: 0181 985 0067
Contact: Angela Flowers, Matthew Flowers, Karen Demuth
Open: Tues-Sun 10-6
Space: 1 gallery
Exhibitions: 12 a year all originated

Flying Colours

Varied and lively stock of Scottish contemporary paintings.
15 Chesham Street, London SW1X 8ND, tel: 0131 235 2831

Footstool Restaurant Gallery

Changing exhibition programme in restaurant setting.
St John's Smiths Square, London SW1, tel: 0171 222 2168, fax: 0171 223 1618
Contact: David Pratt, Exhibition Organiser
Open: Mon-Fri 11.30-5.30; from 5 on concert evenings; Sat & Sun from 6 when concert scheduled.
Space: 1 gallery
Exhibitions: 11 a year all on a hire basis
Details: Sales are primary function of exhibitions.

Forty Hall Museum

Two exhibition spaces in museum housing C17th and C18th furniture, pictures and local history displays.
Forty Hill, Enfield, London EN2 9HA, tel: 0181 363 8196, fax: 0181 367 9098
Contact: J W Griffin, Local History & Museums Officer
Open: Thurs-Sun 11-5
Space: 1 gallery
Exhibitions: 6 a year
Details: Museum built in 1629. The Raynton Room usually booked 4/5 years in advance. The Exhibition Gallery occasionally used to present exhibitions by local societies and travelling shows.

Francis Graham-Dixon Gallery

Gallery showing and dealing in contemporary British, European and American art and specialising in abstract painting and sculpture.
17-18 Great Sutton Street, London EC1V 0DN, tel: 0171 250 1962, fax: 0171 490 1069
Contact: Francis Graham-Dixon, Director
Open: Mon-Sat 11-6
Space: 2 galleries with 60 lin m hanging space and 200 sq m floor space
Exhibitions: 8 a year all originated
Details: Ground-floor gallery with good natural light and 45 m wall space. Lower ground floor space has 11.5 m wall space. Most artists shown are exclusively represented by the gallery.

Francis Kyle Gallery

Gallery shows younger British artists and leading European and American artists.
9 Maddox Street, London W1, tel: 0171 499 6870, fax: 0171 495 0180
Contact: Director
Space: 3 galleries
Details: Paintings, watercolours, drawings and limited edition prints.

Freud's Café/Bar/Gallery

Wall space within fashionable café / bar.
198 Shaftesbury Avenue, London WC2H 8JL, tel: 0171 240 9933
Contact: Pat Thomas, Exhibitions Organiser, Freud's, 36 Great James Street, London, WC1N 3HB, tel: 0171 831 8641, fax: 0171 831 3062
Open: Mon-Sat 11am-11pm; Sun 12-10.30pm
Space: 1 gallery with 19 lin m hanging space
Exhibitions: 13 a year of which 12 originated, 1 on a hire basis
Details: Wide range of work by young artists which may be challenging, even difficult. The nature of the space dictates that work can be hung on walls only. Exhibitions change monthly. Contact exhibition organiser for further information. Commission charged on sales.

Frith Street Gallery

Gallery in Soho showing mainly abstract works on paper and canvas.
59-60 Frith Street, London W1V 5TA, tel: 0171 494 1550, fax: 0171 287 3733
Contact: Jane Hamlyn
Open: Tues-Fri 10-6; Sat 11-4
Exhibitions: 10 a year all originated
Details: Restored C17th house containing ground floor and basement exhibition spaces. Shows work by both young and established artists from Britain and abroad. Tend to be solo shows.

Galeric Kohler

Commercial gallery with personal approach where patrons and artist are encouraged to meet.
14 Osten Mews, London SW7 4HW, tel: 0171 370 0850, fax: 0171 370 2843
Contact: Margot Wong, Director
Open: Tues-Sat 2-6; and by appointment
Space: 1 gallery with 50 lin m hanging space and 18 sq m floor space
Exhibitions: 8 a year all originated
Details: All exhibitions include two and three dimensional works particularly sculpture, ceramics, prints and some oil paintings and photographs. Gallery aims to introduce artist and work to private patrons

and organisations. British and European artists represented.

Galerie Not

Pa Ph Pr Cr Sc ✓ H ♿

Unspoilt Victorian shop with a dividing communicating door which enables two small exhibitions to be shown at one time adapting well to combined art and makers' exhibitions.
54 Mill Lane, West Hampstead, London NW6 1NJ, tel: 0171 433 3526
Contact: Philip Not, Gallery Proprietor
Open: Tues-Fri 10.30-4.30; Sat 10.30-6; private viewing by appointment
Space: 2 galleries with 18 lin m hanging space and 30 sq m floor space
Exhibitions: 24 a year of which 2 originated, 22 on a hire basis
Details: The gallery specialises in oils, watercolours, small sculpture, photography and craftwork. One-person and group exhibitions by established and talented new artists and makers welcome. Gallery has ample natural light. Sale of work is considered gallery's primary role. No commission taken on sales from solo exhibitions; 20% commission on sales made from group shows.

Galerie Vermillion

Pa Ph Pr Cr Sc

Established and non-established artists with work ranging from the traditional and the figurative to the experimental and avant-garde.
120 Upper Tooting Road, London SW17 7EN, tel: 0181 767 5029
Details: Changing display of work with shows by individual artists from time to time. Hopes to act as a warehouse for the fine and applied arts.

Gallery 273 *

Pa Ph Pr Cr Sc ✓

Private gallery with opportunities for young local artists.
Physics Dept, Queen Mary & Westfield College, Mile End Road, London E1 4NS, tel: 0171 975 5051
Contact: Anthony Scivetti
Space: 1 gallery with 20 lin m hanging space and 75 sq m floor space
Exhibitions: 6 a year all originated
Details: Established 30 years ago. No charge made for hire of the gallery and no commission on sales. However, the artist is asked to make a contribution towards cost of the private view and to provide invitation cards at his/her own expense.

Gallery 1885

Ph ✓ ♿

Gallery whose purpose is to exhibit contemporary work by photographers and give publicity to Camera Club.
Camera Club, 16 Bowden Street, Kennington, London SE5 4DS, tel: 0171 587 1809
Contact: Alan Foster-Turner, Exhibitions Secretary
Space: 1 gallery with 56 sq m floor space
Exhibitions: 12 a year all originated
Details: Gallery run by the Camera Club founded 1885. Welcomes approaches from photographers wishing to exhibit. Talks and lectures organised to complement programme. Exhibitions change monthly and opening reception by invitation first Friday in month.

Gallery at Ballantyne & Date

Pa Ph Pr Cr Sc LA ✓ ♿

Shows modern and contemporary fine art from Europe and Asia.
38 Museum Street, London WC1, tel: 0171 242 4249, fax: 0171 430 0684
Space: 2 galleries with 170 sq m floor space
Exhibitions: 10 a year all originated
Details: Programme of solo and group shows of innovative work of quality. Artists contribute to all costs.

Gallery at Bird and Davis

45 Holmes Road, Kentish Town, London NW5 3AN, tel: 0171 485 3797, fax: 0171 284 0509

Gallery at John Jones

Pa Ph Pr Cr Sc ✓ H ♿

Commercial gallery with contemporary British art exhibitions held throughout the year.
4 Morris Place, London N4 3JG, tel: 0171 281 2380, fax: 0171 281 5956
Contact: Frankie Rossi, Director
Open: Mon-Fri 10-6; Sat 10-3
Space: 2 galleries with 14 lin m hanging space plus 1 lin m on screens and 1114 sq m floor space
Exhibitions: 8 a year all originated
Details: Exhibitions held alongside permanent display of master graphics. Forums and talks held in conjunction with exhibitions.

Gallery Differentiate

45 Shad Thames, Tower Bridge, London SE1 2NJ, tel: 0171 257 8909

Gallery in Cork Street

Pa Ph Pr Cr Sc H ♿

Central London gallery available for hire for art exhibitions and events of "internationally recognised high standard."
28 Cork Street, London W1X 1HB, tel: 0171 287 8408, fax: 0171 287 2018
Contact: Michele Fone/Benedikte van Heesewijk, Manager
Open: Mon-Fri 10-6; Sat 10-1

Space: 1 gallery with 60 lin m hanging space and 125 sq m floor space
Exhibitions: 17 a year of which 4 originated, 13 on a hire basis
Details: Gallery available on weekly hire charge with no commission taken on sales. Versatile and fully-equipped display area, hanging systems, security, plinths, display cases, etc. Advice offered on organisation, marketing and promotion of exhibitions and possible assistance with mailing lists. Facilities for disabled people within exhibitions will vary according to client hiring gallery.

Gallery K *

Pa Pr Sc ✓ H

Contemporary art gallery specialising in European & British contemporary art.
101-103 Heath Street, Hampstead, London NW3 6SS, tel: 0171 794 4949, fax: 0171 431 4833
Contact: Ritsa Kyriacou/Katerina Gregos, Directors
Space: 2 galleries with 70 lin m hanging space and 130 sq m floor space
Exhibitions: 12 a year of which 10 originated, 2 on a hire basis
Details: Work shown includes painting, sculpture, works on paper, installations. Exhibits mostly abstract, although some figurative and conceptual work shown. Specialises in Greek painters. Welcomes applications by young contemporary artists with appropriate work.

Gallery of Modern Art

Pa Ph Pr Cr Sc ✓ ♿

Gallery showing two- and three-dimensional work by mainly established artists.
9 Barmouth Road, London SW18 2DT, tel: 0181 875 1481
Contact: Brit Newbery, Gallery Director
Open: Mon-Thurs 10-4; Sat & evenings by appointment
Space: 1 gallery with 22 lin m hanging space and 32 sq m floor space
Exhibitions: 45 a year all originated
Details: Aims to provide exposure to professional artists whose work gallery considers should be better recognised. Abstract and ceramics among contemporary work shown. Features international as well as established UK artists. Sales of work important (commission taken) along with commitment to breaking new ground. Walls 10 feet high.

Gallery on the Lane

205 Acton Lane, Chiswick, London W4 5DA, tel: 0181 742 1754
Open: Mon-Sat 9-6, Sun; other times by appointment.

Gallery (The)

Pa Ph Cr Sc ● H

74 South Audley Street, London W1Y 5FF, tel: 0171 491 2948, fax: 0171 629 0414
Contact: Annabelle Cornelius
Space: 37 lin m hanging space
Exhibitions: 25 a year
Details: Gallery housed in Grade II listed Georgian building in heart of Mayfair. The display space has been restored to include original fireplaces, cornices, a heavily ornamental ceiling and antico flooring. Hanging space on two parallel walls each 60ft x 20ft. Hired out to individuals and groups who administer own exhibitions on a weekly basis.

Gasworks

A Pa Pr ●

Artist-run space showing contemporary art.
155 Vauxhall Street, London SE11, tel: 0171 587 5202
Contact: Rebecca Fortnum & Helen Ireland, Gallery Co-ordinators
Space: 1 gallery with 33 lin m hanging space and 48 sq m floor space
Exhibitions: 15 a year all originated

Gayton Library

Pa Ph Pr Cr Sc ● H

Dedicated area within main lending library run by Harrow Library Service with varied programme featuring work by local artists, both individuals and societies.
Gayton Road, Harrow, Middlesex, London HA1 2HL, tel: 0181 427 6012/ 0181 427 8986
Contact: John Pennells, Principal Librarian, Lending Services
Open: Mon, Tues, Thurs 9.30-8; Fri 9.30-6; Sat 9-5
Space: 1 gallery with 7 lin m hanging space plus 42 lin m on screens and 61 sq m floor space
Exhibitions: 22 a year of which 2 originated, 20 on a hire basis
Details: Exhibition programme designed to encourage existing artists and to increase awareness of opportunities locally to take up art as an interest. Work from local schools and colleges, reflecting diversity of the community is also shown. Exhibitions usually booked for 2 weeks. Library provides limited help with publicity and insurance. Sales not a priority.

Geffrye Museum *

Cr H

Long-term exhibitions staged (3-6 months) on subjects related to history of English domestic interior and related fields.
Kingsland Road, London E2 8EA, tel: 0171 739 9893, fax: 0171 729 5647
Contact: Christine Lalumia, Exhibition Organiser

Space: 1 gallery with 195 sq m floor space
Exhibitions: 3 a year of which 2 originated, 1 on a hire basis

Gilmour Gallery

Pa Ph Pr Sc

A commercial gallery exhibiting work by artists from Britain and abroad including those the gallery represents.
1 Colville Place, London W1, tel: 0171 637 4863
Contact: David Gilmour, Director
Open: Mon-Fri 10-6; Sat 11-1
Space: 2 galleries with 27 lin m hanging space and 74 sq m floor space
Exhibitions: 8 a year all originated
Details: Monthly exhibitions held including those by artists whom the gallery represents. Applications from artists only with prior notice/agreement.

Gimpel Fils

Pa Pr Sc

Major London gallery showing American, British and European artists' paintings and sculpture.
30 Davies Street, London W1Y 1LG, tel: 0171 493 2488, fax: 0171 629 5732
Contact: Rene Gimpel, Simon Lee, Directors
Open: Mon-Fri 10-5.30; Sat 10-1
Space: 2 galleries with 16 lin m hanging space and 80 sq m floor space
Exhibitions: 10 a year all originated
Details: Artists include Robert Adams, Terry Atkinson, Charles Beauchamp, Reg Butler, Hubert Dalwood, Alan Davie, Andrea Fisher, Pamela Golden, Barbara Hepworth, Susan Hiller, Albert Irvin, Peter Kennard, Yves Klein, Peter Lanyon, Louis le Bronquy, Antoni Malinowski, Bernard Meadows, Henry Moore, Ben Nicholson, Nikki de Saint Phalle. Selling work is gallery's primary role.

Glasshouse (The)

A Cr

Gallery and glass blowing studios where work by leading contemporary British makers (Annette Meech, Christopher Williams, Fleur Tookey and David Taylor) can be seen.
21 St Alban's Place, Islington, London N1 0NX, tel: 0171 359 8162, fax: 071 359 9485
Contact: Ann Morgan, Gallery Administrator
Open: Tues-Fri 10-6; Sat 10-5
Space: 1 gallery with 36 sq m floor space
Details: Artist-run studio comprising hot and cold glass working facilities and gallery displaying the work of permanent members. Displays are changed once a week. The selection of studio glass exhibited varies from one-off collector's pieces to limited edition works. Glasshouse also undertakes commissions, restoration of

antique and contemporary glass. The only gallery in Central London to allow the public to view the making of hot glass. On Craft Council selected list. Sale of work not primary role of gallery.

Gloucester Gallery

12 Gloucester Road, London SW7 4RB, tel: 0171 589 4552

Goethe-Institut London

Pa Ph Pr Sc ●

Showcase for predominantly contemporary German art including painting, sculpture, installation, photography and video art.
50 Princes Gate, Exhibition Road, London SW7 2PH, tel: 0171 411 3400, fax: 0171 581 0974
Contact: Helga Wilderotter-Ikonomou, Head of Programme Department
Space: 50 lin m hanging space plus 20 lin m on screens and 170 sq m floor space
Exhibitions: 4 a year of which 2 originated, 2 touring
Details: Works exhibited mainly by German artists living and working in Germany; many showing in UK for the first time. Works by British artists related to a German context also considered. Solo shows a rare exception, occasional lectures organised with exhibitions. Audience with an interest in German art and culture.

Great Western Studios

Pa Ph Pr Cr Sc A ●

5,000 sq feet open plan warehouse space for exhibitions in building with artists' studios, open to proposals from curators and visual artists for exhibitions of contemporary art.
The Lost Property Building, Great Western Road, London W9 3NY, tel: 0171 221 0100, fax: 0171 221 0200
Contact: Nicholas Kirkham, Director
Open: By arrangement, contact N Kirkham
Space: 2 galleries with 85 lin m hanging space and 420 sq m floor space
Details: New large exhibition space planning to show 3 exhibitions a year. Open to proposals. Lots of movable screens available. Sale of work not a priority.

Greenwich Citizens Gallery

Pa Ph Pr Cr Sc A ● H

Gallery targets local people and priority groups historically excluded from participation and representation in visual arts.
147 Powis Street, Woolwich, London SE18
Contact: The Curator, Greenwich Borough Museum, 232 Plumstead High Street, London, SE18 1JT, tel: 0181 855 3240
Open: Tues-Sat 10-5 during displays; can vary
Space: 1 gallery with 35 lin m hanging

space plus 20 lin m on screens and 170 sq m floor space

Exhibitions: 8 a year all originated

Details: Run by the London Borough of Greenwich. Promotes artists who are normally discriminated against by mainstream white art institutions. The gallery wants to improve the relationship between artists and the community. Active education policy to promote critical awareness of visual arts and their relationship to social/political context.

Greenwich Printmakers

A Pa Pr

Small exhibition space showing prints and other works on paper by its members.

1a Greenwich Market, London SE10 9HZ, tel: 0181 858 1569

Contact: John Hurley, 19 Shirley Way, Shirley, CR0 8PF, tel: 0181 777 6527

Open: Tues-Sun 10.30-5.30

Space: 1 gallery with 15 lin m hanging space plus 4 lin m on screens and 27 sq m floor space

Exhibitions: 5 a year

Details: Work of the 46 artist/printmaker members of the association exhibited. Exhibitions organised in other parts of the country or abroad. Works sold seen as priority.

Greenwich Theatre Art Gallery *

Pa Ph Pr Cr ✓

Shows solo exhibitions by local artists, often those exhibiting for the first time.

Crooms Hill, Greenwich, London SE10 8ES, tel: 0181 858 4447, fax: 0181 858 8042

Contact: Joanna Reynolds, Gallery Manager

Space: 2 galleries

Exhibitions: 7 a year all originated

Details: Presents a variety of work for visitors, often people not used to the gallery situation. Aims to create a relaxed and informal atmosphere where potential customers are not made to feel uneasy about asking questions regarding the work and how to buy it. Promotes theatre, dance, performance art related work.

Groucho Club

Pa Ph Pr SG ⊗

First-floor private club with restaurant; reception rooms used for exhibitions.

45 Dean Street, London W1V 5AP, tel: 0171 439 4685, fax: 0171 437 0133

Contact: Nicola Whittington, Manager

Open: 8-1 by appointment or with a member only

Exhibitions: 14 a year all originated

Details: Exhibits work by young artists not represented by agent or gallery. Large mixed media paintings have dominated programme, but has held successful

exhibition of fabrics. One of the restaurants also used to display members' work for sale. Sales not main role.

Gruzelier Modern & Contemporary Art

Pa Pr SG ✓

Gallery offering a range of young contemporary artists and collectors items by established British artists.

16 Maclise Road, London W14 0PR, tel: 0171 603 4540

Contact: John Gruzelier

Space: 5 galleries with 607 sq m floor space

Exhibitions: 10 a year all originated

Details: Exhibition programme combines solo, 2/3 person, and mixed thematic shows. Artists may apply for details in writing.

Hackney Museum

Pa Ph Pr Cr ✓ &Wc

Small temporary exhibition space in museum available for Hackney-based artists only.

Central Hall, Mare Street, London E8 1HE, tel: 0181 986 6914

Contact: Fiona Davison, Curator

Space: 1 gallery with plus 3 lin m on screens and 70 sq m floor space

Exhibitions: 2 a year both originated

Details: Collects and shows work based on history of Hackney and the roots of its people. Shows work in a variety of media by artists who work, study or live in the borough as well as historical works and artifacts. Half the shows are solo and most are by living artists. Target audience is the people of Hackney, of every age and interest. Sales not a priority.

Hales Gallery / Revival Café *

Pa Ph Pr SG ✓

Interested in sculpture/installation and works that cross the boundaries of different art forms.

70 Deptford High Street, London SE8 4RT, tel: 0181 694 1194

Contact: Paul Hedge

Open: Mon-Sat 10-4

Space: 1 gallery with 140 sq m floor space

Exhibitions: 2 a year both originated

Details: Presents the work of newly established artists in a programme of approximately 10 shows a year. Aims for audience of local people and buyers from London and abroad.

Hamilton's Gallery

Ph ✓ ⊗

Commercial gallery specialising in photography; C19th to contemporary.

13 Carlos Place, London W1Y 5AG, tel: 0171 499 9493, fax: 0171 629 9919

Contact: Andrew Cowan, Director

Open: Tues-Sat 10-6

Space: 3 galleries with 325 sq m floor space

Exhibitions: 8 a year all originated

Details: Predominantly solo exhibitions. Aims to attract people interested in photography and introduce and sell work to a wider audience. Portfolio viewing system held on last Friday of every month. 3 different size spaces within the one substantial area.

Hanina Gallery

Pa SG &

Large purpose-built exhibition space in Notting Hill Gate area specialising in unusual and decorative European and American paintings and sculptures from 1890s to 1930s.

180 Westbourne Grove, London W11 2RH, tel: 0171 243 8877, fax: 0171 243 0132

Contact: Yuval Hanina

Open: Mon-Sat 10-6

Space: 1 gallery with 145 sq m floor space

Details: Hanina Gallery opened as European branch of Nanina Fine Arts Ltd, New York. Primary interests is to shed more light on important works by artists and movements which flourished alongside Impressionism, especially Symbolist, Secessionist and modern American works. Gallery's sculpture court, a double volume space, displays large collection of late C19th and early C20th sculptures, strong in animal and sporting pieces. May in future include contemporary work of similar nature.

Hardware Gallery

Pa Pr SG ✓ &

Specialises in contemporary printmaking and British artists' bookworks.

162 Archway Rd, Highgate, London N6 5BB, tel: 0181 341 6415, fax: 0181 348 0561

Contact: Deirdre Kelly, Director

Open: Tues-Sat 2-6

Space: 1 gallery with 16 lin m hanging space and 30 sq m floor space

Exhibitions: 8 a year all originated

Details: Establed in 1986 to direct focus towards new printmaking by young artists. Holds broad spectrum of printwork on consignment basis. Through changing exhibition programme tries to encourage innovative use of printmaking. Since 1993 organised exhibitions of British artists' books and is an established focus for artists' publications. Wide range of books in stock and on permanent display. Exhibits both national and international work.

Harriet Green Gallery

Pa Ph Pr Cr SG ✓ &

Small commercial gallery specialising in contemporary art.

5 Silver Place, Soho, London W1R 3LJ,
tel: 0171 287 8328, fax: 0171 287 3990
Contact: Harriet Green, Director
Open: Tues-Fri 11-6; Sat 12-6
Space: 2 galleries with 43 lin m hanging
space and 46 sq m floor space
Exhibitions: 10 a year all originated
Details: Shows selected by Director.
Emphasis is on showing 2D work and
smaller 3D work at cutting edge of
contemporary art.

Hart Gallery

*A commercial gallery showing contemporary
art, ceramics and sculpture.*
113 Upper Street, Islington, London N1
1QN, tel: 0171 704 1131, fax: 0171 704
1707
Contact: John and Katherine Hart, Owners
Open: Wed-Fri 1-8; Sat & Sun 11-6
Space: 2 galleries with 100 lin m hanging
space and 140 sq m floor space
Exhibitions: 8 a year all originated
Details: Emphasis on high quality and
encouraging people to obtain original
artwork for their own enjoyment and
enrichment. One gallery for ceramics.

Hayward Gallery 21/10 call
again in
the Nov-
Steven.

South Bank Centre, London SE1 8XZ,
tel: 0171 928 3144, fax: 0171 401 2664
Contact: Exhibition Department, South
Bank Centre, London, SE1 8XX, fax: 0171
401 2664
Open: Daily 10-6; late nights Tues & Wed
until 8
Space: 5 galleries with 5364 sq m floor
space
Exhibitions: 4 a year all originated
Details: Exhibiting areas can be used for
educational and entertainment purposes
during exhibitions.

Heinz Gallery (RIBA)

*Shows work by contemporary and past
architects.*
21 Portman Square, London W1H 9HF,
tel: 0171 580 5533 ext 4807
Contact: Andrew Norris, Exhibitions
Officer
Space: 1 gallery with 21 lin m hanging
space plus 12 lin m on screens and 51 sq m
floor space
Exhibitions: 6 a year
Details: Part of the British Architectural
Library Drawings Collection. Five/six
exhibitions a year. See also entry for RIBA,
London.

Heritage Centre

*Local artists and community projects or
artists working within the centre's aims
encouraged to exhibit.*
19 Princelet Street, Spitalfields, London
E1 6QH, tel: 0171 377 6901
Contact: Mark Kiddle, Coordinator
Open: By appointment or when exhibiting
Space: 120 lin m hanging space and 300 sq
m floor space
Exhibitions: 12 a year
Details: Temporary exhibitions and
lectures arranged in unique Eastern
European style Synagogue, built in the
1880s in the back garden of an C18th
Hugenot house. Aims to establish a
resource centre and museum for the study
of immigration and the history of
Spitalfields. Exhibitions held to help
fundraise.

Highgate Gallery

*Part of a lively cultural institution well
used by Highgate residents.*
11 South Grove, Highgate, London N6
6BS, tel: 0181 340 3343
Contact: Antonia Evans, The
Administrator, HLSI, 11 South Grove,
London, N6 6BS, tel: 0181 340 3343
Open: Ring for details
Space: 1 gallery with 23 lin m hanging
space and 90 sq m floor space
Exhibitions: 7 a year
Details: Gallery within institution which
houses library, reading room and holds
lectures and adult education classes. One-
person or group shows. Exhibitions last up
to 3 weeks. Sales not priority. No
commission taken on sales made.

Honor Oak Gallery

*Informal commercial gallery showing works
on paper by wide range of C20th artists
from established masters to compatible
contemporaries.*
52 Honor Oak Park, Forest Hill, London
SE23 1DY, tel: 0181 291 6094
Contact: John Broad, Director
Open: Tues-Fri 9.30-6; Sat 9.30-5
Space: 1 gallery with 11 lin m hanging
space and 22 sq m floor space
Exhibitions: 1 a year originated
Details: About 30 artists represented in
continually changing exhibition. Annual
temporary exhibition provides opportunity
to concentrate on work of one or two
invited artists. Approaches from artists
welcome, but temporary exhibitions are by
invitation only. Not suitable for display of
large works.

Hoxton Hall

130 Hoxton Street, London N1 6SH
Contact: Marketing Officer

Hyde Park Gallery

*Commercial gallery exhibiting paintings
and sculpture with space to rent.*
16 Craven Terrace, London W2 3QD,
tel: 0171 402 2904
Contact: Christopher Moss, Proprietor
Open: Mon-Fri 11-6; Sat 11-4
Space: 5 galleries with 100 lin m hanging
space plus 8 lin m on screens and 91 sq m
floor space
Exhibitions: 15 a year of which 3
originated, 12 on a hire basis
Details: Gallery in residential and tourist
central London area. Flexible space to suite
different exhibitors to rent. Aims to sell
work.

Ice House

*Gallery programmed with temporary
exhibitions April-October.*
Holland Park, Off Kensington High
Street, London W8, tel: 0171 937 2542
Contact: Michael Goggin, Arts Officer,
Leighton House Museum, 12 Holland Park
Road, London, W14 8LZ, tel: 0171 603
1123
Space: 1 gallery
Exhibitions: 810 a year all on a hire basis
Details: Programme of two week
exhibitions. Small irregularly shaped
building, roughly circular with a
rectangular vestibule. Applications go
through selection procedure.

Images, Corporate Art Consultants *

*A consultancy placing art into offices, have
organised a number of exhibitions.*
19 Helenslea Avenue, Golders Green,
London NW11 8NE, tel: 0181 455 3160,
fax: 0181 209 0309
Contact: Mr Niall Fairhead
Exhibitions: 4 a year all originated
Details: Exhibitions organised include 'The
Green-Fund' at Smith's Gallery and The
Patrick Caulfield at The Tricycle Gallery.
Also several successful exhibitions in clients'
offices. Provide a commission service
involving artists based in London.

Imagination Gallery

*Airy atrium space created by fabric roof
stretched between two buildings, spanned by
elegant steel bridges.*
South Crescent, 25 Store Street, London
WC1E 7BL, tel: 0171 323 3300, fax:
0171 323 5810
Contact: Chris Bridge/Julie Hurst
Open: Flexible
Space: 1 gallery with plus 58 lin m on
screens and 33 sq m floor space
Exhibitions: 3 a year all originated

Details: Brief for gallery to 'stimulate, educate and entertain'. Only small amount of wall space but plenty hanging space on movable screen. Rental costs from £2000 per day, however each exhibition is costed separately.

Imperial War Museum

Pa Ph Pr Sc ☼ wc 4

A national museum showing a variety of exhibitions relating to aspects of C20th conflict.
Lambeth Road, London SE1 6HZ, tel: 0171 416 5000, fax: 0171 416 5374
Contact: Dr Christopher Dowling, Press Officer
Open: Daily 10-6
Space: 4 galleries
Exhibitions: 7 a year of which 6 originated, 1 touring
Details: Covers the two world wars and other conflicts involving Britain and the Commonwealth since 1914. Art department holds the largest collection of war paintings and posters in the country. Regular programme of changing exhibitions. Two galleries house permanent displays of paintings and drawings from First and Second World Wars, three others used for temporary exhibitions.

Institute of Contemporary Arts Bookshop: 925-2434

Pa Ph Pr Sc LA ☼ £ ☼ wc

Represents international contemporary arts across all its media, introducing international artists to national audiences, commissioning new British artists and curating thematic exhibitions.
The Mall, London SW1Y 5AH, tel: 0171 930 3647/0493, fax: 0171 873 0051
Contact: Emma Dexter, Director of Exhibitions
Open: Mon-Thurs & Sat-Sun 12-7.30; Fri 12-9
Space: 3 galleries with 130 lin m hanging space plus 22 lin m on screens and 327 sq m floor space
Exhibitions: 7 a year of which 5 originated, 2 touring
Details: Reflects other forms of visual culture, including architecture. Presents art from other centuries to aid understanding of the contemporary, and to re-evaluate the work of well-established artists, or those excluded from orthodox art histories. 2,500 visitors a week composed of professionals (design/media), clerical, artists, teachers, students, tourists. Sales not a priority. Aiming to make gallery fully accessible 1995/96.

Intaglio Gallery *

Pa Pr Sc ☼

Specialises in contemporary printmaking and related work with an international exhibition programme.

15 Corsica Street, Highbury, London N5 1JT, tel: 0171 704 6780, fax: 0171 704 6780
Contact: Karyn White, Partner/Director
Space: 1 gallery with 15 lin m hanging space and 22 sq m floor space
Exhibitions: 6 a year all originated
Details: Whilst many artists represented have established reputations, it is central to our policy to exhibit work by younger artists of exceptional promise.

Interim Art *

Pa Ph Pr Sc

Gallery showing contemporary work including installations.
21 Beck Road, London E8, tel: 0171 254 9607, fax: 0171 254 6445
Contact: Maureen Paley, Director
Open: Fri-Sat 11-6
Space: 1 gallery with 93 sq m floor space
Exhibitions: 5 a year all originated

Islington Arts Factory

Pa Ph Pr Cr Sc LA ☼ ☼ ☼

Aims to exhibit a wide range of visions to a wide range of children and adults who are not necessarily involved in the arts.
2 Parkhurst Road, Holloway, London N7 0SF, tel: 0171 607 0561
Contact: Phillippa Clayden/Denzil Forrester, Visual Arts Co-ordinators
Open: (Madeleine Pearson Gallery) Mon-Sat 10-6; (Kitchen Gallery) Mon-Fri 10-9.30; (Photography Gallery) Sat 10-6
Space: 3 galleries with 38 lin m hanging space and 77 sq m floor space
Exhibitions: 24 a year of which 4 originated, 20 on a hire basis
Details: Aims to create an environment that allows people to be an active participant of the arts and to provide artists the opportunity to exhibit at minimal cost. All exhibitions are on show for 3 weeks. All 3 galleries hold private views on same evening. Audience includes users of IAF. The Madeleine Pearson Gallery is in church building, its 60ft ceiling has inspired sculptors in particular to make work specifically for the gallery. Artists pay for hire of gallery plus posters and private view costs.

Islington Central Library Gallery *

Pa Ph Pr Cr Sc ☼

Exhibition space available to any artist who lives, works or studies in the borough.
London Borough of Islington Libraries Department, Central Library, 2 Fieldway Crescent, London N5 1PF, tel: 0171 609 3051 ext 242, fax: 0171 607 6409
Contact: Brian Armstrong
Space: 1 gallery with 38 lin m hanging space
Details: Shows work of local artists. 28 shows a year, each lasting two to three

weeks, including mixed and solo shows in a variety of media. Exhibitions of interest to the local community, including local history material, also mounted.

Japanese Gallery

Ph ☼ ☼

One room devoted to promotion and encouragement of Japanese wood block print technique.
66D Kensington Church Street, London W8 4BY, tel: 0171 229 2934, fax: 071 938 3056
Contact: Mr C.D. Wertheim, Managing Director
Open: Mon-Sat 10-6; Sun by appointment
Space: 15 lin m hanging space and 21 sq m floor space
Exhibitions: 4 a year all originated
Details: Specialises in Japanese woodcut prints; antique, contemporary or transitional period. Also sells original Japanese woodcut prints. Sales of primary importance.

Jason & Rhodes Gallery

Pa Pr Sc ☼ ☼

Large commercial gallery showing contemporary and modern British art.
4 New Burlington Place, London W1X 1FB, tel: 0171 434 1768, fax: 0171 287 8841
Contact: Benjamin Rhodes or Gillian Jason, Exhibition Organisers
Open: Mon-Fri 10-6; Sat 10.30-1.30
Space: 2 galleries with 60 lin m hanging space and 200 sq m floor space
Exhibitions: 9 a year all originated
Details: Deals in and shows work by young contemporary artists from Britain and abroad in variety of media – painting, drawing, sculpture, prints. Most shows solo with occasional group exhibition of work by gallery artists. Also showing modern British art.

Javier Lopez Gallery

Pa Sc Ph ☼ ☼

Shows international alongside British contemporary art supporting artists with exhibitions here and abroad and assisting in the development of their careers.
41-42 Foley Street, London W1P 7LD, tel: 0171 436 9881, fax: 0171 436 9884
Open: Tues-Fri 10-6; Sat 11-3
Space: 1 gallery with 23 lin m hanging space and 82 sq m floor space
Exhibitions: 8 a year some in collaboration with other galleries
Details: Opened in June 1995.

Jeanette Hayhurst Fine Glass *

Cr

Gallery specialises in high-quality contemporary glass work.

32a Kensington Church Street, London
W8, tel: 0171 938 1539
Contact: Jeanette Hayhurst, Director
Details: Recent shows included work from
Royal College of Art MA students; solo and
two-person shows by makers such as Keith
Brocklehurst, David Pryterch, Jane Beebe
Anthony Stern, Anna Dickinson and Jim
Roddiss. Shows last a fortnight. Permanent
display of antique and contemporary glass
for sale.

Jibby Beane

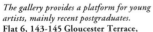

*The gallery provides a platform for young
artists, mainly recent postgraduates.*
**Flat 6, 143-145 Gloucester Terrace,
London W2 6DX, tel: 0171 723 5531**
Contact: Jonathan Goslan/Jibby Beane,
Co-Directors
Open: Wed & Thurs 12-6; or by
appointment
Space: 1 gallery with 154 lin m hanging
space and 33 sq m floor space
Exhibitions: 8 a year all originated
Details: Domestic space converted for
exhibitions. Mainly one-person shows.
Artists invited to design specially for the
space. Large sculptures and installations
accommodated. Events such as
contemporary music concerts and
interactive installations also organised. Sales
of work important to gallery.

Jill George Gallery

*Commercial gallery specialises in paintings,
drawings, watercolours and limited edition
prints by contemporary British artists.*
**38 Lexington Street, Soho, London W1R
3HR, tel: 0171 439 7319, fax: 0171 287
0478**
Contact: Jill George, Director, Jill George
Gallery
Space: 1 gallery with 38 lin m hanging
space and 288 sq m floor space
Exhibitions: 11 a year all originated
Details: Monthly exhibition programme by
invitation only. Permanent selection of
prints and originals on display. Gallery
arranges commissions for its artists.

John Campbell Gallery *

*Contemporary impressionist paintings by
selected gallery artists.*
**164 Walton Street, London SW3 2JL,
tel: 0171 584 9268, fax: 0171 581 3499**
Contact: Mr Hogben
Space: 3 galleries with 95 sq m floor space
Exhibitions: 3 a year all originated
Details: The gallery is also available for
hire.

John Martin of London

Modern British and contemporary fine art.
**38 Albermarle Street, London W1X 3FB,
tel: 0171 499 1314, fax: 0171 493 2842**

JPL Fine Arts

*Commercial gallery with changing stock,
three solo shows and one mixed show a year.*
**26 Davies Street, London W1Y 1LH, tel:
0171 493 2630, fax: 0171 493 1379**
Contact: Christian Neffe, Director
Exhibitions: 4 a year all originated
Details: Specialises in Impressionist and
Post-Impressionist drawings, watercolours,
pastels and paintings and C19th/C20th
French sculpture. Always changing display
of stock in main gallery.

Kaleidoscope

*Open exhibitions on mixed themes, eg.
'Circus', 'Erotica', the 'Political Circus'.*
**64 Willesden Lane, London NW6 7SX,
tel: 0171 328 5833**
Contact: Karl Barrie, Director
Open: Mon-Sat 10-6
Space: 2 galleries with 46 lin m hanging
space
Exhibitions: 12 a year all originated
Details: Visited by a mixed audience. "The
look we are seeking is slick and well
finished, fitting into the 'decor with flair'."
Always looking for paintings and sculpture
(not too large) and for pottery. Occasional
open exhibitions.

Kapil Jariwala Gallery

**4 New Burlington Street, London W1X
1FE, tel: 0171 437 2172**

Karsten Schubert *

*Minimal and conceptual art. Exhibitions of
gallery artists from England, Germany and
USA.*
**41/42 Foley Street, London W1, tel:
0171 631 0031, fax: 0171 436 9255**
Contact: Mr Karsten Schubert, Lady Helen
Windsor, Directors

Kew Gardens Gallery

*Gallery with access through Kew Gardens
aiming to raise awareness of importance
and contribution of botanical and flower
painting to botanical science and to better
understanding of plant kingdom.*
**Royal Botanic Gardens, Kew, London
TW9 3AB, tel: 0181 332 5618, fax: 0181
332 5610**
Contact: Mrs Diana Beevers, Gallery
Manager
Open: (Nov-Jan) 9.30-3.30; (Feb-Mar)
9.30-4; (Apr-Aug) 9.30-5.30; (Sept-Oct)

9.30-4.30; daily except Christmas and New
Year's Day
Space: 1 gallery with 58 lin m hanging
space and 162 sq m floor space
Exhibitions: 6 a year all originated
Details: Displays the best historic and
contemporary paintings and, whenever
possible, exhibits and interprets items from
Kew's collection. Works for sale where
appropriate. Sales important but not main
purpose of gallery. 40% commission +VAT
taken on sales made.

Kew Studio (Staircase Gallery)

*Light and airy staircase exhibition area in
building used for educational projects.*
**St Luke's House, 270 Sandycombe Road,
Kew Gardens, Richmond, Surrey,
London TW9 3NP, tel: 0181 332 2122**
Contact: Exhibitions Organiser
Open: Mon-Fri 10-1
Space: 1 gallery
Details: Solo or group exhibitions. The
Studio encourages both established artists
and art school leavers to show. Wall hung
work only and irregular wall space so
smaller works only. Apply in writing to
exhibitions organiser; booking fee £33 for
one month. 20% commission on sales.

Kingsgate Gallery

*Gallery on 2 levels situated within C19th
warehouse converted into artists'
workshops.*
**110-116 Kingsgate Road, London NW6
2JG, tel: 0171 328 7878**
Contact: Stephen Williams, Co-ordinator,
Kingsgate Workshops
Open: Thurs-Sun 2-6; and by
arrangement.
Space: 1 gallery with 26 lin m hanging
space and 46 sq m floor space
Details: Fortnightly exhibitions. Shows a
wide range of work through solo and group
exhibitions. Proposals considered quarterly.
Apply in writing with CV and photograph
to the coordinator. Commission 10% of
sales. Sale of work important but not
necessarily the gallery's primary role.

Kingston Museum

*Municipal gallery running a programme of
exhibitions by local amateur and
professional artists or work of local
significance.*
**Wheatfield Way, Kingston upon
Thames, London KT1 2PS, tel: 0181 546
5386, fax: 0181 547 6747**
Contact: Tracey Mardles, Public Services
Manager
Open: Mon, Tues, Thurs-Sat 10-5
Space: 1 gallery with 37 lin m hanging
space and 94 sq m floor space

Exhibitions: 9 a year of which 2 touring, 7 on a hire basis
Details: Predominantly by living artists. Most shows are solo and run for two to four weeks. Touring exhibitions taken and in-house object-based exhibitions organised. Available for hire. Sales not a priority.

Kingsway College Kentish Town Gallery

Large open-plan space exhibits fine art and design work from students and staff, and occasional external exhibition.
Kentish Town Centre, 87 Holmes Road, London NW5 3AX, tel: 0171 306 5927/ 5933
Contact: Mark Harris, Art & Design Department
Open: Mon-Fri 9am-9.30pm; Sat 10-3.30
Space: 1 gallery with 20 lin m hanging space and 166 sq m floor space
Exhibitions: 8 a year of which 7 originated, 1 touring
Details: Large art & design education programme. The gallery is a large well-lit space that is also the centre's reception hall. Direct access for street and adjacent coffee bar. Busy, attractive space. Audience mainly of local people studying wide variety of subjects at the centre. Lively openings attract wide range of people. Induction loop due to be installed. Sales not a priority.

Knapp Gallery

An informal gallery that gives an opportunity to artists without financial restrictions.
Regent's College, Inner Circle, Regent's Park, London NW1 4NS, tel: 0171 487 7540, fax: 0171 487 7657
Contact: Joanna Sloman, Exhibition Organiser, Aoife Fennell
Open: Mon-Fri 10-6
Space: 1 gallery with 48 lin m hanging space and 162 sq m floor space
Exhibitions: 10 a year all originated
Details: Solo shows of oils,watercolours and pastels. Also exhibitions of glass and embroidery. Encourages visitors from international student body, staff on campus, the local community and artists' friends and contacts. Sales not a priority.

Knights Park Gallery

Exhibition space in foyer of Design Faculty.
Kingston University, Knights Park Campus, Kingston upon Thames, London KT1 2QJ, tel: 0181 547 2000 ext 4128, fax: 0181 547 7011
Contact: Professor Bruce Russell, Head of School of Fine Art
Open: Mon-Fri 9.30-5.30; Sat 10-12

Space: 1 gallery with 44 lin m hanging space and 140 sq m floor space
Exhibitions: 20 a year of which 16 originated, 2 touring, 2 on a hire basis
Details: Exhibition space has 9' high walls and lighting by fluorescent and spots. Didactic exhibitions of work by staff of Faculty of Design (Fine Art, Foundation, Photography, Computers, Printmaking, Fashion, 3D design, Illustration). Also student-curated shows from these disciplines. Inter-School/Inter-Faculty thematic shows. Some shows of work by invited contemporary artists and occasional international shows resulting from transatlantic exchanges. Sales not a priority.

Kufa

Gallery in Bayswater with café and library specialising in oriental arts and architecture.
26 Westbourne Grove, London W2 5RH, tel: 0171 229 1928, fax: 0171 243 8513
Contact: Mr Walid Atiyeh, Administrator
Open: Mon-Sat 10-6; can be extended by negotiation.
Space: 1 gallery with 105 lin m hanging space and 245 sq m floor space
Exhibitions: 10 a year of which 7 originated, 3 touring
Details: Entrance, café and gallery are programmed as one space. Duration of exhibitions varies according to requirements. Basic aim is to increase public awareness and appreciation of art in general and to make the gallery a welcoming and popular place. Lectures can be held in gallery. Sale of work not a priority.

La Galerie *

Concentrates solely on works by French artists and aims to demonstrate that French art did not cease with the post impressionists.
225 Ebury Street, London SW1W 8UT, tel: 0171 730 9210, fax: 0171 730 9206
Contact: Jenne Aldridge/Emma Vaile
Space: 2 galleries with 199 sq m floor space
Exhibitions: 4 a year all originated
Details: Contemporary artists on show are well known in France but are not in the UK. Hopes to encourage more contemporary French artists to exhibit here in London. Works on show cover a range of oil paintings, watercolours, pastels, drawings and lithographs.

Lamont Gallery

Located in stylishly converted East End pub, with adjoining graphics area, exhibiting and dealing in leading contemporary figurative painters and sculptors.

65 & 67 Roman Road, Bethnal Green, London E2 0QN, tel: 0181 981 6332, fax: 0181 983 0144
Contact: Andrew Lamont, Director
Open: Wed-Sat 11-6
Space: 3 galleries with 39 lin m hanging space plus 5 lin m on screens and 100 sq m floor space
Exhibitions: 10 a year all originated
Details: In heart of the East End, where the largest concentration of artists in Britain live and work, it aims to attract new customers for contemporary art. Prices kept at reasonable level and work in variety of sizes and media shown. Solo shows with occasional theme exhibitions. Work by women particularly successful. Independent access for wheelchair users to 2 out of 3 galleries, one gallery inaccessible.

Lauderdale House

Lower Gallery within entrance hall and Upper Gallery available for hire in community arts centre.
Waterlow Park, Highgate Hill, London N6 5HG, tel: 0181 348 8716/0181 341 2032, fax: 0181 348 4293
Contact: Jenny Tolerton, Admin Officer
Open: Tues-Fri 11-4; Sat opening dependent on private bookings; Sun 12-5; times can vary so phone for details.
Space: 2 galleries with 19 lin m hanging space
Exhibitions: 27 a year of which 3 originated, 24 on a hire basis
Details: Situated in a listed building with an active arts programme. Evenings and weekends the house is used for concerts, children's or adults theatre and private functions. These increase the exposure to the exhibitions. Because of this multi-use there is no facility for free-standing exhibits, except on the night of the private view. Sales a priority. Wheelchair users can reach Upper Gallery with assistance.

Laure Genillard Gallery

Gallery showing mostly European contemporary art focusing on minimal and conceptual work.
38a Foley Street, London W1P 7LB, tel: 0171 436 2300
Open: Tues-Fri 11-6; Sat 11-3
Contact: Laure Genillard
Space: 1 gallery
Exhibitions: 7 a year all originated
Details: Shows installation work.

Laurent Delaye

A commercial gallery acting as agent to small number of young British artists.
44 Connaught Mansions, 398 Coldharbour Lane, London SW9 8LE, tel: 0171 737 2798, fax: 0171 733 3097

Contact: Laurent Delaye
Open: Fri & Sat 12-6; or by appointment
Space: 1 gallery with 25 lin m hanging space and 22 sq m floor space
Exhibitions: 4 a year all originated
Details: Exhibitions may be held in spaces other than the gallery, depending on the nature of the work. International promotion is considered the primary role of the gallery.

Lefevre Gallery

Po

Commercial gallery specialises in C19th and C20th European paintings and drawings.
30 Bruton Street, London W1X 8JB, tel: 0171 493 2107, fax: 0171 499 9088
Contact: Director
Space: 1 gallery
Details: Monthly exhibitions include British and European paintings & drawings.

Leigh Gallery

Po Pr Cr

Gallery specialises in studio pottery, glass, paintings, prints.
17 Leigh Street, London WC1, tel: 0171 388 3522, fax: 0171 388 0654
Contact: Michael Ransom-Witt, Director
Space: 1 gallery
Exhibitions: 3 a year all originated
Details: Exhibitions organised to accompany regularly changing stock.

Leighton House Museum

Po Ph Pr Cr SC LA ✓

Programme of changing exhibitions in museum housing collections of fine and decorative C19th art.
12 Holland Park Road, London W14 8LZ, tel: 0171 602 3316, fax: 0171 371 2467
Contact: Julia Findlater, Curator
Open: Mon-Sat 11-5
Space: 2 galleries with 140 lin m hanging space plus 20 lin m on screens and 1050 sq m floor space
Exhibitions: 9 a year of which 8 originated, 1 touring
Details: Exhibitions run for minimum of two weeks. Solo exhibitions preferred.

Lewisham Art House

A Po Ph Pr Cr SC LA ✓ ✪ ⬤

Run by artists for artists and the local community showing wide range of contemporary fine art.
140 Lewisham Way, New Cross, London SE14 6PD, tel: 0181 694 9011
Contact: John Turner, Gallery Coordinator
Open: Wed-Sun 11-6
Space: 1 gallery with 32 lin m hanging space plus 6 lin m on screens and 74 sq m floor space

Exhibitions: 17 a year of which 3 originated, 14 on a hire basis
Details: Exhibitions programme includes full range of arts practice, including work by individual artists, groups, "opens" and work by community groups. Every show includes talk and discussion programme and may feature practical workshops to explore aspects of work on show in greater depth. Sales not main function of gallery. No commission taken on works sold.

Limelight (The)

Po Ph Pr Cr SC ✓ ⬤⬤④

Dedicated exhibition space within library building.
Lewisham Library, 199/201 Lewisham High Street, London SE13 6LG, tel: 0181 297 8521, fax: 0181 297 8376
Contact: Sally Bushell, Arts Officer
Open: Mon, Tues, Fri, Sat 9.30-5; Tues, Thurs 9.30-8
Space: 1 gallery with 12 lin m hanging space
Details: Seeks to develop high-quality exhibitions and events programme featuring work by local artists, craftspeople and arts organisations, for benefit of local residents. Aims to encourage displays of work by groups and individuals traditionally under-represented. Illuminated glass display cases. Sales of work not priority.

Linda Blackstone Gallery

Po Pr Cr SC ⊗

Converted slaughterhouse showing figurative work by British artists.
The Old Slaughterhouse, r/o 13 High Street, Pinner, London HA5 5QQ, tel: 0181 868 5765, fax: 01923 897153
Contact: Mrs Linda Blackstone, Proprietor
Open: Wed-Sat 10-6
Space: 3 galleries with 50 lin m hanging space
Exhibitions: 6 a year all originated
Details: Selling gallery with natural light exhibiting work of around 40 British artists whose paintings/sculpture/ceramics are in representational manner. Mixed display throughout the year, punctuated by six three-week exhibitions.

Linhof Gallery *

Po Ph Pr Cr SC LA ✓

Linhof Professional Sales, 56 Marchmont Street, London WC1N 1AB, tel: 0171 278 1004, fax: 0171 837 1287
Contact: Mrs Pell-Johnson
Space: 1 gallery
Exhibitions: 3 a year originated
Details: Exhibits work produced by independent artists using Linhof photographic equipment, occasional special exhibitions from Linhof collection. Space free to artists who cover costs of framing, posters, private viewing cards, etc. Audience

predominantly professionals in photography market.

Lisson Gallery

Po Ph Pr SC ✓

Deals in and shows work by living artists in a variety of media, specialising in international avant-garde British sculpture.
67 Lisson Street, London NW1 5DA, tel: 0171 724 2739
Contact: Exhibition Organiser
Open: Mon-Fri 10-6; Sat 10-5
Space: 4 galleries with 3000 sq m floor space
Exhibitions: 10 a year all originated
Details: Interest confined to contemporary art since 1965. Promotes British artists worldwide and represents foreign artists in Britain. Exhibitions include painting, sculpture, drawing, prints and photography. Lisson Gallery also at 52-54 Bell Street, London, NW1 5DA; contact exhibition organiser at 67 Lisson Street.

Livesey Museum

Temporary exhibitions specially for children under 12.
682 Old Kent Road, London SE15 1JF, tel: 0171 639 5604, fax: 0171 277 5384
Contact: Nicky Boyd, Museum Manager
Open: Mon-Sat 10-5
Space: 1 gallery with 1500 sq m floor space
Exhibitions: 1 a year originated
Details: Exhibitions are thematic – past exhibits have been on light, water, circuses, robots and rubbish. Almost always an element of contemporary art.

Llewellyn Alexander (Fine Paintings)

Po Pr SC

Specialises in C20th British and European paintings including oils and watercolours, pastels and miniatures.
124-126 The Cut, Waterloo, London SE1, tel: 0171 620 1322, fax: 0171 928 9469
Contact: Exhibition Organiser
Open: Mon-Sat 10-7.30
Exhibitions: 12 a year all originated
Details: Gallery aims to exhibit the best of British contemporary paintings.

Loggia

A Po Pr SC ⊗

Small gallery and Sculpture Garden run by the Free Painters and Sculptors to promote public interest in the visual arts.
15 Buckingham Gate, London SW1E 6LB, tel: 0171 828 5963
Contact: Roy Rasmussen, Gallery Director
Open: Mon-Fri 6-8; Sat, Sun 2-6
Space: 1 gallery
Exhibitions: 11 a year all originated
Details: Members of the Free Painters and Sculptors voluntarily maintain the gallery and sculpture garden – a registered

Educational Charity. Discussions and exhibitions of members' work are held throughout the year. Applications for membership are welcomed and should be addressed to the Hon. Secretary FPS. Gallery's main function is to give members an opportunity to exhibit in London.

Logos Art Gallery

20 Barter Street, London WC1A 2AH, tel: 0171 404 7091, fax: 0171 430 1739

London Contemporary Art *

Pr

Commercial gallery specialising in prints and originals by contemporary British artists.
132 Lots Road, Chelsea, London SW10 0RJ, tel: 0171 351 7696, fax: 0171 376 3771
Contact: Marketing Manager
Space: 74 sq m floor space
Details: Permanent collection of work from stable of artists. Full staff of sales people and corporate consultants involved in promotion of work. Part of three storey printing complex including etching, lithography, silkscreen and origination & design ateliers.

London Ecology Centre Gallery

Pa Ph Pr Cr Sc LA ✓ H ●

Gallery with large street window hired to artists to show work broadly dealing with environmental issues.
45 Shelton Street, Covent Garden, London WC2H 9HJ, tel: 0171 379 4324, fax: 0171 379 8334
Contact: Michael Waller, Gallery Administrator
Open: Mon-Sat 10-6
Space: 1 gallery with 20 lin m hanging space and 60 sq m floor space
Exhibitions: 40 a year of which 5 originated, 35 on a hire basis
Details: Gallery is hired to artists who are selected for quality and innovation, and whose work is sympathetic to aims of Ecology Centre; raising awareness of environmental concerns. Gallery also available for meetings and lectures during the day. Whether sales important depends on artist.

London Film-makers Co-op

Pa Ph LA ✓

Small exhibitions of film makers' related visual art are held in the gallery and cinema/performance space for video/installation/sound/time-based work.
42 Gloucester Avenue, Camden, London, tel: 0171 586 4806/8516, fax: 0171 483 0068

Contact: John Thomson, Exhibition Organiser
Details: Cinema and performance space with exhibition area. Specialises in screening avant-garde and experimental films rarely. 70 showings a year includes triple screen films, slide and sound works, time-based media events, performance and installation work. Duration of exhibitions in gallery very variable, relates to the screening programme.

London Institute Gallery

65 Davies Street, London W1Y 2DA, tel: 0171 514 6000, fax: 0171 514 6131

London Print Workshop

Pr ✓

Gallery and print workshop presenting mixture of solo and group shows by both young and prestigious artists.
421 Harrow Road, London W10 4RD, tel: 0181 969 3247, fax: 0181 964 0008
Contact: John Phillips, Director
Space: 1 gallery with 17 lin m hanging space and 26 sq m floor space
Exhibitions: 12 a year of which 10 originated, 2 touring
Details: Gallery used and visited by general public and people with special interest in printmaking. Commission charged on sales.

London Printworks Trust

Pr Cr Sc ⓔ ●

Exhibition space housed in converted warehouse with workshops and design studios promoting printed textiles.
Unit 7, Brighton House, Brighton Terrace, Brixton, London SW9 8JD, tel: 0171 738 7841
Contact: Stewart Russell, Education/Exhibitions Co-ordinator
Open: Wed-Sun 10-6
Space: 1 gallery with 19 sq m floor space
Details: New gallery whose exhibition programme aims to promote contemporary printed textiles and stimulate cross disciplinary dialogue by commissioning new work from artists already exploring the field and introducing the medium to artists working in other visual mediums. Sales not a priority.

Long & Ryle Art International

Pa Ph Pr Sc ✓

Deals in broad range of contemporary art in all media with both young and more established artists presented.
4 John Islip Street, London SW1P 4PQ, tel: 0171 834 1434, fax: 0171 821 9409
Contact: Sarah Long
Space: 2 galleries with 35 lin m hanging space and 54 sq m floor space
Exhibitions: 12 a year all originated
Details: Attached to corporate art business.

Monthly exhibitions by young and more established artists. Spanish and South American art a particular feature of the international selection. Charges reasonable prices and offers corporate purchasing service.

McHardy Sculpture Gallery

Pa Sc ✓ ●

Private gallery dedicated to contemporary sculpture and sculptor's drawings.
Cardamon Building, 31 Shad Thames, London SE1 2YR, tel: 0171 403 7555, fax: 0171 378 7300
Contact: Joanne McHardy
Space: 1 gallery with 60 sq m floor space
Exhibitions: 2 a year both originated
Details: Permanent changing display plus two exhibitions of the work of a range of sculptors, many being ideas for larger sculptures or commissions in bronze, stone or other permanent media. All work taken on a sale or return basis.

Mall Galleries

Pa Cr Sc ✓ ⓔ H

Umbrella organisation working on behalf of artists' societies.
17 Carlton House Terrace, The Mall, Nr Trafalgar Square, London SW1, tel: 0171 930 6844, fax: 0171 839 7830
Contact: Danielle Slattery
Open: Mon-Sun 10-5
Space: 3 galleries with 505 sq m floor space
Exhibitions: 24 a year of which 12 originated, 12 on a hire basis
Details: The 9 societies hold annual exhibitions at Mall Galleries, open for any artists' submissions. Also national competitions offer substantial prizes. The gallery is available for hire – only at related events. Lectures, group shows, promotions, etc. Ideally situated on The Mall.

Manor House Society

Pa Ph Pr Cr Sc ✓ H

Shows work by Jewish artists or work of Jewish interest within multi-use progressive Jewish centre.
The Sternberg Centre for Judaism, 80 East End Road, London N3 2SY, tel: 0181 346 2288, fax: 0181 349 0694
Contact: Visual Arts Director
Space: 1 gallery
Exhibitions: 6 a year of which 1 on a hire basis
Details: Programme predominantly work by living artists in month-long exhibitions. Varied – some exhibitions are specialist, others attract interest of a wide public.

Marlborough Fine Art *

Pa Pr Sc

Commercial gallery showing impressionist and C20th work.

6 Albermarle Street, London W1X 4BY, tel: 0171 629 5161, fax: 0171 629 6338
Contact: Director
Exhibitions: 7 a year
Details: Paintings, drawings, watercolours and sculpture, prints and photographs. The print gallery, Marlborough Graphics can be contacted at 6 Albemarle Street also holds regular exhibitions.

Marlene Eleini Gallery

Pa Ph Pr Cr Sc

Gallery dealing in C20th and contemporary art by living artists in a wide variety of media; mainly abstract and non-figurative.
No 12, 69 Westbourne Terrace, London W2 3UY, tel: 0171 706 0373
Contact: Marlene Eleini, Director
Space: 1 gallery
Exhibitions: 3 a year all originated
Details: Concentrates on private dealing with only the occasional show.

Marsden Contemporary Art

Pa Cr Sc ✅

Gallery has small group of artists who fulfil its policy to exhibit new, up-and-coming painters, sculptors and ceramicists.
21 Dulwich Village, London SE21 7BT, tel: 0181 693 2700
Contact: Gary Marsden
Space: 1 gallery with 300 sq m floor space
Exhibitions: 6 a year all originated
Details: Work can be viewed by appointment and at fine art fairs. Also occasional hired venues in the West End. Prices range between £100-£2000 and commission is taken from sales.

Marsham Street Gallery *

Pa Pr Cr Sc ✅

Small commercial gallery showing contemporary art.
55 Marsham Street, London SW1, tel: 0171 222 3882
Contact: Exhibition Organiser
Space: 1 gallery with 18 lin m hanging space and 20 sq m floor space
Exhibitions: 10 a year all originated

Mary Ward Centre Gallery

Pa Ph Pr Cr Sc ✅ ♿ We

Café gallery of popular adult education centre in listed Georgian central London building with monthly exhibitions of 2D work by professional artists and students.
42 Queen Square, London WC1N 3AQ, tel: 0171 831 7711
Contact: Caroline Deane, Part-time Art Tutor
Space: 1 gallery with 21 lin m hanging space and 60 sq m floor space
Exhibitions: 9 a year all originated
Details: Exhibitions held during term-time. Mostly solo shows adhering to non-sexist,

non-racist principles of equal opportunities policy. Audience includes students, visitors to the centre and public using the café. Artists hang their own work. Sales not a priority.

Matt's Gallery

Pa Ph Pr Sc LA £ ♿

Making the improbable possible.
42-44 Copperfield Road, London E3 4RR, tel: 0181 983 1771, fax: 0181 983 1435
Contact: Robin Klassnik, Director
Open: Ring for details
Space: 2 galleries with 73 lin m hanging space and 298 sq m floor space
Exhibitions: 6 a year all originated
Details: Artists work closely with the director in the making of pieces, often for a period of up to three months. Exhibitions last two months and include work in a wide range of media – painting, sculpture, drawing, photography, video and live art. Regular programme of talks and seminars. Sales not a priority.

Mayor Gallery

Pa Sc

Programme, arranged by invitation, consists of mixed and solo exhibitions of C20th British, European and American art.
22a Cork Street, London W1X 1HB, tel: 0171 734 3558, fax: 0171 494 1377
Contact: James Mayor/Andrew Murray, Directors
Space: 1 gallery

Medici Galleries

Pa Pr Cr Sc LA

Commercial gallery with regular exhibitions by contemporary British artists, plus prints and reproductions.
7 Grafton Street, London W1X 3LA, tel: 0171 629 5675, fax: 0171 495 2997
Contact: Director
Space: 2 galleries
Exhibitions: 6 a year all originated
Details: Also at 26 Thurloe Street, South Kensington, 0171 589 1363. Exhibitions held alongside a gallery programme of its own artists.

Mercury Gallery

Pa Pr Sc ♿

Gallery shows contemporary and C20th British art.
26 Cork Street, London W1X 1HB, tel: 0171 734 7800, fax: 0171 287 9809
Contact: Gillian Raffles, Director
Open: Mon-Fri 10-5.30; Sat 10-12.30
Exhibitions: 10 a year all originated
Details: Solo shows by gallery artists, and two mixed exhibitions of gallery artists and C20th.

Mermaid Gallery *

Pa Ph Pr Cr ✅ ♿

Exhibition space in theatre.
Mermaid Theatre, Puddle Dock, Blackfriars, London EC4U 3DB, tel: 0171 410 0102, fax: 0171 410 0202
Contact: Jessica O'Leary, Gallery Manager
Space: 1 gallery with 100 lin m hanging space
Exhibitions: 12 a year all on a hire basis
Details: Approx 100m long with its own lighting, plus natural light from high windows on the opposite wall. Links the main bar and servery to the River Room cocktail lounge. All work needs to be mirror plated for security reasons.It is suggested that all work displayed should be under glass for its own protection.

Merrifield Studios *

Pa Pr

Shows contemporary prints and paintings.
110 Heath Street, Hampstead, London NW3, tel: 0171 794 0343, fax: 0171 433 3874
Contact: Blackie Merrifield, Exhibition Organiser
Exhibitions: 4 a year all originated
Details: Space a substantial size, with flexibility to divide into 3 areas.

Merton Civic Centre

Pa Ph Pr Cr Sc ✅ ♿

Exhibition space on first floor near coffee bar for hire to local artists/groups.
London Road, Morden, London SM4 5DX
Contact: Customer Services Librarian, Merton Library Service, Morden Library, Merton Civic Centre, London Road, Morden, London, SM4 5DX, tel: 0181 545 4040
Open: Mon-Sat 9-5
Space: 1 gallery with plus 18 lin m on screens
Exhibitions: 6 a year all on a hire basis
Details: Hanging space all on screens plus two free standing display cases available. Mostly shows paintings and photographs. Hire charge £72 for 6 day week and 20% commission taken on any sales made. Additional larger space (ground floor foyer) available if required at extra cost.

Metro Photographic Gallery *

Ph ✅

The Metro Cinema, 11 Rupert Street, London W1V 7FS, tel: 0171 437 0757, fax: 0171 286 2112
Contact: Roy Bristow, 79 Wardour Street, London, W1V 3TH, tel: 0171 434 3357
Space: 2 galleries with 70 lin m hanging space
Exhibitions: 12 a year all originated
Details: Changing programme of British

contemporary photography each month. Disabled access by lift to corridor gallery and bar area.

Millfield House Arts Centre

 ✓

Space used as a coffee bar/lounge in arts centre which also houses a theatre and library.
Silver Street, Edmonton, London N18 1PJ, tel: 0181 803 5283, fax: 0181 807 3892
Contact: Penny Wilkinson, Exhibition Organiser
Space: 1 gallery with 19 lin m hanging space
Exhibitions: 12 a year all originated
Details: Varied exhibition programme of 12 monthly shows a year. Solo, mixed and thematic in a wide variety of 2D media – painting, drawing, photography, prints and crafts. Exhibitors mainly local artists and audience made up of casual visitors or those involved in other activities being held at the centre. Offers drama and music events, workshops, classes, rehearsal studio and hosts meetings.

Milne & Moller

Pa

Gallery specialises in watercolour paintings 1850-1950 and contemporary oil paintings, watercolours and ceramics.
35 Colville Terrace, London W11 2BU, tel: 0171 727 1679
Contact: Juliet Moller, Director
Open: By appointment
Exhibitions: 2 a year both originated
Details: Regular solo and mixed exhibitions. Exhibitor at C20th British Art Fair and Olympia Fine Art & Antique Fair.

Mistral Galleries

Pa ✓

Selling gallery showing solo and mixed exhibitions.
10 Dover Street, London W1X 3PJ, tel: 0171 499 4701; 01959 564477, fax: 0171 499 0618
Contact: Gallery Manager
Open: Mon-Fri 10-6; Sat 10-4
Space: 2 galleries with 92 lin m hanging space and 161 sq m floor space
Exhibitions: 8 a year all originated
Details: Established client list and passing trade due to prime position. Exhibits paintings by young as well as established artists. Always interested in seeing new work.

Montpelier Sandelson

Pa Pr Sc ✓

Gallery specialising in contemporary British art.

4 Montpelier Street, London SW7, tel: 0171 584 0667, fax: 0171 225 2280
Contact: Bernice Sandelson/Robert Sandelson, Directors
Space: 2 galleries
Exhibitions: 6 a year all originated
Details: Regular mixed exhibitions of C20th British painters and sculptors.

Morley Gallery

Pa Ph Pr Cr Sc LA ✓ H ⊕

Gallery linked to Morley College representing all art forms.
61 Westminster Bridge Road, London SE1 7HT, tel: 0171 928 8501 ext 226, fax: 0171 928 4074
Contact: Jane Hartwell
Open: Mon 1-6; Tues, Thurs, Fri 10-6; Wed 10-7.30; contact gallery for details of Sat opening times.
Space: 1 gallery with 44 lin m hanging space
Exhibitions: 10 a year of which 7 originated, 3 on a hire basis
Details: Offers space to new and innovative work to enhance the teaching of the college. Tries to broaden audience base for contemporary fine art by representing work in an accessible manner. Reflects the equal opportunities policy of the college. Schools and colleges are invited to every exhibition and talks by artists are organised on a regular basis. Sale of work not gallery's primary consideration.

Mortimer Arms Pub

405 Green Lanes, Tottenham, London N4, tel: 0181 341 7472

Museum of Installation *

Sc ✓

Extensive archive and publication facilities dedicated to field of installation art with temporary exhibition programme.
33 Great Sutton Street, London EC1V 0DX, tel: 0171 253 0802, fax: 0171 582 7022
Contact: The Directors
Space: 1 gallery with 190 sq m floor space
Exhibitions: 5 a year all originated
Details: Work made specifically for MOI crosses over into a variety of media. In addition to main venues, installations chosen and made in direct response to the context of 5 other sites. As programme is continuously being assessed, new projects and proposals are planned only 6 months in advance. Awareness of context and content on the artist's behalf is of importance when being considered. Advisable for interested artists to visit the museum before making an application.

Museum of London

Pa Ph Pr ✓ ⊕ We 4

Museum concerned with capital's history from prehistoric times to present.

150 London Wall, London EC2Y 5HN, tel: 0171 600 3699, fax: 0171 600 1038
Contact: Russell Clark, Exhibitions Officer
Open: Tues-Sat 10-6; Sun 12-6; Mon closed except BH
Space: 2 galleries with plus 12 lin m on screens and 220 sq m floor space
Exhibitions: 4 a year all originated
Details: Proposals for temporary exhibitions which complement theme of museum are looked at by Exhibition Committee. Exhibition space in foyer and in gallery. Some free standing showcases available. Selling work not gallery's main aim.

Music Theatre Gallery

Pa Pr Cr ✓ ⊕

Commercial gallery specialising in C20th original artwork connected with performing arts.
1 Elystan Place, London SW3 3LA, tel: 0171 823 9880, fax: 0171 823 9790
Contact: Joseph Karaviotis
Open: Tues-Fri 10-6; Sat 10-1
Space: 2 galleries with 95 sq m floor space
Exhibitions: 4 a year all originated
Details: Programme of C20th original drawings of costume and set designs for opera, ballet and theatre. Each year organises exhibitions at Royal Opera House, Glyndebourne, Royal National Theatre and Barbican.

Narthex Gallery

Pa Ph Pr Cr ✓ H ⊕ We 4

Gallery aims to promote work by artists representative of groups who use the church café.
Chelsea Methodist Church, 155a Kings Road, London SW3 5TX, tel: 0171 352 9305
Contact: Church Community Worker
Open: Mon-Thurs 10-5; Fri 10-2; Sun 10.30-12.30
Space: 1 gallery with 26 lin m hanging space
Exhibitions: 6 a year all on a hire basis
Details: Gallery shares reception area with the Welcome In which sells hot drinks and snacks to passers-by. In promoting work by people who use this facility the gallery has, for example, exhibited work by homeless artists, those with learning difficulties, by pensioners in sheltered accommodation and by an advanced embroidery class. No charge for using the gallery. Sales are welcome (10% commission taken) but not a priority.

National Army Museum

Pa ⊕ ⊕ We

National museum telling the story of British Army in peace and war.
Royal Hospital Road, London SW3, tel: 0171 730 0701
Contact: Mr I G Robertson, Director

Open: Daily
Space: 1 gallery with 120 lin m hanging space and 830 sq m floor space
Exhibitions: 1 a year on a hire basis
Details: Museum illustrates history of Britain's Army with emphasis on experiences of individual soldier in peace as well as in war. Annual Armed Forces Art Society Exhibition plus occasional contemporary shows. Sales not a priority.

National Maritime Museum, Queen's House Greenwich, Old Royal Observatory

Museum used occasionally for contemporary sculpture or other creative arts and for Greenwich Festival events.
Greenwich, London SE10 9NF, tel: 0181 858 4422, fax: 0181 312 6632
Contact: Helen Mitchell
Space: 4 galleries
Exhibitions: 2 a year of which 1 originated, 1 on a hire basis
Details: Houses the Greenwich Hospital collection of oils of maritime occasions throughout history of British Navy. Large collection of Dutch marine art. Sailors crafts, ship models. Handling session for blind visitors (Sun).

National Portrait Gallery

Pa Ph Pr Sc ⚫ wc 4

Primary collection of over 9,000 works with constantly changing displays, programme of international exhibitions, acquisitions and commissions and annual portrait competition for young artists.
St Martin's Place, London WC2H 0HE, tel: 0171 306 0055, fax: 0171 306 0056
Contact: Kathleen Soriano, Exhibitions Officer
Open: Mon-Fri 10-6; Sat 10-6; Sun 12-6
Space: 3 galleries with 154 lin m hanging space plus 67 lin m on screens and 395 sq m floor space
Exhibitions: 6 a year of which 5 originated, 1 touring
Details: Programme of eight twelve-week exhibitions includes major international loan exhibitions, small solo shows and biographical and photographic exhibitions. Gallery also collects portraits of famous British men and women. Education Department runs continuous programme of lectures, talks, films and demonstrations.

Natural History Museum

Pa Ph Pr Sc ⚫ wc 4

Museum whose main purpose is to increase public awareness and understanding of the natural world.
Cromwell Road, London SW7
Contact: Giles Clarke, Head of Exhibitions & Education
Open: Mon-Sat 10-6; Sun 11-6

Space: 2 galleries with 850 sq m floor space
Exhibitions: 2 a year of which 1 originated, 1 touring
Details: Natural History Museum concentrates all resources on permanent collection. Able to accommodate exhibitions only if sponsored and organised externally. Thus, applications very rarely considered. For exhibitions that do go ahead, Museum offers one of Britain's most popular and entertaining venues, attracting up to 1.7 million visitors a year.

Naturally British *

Specialist craft outlet retailing cottage industries with basement area used for exhibitions.
13 New Row, London WC2N 4LF, tel: 0171 240 0551, fax: 0171 497 8812
Contact: Jon Blake, Managing Director
Details: Stock includes pottery, textiles, toys, jewellery, glass, clothes, firescreens and ceramic plaques. Divided into two floors, the basement is used for exhibitions. All applications must be arranged first by telephone.

New Academy Gallery/ Business Art Galleries

Pa Pr Sc ⚫ ♿

Gallery showing and dealing in work by established and emerging artists.
34 Windmill Street, Off Charlotte Street, London W1P 1HH, tel: 0171 323 4700, fax: 0171 436 3059
Contact: Jill Hutchings, Exhibition Organiser
Open: Mon-Wed, Fri & Sat 10-6; Thurs 10-8; Sat 11-5; closed BH weekends.
Space: 2 galleries with 48 lin m hanging space and 160 sq m floor space
Exhibitions: 12 a year
Details: Holds work by over 200 artists, mainly British, either on slide or in the gallery. Solo, group and theme exhibitions of paintings, prints and some sculpture. Aims to encourage private and corporate buyers and provide a strong stable of artists. Arranges commissions.

New Grafton Gallery

Pa Pr ⚫

Commercial gallery with established reputation for contemporary British painting – watercolours, oils, pastels, etc.
49 Church Road, Barnes, London SW13 9HH, tel: 0181 748 8850, fax: 0181 748 9818
Contact: David Wolfers, Director
Open: Tues-Sat 10-5.30
Space: 1 gallery
Exhibitions: 12 a year all originated
Details: Applications welcome from established and new artists who may send slides to director. Majority of shows are solo, occasionally two-person. Mixed show

every summer and Christmas. Wide audience.

New Richmond Gallery

Pa Pr

Small gallery specialising in etchings by contemporary artists.
63 Sheen Road, Richmond, Surrey, London TW9 1YT, tel: 0181 940 9629
Open: Tues-Sat 10-5.30
Exhibitions: 2 a year both originated
Details: Also selling contemporary limited edition prints and watercolours. Galleries on 2 floors. Two solo shows held each year to supplement continuous turnover of work by a stable of artists.

Nigel Greenwood Gallery *

Pa Ph Pr Sc

Commercial gallery which deals and shows selected artists specialising in paintings and prints.
4 New Burlington Street, London W1X 1FE, tel: 0171 434 3795, fax: 0171 287 2396
Contact: Nigel Greenwood, Exhibition Organiser
Space: 2 galleries
Exhibitions: 8 a year all originated
Details: Incorporates Nigel Greenwood Books and stocks a wide range of catalogues, artists' books and monographs.

No 4 Hamilton Place

Pa Ph Pr Cr Sc ⚫ ♿

Lecture theatre and small room available for artists who would like to construct own exhibitions within space provided.
4 Hamilton Place, London W1V 0BQ, tel: 0171 499 3515, fax: 0171 499 6230
Contact: Mrs Conway Holland
Open: Mon-Fri 9-5.30; evenings & weekends by arrangement
Space: 2 galleries with 222 sq m floor space
Exhibitions: 2 a year of which 1 originated, 1 on a hire basis
Details: Group and solo shows welcome in programme that features mainly painting and small sculpture.

North Bank Gallery

Pa Ph Pr Sc ⚫ ♿

Gallery with large windows at street level and modern interior aims to give young artists opportunity to exhibit their work which is affordable to a wide public.
96 Gillespie Road, London N5 1LN, tel: 0171 226 7261
Contact: Anna Banks
Open: Times vary, 5 days a week & always 2-7
Space: 1 gallery with 21 lin m hanging space and 39 sq m floor space
Exhibitions: 13 a year of which 9 originated, 4 on a hire basis
Details: Ample daylight, high ceiling and

lighting by spots. Aims to supply artists exhibiting with a support network. Gallery available for hire in evenings as well as for exhibitions. Low commission in return for artists invigilating own exhibitions. Artists pay for publicity costs. Sales not considered gallery's primary role.

North Peckham Exhibition Gallery

 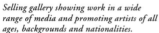

Municipal gallery staging small photographic and painting exhibitions by local artists.
North Peckham Library, Civic Centre, 600-608 Old Kent Road, London SE15, tel: 0171 639 1255
Contact: Library Manager
Details: Mixture of group and solo shows. Policy is to provide space for local artists who are showing for the first time. Audience from North Peckham area who often have little access to original art.

Northcote Gallery

Pa Pr Sc ✓ ♿

Selling gallery showing work in a wide range of media and promoting artists of all ages, backgrounds and nationalities.
110 Northcote Road, Battersea, London SW11 6QP, tel: 0171 924 6741
Contact: Ali Pettit
Open: Tues-Sat 11-7
Space: 1 gallery with 35 lin m hanging space
Exhibitions: 16 a year all originated
Details: Gallery with plaster walls and wooden floors designed to exhibit high standard of work from home and abroad. Sales a priority.

O'Leary Gallery

Pa Ph Pr Cr Sc ✓ ⊗ wc

Gallery used for community temporary exhibitions and special events.
Valence House Museum, Becontree Avenue, Dagenham, London RM8 3HT, tel: 0181 595 8404
Contact: Sue Curtis, Curator
Open: Tues-Fri 9.30-1, 2-4.30; Sat 10-4
Space: 1 gallery with 31 lin m hanging space plus 46 lin m on screens
Exhibitions: 4 a year of which 2 originated, 2 touring
Details: Exhibitions relate to historic and artistic heritage of Barking and Dagenham. Aims to educate and entertain. Sales not priority.

October Gallery

Pa ✓ ♿

Large exhibition space in central London whose policy it is to shows works by the international transvangarde with the primary aim of selling work.

24 Old Gloucester Street, London WC1N 3AL, tel: 0171 242 7367, fax: 0171 405 1851
Contact: Elisabeth Lalouscheck, Artistic Director
Open: Tues-Sat 12.30-5.30
Space: 2 galleries with 59 lin m hanging space and 131 sq m floor space
Exhibitions: 8 a year
Details: Shows work of living artists from around the world: Europe, Asia, Africa, Middle East, the Americas, Japan and Australia. Mainly solo exhibitions each lasting 4 to 6 weeks. Permanent collection of selected pieces by artists the gallery represents. Education programme with workshops run by artists.

Old Bull Arts Centre

Pa Ph Pr Cr Sc ✓ ♿

68 High Street, Barnet, London EN5 5SJ, tel: 0181 449 5189, fax: 0181 364 9037
Contact: Visual Arts Officer
Open: Tues-Sun 10-5.30
Space: 1 gallery with 30 lin m hanging space and 80 sq m floor space
Exhibitions: 12 a year
Details: Exhibitions iclude local artist's first solo shows. Fouthcoming seasons include photography, textiles and Asian art.

Oliver Swann Galleries *

Pa ✓

Commercial gallery dealing and showing 2D work by living artists.
170 Walton Street, London SW3 2JL, tel: 0171 581 4229/ 071 584 8684
Contact: Oliver Swann, Exhibition Organiser
Space: 1 gallery with 20 lin m hanging space and 20 sq m floor space
Exhibitions: 6 a year all originated
Details: A subjective choice of representational work in oils, watercolour and pastels. Subject matter is wide ranging and aims to exhibit growing number of artists with reputations amongst critics and collectors. Six exhibitions each lasting 2-3 weeks a year. Most solo shows. Gallery houses permanent collection and changing display of gallery artists.

Orangery (The)

Pa Ph Pr Cr Sc ✓ ♨

Gallery with exhibitions between April and October.
Holland Park, Off Kensington High Street, London W8, tel: 0171 937 2542
Contact: Michael Goggin, Arts Officer, Leighton House Museum, 12 Holland Park Road, London, W14 8LZ, tel: 0171 603 1123
Space: 1 gallery with 108 sq m floor space
Exhibitions: 8 a year all on a hire basis
Details: Programme of 6-8 two week exhibitions. Space unusual as there are

many windows. Possible to hang work from rails in front of windows or artists may make use of screens and plinths. Applications to gallery go through selection panel.

Oriel Contemporary Art

45 Chalcot Road, Primrose Hill, London NW1 8LS, tel: 0171 483 1375, fax: 0171 483 1363
Contact: Geoff Evans, Art Director

Orleans House

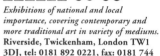

Exhibitions of national and local importance, covering contemporary and more traditional art in variety of mediums.
Riverside, Twickenham, London TW1 3DJ, tel: 0181 892 0221, fax: 0181 744 0501
Contact: Stephen Nicholls, Acting Curator
Open: Tues-Sat 1-5.30; Sun & BH 2-5.30; (1 Oct – 31 Mar) closes at 4.30
Space: 2 galleries with 46 lin m hanging space plus 32 lin m on screens and 115 sq m floor space
Exhibitions: 18 a year of which 16 originated, 2 touring
Details: Set in woodland by the Thames. Shows exhibitions on a wide range of subjects. Audience mainly regular local visitors of all ages. Owned by the London Borough of Richmond upon Thames. Exhibitions usually booked one year in advance. Two exhibition spaces, Main Gallery and the Stables. Selling work not primary role.

Outlaws Club *

Cr

Gallery specialises in 'designer' jewellery with changing display of work for sale.
49 Endell Street, London WC2, tel: 0171 379 6940
Contact: Angela McLoughlin, Exhibition Organiser
Details: Aims to provide best selection of new work for most competitive prices. Many items on show are exclusive.

Oval House *

Pa Ph Pr Sc ✓

Unusually shaped café space more suited to painting, sculpture etc than small works of craft.
52-54 Kennington Oval, London SE11 5SW, tel: 0171 735 2786
Contact: The Director
Space: 1 gallery with 114 sq m floor space
Exhibitions: 2 a year both originated
Details: Solo shows only. Artists responsible for own hanging/framing. Small commission on sales. In addition to café customers, visitors drawn from theatre-goers and students on art education programmes and workshops.

Park Walk Gallery

Commercial gallery specialising in C20th English, European and contemporary art.
**20 Park Walk, London SW10 0AQ, tel:
0171 351 0410**
Contact: Jonathan Cooper, Director
Open: Mon-Fri 10-6.30; Sat 11-3
Space: 2 galleries with 600 sq m floor space
Exhibitions: 4 a year all originated
Details: Contemporary work represented at
shows such as C20th British Art Fair.
Gallery is irregular with alcoves etc, so
check details on application.

Paton Gallery *

**London Fields, 282 Richmond Road,
London E8 3QS, tel: 0181 986 3409**
Contact: Graham Paton, Director
Space: 2 galleries
Exhibitions: 9 a year all originated
Details: A platform for new generation
British artists, chiefly painters who show
the potential for international careers.
Audience are serious UK collectors and
museums, with growing interest from US
collectors and museums.

Pentagram Gallery

**11 Needham Road, London, tel: 0171
229 3477**

Phinns Gallery

**16 Clifford Street, London W1, tel: 0171
734 1228, fax: 0171 734 2778**

Photofusion

*Dedicated exhibition space within lively
photography centre, mixing prestigious
exhibitions at leading edge of photographic
arts with community exhibitions and work
of students.*
**17a Electric Lane, Brixton, London SW9
8LA, tel: 0171 738 5774, fax: 0171 738
5509**
Contact: Julia Martin, Director
Open: Tues-Fri 10.30-5.30; Sat 12-4
Space: 1 gallery with 19 lin m hanging
space plus 40 lin m on screens and 600 sq
m floor space
Exhibitions: 10 a year of which 8
originated, 2 on a hire basis
Details: Specialised centre with darkrooms,
studio, picture library and agency. Also
provides space for talks, debates and active
demonstrations. Annual programme
includes one open exhibition and seven
submission shows. Professional and non-
professional photographers welcome to
apply. Aims to provide exhibition space for
young and unknown photographers.
Available for hire. Chairlift available for
wheelchairs. Sales not priority.

Photographers Gallery

*Major international photography centre
exploring contemporary photography
culture through integrated programme of
exhibitions and education events.*
**5-8 Great Newport Street, London
WC2H 7HY, tel: 0171 831 1772, fax:
0171 836 9704**
Contact: David Chandler, Senior
Exhibitions Organiser
Open: Mon-Sat 11-6
Space: 3 galleries with 117 lin m hanging
space plus 61 lin m on screens and 232 sq
m floor space
Exhibitions: 22 a year of which 18
originated, 4 touring
Details: Programme of exhibitions and
education events presented in 7 six-week
periods a year. Emphasis on new and
developing photographic practices within
context of contemporary visual arts, and on
work dealing with relevant issues; social or
aesthetic. Thematic exhibitions with
historical material included where
appropriate. Sales not primary role of
gallery but actively promoted through print
sales room.

Piccadilly Gallery

*Small commercial gallery with monthly
exhibitions of contemporary figurative
work, symbolist and C20th drawings and
watercolours.*
**16 Cork Street, London W1X 1PF, tel:
0171 629 2875, fax: 0171 499 0431**
Contact: C Briggs, Director
Space: 1 gallery
Exhibitions: 12 a year all originated

Piers Feetham Gallery

*Shows contemporary 2D work with
increasing specialism in drawings.*
**475 Fulham Road, London SW6 1HL,
tel: 0171 381 5958**
Contact: Piers Feetham, Owner
Open: Tues-Fri 10-1, 2-6; Sat 10-1
Space: 1 gallery with 17 lin m hanging
space and 23 sq m floor space
Exhibitions: 8 a year all originated
Details: Shows small- to medium-sized
paintings, watercolours, pastels, drawings;
representational, figurative and semi-
abstract. Three mixed shows a year of
contemporary British drawings. Clients like
middle-of-the-road C20th British painting.

Pictoons Gallery

*British cartoons and international C20th
art.*
**12a Piccadilly Arcade, London SW1Y
6NH, tel & fax: 0171 493 4094**

Pinner Library

*Library space showing temporary
exhibitions by local amateur artists.*
**Marsh Road, Pinner, London HA5 5NQ,
tel: 0181 866 7827**
Contact: MaggieTimms, Branch Librarian
Open: Mon, Tues, Thurs 9.30-1, 2-8; Fri
9.30-1; Sat 9-5
Space: 1 gallery with 11 lin m hanging
space
Exhibitions: 16 a year all on a hire basis
Details: Promote work of local artists and
art societies and increase awareness and
generally raise profile of art within
community through active participation.
Sales not priority; 10% commission taken.

Plantation House

*Exhibition cases along ground-floor
corridors of City office building.*
**31-35 Fenchurch Street, London EC3M
3DX, tel: 0171 626 7438, fax: 0171 283
4864**
Contact: Alison Gourlay, Marketing
Manager
Open: Mon-Fri 9-5.30
Exhibitions: 12 a year all on a hire basis
Details: Plantation House is a landmark
City office-building. Ten exhibition cases,
each 80x95x15cm, are available for
exhibitions. Over 2000 people work in the
building housing 70 City concerns. In
addition the ground floor is a public
thoroughfare and upwards of 2000
members of the public pass through. Selling
work not the main purpose.

Polish Cultural Institute

*Gallery is part of Cultural Department of
the Polish Embassy.*
**34 Portland Place, London W1, tel: 0171
636 6032/3/4, fax: 0171 637 2190**
Contact: Mrs Aleksandra Czapiewska,
Deputy Director
Open: Mon-Fri 10-4; Thurs 10-8
Space: 1 gallery with 44 lin m hanging
space and 90 sq m floor space
Exhibitions: 6 a year of which 4
originated, 2 touring
Details: Polish Cultural Institute promotes
Polish contemporary art in Britain. Exhibits
work by artists from Poland or of Polish
origin. Gallery also used for book
launchings and literary meetings.

Portal Gallery

*Exhibits exclusively British contemporary
idiosyncratic painters.*
**16a Grafton Street, Bond Street, London
W1X 3LF, tel: 0171 629 3506/071 493**
Contact: Jess Wilder/Lionel Levy,
Directors

Space: 2 galleries
Exhibitions: 8 a year all originated
Details: One-person shows plus continuous display of gallery artists including Beryl Cook, Jane Lewis, Lizzie Riches and Kit Williams. Wooden bird sculptures by Guy Taplin.

Portland Gallery

Gallery specialising in C20th Scottish painting.
9 Bury Street, St James's, London SW1Y 6AB, tel: 0171 321 0422, fax: 0171 321 0230
Contact: Tom Hewlett, Director
Open: Mon-Fri 10-5
Space: 2 galleries with 32 lin m hanging space and 80 sq m floor space
Exhibitions: 6 a year all originated
Details: Small commercial gallery concentrating on C20th and contemporary British art, especially Scottish work. Predominantly representational and figurative art. Applications to exhibit should include a CV and slides. Sales a priority.

Posk Gallery

Gallery available for exhibitions in all media.
238-246 King Street, Hammersmith, London W6 0RF, tel: 0181 741 1940, fax: 0181 746 3798
Contact: J. Baranowska, Director
Open: Mon-Sun 11-9
Space: 1 gallery with 23 lin m hanging space plus 12 lin m on screens and 46 sq m floor space
Exhibitions: 26 a year
Details: Every second Sunday private view, 5pm. Audience about 300 weekly. The exhibitor is solely responsible for printed matter advertising them and for invitations. The exhibitor must care for the aesthetic side of his exhibits, their artistic standard and their display and arrangements in the gallery. 15% commission on sales. Sales not gallery's primary role.

Pump House Gallery

Popular space in London park available to individuals and groups for contemporary shows.
c/o Park Managers Office, Battersea Park, Albert Bridge Road, London SW11, tel: 0181 871 7572
Contact: Charlie Catling, Senior Arts Officer, Wandsworth Arts Office, Room 224A MB, Town Hall, Wandsworth High Street, London, SW18 2PU, tel: 0181 871 7037, fax: 0171 871 7630
Open: (Summer) Tues-Sun 11-6; (Winter) Tues-Fri 11-3, Sat & Sun 11-4

Space: 1 gallery with 34 lin m hanging space
Exhibitions: 22 a year of which 2 originated, 20 on a hire basis
Details: 2 floors of Battersea Pump House building, Victorian landmark in Battersea Park, one of London's busiest parks. (See also Battersea Library Gallery). Selling work not gallery's main purpose.

Purdy Hicks Gallery

Large commercial exhibition space concentrating on painting.
Jacob Street Film Studios, Mill Street, London SE1 2BA, tel: 0171 237 6062, fax: 0171 237 3049
Contact: Jayne Purdy/Rebecca Hicks, Directors
Open: Tues-Fri 10-5.30; Sat 11-3
Space: 3 galleries with 279 sq m floor space
Exhibitions: 9 a year of which 7 originated, 2 on a hire basis
Details: Shows work by well-known artists. Exhibitions last 3-4 weeks. All work by living artists; painting, sculpture, drawing, prints, photography, installation. Tends to centre on painting and photography and cross-over between the two. Audience from surrounding area and City. Attract serious collectors and curators from Britain and abroad. Gallery on third floor of warehouse, wheelchair access not possible.

Quaker Gallery

West End gallery with busy street frontage and eclectic programme of short-term exhibitions with accent on diversity and surprise.
52 St. Martins Lane, London WC2, tel: 0171 836 7204
Contact: John Olsen, Co-ordinator
Open: Mon-Sat 11-7; Sun 10-2
Space: 1 gallery with 22 lin m hanging space and 30 sq m floor space
Exhibitions: 21 a year all on a hire basis
Details: Operated by an active charity, the gallery encourages a diversity of exhibitions reflecting tastes of West End. Whether sales a priority depends on artists exhibiting. No commission taken. Interested artists contact gallery by telephone initially.

Questors Theatre

12 Mattock Lane, London W5 5BQ
Contact: Christine Greening, Exhibitions Secretary

Railings Gallery *

Gallery showing and selling contemporary limited edition original prints and drawings by abstract and representational artists.
5 New Cavendish Street, London W1, tel: 0171 935 1114, fax: 0171 486 9250

Contact: Eric Sandes/Geihle Sander, Director
Space: 2 galleries with 45 lin m hanging space plus 30 lin m on screens and 100 sq m floor space
Exhibitions: 4 a year all originated
Details: Some paintings. Commission: rates by arrangement.

Raw Gallery

Spacious modern gallery that aims to show an exciting range of painting and sculpture.
7 Gainsford Street, Tower Bridge, London SE1 2NE, tel: 0171 357 7570
Contact: Haydn Reynolds, Director
Open: Tues-Sat 11-6; Thurs 11-8; Sun 2-5
Space: 1 gallery with 46 lin m hanging space plus 4 lin m on screens and 121 sq m floor space
Exhibitions: 12 a year of which 10 originated, 2 on a hire basis
Details: Range of contemporary British and international painting and sculpture. Specialises in large scale work. Represents new and established artists. Occasionally available to hire by regional art colleges.

Rebecca Hosack Fitzrovia

Gallery promotes British and non-European contemporary art including Australian Aboriginal and African art.
35 Windmill Street, off Charlotte Street, London W1, tel: 0171 409 3599, fax: 0171 323 3182
Contact: Rebecca Hossack, Director/Owner
Open: Mon-Sat 10-6
Space: 2 galleries with plus 61 lin m on screens and 93 sq m floor space
Exhibitions: 12 a year all originated
Details: Salling is primary role of gallery.

Rebecca Hossack Gallery

Gallery promotes British and non-European contemporary art.
Fitzrovia, 35 Windmill Street, London W1P 1HH, tel: 0171 436 4899, fax: 0171 323 3182
Contact: Lucy Field, Gallery Director
Open: Mon-Sat 10-6
Space: 2 galleries with 93 sq m floor space
Exhibitions: 12 a year all originated
Details: 35 Windmill Street shows work by exciting young British artists, both figurative and abstract. The gallery also specialises in contemporary non-western arts, including Australian Aboriginal and African. Also Rebecca Hossack Sculpture Garden, St James's, 197 Piccadilly, exhibiting sculpture by young artists during 1995 (contact as above).

Redfern Gallery

Specialises in C20th paintings, sculpture, drawings and graphics.
20 Cork Street, London W1X 2HL, tel: 0171 734 1732/0578, fax: 0171 494 2908
Contact: David Gault, Margaret Thornton, Gordon Samual, The Lady Tanlaw, Directors
Open: Mon-Fri 10-5.30; Sat 10-1
Space: 1 gallery with 65 lin m hanging space
Exhibitions: 9 a year of which 7 originated, 2 on a hire basis
Details: Monthly exhibitions of contemporary British and European artists.

Reed's Wharf Gallery

Commercial gallery exhibiting work by young, relatively unknown as well as more established artists.
Mill Street, London SE1 2BA, tel: 0171 252 1802, fax: 0171 231 5633
Contact: Stephen Lacey
Open: Tues-Fri 10-6; Sat 11-3
Space: 1 gallery with 28 lin m hanging space plus 18 lin m on screens and 150 sq m floor space
Exhibitions: 8 a year all originated
Details: Contemporary exhibition space showing work by artists from this country and abroad. Visits by school and college groups encouraged.

RIBA *

Exhibition space occasionally available for visual art and architecture exhibitions.
66 Portland Place, London W1N 4AD, tel: 0171 580 5533, fax: 0171 255 1541
Contact: Janette Donaldson, Bookings Officer
Open: Mon, Wed, Fri, Sat 8-6; Tues & Thurs 8-9
Space: 3 galleries with 39 lin m hanging space plus 54 lin m on screens and 550 sq m floor space
Exhibitions: 4 a year
Details: See also Heinz Gallery (RIBA), London.

Rich and Famous

Front room of large Victorian house offering an 'alternative' space for unrepresented artists.
81 Sandringham Road, Dalston, London E8 2LL, tel: 0171 241 1006
Contact: Mark Bishop, Exhibition Organiser
Open: Fri & Sat; ring to check
Space: 1 gallery with 15 lin m hanging space
Exhibitions: 12 a year all originated

Details: 'Alternative' space run by artists' co-op with flexible approach exploring new and contemporary issues. Providing public access to under-represented art (eg by artists from under-represented sections of society or in terms of media, new technologies, etc) Welcomes artists' proposals in these areas. Open to external influences. Close contacts with artists and spaces in Berlin. Co-op organises events/installations etc in other, often temporary, venues and outdoor spaces. Sales not a priority but 33% commission on any sales made.

Richard Dickens

Small gallery in framing workshop giving occasional shows of representational work in watercolour, print and oil.
1 Burland Road, London SW11 6SA, tel: 0171 223 8754
Contact: Richard Dickens
Open: Mon-Sat 10-5
Space: 1 gallery with 14 lin m hanging space plus 10 lin m on screens and 28 sq m floor space
Exhibitions: 1 a year originated
Details: Corner gallery in backwater of Battersea. Plenty of wealthy potential customers, most of whom seem extremely reluctant to spend on art. Very small gallery looking for representational watercolours.

Rico

Café bar space where monthly exhibitions are held.
118 Westbourne Grove, London W112RR
Contact: Mike Nayla, Director
Open: Daily 8am – 11pm
Space: 4 galleries with 10 lin m hanging space and 20 sq m floor space
Exhibitions: 7 a year all originated
Details: Aim is to create relaxed and informal atmosphere in which café goers can enjoy viewing and hopefully buy work. 15% commission taken on work sold.

Riverside Room

Space in a riverside tea room.
Old Town Hall, Whittaker Avenue, Richmond, London TW9 1TP, tel: 0181 940 9125, fax: 0181 940 6899
Contact: Nigel Cutting, Principal Arts Officer, London Borough of Richmond, Langholm Lodge, 146 Petersham Road, Richmond, TW10 6UX, tel: 0181 332 0534, fax: 0181 940 7568
Open: Mon-Sat 10-5
Space: 1 gallery with 19 lin m hanging space plus 4 lin m on screens and 40 sq m floor space
Exhibitions: 9 a year all originated
Details: Programme concentrates primarily on local artists, but happy to take

occasional touring shows. Tends to concentrate on one- or two-person shows rather than group exhibitions.

Riverside Studios

Exhibition space within busy arts centre.
Crisp Road, Hammersmith, London W6 9RL, tel: 0181 741 2251, fax: 0181 563 0336

Rocket Gallery

London showroom for the Rocket Press, where exhibitions combining fine print and contemporary art are brought to a wide audience.
13 Old Burlington Street, London W1X 1LA, tel: 0171 434 3043, fax: 0171 434 3384
Contact: David Stephenson, Co-director
Open: Tues-Sat 10-6
Space: 1 gallery with 22 lin m hanging space plus 183 lin m on screens
Exhibitions: 8 a year all originated
Details: Rocket Gallery launches and presents each new book from The Rocket Press, and exhibits artists represented by Rocket Contemporary Art. Also exhibitions of C20th British, North American and European fine printing, printmaking, painting and photography. Holds a stock of limited edition books and livres de peintres. Sale of work not gallery's primary consideration.

Rona Gallery *

Exclusively C20th British naive painters.
1-2 Weighhouse Street, London W1Y 1YL, tel: 0171 491 3718, fax: 0171 491 4171
Contact: Stanley Harries, Director
Space: 2 galleries with 102 sq m floor space
Details: A stock of work which evolves by sales and new acquisitions – no regular exhibition programme as such. Gallery is on two levels linked by a spiral staircase.

Rowley Gallery Contemporary Art

Gallery attached to framing business.
115 Kensington Church Street, London W8 7LN, tel: 0171 229 5561

Roy Miles Gallery

Commercial gallery which pioneered the market in contemporary Russian, E European, Vietnamese and Asian art.
29 Bruton Street, London W1X 7DB, tel: 0171 495 4747, fax: 0171 495 6232
Contact: Roy Miles
Space: 3 galleries with 100 lin m hanging space and 199 sq m floor space
Exhibitions: 8 a year
Details: Quality of work on show richly

complemented by style and decoration of the gallery. Purchasers include many prestigious museums.

Royal Academy of Arts *

Pa Pr Sc

Oldest institution in Britain devoted to fine arts which hosts major international touring exhibitions and 'Summer Exhibition'.
Piccadilly, London W1V 0DS, tel: 0171 439 7438, fax: 0171 434 0837
Contact: Piers Rodgers
Open: Daily 10-6
Space: 2 galleries
Exhibitions: 4 a year all originated
Details: Run by council of 80 academy members (painters, architects, engravers and sculptors). Exists to encourage the widest possible participation in, and enjoyment of, visual arts. Competitive entry to its 'Summer Exhibition' offers a unique exhibition opportunity to over 1000 participants each year.

Royal Air Force Museum

Pa Ph Pr Sc H & Wc 4

Britain's National Museum of Aviation.
Grahame Park Way, Hendon, London NW9, tel: 0181 205 2266, fax: 0181 205 8044
Contact: Sarah El-Doori, Press & Conference Manager
Open: Mon-Sun 10-6
Space: 3 galleries with 653 sq m floor space
Exhibitions: 3 a year all originated
Details: Situated within Britain's only national museum devoted entirely to aviation. All exhibitions are aviation oriented. Of these 80% are from the museum's own collection, 20% from other sources, primarily the Guild of Aviation Artists. Sales not a priority.

Royal College of Art (Henry Moore Gallery) *

Pa Pr Cr Sc O H

Mostly shows work by staff and students within the college with some outside exhibitions.
Kensington Gore, London SW7 2EU, tel: 0171 584 5020, fax: 0171 225 1487
Contact: Ingrid Bleichroeder, Public Relations Director
Space: 6 galleries with 1500 sq m floor space
Exhibitions: 20 a year of which 15 originated, 5 on a hire basis
Details: Work by staff and students from all departments within the college, annual degree shows in mid-June & July, other College shows during the year. Also outside exhibitions, including C20th British Art Fair and the London & Provincial Antique Dealers Antique Show.

Royal Festival Hall Galleries

South Bank Centre, London SE1 8XX, tel: 0171 921 0600, fax: 0171 921 0663
Contact: Alison Wright

Rudolf Steiner House

Pa Ph Pr O H &

Exhibition space in multi-functioning foyer.
35 Park Road, London NW1 6XT, tel: 0171 723 4400, fax: 0171 724 4364
Contact: Dorian Keller
Open: Mon-Sat 10-6
Space: 1 gallery with 11 lin m hanging space
Exhibitions: 14 a year all on a hire basis
Details: Preference given to artists who are familiar with the teaching of Rudolf Steiner. Audience mainly people who come to the house for the wide range of activities available. 10% commission of sold works as a hiring fee, or £50 per week.

Rutland Gallery *

Pa

Shows selected modern masters, British primitives of the C18th and C19th, also work from the South China Coast.
32a St George Street, London W1R 9FA, tel: 0171 499 5636
Contact: Exhibition Organiser
Space: 2 galleries with 70 lin m hanging space and 40 sq m floor space

S.A.S. Gallery *

Pa O

Commercial gallery aims to offer smaller-scale work, drawings and sketches by young artists of some reputation.
72 Lupus Street, Pimlico, London SW1V 3HB, tel: 0171 821 5801
Contact: Robert Castelo, Art Director, PO Box 242, London, SW1V 3HB
Space: 1 gallery with 18 lin m hanging space plus 5 lin m on screens
Exhibitions: 9 a year all originated
Details: Draws on context of a busy, adjoining office to create atmosphere. Gallery looking for variety and quality. Applications welcomed but more likely the gallery will seek out work rather than wait for it to come to them.

Saatchi Gallery 21/10 curators

Pa Pr Sc & Wc Office & shop?
328 - 8299 cm THURS FRI

Contemporary art museum in converted warehouse which aims to introduce new art to a wide audience. SAT SUN
98a Boundary Road, London NW8 0RH, tel: 0171 624 8299, fax: 0171 624 3798
Contact: Jenny Blyth, Curator
Open: Thurs-Sun 12-6
Space: 6 galleries with 2790 sq m floor space
Exhibitions: 3 a year
Details: Private collection of contemporary

art by living artists. Only exhibits work from the collection. Large number of works by relatively few artists make up the collection of painting and sculpture. Each show lasts four months. Works not on display are frequently on loan to museums around the world. £2.50 admission charge on Fri (free on Thurs). No sales.

St Martin's Gallery

Pa Ph Pr Cr O H &

Commercial gallery in vaulted crypt of St Martin in the Fields church with all profits going to church for its work with the homeless.
St Martin-in-the-Fields, Trafalgar Square, London WC2N 4JJ, tel: 0171 930 0089, fax: 0171 839 5163
Contact: Allyson Hargreaves, Gallery Manager
Open: Mon-Sat 10-6
Space: 1 gallery with 180 lin m hanging space and 56 sq m floor space
Exhibitions: 34 a year all on a hire basis
Details: Gallery space next to the popular Café-in-the-Crypt. Exhibitions seen by large numbers of visitors to London. Hire charges are competitive, and work sells well. 20% commission on sales. Group and student shows welcomed.

Salama-Caro Gallery *

Pa Ph Pr Sc

Commercial gallery showing own stable of artists.
5-6 Cork Street, London W1X 1PB, tel: 0171 734 9179, fax: 0171 494 2773
Contact: Laura Baker
Space: 4 galleries
Exhibitions: 6 a year all originated
Details: Artists represented include Robert Indiana, Ed Albers, Arshile Gorky, Louise Nevelson, John Stezaker, Guillermo Kuitca, Robert Morris, Adam Fuss.

Sally Hunter Fine Art

Pa O

Small gallery, specialising in modern British art with a few contemporary exhibitions.
11 Halkin Arcade, Motcomb Street, London SW1X 8JT, tel: 0171 235 0934
Contact: Sally Hunter, Director
Open: Mon-Fri 10-6
Space: 1 gallery with 60 lin m hanging space and 400 sq m floor space
Exhibitions: 13 a year all originated

Savannah Gallery *

Pa Ph Pr Cr Sc LA O

A changing programme of modern and contemporary African art put together to form mixed travelling and solo shows.
45 Derbyshire Street, London E2 6NQ, tel: 0171 613 3072
Contact: Mr L Coubagy

Space: 2 galleries with 940 sq m floor space
Exhibitions: 4 a year all originated
Details: Artists included in this programme are those with established reputations and those who show potential.

Seen Galleries *

 ✔

Private gallery selling originals to corporate and private clients worldwide.
8 Frederic Mews, London SW1X 8EQ, tel: 0171 245 6131, fax: 0171 245 9007
Contact: Jeffrey Sion, Director
Space: 1 gallery
Exhibitions: 3 a year all originated
Details: Private gallery selling originals to corporate and private clients worldwide. Representational and figurative. Always seeking new artists.

Serpentine Gallery

Pa Ph Pr SC LA ✔✆ ♿4

Exhibitions programme recognises achievements of established British artists while reflecting new international developments and presenting work by younger artists.
Kensington Gardens, London W2 3XA, tel: 0171 402 6075, fax: 0171 402 4103
Contact: Julia Peyton-Jones/Andrea Schlicker, Director/Deputy Director
Open: Daily 10-6 except during installation of exhibitions.
Space: 4 galleries with 500 sq m floor space
Exhibitions: 8 a year all originated
Details: Launched in 1970 by the Arts Council, also funded by Westminster. Annual attendance is 200,000. Offers four finely-proportioned rooms with an abundance of natural light. Selling work not a primary function.

Showroom (The)

Pa SC LA ♿

Publicly-funded contemporary art gallery with visual and live arts programme.
44 Bonner Road, Bethnal Green, London E2 9JS, tel: 0181 983 4115
Contact: Kim Sweet, Director
Open: Wed-Sun 1-6
Space: 2 galleries with 70 lin m hanging space and 400 sq m floor space
Exhibitions: 6 a year all originated
Details: Supports production and presentation of innovative new developments within the contemporary arts, by emerging and established artists from UK and abroad. Commissions and exhibits work which is of high quality, is suited to gallery space and is relevant both within context of current art practice and broader cultural concerns.

Slade Gallery

University of Central London, Gower Street, London, tel: 0171 387 7050

Sladmore Gallery of Animal Sculpture

SC

Commercial gallery dealing in C19th and C20th sculpture and antiques and shows sculpture by living artists, particularly animal sculpture.
32 Bruton Place, London W1X 7AA, tel: 0171 499 0365
Contact: Edward Horswell, Exhibition Organiser
Details: Specialises in 'fine antiques' and animal sculpture, and promotes work of two contemporary sculptors. Programme includes three shows of three to four weeks and a changing selection of antiques. Permanent collection of C19th and early C20th animal bronzes.

Slaughterhouse Gallery

Pa Ph Pr Cr SC LA ✔♿ ⊗

Unconventional space for multi-media exhibitions, performance, music, dance, film, photography, theatre.
63 Charterhouse Gallery, Smithfield, London EC1M 6HJ, tel: 0171 251 5888, fax: 0171 490 0847
Contact: Marguerite Smith, Director
Open: Tues-Sat 11-6; or by appointment
Space: 4 galleries with 185 sq m floor space
Exhibitions: 13 a year of which 2 originated, 11 on a hire basis
Details: Opposite Smithfield Meat Market. Three spectacular subterranean vaults in the style of a Byzantine crypt. Overlooked by the upper floor of the gallery, a more conventional white-walled space which provides balance and excellent views to the chambers below. Has shown many college degree shows and has very good support from firms in the area. Sales not a priority.

Small Mansion Arts Centre *

Pa Pr SC ✔✆♿

Equal access policy arts centre gallery space.
Gunnersbury Park, Popes Lane, Hounslow, London TW3 8LQ, tel: 0181 993 8312
Contact: Fred Lightfoot, Administrator
Space: 3 galleries with 51 lin m hanging space plus 20 lin m on screens and 153 sq m floor space
Exhibitions: 13 a year of which 11 originated, 2 on a hire basis
Details: Seeks to arrange a varied programme embracing all media, and to try and ensure equal representation between gender and provide access to Asian and other ethnic artists. Thematic exhibitions and occasional one-person shows preferred. The Orangery (see separate entry) is used for limited periods in the year and favours local (West London) artists. Audiences are typical cross-section. Encourages artists to submit proposals for exhibition.

South London Gallery

 Pa Ph SC LA ✔♿

Victorian gallery with excellent natural light showing changing exhibitions of contemporary art.
65 Peckham Road, London SE5 8UH, tel: 0171 703 6120, fax: 0171 252 4730
Contact: David Thorp, Gallery Director
Open: Tues, Wed, Fri 11-6; Thurs 11-7; Sat & Sun 2-6
Space: 1 gallery with 54 lin m hanging space and 260 sq m floor space
Exhibitions: 7 a year of which 5 originated, 2 touring
Details: Regionally significant venue for contemporary art, with policy to explore new developments in visual arts by British and foreign artists. Exhibitions programme is accompanied by education activities which are seen as an essential element within the gallery's programme. Selling not considered primary role.

Soviet Carpet & Art Centre

Pa Ph Pr Cr SC ⊗

A private gallery showing East European works of art.
303-305 Cricklewood Broadway, London NW2 6PG, tel: 0181 452 2445, fax: 0181 450 2642
Contact: Dr Robert Rabi, Manager
Open: Mon-Fri by appointment; Sun 10.30-5.30
Space: 1 gallery with 70 lin m hanging space and 250 sq m floor space
Exhibitions: 2 a year both originated
Details: Gallery above large trade warehouse that sells hand-made rugs. Specialises in fine and applied arts from Russia and other republics of the former USSR. Happy to act as the originator and organiser of touring exhibitions. Exhibits other art forms connected to the former Soviet republics. Specialises in fine hand-made rugs from the southern regions, eg Turkmenistan & the Caucasus. Sales a priority.

Special Photographers Co

Ph SC ✔♿ ♿

Active exhibitions promoting work of new and established photographers addressing contemporary issues in local and international context.
21 Kensington Park Road, London W11 2EU, tel: 0171 221 3489, fax: 0171 792 9112
Contact: Catherine Turner, Director
Open: Mon-Fri 10-6; Sat 11-5
Space: 1 gallery with 30 lin m hanging space and 1300 sq m floor space
Exhibitions: 10 a year of which 9 originated, 1 on a hire basis
Details: Exhibits photographs which reflect the personal expression or obsession of the

artist. More interested in photographs that talk of the artist than of the subject – ie fine art rather than reportage. An independent gallery which receives no funding therefore the financial feasibility of each exhibition must be carefully considered. Sales therefore important to gallery.

Spink & Son

Gallery dealing in 18th, 19th and 20th Century watercolours, drawings and paintings with annual exhibitions.
5, 6 & 7 King Street, St James's, London SW1Y 6QS, tel: 0171 930 7888, fax: 0171 839 4853
Contact: Iona Sale, Public Relations Manager
Open: Mon-Fri 9-5.30
Space: 2 galleries with 45 lin m hanging space and 91 sq m floor space
Exhibitions: 4 a year all originated
Details: Gallery holds annual watercolour exhibitions in Spring and Autumn and C20th British modern art exhibition in the summer. Situated in the heart of St James's in close proximity to many fine art galleries, antique dealers and auctioneers. Sales a priority.

Stables Gallery

Gallery in converted stables whose main objective is to display high-quality works of art in variety of styles and media.
Gladstone Park, Dollis Hill Lane, London NW2 6HT, tel: 0181 452 8655
Contact: Vernon Fletcher, Exhibitions Manager
Open: (Oct-Mar) Thurs-Sun 11-5; (April-Sept) Thurs-Sun 11-6
Space: 1 gallery with 27 lin m hanging space and 28 sq m floor space
Exhibitions: 12 a year all originated
Details: Exhibitions cover all art disciplines and solo and group shows. Gallery well suited to showing small to medium sized pictures. Artists include college graduates, self-taught and established artists. Work selected by a visual arts panel. Selling work not gallery's primary role.

Stalls Gallery/Circle Gallery/Roof Garden Restaurant Gallery

Theatre-based gallery.
Lyric Theatre, King Street, Hammersmith, London W6 0QL, tel: 0181 741 0824, fax: 0181 741 7694
Contact: Yvonne Joyce, Head of Education
Open: Mon-Sat 10-11
Space: 1 gallery with 20 lin m hanging space
Exhibitions: 12 a year all originated
Details: Audience of the general public and theatre goers. Welcomes artists who are looking for their first exhibition space after leaving college.

Standpoint Gallery

Standpoint Studios, 45 Coronet Street, London N1 6HD, tel: 0171 729 5272

Stanmore Library

Dedicated exhibition space within main library building with primary purpose of supporting and promoting development of art in local community.
8 Stanmore Hill, Stanmore, London HA7 3BQ, tel: 0181 954 9955
Contact: Derek Knight, Branch Librarian
Open: Mon, Tues, Thurs 9.30-1, 2-8; Fri 9.30-1; Sat 9-5
Space: 1 gallery with 13 lin m hanging space plus 22 lin m on screens and 33 sq m floor space
Exhibitions: 26 a year all on a hire basis
Details: Priority given to artists based in local community. No selection policy is enforced. Small booking fee is charged and library takes 10% commission on sales but sale of work not a priority. Display cases for craft work available.

Stephen Friedman Gallery

25-28 Old Burlington Street, London W1X 1LB, tel: 0171 494 1434, fax: 0171 494 1431
Contact: Stephen Friedman
Open: Tues-Fri 10-5; Sat 11-3

Studio & Education Access *

Founded to promote under-represented art of the community.
The Boilerhouse, Brick Lane, London E1
Contact: Chris Anstice, 37 Elliots Row, London, SE11 4FZ, tel: 0171 735 5926
Space: 1 gallery with 160 lin m hanging space and 93 sq m floor space
Exhibitions: 12 a year of which 9 originated, 3 touring
Details: Provides rent-free space with no commission on sales. Aims to encourage experimentation, and bring into the open cultural expression of a mixed society. May incorporate any number of media and circumvent established cultural boundaries. Artists selected by committee and expected to invigilate their exhibition.

Studio l'Image

Purpose-built brick space exhibiting up and coming young artists from southern England.
2a Tabernacle Street, London EC2A 4LU, tel: 0171 256 9969, fax: 0171 256 9959
Contact: Jonathon or Lucia, Owner or Co-ordinator

Open: Daily 10-4
Space: 2 galleries with 30 lin m hanging space and 46 sq m floor space
Exhibitions: 4 a year all on a hire basis
Details: Narrow gallery plus foyer/reception area showing work by young illustrators, photographers and artists from Southern England. Artists selected for their individuality and style. Visitor feed-back encouraged. Sales not high priority but encouraged. Small commission taken which is fed back into space.

Studio (The)

Exhibition space divided into working areas; small gallery shop, small porcelain restoration workshop, large cellar picture framing workshop.
Porcelain and Pictures Ltd, 1(b) Gastein Road, Fulham, London W6 8LT, tel: 0171 385 7512
Contact: Edward & David Toms, Exhibition Organiser
Open: Daily 9.30-5.30
Space: 1 gallery with 31 lin m hanging space and 84 sq m floor space
Exhibitions: 3 a year of which 2 originated, 1 touring
Details: Deals in C19th and C20th watercolours, and contemporary limited edition prints and watercolours by both established and young unestablished artists. Workshops provided for picture framers and porcelain restorers. Programme of tuition and seminars held on both subjects. Specialist in publishing prints. Sales a priority and commission of 25% taken on sales made.

Sutton College Gallery

Aims to help young artists and makers who would find it difficult to show in London galleries.
Sutton College of Liberal Arts, St Nicholas Way, Sutton, London SM1 1EA, tel: 0181 770 6901, fax: 0181 770 6933
Space: 1 gallery with 24 lin m hanging space and 75 sq m floor space
Exhibitions: 8 a year all originated
Details: All exhibits in lockable showcases. Leading artists and makers invited to show at intervals (two or three a year). Particularly suitable for ceramics, jewellery, prints and small sculptural items.

Sunshine Gallery

Hays Galeria, Tooley Street, London SE1 2HD, tel: 0171 403 0933, fax: 0171 403 0934

Sutton House

Pa Pr Sc ✓ &wc 4

Contemporary art gallery within National Trust owned Tudor building in East London, with varied exhibitions.
2 & 4 Homerton High Street, Hackney, London E9 6JQ, tel: 0181 986 2264, fax: 0181 533 0556
Contact: Carole Mills, Project Manager
Open: Wed-Sun 11.30-5.30; closed January
Space: 1 gallery with 8 lin m hanging space plus 14 lin m on screens and 11 sq m floor space
Exhibitions: 9 a year of which 2 originated
Details: Monthly exhibitions in gallery providing show space primarily for locally based artists. Aim is to show contemporary work as a complement to the historic house.

Swiss Cottage Central Library Exhibition Hall

Pa Ph Pr Sc ✓ H &

Exhibition space in the heart of Swiss Cottage Library.
88 Avenue Road, London NW3 3HA
Contact: David Law, Exhibitions Officer, Camden Arts Services, London Borough of Camden, Crowndale Centre, 218 Eversholt Street, London, NW1 1BD, tel: 0171 911 1596, fax: 0171 911 1615
Open: Mon, Thurs 10-7; Tues, Fri 10-6; Sat 10-5
Space: 1 gallery with 55 lin m hanging space plus 14 lin m on screens and 126 sq m floor space
Exhibitions: 8 a year all on a hire basis
Details: Exhibitions space located centrally in the building with both natural and artificial light, it offers exhibitors exposure to a wide and receptive audience. The programme aims to reflect local, regional and national developments in contemporary art, craft and photography. Exhibitions Officer provides assistance in presenting the exhibitors' work. Individuals, groups, societies and guilds are welcome to apply.

Tabernacle Art Gallery

Pa Ph Pr C Sc LA ✓ H &wc

Gallery forms centre of large community centre based on the arts.
Powis Square, London W11, tel: 0171 243 8621/0181 964 5740 after 6 pm, fax: 0171 727 0296
Contact: Mary McGowan, Gallery Coordinator
Open: Mon-Fri 10-8; Sat 10-3 (longer hours for special exhibitions)
Space: 1 gallery with 61 lin m hanging space and 118 sq m floor space
Exhibitions: 12 a year of which 6 originated, 1 touring, 5 on a hire basis
Details: Specialises in artists in last 2 years

of art school through the 5 years following, mounting large open exhibitions regularly. Can be hired by groups or single artists. Sometimes sponsors groups of students and raises sponsorship for the opens. Ceramics on display in cabinets which can be hired individually by the month.

Talent Store Gallery *

Pa ✓

Exhibits work to suit conventional tastes of its clientele and aims to provide a start for young artists and those who have not previously exhibited much.
11 Eccleston Street, London SW1W 9LX, tel: 0171 730 8117
Contact: Mrs Kabby Streater, Gallery Manager
Space: 1 gallery with 102 lin m hanging space
Exhibitions: 12 a year all originated
Details: Target audience is the ordinary person in the street.

Tate Gallery

Publishing (Rosemary) Bennett. 21/10

Pa Ph Pr Sc LA

Houses national collections of British art from the C16th to the present day (including Turner collection in the Clore Gallery) and international C20th art.
Millbank, London SW1P 4RG, tel: 0171 887 8000, fax: 0171 887 8007
Contact: Nicholas Serota, Director
Open: Mon-Sat 10-5.50; Sun 2-5.50
Exhibitions: 5 a year all originated
Details: Displays change annually to explore the wealth and variety of the collection. Admission is free except for three major loan exhibitions each year. Bookshop, restaurant, coffee shop.

Tannery (The)

46 Bermondsey Street, London SE1, tel: 0171 340 5650

Tea Rooms Des Artistes

Pa Ph Pr C LA ✓ H

Licensed café with artwork and performance as the main focus.
697 Wandsworth Road, Clapham, London SW8 3JF, tel: 0171 652 6526
Contact: David Attwater, Proprietors
Open: Mon 6-12; Tues-Thurs, Sat & Sun 12-12; Fri 4.30-12
Space: 60 lin m hanging space and 3000 sq m floor space
Exhibitions: 12 a year of which 10 originated, 2 on a hire basis
Details: C16th barn on edge of Clapham Old Town. Original beams, pitched ceiling. Vegetarian food, licensed bar, stage and PA system. Courtyard area for sculptural displays. Exhibitions change monthly. No commission taken. 2D work preferred. 200 visitors daily from wide cross section.

Thackeray Gallery

18 Thackeray Street, Kensington Square, London W8 5ET, tel: 0171 937 5883

Theatro Technis

Pa Ph Pr Cr Sc ✓ & wc

Promotes visual art through programme of one-person and group shows in theatre foyer space.
26 Crowndale Road, London NW1 1TT, tel: 0171 387 6617, fax: 0171 388 7971
Contact: George Eugeniou, Artistic Director
Open: Mon-Sat 10-5.30
Space: 1 gallery with 5 sq m floor space
Exhibitions: 2 a year both originated

Theo Waddington Fine Art

Pa Pr Sc ✓ &

Major London commercial gallery showing and selling contemporary work.
5a Cork Street, London W1X 1PB, tel: 0171 494 1584, fax: 0171 287 0926
Contact: Terence Sims, Gallery Director
Open: Mon-Fri 10-5.30; Sat 10-1
Space: 100 lin m hanging space and 240 sq m floor space
Exhibitions: 11 a year
Details: Applications from artists seeking exhibitions occasionally welcomed. Independent access for wheelchair users to half of the gallery only.

Thompson's Gallery

Pa Sc &

Commercial gallery showing contemporary painting and sculpture from Britain and Ireland.
38 Albemarle Street, London W1X 3FB, tel: 0171 499 1314
Contact: John Martin & Sara Pearce
Space: 1 gallery with 22 lin m hanging space and 36 sq m floor space
Exhibitions: 8 a year all originated

Tiller Centre

Pa Ph Pr Cr ✓ H & wc

Public hall with exhibition boards for display of 2D work.
The Tiller Centre, Tiller Road, Isle of Dogs, London E14 8PX, tel: 0171 987 7925, fax: 0171 538 3314
Contact: Denise Terry-Roberts, Community Arts Development Officer
Space: 2 galleries with 23 lin m hanging space and 173 sq m floor space
Exhibitions: 6 a year of which 3 originated, 1 on a hire basis
Details: 14m of exhibition boards. Additional 9m of exhibition boards in corridor. Most work shown originates from art centre users or local artists.

Todd Gallery

Gallery interested in the work of young British artists and aims to present exhibitions in an international context.
1-5 Needham Road, London W11 2RP, tel: 0171 792 1404, fax: 0171 792 1505
Contact: Anthony Stokes/Jenny Todd, Directors
Open: Tues-Fri 11-6; Sat 11-4
Space: 1 gallery with 40 lin m hanging space
Exhibitions: 8 a year all originated
Details: Gallery does not consider sale of work as its main role.

Tom Allen Gallery *

A small, well-lit but personal space mostly used by local artists and community groups.
Grove Crescent Road, Stratford, London E15 2BJ, tel: 0181 555 7289
Contact: Hilary Wilhelm (Mrs)
Space: 1 gallery with 105 lin m hanging space and 34 sq m floor space
Exhibitions: 12 a year all originated
Details: The aim is to offer artists an exhibition as a stepping stone.

Tom Blau Gallery at Camera Press

Selling contemporary photography gallery in foyer of international photographic features agency Camera Press.
21 Queen Elizabeth Street, London SE1 2PD, tel: 0171 378 1300, fax: 0171 278 5126
Contact: Helen Dent, Gallery Manager
Open: Mon-Fri 10-6.30
Space: 1 gallery with 31 lin m hanging space plus 6 lin m on screens and 70 sq m floor space
Exhibitions: 7 a year of which 5 originated, 1 touring, 1 on a hire basis
Details: Exhibits and sells work by emerging and established photographers. Generally two exhibitions a year are of work by individual photographers. Other exhibitions generated by Camera Press archives, by taking touring shows from other galleries or by private hire. Gallery aims to encourage visitors to appreciate broad spectrum of contemporary photography.

Tram Depot Gallery

38-40 Upper Clapton Road, London E5, tel: 0181 806 3479

Tricycle Gallery

Committed to exhibiting contemporary art in a theatre environment.

269 Kilburn, High Road, London NW6, tel: 0171 372 6611, fax: 0171 328 0755
Contact: Jeremy R. Cole, Coordinator
Open: Mon-Sat 10.30am-10.30pm
Space: 1 gallery with 450 sq m floor space
Exhibitions: 12 a year all originated
Details: Solo and group shows. Gallery based within Tricycle Theatre. Well-known and up-and-coming artists. Paintings, drawings, prints (no photo work, no 3D work). Private view cards and mailshot free for artists. 25% commission on sales which are an important function of gallery.

Tryon & Swann Gallery

Specialists in sporting, wildlife and marine pictures, prints, bronzes and books.
23-24 Cork Street, London W1, tel: 0171 734 6961, fax: 0171 287 2480
Contact: The Hon J E H Bigham, Chairman
Open: Mon-Fri 9.30-5.30
Space: 3 galleries
Exhibitions: 8 a year all originated
Details: Exhibitions of work by C19th and C20th artists with subject matter appropriate to gallery's specialisms. Sales a priority.

Two 10 Gallery

Small gallery (at the Welcome Centre for Medical Science) displaying temporary exhibitions that explore the interaction and intersection between art and the medical sciences.
210 Euston Road, London NW1, tel: 0171 611 8351, fax: 0171 611 8526
Contact: Dr Ken Arnold
Space: 1 gallery
Exhibitions: 2 a year both originated
Details: Opened in april 1995, the gallery aims to show how art can play a role in poromoting the public's understanding of science. Exhibitions available for loan.

Union Chapel Project *

A complex of Victorian gothic buidings with a range of arts and community activities.
Compton Avenue, Off Upper Street, London N1, tel: 0171 226 1686, fax: 0171 354 8343
Contact: Martin Frost, Exhibition Organiser
Space: 2 galleries with 390 sq m floor space
Exhibitions: 4 a year of which 2 touring, 2 on a hire basis
Details: 1,200 seater auditorium/chapel, studio theatre, three halls of varying sizes. Exhibitions considered for café/bar and studio theatre (2D and 3D).No selection committee – the artists select the work and decide how and where to show it.

Uxbridge Central Library

Exhibition space in library.
Central Library, High Street, Uxbridge, London UB8 1HD, tel: 01895 250711, fax: 01895 239794
Contact: Joan Gallacher, Arts Co-ordinator
Space: 1 gallery with 30 lin m hanging space and 68 sq m floor space
Exhibitions: 22 a year all originated
Details: Will consider for display any work but retain overall control. Around 13,000 visitors per week. The fortnightly/monthly exhibitions are predominantly mixed.

Victoria Gallery *

Promotes both young and established artists in group or solo shows.
158 Hermon Hill, London E18 1QH, tel: 0181 898 1195, fax: 0181 530 7978
Contact: John Barratt
Open: Mon-Fri 10-5.30; Sat 11-1
Space: 1 gallery with 100 sq m floor space
Exhibitions: 2 a year both originated
Details: Exhibitions held in single gallery space and include painting, sculpture, craft, and occasionally photography. Also publishes limited edition art books, open editions, trade cards.

Victoria Miro

Commercial gallery showing and dealing work by living British and foreign artists working in a variety of media.
21 Cork Street, London W1X 1HB, tel: 0171 734 5082, fax: 0171 494 1787
Contact: Clare Rowe, Exhibition Organiser
Space: 1 gallery with 10 lin m hanging space and 500 sq m floor space
Exhibitions: 10 a year all originated
Details: Exhibitions mainly solo shows lasting 4-6 weeks. Only looks at new works on recommendation.

Village Coffee Shop & Gallery

Informal café gallery specialising in emerging artists.
27 Shepherd Market, Mayfair, London W1Y 7HR, tel: 0171 499 4592
Contact: Dave Williams
Open: Mon-Fri 7-9; Sat-Sun 9-7
Space: 1 gallery with 11 lin m hanging space
Exhibitions: 4 a year all originated
Details: Showing art for arts sake with only a 20% commission. All monies raised from commission used to help other artists.

Vortex Galleries *

Above a bookshop and shop selling art cards, prints and frames.
139-141 Stoke Newington Church Street, London N16, tel: 0171 254 6516
Contact: Irving Kinnersley, Exhibition Organiser
Space: 1 gallery
Exhibitions: 12 a year all on a hire basis
Details: Contains a cafe doubling at night as jazz bar. Exhibitions generally by invitation although applications considered. Paintings generally shown, some relief work considered.

Waddington Galleries

Three spaces used for monthly exhibitions of contemporary and modern art from the gallery's stock.
11, 12 & 34 Cork Street, London W1, tel: 0171 439 6262/437 8611, fax: 0171 734 4146
Open: Mon-Fri 10-5.30; Sat 10-1; (Aug) closed Sat
Space: 3 galleries
Exhibitions: 10 a year all originated
Details: Commercial gallery dealing in C20th works of art: paintings, sculptures, drawings, prints and illustrated books. Substantial inventory of works by major artists of the century including Picasso, Matisse, Miro, Dubuffet, Calder, Moore, Leger and Gris. In addition, the gallery represents approximately 20 contemporary artists, mainly British, but also a number from N. America and Europe. Regular mixed exhibitions composed of important works from stock, interspersed with solo shows of work by gallery artists.

Walpole Gallery

Gallery with changing stock of Italian paintings, sculpture, prints and drawings and occasional exhibitions.
38 Dover Street, London W1X 3RB, tel: 0171 499 6626, fax: 0171 493 4122
Contact: Elisabetta Genuizzi, Secretary
Exhibitions: 1 a year originated
Details: Deals in Italian art up to the C18th. Exhibitions last two months. Devoted to specific themes as well as anthologies representing kind of stock for sale.

Walton Contemporary Art

Contemporary artists' and sculptors' work in original print and edition form is presented throughout the year.
188 Walton Street, London SW3 2JL, tel: 0171 581 9011, fax: 0171 581 0585
Contact: Betty Kitching, Gallery Director
Open: Mon-Fri 9.30-6.30; Sat 10-3.0-6
Space: 1 gallery with 121 sq m floor space

Exhibitions: 2 a year both originated
Details: Gallery represents contemporary artists and supplies both the trade and private sectors for residential and business interiors.

Warren Wine Bar & Gallery

The Grafton Hotel dedicates wall space to contemporary art and so promotes its wine bar.
Fitzroy Court, Off Tottenham Court Road, London W1, tel: 0171 388 4131
Contact: Antony Brunt, Manager
Space: 6 galleries with 35 lin m hanging space
Exhibitions: 10 a year all on a hire basis
Details: Shows last 4-6 weeks and include the work of 6 artists. No fee for hiring the space but artists must organise insurance. 10% commission.

Waterman Fine Art

74a Jermyn Street, St James's, London SW1Y 6NP, tel: 0171 839 5203, fax: 0171 321 0212
Open: Mon-Fri 9-6, Sat 10-4

Watermans Arts Centre

Gallery, theatre, cinema, restaurant and bar where main gallery exhibits new and innovative work in all fine art media.
40 High Street, Brentford, London TW8 0DS, tel: 0181 847 5651, fax: 0181 569 8592
Contact: Penny Precious, Visual Arts Officer
Space: 3 galleries with 375 lin m hanging space and 2950 sq m floor space
Exhibitions: 8 a year of which 4 originated, 1 touring, on a hire basis
Details: Aims for "Artists' advocacy giving greater access to their audiences." Site-specific projects are encouraged along with non-gallery sited work. Artists expected to participate in the community education programme, the results of which form exhibitions in the Foyer Gallery and Stairway Gallery.

Westminster Gallery

Extensive and adaptable gallery space available in the heart of London.
Westminster Central Hall, Storey's Gate, London SW1H 9NH, tel: 0171 222 2723, fax: 0171 222 6883
Contact: Peter Tudor, General Manager
Open: By arrangement
Space: 2 galleries with 69 lin m hanging space and 547 sq m floor space
Exhibitions: 8 a year all originated
Details: In the basement of Westminster Central Hall with one main area that can be divided into several smaller spaces. Also

a lecture hall and a library which give additional temporary space. Makes its facilities available to a variety of artists and art societies in mixed shows, ranging from the conventional to the contemporary. Lighting and plinths available for use if necessary. Sale of work not gallery's primary role.

Westminster Library Service

Headquarters of the City of Westminster's Education and Leisure Department, including the Library Service which has exhibition spaces in 13 libraries.
PO Box 240, Westminster City Hall, Victoria Street, London SW1E 6QP, tel: 0171 798 2496, fax: 0171 798 3404
Contact: D Ruse, Assisant Director

Whitechapel Art Gallery

Reopens JAN 98

One of London's most exciting public galleries.
80/82 Whitechapel High Street, London E1 7QX, tel: 0171 522 7888, fax: 0171 377 1685
Contact: James Peto/Felicity Lunn, Curators
Open: Tues, Thurs-Sun 11-5; Wed 11-8
Space: 3 galleries with 161 lin m hanging space plus 24 lin m on screens and 576 sq m floor space
Exhibitions: 7 a year of which 4 originated, 3 touring
Details: Temporary exhibitions, mainly of modern and contemporary art. Organises talks, lectures, school and community group workshops, an artists in schools scheme and small exhibitions in local venues. Audience includes children/students, local community, artists, city workers, overseas visitors. Sales not a priority.

Whiteleys Atrium Gallery

Gallery in shopping centre with space for hire.
Queensway, London W2, tel: 0171 229 8844
Contact: Alan Thornton
Space: 1 gallery with 492 sq m
Details: Hire charge is £1000 per week – no sales commission taken.

Wigmore Hall

Concert hall with exhibition space running the length of the foyer.
36 Wigmore Street, London W1H 0BP, tel: 0171 486 1907, fax: 0171 224 3800
Contact: Exhibition Organiser
Open: (Winter) Mon-Sat 10-9.30, Sun 11-1 & 3.30-6; (Summer) Mon-Sat 10-9.30, Sun 11-1, 3.30-6, 6.30-9; closed August
Space: 1 gallery

Exhibitions: 11 a year all on a hire basis
Details: Visitors generally concert-goers and tourists. Exhibitions run for one calendar month. The space available is suitable for paintings, drawings, sketches etc. Commission of 20% on all paintings sold.

Wildenstein & Co

Pa

Old gallery showing well-established artists in combination of mixed and solo shows
147 New Bond Street, London W1Y 0NX, tel: 0171 629 0602, fax: 0171 493 3924
Contact: David Ellis-Jones, Director
Open: Mon-Fri 10-5.30
Space: 3 galleries
Exhibitions: 3 a year all originated
Details: Programme of contemporary and modern painting augmenting permanent dealership of old masters and impressionists. Audience made up of collectors and buyers of art.

Willesden Gallery

Pa Ph Pr Cr Sc ✓ ⬤ Wc

Dedicated exhibition spaces within modern building comprising library, cinema, restaurant/bar, bookshop and conference.
Willesden Green Library Centre, 95 Willesden High Road, London NW10 2ST, tel: 0181 908 7503
Contact: Maps Business Unit c/o Willesden Gallery
Open: Daily 9 am-11pm
Space: 31 lin m hanging space
Exhibitions: 10 a year
Details: Offers artists and residents of Brent wide range of arts and events. Library has long walkway and 2 additional spaces ideal for large sculptural pieces. Plinths, perspex boxes and display cases available. Programme includes major touring shows (eg from the South Bank), work from Brent artists in residence, studio groups, and members of the Brent Artists Register. Visual arts festival held each year. Commission on some sales.

William Jackson Gallery

New Burlington Street, London W1, tel: 0171 287 0495

William Morris Gallery

Pa Cr ⬤ 4

Permanent exhibition of life and work of William Morris and of his associates in the Arts and Crafts Movement with some contemporary art exhibitions mounted.
Lloyd Park, Forest Road, Walthamstow, London E17 4PP, tel: 0181 527 3782
Contact: Norah Gillow, Keeper
Open: Tues-Sat & 1st Sun in each month 10-1, 2-5
Space: 1 gallery with 14 lin m hanging space plus 10 lin m on screens and 30 sq m floor space

Exhibitions: 4 a year of which 2 originated, 2 touring
Details: Promotes the work of William Morris and the Pre-Raphaelite movement. For temporary exhibitions favours work by local artists. Artists' residencies, talks and workshops accompany exhibitions. Sale of work not primary function of gallery.

Wimbledon Library Gallery

Pa Ph Pr Cr Sc ✓ ⬤ ⊗

Gallery used for displays and exhibitions by artists, craftspeople and by Wimbledon School of Art.
Wimbledon Hill Road, Wimbledon, London SW19 7NB, tel: 0181 946 7432, fax: 0181 944 6804
Contact: Alison Williams, Customer Services Librarian
Open: Mon, Tues, Thurs, Fri 9.30-7; Wed 9.30-1; Sat 9.30-5
Space: 1 gallery with 30 lin m hanging space plus 8 lin m on screens and 70 sq m floor space
Exhibitions: 15 a year all on a hire basis
Details: Panelled room with white display screens and high glass ceiling, giving good natural light. Aims to promote arts and crafts to the community by providing attractive exhibition space in busy public library. Fee charged to hire gallery and commission taken on sales but work exhibited does not have to be for sale. Gallery is on first floor.

Wine Gallery

Pa Pr

Wine bar/restaurant/gallery.
49 Hollywood Road, London SW10, tel: 0171 352 7572, fax: 0171 376 5083
Contact: Director
Exhibitions: 6 a year all originated
Details: Specialises in promotion of local artists. Also at 294 Westbourne Grove, London W11, tel 071 299 1877.

Wingfield Sporting Art *

Pa Pr Sc ✓

Commercial gallery showing all forms of sport in art and sculpture by contemporary artists.
35 Sibella Road, London SW4 6JA, tel: 0171 622 6301
Contact: Mr David Wingfield, Exhibition Organiser
Space: 4 galleries
Exhibitions: 4 a year all originated
Details: Clients range from private individuals to multinationals commissioning art to complement their sponsorship programme in sports. Limited edition prints published to encourage collectors of affordable sporting art.

Wood Green Central Library

Pa Pr Cr ✓ ⬤ ⬤ Wc

Purpose-built exhibition room attached to main library, plus additional space outside exhibition room.
High Road, London N22 6XD, tel: 0181 888 1292, fax: 0181 889 0110
Contact: Gill Harvey, Neighbourhood Librarian
Open: Mon-Thurs 9.30-7; Sat 9.30-5
Space: 2 galleries with 24 lin m hanging space plus 8 lin m on screens
Exhibitions: 11 a year of which 7 originated, 4 on a hire basis
Details: Two exhibition spaces in library showing temporary exhibitions of contemporary art. Priority given to work by local artists, and/or exhibitions of particular relevance to the local community. New Gallery – purpose built, enclosed. Long Gallery – movable screens outside New Gallery. Both on 1st floor with lift access.

Workfortheeyetodo

51 Hanbury Street, London E1, tel: 0171 278 2885

Woodlands Art Gallery

Pa Ph Pr Cr Sc ✓ ♿

Four large well-lit galleries showing one-person and group shows and exhibitions of schools' and community groups' work.
90 Mycenae Road, Blackheath, London SE3 7SE, tel: 0181 858 5847
Open: Mon-Sat 11-5; Sun 2-5; closed BH
Space: 4 galleries with 63 lin m hanging space and 159 sq m floor space
Exhibitions: 10 a year
Details: Located on ground floor of C18th building surrounded by garden. Friends of the Gallery organise lectures, films and demonstrations. Education committee organises visits by schools and workshops for adults and children. Sales encouraged. Strict selection of work by committee.

Wren Café Gallery

Pa Ph Pr Cr ✓

Busy varied programme for extensive passing audience.
35 Jermyn Street, London SW1Y 6DT, tel: 0171 437 9419
Contact: Donald Mullis, Arts Administrator, 197 The Rectory, Piccadilly, London, SW1Y, tel: 0171 734 4511
Space: 27 lin m hanging space
Exhibitions: 12 a year
Details: Most exhibitions are one-person; december show features every artist who has exhiibited in the previuos 11 months. Open to all artists whose work is wall mounted, from enthusiastic amateur to students and professionals. Only firm rule that work should not put people off their lunch!

Wyllie Gallery

[Pa][Pr] [H]

Commercial gallery dealing in and showing C19th, C20th and contemporary marine paintings and prints.

44 Elvaston Place, London SW7 5NP, tel: 0171 584 6024

Contact: John Wyllie, Exhibition Organiser
Open: By appointment
Space: 40 galleries
Exhibitions: 4 a year of which 1 originated, 3 on a hire basis
Details: Specialises in the work of the Wyllie family from the C19th onwards. Four mixed exhibitions a year of varying length, including annual exhibition in November/December. Also holds shows at Cowes, Bosham, Seaview and Bembridge.

Zebra One Gallery *

[Pa][Pr]

Small space with own stable of artists.

Perrins Court, Hampstead, London NW3, tel: 0171 794 1281

Contact: Director
Exhibitions: 6 a year all originated
Details: Presents regular programme of contemporary work. Framing service on premises.

Zelda Cheatle Gallery

[Ph][Pr] [H] ♿

Gallery aiming to exhibit best in photography from around the world by both new and established artists.

8 Cecil Court, London WC2N 4HE, tel: 0171 836 0506, fax: 0171 497 8911

Contact: Gareth Abbott
Open: Tues-Fri 11-6; Sat 11-4; Mon by appointment
Space: 2 galleries with 31 lin m hanging space and 56 sq m floor space
Exhibitions: 12 a year of which 11 originated, 1 on a hire basis
Details: Selling gallery. All photography, shows changing every five weeks. From C19th to contemporary installation. Audience ranging from students to serious private and corporate collectors.

Zella Nine Gallery

[Pa][Ph] ♿

Promotes contemporary works on paper – mainly original prints and watercolours.

2 Park Walk, Fulham Road, London SW10 0AP, tel: 0171 351 0588, fax: 0171 352 4752

Open: Daily 10-9
Space: 1 gallery with 120 lin m hanging space and 90 sq m floor space
Details: Exhibits works by contemporary artists and all work is taken on sale or return basis. 40% commission taken and prices range between £10 and £1000. Wheelchair access with assistance to half the exhibition space.

Zwemmer Fine Photographs

[Ph] ✔ ♿

Gallery showing and selling original photographic prints.

28 Denmark Street, London WC2H 8NJ, tel: 0171 379 6348, fax: 0171 240 5250

Contact: Francis Hodgson, Managing Director
Open: Tues-Sat 11-7
Space: 1 gallery with 18 lin m hanging space and 46 sq m floor space
Details: Gallery opened early 1994 aiming to hold monthly exhibitions intended to make fine original photography for sale. Deals with major institutions and casual buyers. Only selection criteria is excellence of work and mainly shows work by photographers with established reputation. Aims to be serious but not forbidding place.

Loughborough
LEICESTERSHIRE EMA

Loughborough College of Art and Design *

[Pa][Ph][Pr][Cr][SC] ✔

Space in entrance of Fine Art Department with range of exhibitions shown primarily for educational reasons.

Radmoor, Loughborough LE11 3BT, tel: 01509 261515

Contact: Pete Wheeler, Exhibition Organiser
Space: 1 gallery with 31 lin m hanging space and 90 sq m floor space
Exhibitions: 2 a year of which 1 originated, 1 touring
Details: Exhibitions include group, thematic, solo and touring exhibitions.

Rawlins School & Community College

[Pa][Ph][Pr][Cr][SC][LA] ✔ [H] ♿ [4]

Gallery in community centre showing mainly local artists' work or work of particular interest to the community.

Quorn, Loughborough LE12 8DY, tel: 01509 412406

Contact: Jackie Edwards, Vice-Principal (Community)
Exhibitions: 4 a year all originated
Details: Exhibition space used by local and regional artists. It is a multi-purpose area and used by a number of local groups therefore not suitable for large or vulnerable pieces.

Loughton
ESSEX EA

Loughton Library

[Pa][Pr][Cr] ✔ [H] ♿

Space within library that encourages and supports local arts activity by showing work by local artists and arts societies.

Traps Hill, Loughton IG10 1HD, tel: 0181 502 0181, fax: 0181 508 5041

Contact: Daphne Powell
Open: Mon, Tues, Wed, Fri 9-7.30; Sat 9-5
Space: 2 galleries with 25 lin m hanging space
Exhibitions: 30 a year all on a hire basis
Details: Hanging onto 6'x4' panels. Sale of work not primary role of exhibition space.

Lowestoft
SUFFOLK EA

Arts Centre Gallery

[Pa][Ph][Pr][Cr][SC][LA] ✔ [£] ♿

Gallery provides the public with free entry to exhibitions that cover a balanced variety of contemporary visual art forms.

Regent Road, Lowestoft NR32 1PA, tel: 01502 525154

Contact: Tony Collins c/o Mari Warner-Craig, Gallery Chairman
Open: Tues-Sat 10-12, 1-4
Space: 1 gallery with 32 lin m hanging space and 81 sq m floor space
Exhibitions: 12 a year all originated
Details: Gallery aims to provide accessible and professional exhibitions which provide information, entertainment, variety and challenging experience of the visual arts across many themes, forms, modes of making and communicating. Programme of workshops, illustrated talks and lectures accompany specific exhibitions. Sale of work not gallery's primary role.

Ludlow
SHROPSHIRE WMA

Silk Top Hat Gallery

[Pa][Ph][Pr][Cr] ✔ ♿

Gallery on two floors showing work by individual artists and groups.

4 Quality Square, Ludlow SY8 1AR, tel: 01584 875363

Contact: Jill Howorth, Proprietor
Open: Mon-Sat 10-5
Space: 2 galleries with 46 lin m hanging space and 49 sq m floor space
Exhibitions: 12 a year all originated
Details: As well as exhibitions gallery sells art materials and runs Friends' Group with talks, trips, newsletter, etc. Sales of work a priority; occasionally negotiates payments

by instalments. Mixture of fluorescent, spots and natural light.

Luton
BEDFORDSHIRE EA

33 Arts Centre

Pa Ph Pr Cr Sc ✓ & wc

Exhibitions of contemporary visual art organised by a local artists' group, the Centre Group.
33-35 Guildford Street, Luton LU1 2NQ, tel: 01582 419584, **fax:** 01582 459401
Contact: Caroline Jones, Administrator
Open: Mon-Fri 11-6
Space: 1 gallery with 23 lin m hanging space and 35 sq m floor space
Exhibitions: 7 a year of which 6 originated, 1 touring
Details: Two rooms in old converted hat factory with windows onto street. Exhibitions of mixed contemporary work. Emphasis on local artists, young artists and exhibitions with educational link with schools. Also in art centre: video editing suite, small theatre, darkroom and 16 track recording studio. Sales not a priority.

Luton Central Library

Pa Ph Cr Sc ✓ £ & 4

One of five spaces run by Bedfordshire County Council Leisure Services, this gallery has equal commitment to exhibition of local and national work.
St George's Square, Luton LU1 2NG, tel: 01582 30161 ext 217, **fax:** 01582 24638
Contact: Stephanie Record, County Arts Officer, South & Luton
Open: Mon-Fri 9-7; Sat 9.30-4
Space: 1 gallery with 17 lin m hanging space plus 30 lin m on screens and 30 sq m floor space
Exhibitions: 14 a year of which 3 originated, 2 touring
Details: Set to one side of the main staircases and lift leading from lending library to reference library and St George's Theatre on the third floor. On average 50,000 people a month enter building. Programme approximately 50% county/national and 50% local work. Stephanie Record co-ordinates exhibitions in libraries throughout South Bedfordshire. Sales not a priority.

Luton Museum & Art Gallery

Pa Ph Pr ✓ H

Most exhibitions are of local artists' work with two open exhibitions organised each year.
Wardown Park, Luton LU2 7HA, tel: 01582 746719
Contact: Robin Holgate, Curator
Open: Mon-Sat 10-5; Sun 1-5

Space: 1 gallery with 33 lin m hanging space plus 9 lin m on screens and 75 sq m floor space
Exhibitions: 15 a year of which 2 originated, 2 touring, 11 on a hire basis
Details: Although a Victorian mansion, can be considered for use as fully-equipped art gallery with exhibition standard lighting. Security meets the Museum & Gallery Commission requirement. Refurbishment work over the next two years will affect available space.

St George's Theatre

Pa Ph ✓ & wc

Exhibition area within professional theatre and film theatre.
Luton Central Library, St George's Square, Luton LU1 2NG, tel: 01582 30637, **fax:** 01582 24638
Contact: Alan Smith, Arts and Entertainments Manager, Luton Borough Council
Open: Mon-Fri evenings 7.30-11
Space: 2 galleries with 8 lin m hanging space
Exhibitions: 8 a year of which 7 originated, 1 touring
Details: Exhibition area in the bar and green room of this professional theatre and film theatre. Exhibition area only open to public during theatre opening hours. Contemporary painting and photography are prioritised. Sales not a priority.

Lymington
HAMPSHIRE SA

Solent Gallery

Pa Pr

Commercial gallery promoting representational and impressionist painting.
11 Gosport Street, Lymington SO41 9BG, tel: 01590 679178, **fax:** 01590 670000
Contact: H. Bagnall, Gallery Director
Open: Mon-Sat 10-5
Space: 1 gallery with 26 lin m hanging space and 60 sq m floor space
Details: A changing display of paintings by artists from UK. Also abroad, including France, Australia, S. Africa and Canada. 2-3 one person exhibitions annually appeal to buyers of paintings from cross-section including locals, yachtsmen, visitors, also 2nd home owners in the area and persons visiting the New Forest. A selection of marine, coastal, landscape and wildlife painting, for sale between exhibitions

Lytchett Minster
DORSET SWA

Courtyard Centre

Pa Ph Pr Cr Sc IA ✓ H &

Converted Georgian barn for multi-purpose hire but primarily for arts events.
Cottage Farm, Huntick Road, Lytchett Minster BH16 6BA, tel: 01202 623423
Contact: Lynda Wise
Open: Mon-Fri 10-5
Space: 1 gallery with 205 sq m floor space
Details: Very flexible approach; open to hire for any purpose providing it's not too messy. Book well in advance. Artists hiring space to organise all aspects of exhibition/event. Centre has links with schools who visit regularly.

Maidstone
KENT SEA

County Hall Gallery

Pa Ph Pr &

Purpose-designed gallery which promotes occasional programme of exhibitions on themes relating directly to county.
County Hall, Maidstone, tel: 01622 694456
Contact: John Brazier, Head of Arts Promotion
Open: Mon-Fri 9-5
Space: 1 gallery with 32 lin m hanging space plus 5 lin m on screens and 58 sq m floor space
Exhibitions: 4 a year all originated
Details: Sales not priority.

Gallery, Kent Institute of Art & Design at Maidstone

Pa Ph Pr Sc ✓

Broad programme geared toward exhibitions of illustration, media communications and photography.
Kent Institute of Art & Design, Oakwood Park, Maidstone ME16 8AG, tel: 01622 757286
Contact: Christine Gist, Exhibitions Officer
Space: 1 gallery with 23 lin m hanging space plus 9 lin m on screens and 54 sq m floor space
Exhibitions: 5 a year all originated
Details: Some individual exhibitions may be incorporated into the programme. Institute has its main facilities for exhibition at Canterbury site (see entry for Herbert Read Gallery).

Hazlitt Theatre Foyer

Pa Ph Pr ✓

Upstairs foyer of busy theatre.

The Corn Exchange Complex, Earl Street, Maidstone ME14 1PL, tel: 01622 602179, fax: 01622 675401
Contact: Stephen Young
Open: Mon-Sat 10-4
Space: 2 galleries with 14 lin m hanging space and 76 sq m floor space
Exhibitions: 3 a year all originated
Details: Either takes commission from sales or hires space to artists. Three wall spaces and three permanent screens. Mainly local artists and photographers. Solo and group shows.

Maidstone Library Gallery

Pa Ph Pr Gr Sc ⬢ ◐ ⦸

Dedicated gallery and external sculpture court showing work by established and new, emerging artists.
St Faith's Street, Maidstone ME14 1LH, tel: 01622 752344, fax: 01622 754980
Contact: Jenny Bowmer, Arts Promotion Officer
Open: Mon & Wed 10-7; Sat 9.30-5.30; Tues & Fri 9.30-5.30; Thurs 10-5.30
Space: 2 galleries with 50 lin m hanging space plus 7 lin m on screens and 255 sq m floor space
Exhibitions: 8 a year of which 6 originated, 1 touring, 1 on a hire basis
Details: Three exhibition spaces; open-air sculpture court, main gallery and small gallery. Flexible panels can be removed between galleries. Lighting by track mounted spots, also natural light. All media considered. Gallery committed to providing access to programme through educational workshops/artists' talks etc. Aims to become a resource for artists and help establish professional practice of emerging artists through training programme. Small exhibitions of local interest at branch libraries and projects for local schools and community groups in branches and at Library Gallery. Sales not a priority.

Maldon
ESSEX EA

Oakwood House

Pa Ph Gr Sc ◐ ⬡

Commercial gallery in Georgian town house with programme of monthly exhibitions by local artists.
2 High Street, Maldon CM9 7PJ, tel: 01621 852317
Contact: Muriel Lacey, Director
Open: Mon-Sat 10-4
Space: 2 galleries with 15 lin m hanging space and 9 sq m floor space
Exhibitions: 6 a year all originated
Details: Exhibition space suitable for smaller-sized works. Stock of land/seascapes held in other rooms of house. Room available for talks/workshops etc.

Manchester
GREATER
MANCHESTER NWA

Castlefield Gallery

A Pa Pr Sc ◐⬤ ⬡

Artist-run gallery promoting and exhibiting a wide range of contemporary art.
5 Campfield Avenue Arcade, Off Deansgate, Manchester M3 4FN, tel: 0161 832 8034
Contact: Kate Jesson, Exhibitions Co-ordinator
Open: Tues-Fri 10.30-5; Sat & Sun 12-5
Space: 2 galleries with 45 lin m hanging space and 78 sq m floor space
Exhibitions: 7 a year all originated
Details: Set up by Manchester Artists Studio Association to increase access to contemporary art, encouraging enjoyment and awareness through education. Shows artists of international standing and emerging talent. A third of exhibitions show work by North West artists. Offers opportunities within and outside gallery. Exhibitions selected by committee of artists in consultation with Exhibitions Coordinator and reflect broad spectrum of current contemporary artistic development. Gallery houses Slidex, public access slide index of North West artists. Commissioning of new art for public and private clients. All works for sale but sales not gallery's primary role.

Chinese Arts Centre

Pa Ph Pr Gr Sc ◐⬤ ⬡⬡

Specialises in creating issue-based exhibitions in other galleries, with occasional complementary display/event at centre's own gallery.
Fraser House, 36 Charlotte Street, Chinatown, Manchester M1 4FD, tel: 0161 236 9251
Contact: Kwong Lee, Exhibition Officer
Open: By appointment
Space: 1 gallery with 35 lin m hanging space plus 16 lin m on screens and 71 sq m floor space
Exhibitions: 2 a year both originated
Details: Promotes contemporary Chinese arts and crafts to people of all cultural backgrounds. Touring exhibitions curated and organised in collaboration with other art organisations/venues. Exhibitions usually issue-based with underlying aim of challenging stereotypes and prejudices encountered by artists of Chinese descent. No restriction on artforms. Innovative works selected to contrast with traditional styles. Education programme organised to explore themes of exhibitions. Sale of work not gallery's primary role.

Colin Jellicoe Gallery

Pa Pr ◐ ⦸

Small basement gallery selling work by contemporary artists.
82 Portland Street, Manchester M1 4QX, tel: 0161 236 2716
Contact: Colin Jellicoe
Open: Mon-Fri 11-5; Sat 1-5
Space: 1 gallery with 15 lin m hanging space and 24 sq m floor space
Exhibitions: 7 a year all originated
Details: About sixty artists exhibit drawings, paintings and graphics, mainly traditional and modern landscape and figure themes in three mixed shows: Spring Exhibition April-May; Summer Exhibition July to September; Winter Exhibition November to February. Other months solo shows; group shows; theme shows by gallery artists. Open to all. Sale of work gallery's primary role.

Cornerhouse

Pa Ph Pr Sc IA ◐⬤ ⬤⬡

Gallery specialising in innovative contemporary art and issues.
70 Oxford Street, Manchester M1 5NH, tel: 0161 228 7621 or Box office 0161 228 2463, fax: 0161 236 7323
Contact: Stephen Snoddy, Exhibitions Director
Open: Tues-Sat 11-6; Sun 2-6
Space: 3 galleries with 198 lin m hanging space
Exhibitions: 18 a year of which 14 originated, 4 touring
Details: Exhibits innovative work in most media. Also exhibitions on architecture. Sales not priority.

Counter Image

A Ph ◐

A film and photography resource centre with black and white and colour darkrooms, and an independent photography gallery.
3rd Floor Fraser House, 36 Charlotte Street, Manchester M1 4FD, tel: 0161 228 3551
Contact: Tony Clancy, Photography Coordinator
Space: 1 gallery with 20 lin m hanging space and 50 sq m floor space
Exhibitions: 5 a year of which 4 originated, 1 touring
Details: Exhibition programme varied, includes work by members and non-members. Welcomes new work produced in the North West. Audience are the 300 members, art groups people on training courses and the general public. Frames are available.

Gallery Manchester's Art House

Pa Ph Pr **G** SC ⬤H ⬤

Gallery on two floors with changing exhibition programme, specialising in promotion of northern artists.
131 Portland Street, Manchester M1 4PY, tel: 0161 237 3551
Contact: Elaine Mather, Proprietor
Open: Mon, Tues, Wed, Fri 10-5; Thurs 10-7; Sat 10-4
Space: 2 galleries with 62 lin m hanging space and 186 sq m floor space
Exhibitions: 9 a year of which 8 originated, 1 on a hire basis
Details: One of largest private galleries in North West committed to promotion and display of Northern art. Education programme being developed in conjunction with local community with aim of introducing exhibiting artists to wider audience. Also provides showcase for occasional international exhibitions and artists.

Generation X

3rd Floor, Hanover Mill, off Berry Street, Manchester M1 2PT, tel: 0161 795 9813
Contact: Alyson Doocey

Hacienda Club

Pa Ph Cr SC LA ⬤H ⬤

Café area and one small bar plus two main spaces with video screens and large stage.
11-13 Whitworth Street West, Manchester M1 5WG, tel: 0161 236 5051/ 01850 969832, fax: 0161 236 0518
Contact: Ang Matthews, Manager/Licensee
Open: As required.
Space: 3 galleries
Exhibitions: 2 a year of which 1 originated, 1 on a hire basis
Details: City centre night club showing a number of exhibitions and live art works as part of its programme. Responds to interesting ideas for exhibitions, installations and performances designed to work at night and in a night club situation. Occasionally commissions temporary installations or sculptures. Venue covers exhibition/event costs. Sale of work not a concern.

Horniman Bar

Pa Ph Pr ⬤H ⬤W4

Primarily a theatre with small gallery in the bar area.
Library Theatre, St Peter's Square, Manchester M2 5PD, tel: 0161 834 1921, fax: 0161 228 6481
Contact: Deborah Holden, Publicity Assistant
Open: Only open when shows on at library theatre

Space: 2 galleries with 12 lin m hanging space
Exhibitions: 6 a year all on a hire basis
Details: Wall space only available. Only open when shows on in the theatre. Large theatre audience, seats 308. Sales not primary concern.

Manchester Central Library

Pa Ph Pr Cr

Exhibition space within library.
St Peters Square, Manchester M2 5PD, tel: 0161 234 1936
Contact: Bill Nuttall, Exhibitions Officer
Open: Mon-Thurs 10-8; Fri & Sat 10-5
Space: 29 lin m hanging space
Exhibitions: 8 a year of which 7 originated
Details: Facility to exhibit work in display cases and on screens. On a 1st floor corridor so inconvenient for free-standing or large works. Local artists and community programmes provide some of work shown. Most exhibitions now mounted by the Central Library departments. Disabled access by lift.

Manchester City Art Galleries

Pa Ph Pr Cr SC LA ⬤£ ⬤W

Gallery showing wide-ranging programme of visual art.
Princess Street, Manchester M14HR, tel: 0161 236 5244, fax: 0161 236 7369
Contact: Howard Smith, Keeper of Art (Exhibitions), Manchester City Art Galleries, Mosley Street, Manchester, M2 3JL, tel: 0161 236 5241, fax: 0161 236 7369
Open: Mon-Sat 10-5.45; Sun 2-5.45
Space: 1 gallery with 100 lin m hanging space plus 30 lin m on screens and 310 sq m floor space
Exhibitions: 7 a year of which 5 originated, 2 touring
Details: Majority of exhibitions are by fairly established artists although less well-known artists are shown, particularly in the City Art Galleries, Mosley Street. The keystone of the artistic policy is a determination to enlarge the audience for the visual arts in Manchester and beyond. Sales not a priority.

Manchester Craft Centre

Pa Cr SC ⬤ ⬤W

Converted Victorian market building providing workshop space for craftspeople and exhibition space.
17 Oak Street, Smithfield, Manchester M4 5JD, tel: 0161 832 4274, fax: 0161 832 3416
Contact: Sarah Rowland, Manager
Open: Mon-Sat 10-5.30
Space: 1 gallery with 23 lin m hanging space and 22 sq m floor space
Exhibitions: 8 a year all originated

Details: Workshop space for craftspeople, combining sympathetic working environment with retail centre. Glass cabinets and "museum" cases to display crafts. Walls on ground level used to display 2D work. Welcomes exhibitions by new or unknown artists. Sales not primary function.

Manto

Pa Ph Pr LA ⬤ ⬤W

Contemporary café/bar in lively area of the city centre.
46 Canal Street, Manchester M1 3WD, tel: 0161 236 2667
Contact: Nikki Pennington, Promotions Manager, Out on Vinyl, 44 Canal Street, Manchester, M1 3WD, tel: 0161 228 2966, fax: 0161 228 3966
Open: Mon-Sat 12-11.30; Sun 12-11
Space: 1 gallery with 20 lin m hanging space and 200 sq m floor space
Exhibitions: 12 a year of which 2 originated, 10 touring
Details: Shows local artists and attracts a diverse audience. Works closely with local universities and colleges to enable young artists and students to gain much needed exposure. Sales not main purpose of exhibition space.

Met Arts Centre

Pa Cr ⬤ ⬤W

Visual arts input to centre through cabinets for displaying crafts.
Market Street, Bury, Manchester BL9 0BW, tel: 0161 761 7107, fax: 0161 763 5056
Contact: Margi Merriman, Marketing Manager
Exhibitions: 6 a year all originated
Details: Three cabinets for exhibiting; one for jewellery and two for other crafts.

Metropolitan Galleries

Pa Ph Pr Cr SC LA ⬤£ ⬤

Three main galleries in different buildings, all run by Manchester Metropolitan University and each with a different brief as regards types of exhibitions shown.
c/o Room 17, Grosvenor Building, Manchester Metropolitan University, Cavendish Street, Manchester M15 6BR, tel: 0161 247 1708, fax: 0161 247 6393
Contact: Alison Radovanovic, Curator
Open: Mon-Fri 10-6
Space: 3 galleries
Exhibitions: 16 a year all originated
Details: Three main galleries; Holden Gallery in Grosvenor Building, Cavendish Street; Righton Gallery in Righton Building, Cavendish Street and Aytoun Gallery in Aytoun Street. Welcomes approaches from national/international artists. Generates touring shows. All 3 galleries very large spaces; Aytoun a neutral space, other 2 have strong architectural

features. Holden supports research and development work with emphasis on site-specific projects with interactive and multi-media work of particular interest. Righton has experimental design brief – textiles, landscape architecture, architecture, etc – with limited exhibition slots. Aytoun run in conjunction with Slidex (slide register of North West artists) & offers space for wall hung work. Aytoun sells work but more interested in generating commissions. Sales not primary role of any of 3 galleries.

Pankhurst Centre

[Po] [Ph] [Pr] [Cr] ⊘ ⊕ ⚫

Space for women artists and craft workers to exhibit work.
60-62 Nelson Street, Chorlton on Medlock, Manchester M13 9WP, tel: 0161 273 5673
Contact: Rachelle Warburton, Administrator
Space: 3 galleries with 15 lin m hanging space plus 15 lin m on screens and 36 sq m floor space
Exhibitions: 12 a year all on a hire basis
Details: Aimed primarily at those with no previous opportunity to show, but would like the experience of holding an exhibition in a supportive environment. Exhibitions usually on display for four to six weeks.

Portico Library & Gallery

[Po] [Ph] [Cr] ⊘ ⊕ ⊗

Housed under stained glass dome of city-centre Georgian Subscription Library, the gallery shows monthly exhibitions of traditional and contemporary work by local and national artists.
57 Mosley Street, Manchester M2 3HY, tel: 0161 236 6785
Contact: Emma Marigliano, Assistant Librarian
Open: Mon-Fri 9.30-4.30
Space: 1 gallery with 183 lin m hanging space plus 49 lin m on screens and 93 sq m floor space
Exhibitions: 12 a year of which 1 originated, 11 on a hire basis
Details: Exhibits mainly local artists. Evening previews held on the first day of each exhibition. Space booked 18 months ahead. Artists pay exhibition fee in return for comprehensive service. Written details on request. Sales considered gallery's primary role. All hanging space movable.

Royal Exchange Craft Centre & Foyer Gallery

[Po] [Ph] [Pr] [Cr] [Sc] ⊘

Promotes British crafts.
Royal Exchange Theatre, St Ann's Square, Manchester M2 7DH, tel: 0161 833 9333 ext 212, fax: 0161 832 0881
Contact: Claire Lowen, Craft Centre Manager
Open: Mon-Thurs 10-7.30; Fri-Sat 10-8

Space: 2 galleries with 33 lin m hanging space and 49 sq m floor space
Exhibitions: 18 a year all originated
Details: Aims to give as broad a view of contemporary crafts stocking ceramics, glass, wood and jewellery from over 50 jewellers. Up to 8 solo or group shows bring in work that would not usually be purchased as stock. Organises events in schools and within community groups to help promote awareness and enjoyment of contemporary crafts. Twelve selling exhibitions throughout the year promote the work of established printmakers and painters.

Tib Lane Gallery

[Po] [Pr] ⊘ ⊗

Selling gallery showing paintings with some facilities for displaying sculpture but not cabinets.
14a Tib Lane, Off Cross Street, Manchester M2 4JA, tel: 0161 834 6928
Contact: Jan Green
Open: Mon-Fri 11-2, 3-5; Sat 11-1; closed when no exhibition taking place
Space: 1 gallery with 17 lin m hanging space and 30 sq m floor space
Exhibitions: 6 a year all originated
Details: Exhibits C20th figurative paintings, drawings and sculpture by established, local and regional artists. Programme of solo shows plus a mixed show summer and winter. Audience drawn mainly from regular visitors and city working community. Sales of work a priority.

Whitworth Art Gallery

[Po] [Ph] [Pr] [Sc] ⊘ ⊛ ⚫ [we] [4]

University gallery that combines an accessible modern collection with exhibition and events programme.
University of Manchester, Oxford Road, Manchester M15 6ER, tel: 0161 273 4865, fax: 0161 274 4543
Contact: Michael Simpson, Curator, Modern Art
Open: Mon-Wed, Fri-Sat 10-5; Thurs 10-9
Space: 2 galleries with 210 lin m hanging space plus 370 lin m on screens and 440 sq m floor space
Exhibitions: 3 a year of which 2 originated, 1 touring
Details: Prime audience students, although strong holdings of C18th/C19th landscape watercolours are popular locally and nationally. Have a collection of C20th drawings and watercolours. Exhibition programme used to complement the permanent collection. Doesn't always pay exhibition fee. Sales not gallery's primary role.

Mansfield
NOTTINGHAMSHIRE EMA

Mansfield Community Arts Centre *

[Po] [Ph] [Pr] [Cr] [Sc] ⊘ ⊛ ⊕

Busy community arts centre.
Leeming Street, Mansfield NG18 1NG, tel: 01623 653309
Contact: Ms C Drury
Space: 2 galleries with 111 lin m hanging space and 221 sq m floor space
Exhibitions: 9 a year of which 3 touring, 6 on a hire basis
Details: Attracts mainly local audience of around 34,000 a year. People travel from further afield for specific exhibitions. Temporary exhibition policy is designed to attract people back and to cater for a wide variety of tastes.

Mansfield Museum & Art Gallery

[Po] [Ph] [Pr] [Cr] [Sc] ⊘ ⊛ [4]

Municipal museum catering for a wide variety of tastes by providing an ever-changing temporary exhibition programme.
Leeming Street, Mansfield NG18 1NG, tel: 01623 663088, fax: 01623 663086
Contact: Elizabeth Weston, Curator
Open: Mon-Sat 10-5; closed BH
Space: 2 galleries with 71 lin m hanging space and 200 sq m floor space
Exhibitions: 5 a year of which 4 originated, 1 touring
Details: Approximately twenty temporary exhibitions a year ranging from natural history to contemporary art. Contemporary art exhibitions mostly of work by local artists with occasional touring exhibitions shown. Sale of work not a priority.

Margate
KENT SEA

Margate Library Gallery

[Po] [Ph] [Pr] [Cr] [Sc] ⊘ ⊛

First-floor open balcony-like space overlooking main public lending library.
Cecil Square, Margate CT9 1RE, tel: 01843 223626, fax: 01843 293015
Contact: Sheena Watson, Arts Promotion Officer
Open: Mon-Thurs 9.30-6; Fri 9.30-7; Sat 9.30-5
Space: 1 gallery with 30 lin m hanging space and 90 sq m floor space
Exhibitions: 12 a year all originated
Details: Broad-based exhibitions by contemporary visual artists and makers with links with the area, as well as national and regional touring shows. Promotes work of living artists in the South East, showing exhibitions that educate, inform and entertain. Audience drawn from cross-

section of residents and visitors. Occasional museum and archive exhibitions. Sales not a priority.

Salmestone Grange *

Pa Pr Cr Sc LA ✓

Wide variety of exhibitions possible in mediaeval grange and grounds.
Nash Road, Margate CT9 4BX, tel: 01843 226909
Contact: William Whelan, Organiser
Details: Mediaeval grange with two great halls and permanent exhibition of stained glass by Australian C20th artist John Teinick. Occasional craft exhibitions, but many possibilities for exhibitions in 4.5 acres of grounds, reception area, 3 main halls, chapel and a ruin.

Market Harborough
LEICESTERSHIRE EMA

Frank Haynes Gallery

Pa Ph Cr Sc ✓ ⬤

Picture gallery and pottery shop on single site exhibiting regional work, all of which is for sale.
50 Station Road, Great Bowden, Market Harborough LE16 7HN, tel: 01858 464862
Contact: Frank Haynes, Owner
Open: Thurs-Sun 10-5
Space: 2 galleries with 20 lin m hanging space plus 3 lin m on screens and 46 sq m floor space
Exhibitions: 10 a year all originated
Details: Two galleries designed to promote regional art and ceramics. Hanging space in picture gallery only; pottery shop fitted with lots of shelves. Pottery comes mainly from Midlands Potters members. Special exhibition of The Human Figure in Art each October. Carries and makes available leaflets and posters from other organisers. Range of original cards stocked, interested to see more. Picture framing. Sells clay. Sales a priority.

Harborough Museum

Ph Pr Cr ✓ ⬤ wc

Temporary exhibition area in small social history museum.
Council Offices, Adam and Eve Street, Market Harborough LE16 7LT, tel: 01858 432468, fax: 01858 462766
Contact: Steph Mastoris, Keeper
Open: Mon-Sat 10-4.30; Sun 2-5
Space: 1 gallery with 12 lin m hanging space and 5 sq m floor space
Exhibitions: 2 a year both originated
Details: Exhibitions are mainly historical, though to attract other sectors of the public occasional contemporary art/craft exhibitions held. Talks and demonstrations sometimes arranged. Sales not a priority.

Marlborough
WILTSHIRE SA

Marlborough Studio Art Gallery *

Pa Pr Cr

Exhibits works by proprietor and other local professional artists.
4 Hughenden Yard, High Street, Marlborough SN8 1LT, tel: 01672 514848
Contact: Andy Le Poidevin, Proprietor
Space: 1 gallery
Exhibitions: 2 a year both originated
Details: Limited edition prints by David Shepherd, OBE, FRSA, at least two exhibitions a year. Otherwise a continuous display.

Mount House Gallery *

Pa Ph Pr Cr Sc ✓

Varied programme of contemporary art, craft and design.
Bridewell Street, Bath Road, Marlborough
Contact: Stephen Murfitt, Exhibition Organiser
Space: 1 gallery with 60 lin m hanging space and 80 sq m floor space
Exhibitions: 6 a year all originated
Details: Each exhibition has an educational value to town and college, and artists run workshops/talks/sessions in return for use of the gallery.

Melton Mowbray
LEICESTERSHIRE EMA

Melton Mowbray Library

Pa Ph Pr ✓ H

Gallery within library for display of work by artists trying to make their living from art, ie not 'hobby' artists.
Wilton Road, Melton Mowbray LE13 0UJ, tel: 01664 60161, fax: 01664 410199
Contact: Area Librarian or Area Administration Officer
Open: Mon-Thurs 9-7; Fri 9-5; Sat 9-4
Space: 1 gallery with 18 lin m hanging space and 30 sq m floor space
Exhibitions: 9 a year of which 7 originated, 2 on a hire basis
Details: Gallery provides an extra facility/dimension for library users and local people. 20% commission on sales.

Middlesbrough
CLEVELAND NA

Captain Cook Birthplace Museum

Pa Ph Cr ✓ ⬤ wc

Temporary exhibition space showing exhibitions fitting into theme of museum.
Stewart Park, Marton, Middlesbrough TS7 6AS, tel: 01642 311211
Contact: Hilary Wade, Curator, Dorman Museum, Linthorpe Road, Middlesbrough, TS5 6LA, tel: 01642 813781
Open: (Summer) Tues-Sun 10-5.30; (Winter) Tues-Sun 9-4
Space: 1 gallery with 20 lin m hanging space plus 6 lin m on screens and 120 sq m floor space
Exhibitions: 4 a year of which 2 originated, 2 touring
Details: Exhibitions need to fit into the theme of the Museum and relate to Captain Cook, the sea, C18th or Australia, New Zealand, North America and the South Seas. Display boards and cases. Sales not a priority.

Cleveland Crafts Centre

Cr

Major crafts exhibitions complemented by smaller 'sideshows'.
57 Gilkes Street, Middlesbrough TS1 5EL, tel: 01642 226351
Contact: Barry Hepton, Craft Officer
Open: Tues-Sat 10-5
Space: 1 gallery with 20 lin m hanging space and 65 sq m floor space
Exhibitions: 8 a year of which 2 originated, 6 touring
Details: Broad remit to promote the crafts, taking a national view. Thriving retail shop, collections of studio pottery and contemporary jewellery. 1st floor textiles, ceramics and jewellery workshops.

Cleveland Gallery

Pa Ph Pr Sc LA ✓ £ ⬤ wc 4

A visual arts resource of local, regional and national importance.
Victoria Road, Middlesbrough TS1 3QS, tel: 01642 262375, fax: 01642 253661
Contact: Gary Topp, Exhibitions Officer
Open: Tues-Sat 10-5
Space: 3 galleries with 100 lin m hanging space and 175 sq m floor space
Exhibitions: 9 a year of which 5 originated, 4 touring
Details: Two galleries devoted to temporary exhibitions of national quality. Third gallery is a showcase for works in the Cleveland County Fine Art Collection. Broad and active education provision with adult classes, youth club and many school activities. Sales not a priority.

Dorman Museum

Museum describing local history, archaeology and natural sciences with exhibitions of local interest or that relate to collections.
Linthorpe Road, Middlesbrough, tel: 01642 813781
Contact: Hilary Wade, Curator
Open: Tues-Sat 10-5.30
Space: 1 gallery with 57 lin m hanging space and 160 sq m floor space
Exhibitions: 4 a year of which 1 originated
Details: Collections of social, local, industrial and natural history,permanent displays of regional and Linthorpe Pottery and temporary exhibition programme. Exhibitions of local interest or relate to the museum collections. Sales not a priority.

Easterside Library

Library with space for exhibitions/functions in community setting.
Broughton Avenue, Easterside, Middlesbrough TS4 3PZ, tel: 01642 317535
Contact: Graham Jarritt, Branch Librarian
Open: Mon-Tues & Thurs-Fri 9.30-12.30, 1-7; Wed & Sat 9.30-12.30
Space: 1 gallery with 20 lin m hanging space plus 10 lin m on screens and 200 sq m floor space
Exhibitions: 1 year originated
Details: Modern library building with good natural light. Provides exhibition space to regional artists. Commission negotiable.

Middlesbrough Art Gallery

Municipal gallery run by Middlesbrough Museums & Galleries presenting a varied programme of contemporary visual arts and related events.
320 Linthorpe Road, Middlesbrough TS1 4AW, tel: 01642 247445, fax: 01642 813781
Contact: Alison Lloyd, Assistant Curator (Fine Art)
Open: Tues-Sat 10-5
Space: 3 galleries with 116 lin m hanging space
Exhibitions: 15 a year of which 7 originated, 8 touring
Details: Gallery presents varied programme of contemporary and historical art and has fine collection of C20th art. Supports new work, including commissions beyond the 'gallery walls' to communicate with new audiences. Three main exhibition areas within gallery: one in which initiated and touring exhibitions are shown, an Artist-in-Focus space which profiles regionally-based artists, and a 'community' space showing collaborative projects with local groups, colleges and schools. Sales not primary role of gallery.

Ormesby Hall

National Trust property with exhibition room for shows of local art & craft.
Ormesby, Middlesbrough TS7 9AS, tel: 01642 324188
Contact: John Baxter, Administrator
Space: 15 lin m hanging space and 60 sq m floor space
Exhibitions: 6 a year
Details: Wing of Ormesby Hall with room to present temporary exhibitions. Access to tea rooms and other facilities, can also be used as lecture room.

University of Leeds Adult Education Centre

Space in centre's common room used mainly by students and some members of the public to exhibit work in informal environment.
37 Harrow Road, Middlesbrough TS5 5NT, tel: 01642 814987, fax: 01642 820015
Contact: Ms Samantha Fielding
Space: 1 gallery with 11 lin m hanging space
Exhibitions: 2 a year both on a hire basis
Details: Commission on sales negotiable.

Milton Keynes

BUCKINGHAMSHIRE SA

Milton Keynes Exhibition Gallery

Monthly changing exhibitions of mainly contemporary art.
555 Silbury Boulevard, Milton Keynes MK9 3HL, tel: 01908 835025
Contact: Emma Gregory, Acting Keeper of Exhibitions
Space: 1 gallery with 45 lin m hanging space
Exhibitions: 10 a year of which 6 originated, 4 touring
Details: An education programme of talks, films and workshops is run in conjunction with every exhibition. To apply send CV and slides/photographs of work.

Minehead
SOMERSET SWA

Little Gallery

Commercial gallery showing work by professional Exmoor artists.
Harbour Quay, Porlock Weir, Minehead TA24 8PA, tel: 01643 863113
Contact: John Hammond, Gallery Director
Open: Daily 10-5
Space: 1 gallery with plus 3 lin m on screens and 9 sq m floor space

Exhibitions: 2 a year both on a hire basis
Details: Shows work by professional local painters and by those who live on Exmoor but exhibit in London and abroad. Commission taken on sales.

Mirfield
WEST YORKSHIRE YHA

Eastthorpe Gallery

Converted school in centre of town showing work by new or young artists especially from the North.
Huddersfield Road, Mirfield WF14 8AT, tel: 01924 497646
Contact: Jo Gorner/Liz Hammond, Administrators
Open: Tues-Fri 1-5; Sat 10-5
Space: 2 galleries with 42 lin m hanging space plus 10 lin m on screens and 43 sq m floor space
Exhibitions: 6 a year
Details: Attracts visitors via classes and workshops. Balances challenging shows with more accessible ones. Proposals for projects (including public involvement) welcomed. Houses 8 artist's studios and St Paul's Printworkshop (open access) with screenprinting, etching, darkroom facilities – usage by membership fee.

Morpeth
NORTHUMBERLAND NA

Chantry Silver

Silversmith workshop with gallery above showing silver jewellery and silverware and 12 months continuous exhibits of paintings by 6 local artists.
The Chantry Courtyard, Morpeth, tel: 01670 518817
Contact: Alan le Chard, Exhibition Organiser
Open: 9.30-5
Details: Over 60 paintings on show at all times.

Nailsworth
GLOUCESTERSHIRE SWA

Hand Prints & Watercolours Gallery *

3 Bridge Street, Nailsworth GL6 0AA, tel: 01453 834967
Contact: Alex Hargreaves
Space: 1 gallery with 6 lin m hanging space and 10 sq m floor space
Exhibitions: 2 a year both originated
Details: Presents local artists to tourists and general public. 35% commission on sales. Mainly solo shows.

Nelson
LANCASHIRE NWA

Barrowford Library *

 ✔

A branch of Lancashire Libraries acting as focal point where local artists and others (including schools) can show their work.
Ann Street, Barrowford, Nelson BB9 8QH, tel: 01282 63038
Contact: Mrs C Ashworth, Branch Librarian
Space: 1 gallery with 6 lin m hanging space
Exhibitions: 8 a year of which 5 originated, 3 touring
Details: Audience of mainly library users.

Brierfield Library *

Pa Ph Pr Cr

Wall space above bookshelves and free standing displays for exhibitions.
Colne Road, Brierfield, Nelson BB9 5HW, tel: 01282 615816
Contact: Miss Linda Medley
Space: 1 gallery with plus 5 lin m on screens
Exhibitions: 3 a year all originated
Details: Part Asian audience.

Nelson Library

Pa Ph ✔ ♿ ⓛ

Wall space in upstairs reading room of library creating focal point for local artist and others, including schools, to show work to a wide audience.
Market Square, Nelson BB9 7PU, tel: 01282 692511
Contact: Mrs S. Byrne, Reference Librarian
Open: Mon, Wed & Fri 9.30-7; Tues & Thurs 9.30-5; Sat 9.30-4
Space: 1 gallery with 9 lin m hanging space and 12 sq m floor space
Exhibitions: 11 a year all on a hire basis
Details: Permanent collection of paintings and photographs on history of Nelson and surrounding area. One new exhibition each month in reading room. Large Asian audience. Sales not a priority.

Pendle Arts Gallery

Pa Ph Pr Cr SC ✔ ♿ ⬤

Gallery in town hall foyer aiming to bring examples of contemporary art to Nelson and to show work by appropriate local artists.
Tourist Information Centre, Town Hall, Market Street, Nelson BB9 7IE, tel: 01282 617731
Contact: Roy Shoesmith, Exhibition Organiser, Pendle Arts Gallery, 120 Waidshouse Road, Nelson, BB9 0RS, tel: 01282 694325
Open: Mon-Fri 9.30-5; Sat 9.30-4
Space: 1 gallery with 15 lin m hanging space plus 23 lin m on screens

Exhibitions: 9 a year of which 2 touring, 7 on a hire basis
Details: Exhibitions primarily of local artists/photographers, but occasional shows by artists from outside the Pendle area. Two shows per year by The Gallery Downstairs (Burnley). Gallery is run by voluntary 'friends' but is invigilated by town hall staff. Sales not a priority.

Pendle Heritage Centre *

Pa Ph Pr Cr ✔

Four areas within the Centre for contemporary and other exhibitions.
Park Hill, Barrowford, Nelson BB9 6JQ, tel: 01282 695 366, fax: 01282 611 718
Contact: Roger Dyson, Development Officer
Details: Centre in an historic building dating from the C17th. Contains displays relating to the building's development, and the history of the area (landscape, architecture, social, etc). Has a reconstructed C18th walled garden and planning a woodland and wildlife area. Aims to develop a lively programme of displays, lectures and demonstrations.

Neston
CHESHIRE NWA

Ness Gardens

Pa Cr ✔ ♿ ⬤ ⓦ

Exhibition room within University Botanic Gardens for hire to local artists.
University Botanic Gardens, Ness, Neston L64 4AY, tel: 0151 353 0123, fax: 0151 353 1044
Contact: Dr E Joanna Sharples, Business Administrator
Open: Daily 10.30-5
Space: 1 gallery with 26 lin m hanging space plus 7 lin m on screens and 42 sq m floor space
Exhibitions: 20 a year all on a hire basis
Details: Exhibitions lasting one week from Easter till October. Local artists are encouraged to display and sell their work. Sales not main purpose of gallery but 27.5% commission taken with guarantee of £100 minimum for the week.

Newark
NOTTINGHAMSHIRE EMA

Millgate Museum

Pa Cr ✔ ♿ ⊘

Gallery for broad range of temporary exhibitions within local history museum.
48 Millgate, Newark NG24 4TS, tel: 01636 79403, fax: 01636 613279
Contact: Richard Harvey, Assistant Museum Manager
Open: Mon-Fri 10-5; Sat & Sun & BH 1-5

Space: 1 gallery with 28 lin m hanging space plus 11 lin m on screens and 250 sq m floor space
Exhibitions: 6 a year of which 2 touring, 4 on a hire basis
Details: Four-week exhibitions, about half of which are contemporary work. Hire fee but museum does not take any commission on sales. Temporary exhibitions are shown in an informal setting alongside museum's permanent social history collections. Sales not a priority.

Pierrepont Gallery

Pa Ph Pr Cr ✔ ⬤ ⓦ

Gallery set in old stables and part of thriving leisure activities business.
Thoresby Park, Ollerton, Newark NG22 9EH, tel: 01623 822365/822009, fax: 01623 822315
Contact: Janet McFerran, Gallery Manager, Thoresby Exhibition Centre, Thoresby Park, Newark, NG22 9EH, tel: 01623 822365, fax: 01623 822009
Open: (April-Oct) Fri-Mon 2-5
Space: 2 galleries with 33 lin m hanging space plus 11 lin m on screens and 74 sq m floor space
Exhibitions: 5 a year all originated
Details: Work exhibited by established national and international artist and also work by young and less well known artists. Mixed exhibition at Christmas. Third gallery, "The Loose Box" shows work by variety of artists at accessible prices for immediate purchase and collection. Aims to educate, entertain and sell to members of the art world, students and general public. Sales not gallery's primary function.

Rufford Craft Centre

Pa Ph Pr Cr SC A ✔ ⬤ ⓦ

Main gallery stages major contemporary craft exhibitions specialising in ceramics.
Rufford Country Park, Nr Ollerton, Newark NG22 9DF, tel: 01623 822944, fax: 01623 824702
Contact: Peter Dworok, Interpretation/ Craft Officer
Open: Daily 10.30-5
Space: 2 galleries with 120 lin m hanging space plus 60 lin m on screens and 400 sq m floor space
Exhibitions: 10 a year all originated
Details: Converted stable block and sculpture garden, once part of a country estate now Rufford Country Park. The main gallery stages up to 8 exhibitions a year, specialising in exhibitions of contemporary crafts, in particular ceramics. Features work from country's leading makers. There is also a print gallery which displays printmaking techniques, craft library and video area off the main gallery.

Newbury
BERKSHIRE SA

Arts Workshop

PaPhPrSc ✓Ⓗ

Two exhibition spaces with varied programme including contemporary work.
Northcroft Lane, Newbury RG4 1BU, tel: 01635 47851
Contact: Trish Lee, Exhibition Organiser
Space: 2 galleries with 40 lin m hanging space and 144 sq m floor space
Exhibitions: 12 a year of which 8 originated, 3 touring, 1 on a hire basis
Details: First-floor exhibition space. Mainly shows contemporary artists and craftspeople. Large ground-floor space for special exhibitions, festivals etc.

Granary Exhibition Room

PaPhPrGrSc ✓ Ⓐ

Self-contained exhibition space attached to Newbury District Museum which may be hired by artists and exhibitors.
The Wharf, Newbury RG14 5AS
Contact: Assistant Curator, Newbury District Museum, The Wharf, Newbury, RG14 5AS, tel: 01635 30511, fax: 01635 519562
Space: 1 gallery with 22 lin m hanging space plus 14 lin m on screens and 51 sq m floor space
Details: Exhibition Room can be made available for hire to individuals or groups of artists whenever it is not being used by Museum for its own exhibitions. Sales not seen as priority.

Newcastle under Lyme
STAFFORDSHIRE WMA

New Victoria Theatre

PaPhPr ✓ Ⓐ Ⓦ

Foyer space in new purpose-built theatre.
Eturia Road, Newcastle under Lyme ST5 0JG, tel: 01782 717954, fax: 01782 712885
Contact: Judy Bowker, Front-of-House Manager
Space: 1 gallery with 70 lin m hanging space
Exhibitions: 12 a year of which 9 originated
Details: Programme draws mainly on artists in town and West Midlands region, particularly those who would not normally have opportunity of large exhibition.

Newcastle under Lyme Museum & Art Gallery

PaPhGr Ⓐ Ⓦ

Local authority funded museum with permanent displays of local & social history and an active temporary exhibition programme, mostly historical.
Brampton Park, Newcastle under Lyme ST5 0QP, tel: 01782 619705
Contact: Miranda Goodby, Senior Museum & Arts Officer,
Open: Mon-Sat 10-5.30; Sun 2-5.30; closed BH
Space: 1 gallery with 54 lin m hanging space plus 20 lin m on screens and 135 sq m floor space
Exhibitions: 3 a year all originated
Details: Exhibitions of fine art and crafts from the Museum's permanent collection and outside sources each lasting two months. Two-three per year are contemporary, usually originated and selected to be relevant to the local community. Sales not a priority.

Wavertree Gallery

PaPrGr ✓ Ⓐ Ⓦ

Selling gallery with eclectic policy showing both young and established artists, British and European.
Berkeley Court, Borough Road, Newcastle under Lyme ST5 1TT, tel: 01782 712686
Contact: Malcolm Speirs, Director
Open: Mon-Wed, Fri & Sat 10-5.15; Thurs 10-2
Space: 1 gallery with 27 lin m hanging space plus 8 lin m on screens and 600 sq m floor space
Exhibitions: 9 a year all originated
Details: Contemporary art; stable of 35 gallery artists. Commission taken on sales.

Newcastle upon Tyne
TYNE & WEAR NA

Browns

PaGr ✓ Ⓧ

Small gallery aiming to exhibit and sell quality work.
15 Acorn Road, Jesmond, Newcastle upon Tyne NE2 2DJ, tel: 0191 281 1315
Contact: Maureen Morgan, Gallery Proprietor
Open: Tues-Sat 10.30-5
Space: 1 gallery with 84 lin m hanging space
Exhibitions: 10 a year all originated
Details: Displays work from local artists, mainly watercolours and pastels. Selection of screenprints from international artists from London Contemporary Arts. Most are originals. Busy residential and shopping area with mix of lecturers, students, doctors – cosmopolitan mix. Adjacent to specialist tea & coffee room which attracts a good clientele.

Café Procope *

PaPrSc ✓

Café with active exhibition programme.
35 The Side, Quayside, Newcastle upon Tyne NE1, tel: 0191 232 3848
Contact: Exhibition Organiser
Space: 1 gallery with 12 lin m hanging space
Exhibitions: 12 a year all originated

Calouste Gulbenkian Gallery

PaPhPrGrSc ✓

Gallery in theatre with exhibitions often of work by recent graduates.
Stephenson Road, Newcastle upon Tyne
Contact: Chairman Calouste Gulbenkian Committee, Peoples Theatre Arts Group
Space: 2 galleries with 27 lin m hanging space
Exhibitions: 12 a year all originated
Details: Each exhibition coincides with a play. Large well-lit space. In addition, the 'Circle Bar Gallery' can show more intimate works. Showcase for displaying pottery or jewellery.

Chameleon Gallery *

PaPrGr ✓

Commercial gallery run with picture framing business selling original work and reproduction prints by local and national artists.
Milburn House, Dean Street, Newcastle upon Tyne NE1 1PQ, tel: 0191 232 2819, fax: 0191 230 2026
Contact: Anne Collier, Owner
Space: 1 gallery with 30 lin m hanging space and 60 sq m floor space
Exhibitions: 2 a year both originated
Details: Gallery caters for a wide range of tastes. A varied changing stock of work, including that of local artists, is shown alongside temporary shows. Theme exhibitions featuring several artists preferred to solo shows.

Clayton Gallery

PaPrGrSc ✓ Ⓐ

Independent gallery specialising in contemporary art and crafts including wide range of ceramics, textiles and jewellery.
14 Clayton Road, Jesmond, Newcastle upon Tyne NE2 4RP, tel: 0191 281 2560, fax: 0191 281 6734
Contact: Margaret Walker, Director
Open: Mon-Wed, Fri & Sat 10-5; Thurs 10-6
Space: 1 gallery with 30 lin m hanging space plus 3 lin m on screens and 50 sq m floor space
Exhibitions: 12 a year all originated
Details: Regular exhibitions by well-

established and emerging contemporary artists. Permanent stock of work always available to view and buy. Art purchase plan.

Denton Park Library

Pa Sc ✓ ❶ ⬤

Wall hanging space in main library area.
West Denton Way, West Denton, Newcastle upon Tyne NE5 2QZ, tel: 0191 264 2737
Contact: Mrs J Biggins, Gruop Librarian
Open: Mon & Thurs 9.30-8; Tues & Fri 9.30-5; Wed 9.30-1; Sat 9-1, 2.15-5
Space: 12 lin m hanging space
Exhibitions: 5 a year all on a hire basis
Details: Exhibits work by local people free of charge. Purchase of items must be arranged directly between purchaser and exhibitor. Selling work not a priority for library.

Hancock Museum

Pa Ph Cr Sc ✓ ❶ ⬤ We 4

Museum of natural history, cultural diversity and Egyptology that exhibits contemporary art relating to its major themes.
Barras Bridge, Newcastle upon Tyne Ne2 4PT, tel: 0191 222 7418, fax: 0191 222 6753
Contact: Alec Coles, Curator
Open: Mon-Sun 10-5
Space: 3 galleries with 480 sq m floor space
Exhibitions: 2 a year of which 1 touring, 1 on a hire basis
Details: Sales not a priority.

Hatton Gallery

Pa Ph Pr Sc ✓ ⬤

The Hatton Gallery hosts a changing programme of temporary art exhibitions and displays its own permanent collection.
The Quadrangle, The University, Newcastle upon Tyne NE1 7RU, tel: 0191 222 6057, fax: 0191 261 1182
Contact: Mr A. Parton, Temporary Secretary
Open: Mon-Fri 10-5.30; (term-time) Sat 10-4.30; (vacation) Sat & Sun closed
Space: 5 galleries with 130 lin m hanging space and 430 sq m floor space
Exhibitions: 10 a year of which 8 originated, 2 touring
Details: Five rooms used for temporary exhibitions; historical, contemporary and student shows. Audience is widespread and well-established comprising staff and students from Newcastle University, but also general public from Northumberland & Durham. Cannot organise exhibitions for artists. Not suitable for heavy or large-scale sculpture. Sales not a priority.

Laing Art Gallery

Pa Ph Pr Cr Sc LA ✓ ⬤ ⬤ We 4

Municipal gallery with key aim of promoting innovative regional, national and international art in all media to a wide audience.
Higham Place, Newcastle upon Tyne NE1 8AG, tel: 0191 232 7734, fax: 0191 222 0952
Contact: Samantha Hill, Art Exhibitions Officer
Open: Mon-Sat 10-5; Sun 2-5
Space: 4 galleries with 187 lin m hanging space and 620 sq m floor space
Exhibitions: 10 a year of which 9 originated, 1 touring
Details: Enables artists to use spaces and environments throughout Newcastle including the gallery. Work ranges from painting & sculpture, to photo & video installations, publicly-sited works, artists' placements, performance and other live art 'events'. Focal point for a range of debates about art, architecture and the environment in the 1990s. Sale of work not a priority.

Locus+

Pa Sc LA ✓ ⬤

An office-based agency which commissions projects by visual artists in a wide cariety of media for non-gallery contexts across the northern region.
Room 17, Third Floor, Wards Building, 31-39 High Bridge, Newcastle upon Tyne, NE1 1EW, tel: 0191 233 1450, fax: 0191 233 1451
Contact: Jon Bewley & Simon Herbert
Exhibitions: 10 a year

Newcastle Central Library

Pa Ph Pr Cr Sc LA ✓ ❶

Exhibition space off the entrance area mainly showing work by local arts societies.
Princess Square, Newcastle upon Tyne NE99 1DY, tel: 0191 261 0691, fax: 0191 261 1435
Contact: Pat Dale, Promotion & Arts Assistant
Space: 1 gallery with 12 lin m hanging space plus 40 lin m on screens and 30 sq m floor space
Exhibitions: 13 a year

Newcastle Playhouse Galleries

Pa Ph Pr ✓

Newcastle Playhouse, Barras Bridge, Newcastle upon Tyne NE1 7RH, tel: 0191 232 3366
Contact: Front-of-House Manager
Space: 2 galleries
Details: Gallery programme under review. Suggest any artists wishing to apply for an exhibition contact Front-of-House Manager first.

Newcastle University Long Gallery

Pa Ph Pr Sc ❶

Space in a long, wide corridor outside the Hatton Gallery within the Fine Art Department.
Fine Art Department, The University, Barrass Bridge, Newcastle upon Tyne NE1, tel: 0191 232 8511
Contact: Sia Patsalides, Exhibition Organiser
Open: Mon-Fri 9-5
Space: 1 gallery with 60 lin m hanging space and 600 sq m floor space
Details: Exhibitions change fortnightly. Seen by all visitors to the department, including visiting artists. Gallery is central to department. Exhibits mainly student work from University and University of Northumbria which leads to an open atmosphere and great diversity.

People's Gallery

Cr Sc ⬤ We 4

Community exhibition area with priority given to West End groups but with consideration given to approaches from other parts of the City.
Newcastle Discovery, Blandford Square, Newcastle upon Tyne NE1 4JA, tel: 0191 232 6789, fax: 0191 230 2614
Contact: Gina Barron, Museum Outreach Worker, Tyne and Wear Museums, c/o Outreach Project, Benwell Library, Newcastle upon Tyne, tel: 0191 272 5299
Open: Mon-Sat 10-4
Space: 1 gallery with 324 lin m hanging space plus 29 lin m on screens and 257 sq m floor space
Exhibitions: 13 a year of which 12 originated, 1 touring
Details: Gallery set up to provide opportunity for West End community groups to interpret contemporary lives. This could be achieved by using any form of expression from recorded projects (audio) to artwork or performance. Artists working with groups are welcome, but not part of policy to promote individuals. Groups work alongside outreach team and skills can be set up within community. Sale of work not a priority's primary function.

Red Herring Café

Pa Ph Cr Sc ✓ ⬤

Café/restaurant in West End residential area showing exhibitions.
4 Studley Terrace, Fenham, Newcastle upon Tyne NE4 5AH, tel: 0191 272 3484
Contact: Nichole Messier, Exhibition Organiser
Open: Tues-Sat 10-10
Space: 2 galleries with 8 lin m hanging space
Exhibitions: 12 a year all originated

Details: Busy vegetarian restaurant run by co-operative. Recently began devoting wall space to exhibitions of work by locally-based artists and intends also to show work of community group artwork. Flexible approach. Mainly 2D work but can accommodate small sculpture/craft. 10% commission on sales. No insurance provided. Artists hang work with assistance.

Side Gallery

Exhibition programme of contemporary and historical photography with strong social documentary bias.
9 Side, Newcastle upon Tyne NE1 3JE, tel: 0191 232 2208, fax: 0191 230 3217
Contact: Richard Grassick, Exhibitions Organiser
Open: Mon-Sat 10-5; Sun 11-3
Space: 1 gallery with 37 lin m hanging space plus 39 sq m floor space
Exhibitions: 8 a year of which 7 originated, 1 touring
Details: Gallery covers all exhibition costs.

University Gallery

Public gallery with temporary and touring exhibition programme.
University of Northumbria, Sandyford Road, Newcastle upon Tyne NE1 8ST, tel: 0191 227 4424, fax: 0191 227 4718
Contact: Mara-Helen Wood, Director
Open: (Term-time) Mon-Thurs 10-5, Fri & Sat 10-4; (vacation) Mon-Fri 10-5; closed BH
Space: 2 galleries with 76 lin m hanging space and 232 sq m floor space
Exhibitions: 12 a year of which 10 originated, 2 touring
Details: Exhibition programme includes temporary and touring exhibitions by major contemporary artists as well as exhibitions by promising but less established artists. Lectures, seminars and adult weekend and evening classes organised in conjunction with the programme, as are Saturday and Summer art clubs for 6 8 year olds. Sale of work not considered primary role of gallery, but always welcomed.

Waygood Gallery and Studios

Artist-run gallery alongside four artists studios.
Section C Floor 2, 39 Highbridge, Newcastle upon Tyne NE1 1EW, tel: 0191 221 1712
Contact: Helen Smith
Space: 1 gallery with 23 lin m hanging space and 64 sq m floor space
Exhibitions: 6 a year of which 3 originated, 3 on a hire basis
Details: The space, on second floor of old textile warehouse in central Newcastle lends

itself for use by artists to make work on site. Sculpture and installations are more appropriate than two-dimensional work.

X-Site Gallery

Small front room in terraced house for local artists to explore work in progress or to show finished work.
10 Crossley Terrace, Arthur's Hill, Newcastle upon Tyne NE4 5NY, tel: 0191 272 3535
Contact: Tim Bailey, Co-ordinator
Open: By appointment; please ring
Space: 1 gallery with 12 lin m hanging space and 15 sq m floor space
Exhibitions: 12 a year all originated
Details: Exhibits local artists' work non-judgmentally, offering opportunity for them to explain own work in an informal atmosphere. Aims to show work not able to see elsewhere in the city. Community focus for all sections of the community. Open to approaches from artists working in all artforms, including architecture. Gallery offers free mail-out service. Sales not a priority. Work to be ready to hang.

Zone Gallery

Premier photography gallery in Northern Arts region with a broad programme of contemporary photography exhibitions.
83 Westgate Road, Newcastle upon Tyne NE1 1SG, tel: 0191 232 8833
Contact: Michelle Hirschhorn, Curator
Open: Tues-Sun 12-6
Space: 2 galleries with 64 lin m hanging space and 120 sq m floor space
Exhibitions: 14 a year of which 7 originated, 7 touring
Details: Shows work by major international and national artists as well as promoting the work of northern region artists. Main exhibition space plus additional space for hanging work only on walls of Heaven Café. 8-10 main exhibitions and 5 smaller exhibitions per year. Initiates public talks, seminars and workshops by leading photographic artists, writers and curators. Close to railway station in centre of the city and attracts wide audience for exhibitors.

Newmarket
SUFFOLK EA

Equus Gallery

Gallery specialising in contemporary equestrian art.
Sun Lane, Newmarket CB8 8EW, tel: 01638 560445
Contact: Lydia Minanon
Open: Mon-Sat 9.30-5.30; Wed 9.30-1
Space: 2 galleries
Exhibitions: 10 a year all originated

Details: Specialist in contemporary racing art showing painting, prints and some drawing. Spread over two floors with courtyard. Attracts varied international audience of all ages. Conservation framing service. Sale of work is gallery's primary role.

Newport
ISLE OF WIGHT SA

Isle of Wight Cultural & Leisure Services Department

Handles local authority galleries at Newport, Ryde and Freshwater and Ventnor.
The Guildhall, High Street, Newport PO30 1TY, tel: 01983 823822, fax: 01983 823841
Contact: A D Payne, Head of Libraries & Arts
Space: 4 galleries
Exhibitions: 48 a year of which 10 originated, 2 touring, 36 on a hire basis
Details: Exhibitions change monthly and include all art forms. Prospective exhibits viewed prior to confirmation of acceptance (see entries for Freshwater Gallery, Freshwater; Ryde Gallery, Ryde; Seely Gallery, Newport and Ventnor Library, Ventnor).

Quay Arts Centre

Visual arts and crafts galleries in arts centre complex within restored C18th warehouse hosting touring exhibitions, solo and group shows, both national and local.
Sea Street, Newport PO30 5BD, tel: 01983 528825
Contact: Philip Cundall, Exhibitions Organiser
Open: (1 May – 31 Oct) Mon-Sat 10-5, Sun 11-5; (1 Nov – 31 April) Tues-Sat 10-4, Sun 11-4
Space: 3 galleries with 88 lin m hanging space and 180 sq m floor space
Exhibitions: 20 a year of which 14 originated, 4 touring, 2 on a hire basis
Details: Shows contemporary work of all kinds plus occasional historical touring shows. Aims to introduce to the people of the Isle of Wight the best in contemporary art work; to aid in educational processes in the county; to provide space for historical exhibitions, dance and art related events; to enhance the cultural life of the community. Sale of work not a main aim.

Seely Gallery

Busy library gallery.
Lord Louis Library, Newport PO30 1LL, tel: 01983 527655

Contact: A D Payne, Head of Libraries & Arts, Cultural & Leisure Services Directorate, I.W. County Council, The Guildhall, High Street, Newport, PO30 1TY, tel: 01983 823822, fax: 01983 823841
Open: Mon-Sat library opening hours
Space: 1 gallery with 39 lin m hanging space and 47 sq m floor space
Exhibitions: 12 a year all originated
Details: Eight-sided open-plan above lending library. Professional and amateur individual artists and groups. Island population and seasonal visitors. No hanging fee. Payment by picture donation or 10% of sales at discretion.

North Shields
TYNE & WEAR NA

Globe Gallery

Pa Ph Pr Sc ☑ ❸ Wc

Temporary exhibitions, installations, multi-media work and events, plus craft shop and artists' studios. Opened May 1995.
97 Howard Street, North Shields NE30 1NA, tel & fax: 0191 259 2614
Contact: Rashida Davison, Director
Space: 1 gallery with 76 lin m hanging space and 113 sq m floor space
Exhibitions: 8 a year all originated
Details: Focus on younger artists, mainly from the North of England. Exploring contemporary art practice and alternative uses of gallery space. Rear gallery space can be used for separate smaller-scale exhibitions, installations, etc. Artists make contribution to publicity and marketing costs. gallery charges 30% commission.

Knotts Exhibition Centre

Pa Ph Pr Cr Sc ☑ ❶ ❸ Wc ▣

Space comprises café, sculpture courtyard and connecting corridors offering weekly audience of 1000 people.
YMCA, Church Way, North Shields NE29 0AB, tel: 0191 2575434
Contact: Douglas Hunter, Visual Arts Co-ordinator
Open: Mon-Fri 9-9; Sat & Sun 9-2
Space: 3 galleries with 40 lin m hanging space and 30 sq m floor space
Exhibitions: 10 a year of which 6 originated, 4 on a hire basis
Details: Aims to offer broad and varied programme for users of YMCA. Encourages artists to show in very accessible and well used public space. When space is "hired" to artists this is free. Some teaching opportunities available, particularly for sculptors, to help cover costs etc. Sales not priority.

Northern Print Studio

Pr ☑ ❸ Wc

Studio display space showing changing selection of works made in studio and elsewhere in the Northern Arts region
Fish Quay Design Centre, 42/47 Fish Quay, North Shields NE30 1JA, tel: 0191 2591996
Contact: Ken Duffy, Director
Details: Aims to attract visitors by rotating a changing selection of new work for sale throughout the studio.

Vicarage Cottage

Pa Pr Cr Sc ☑ ❺

Commercial gallery specialising in contemporary (mainly northern and Scottish) painting.
Preston Road, North Shields NE29 9PJ, tel: 0191 257 0935
Contact: George Lilly, Director
Open: Thurs-Sat 10-5; Sun 11-5
Space: 3 galleries with 41 lin m hanging space and 45 sq m floor space
Exhibitions: 9 a year all originated
Details: Provides a programme of serious exhibitions to a wide clientele from north east England and beyond. Both emerging and established artists are shown. Artists are welcome to approach the gallery but should do so initially in writing with slides or photographs of work and CV.

North Walsham
NORFOLK EA

Angel Gallery

Pa Ph Pr Cr Sc IA ☑ ❽

Two-room dedicated exhibition space above bookshop with varied programme of temporary exhibitions specialising in work by North Norfolk artists.
4 Aylsham Road, North Walsham NR28 0BH, tel: 01692 404 054
Contact: Edward Green, Exhibition Organiser
Open: Mon & Tues, Thurs-Sat 10-5.30; Wed 10-1
Space: 2 galleries with 31 lin m hanging space and 28 sq m floor space
Exhibitions: 12 a year all originated
Details: Aims to exhibit quality work that is visually stimulating and different. Provides space for local organisations, and two open exhibitions each year. Selling not main motivation, genuinely interested in enabling artists to show work. Would consider hiring out space and would be interested in organising exhibitions for tour. Applicants should enclose SAE with slides or prints.

Northampton
NORTHAMPTONSHIRE EMA

Derngate

Pa Ph Pr Cr ☑ ❶ ❸ Wc

Purpose-built theatre, concert hall, conference centre and exhibition space.
19/21 Guildhall Road, Northampton NN1 1DP, tel: 01604 26222, fax: 01604 250901
Contact: Kenneth Anthonisz, Assistant Customer Services Manager
Space: 2 galleries
Exhibitions: 24 a year all on a hire basis
Details: Two exhibition areas available in the foyer and circle. Mainly local and regional artists and work from local schools and colleges. Workshops and craft fairs are arranged. The restaurant and bar ensure day-time visitors. 20% sales commission or free hire.

Four Seasons Gallery

Pa Ph Pr Cr ☑

Predominantly contemporary printmakers' gallery with mixed 2D and 3D contemporary art and craft exhibitions.
39 St Giles Street, Northampton NN1 1JF, tel: 01604 32287, fax: 01604 880212
Contact: George Hammershmidt, Partner
Open: Mon-Fri 9.30-5.30; Sat 9.15-5
Space: 1 gallery with 14 lin m hanging space and 20 sq m floor space
Exhibitions: 2 a year both originated
Details: Permanent display of prints on show. For exhibitions always looking for new work. Keen to encourage new talent. Due to limitations of space unable to accept very large works. Also undertakes framing.

Northampton Local Education Authority *

Pa Ph Pr Cr Sc ☑

Works in schools and colleges alongside artists and makers through residencies and displays work together of artists and students/pupils.
Spencer Centre, Lewis Road, Northampton NN5 7BJ, tel: 01604 580119
Contact: Ian Middleton, Advisory Teacher for Art & Design
Details: Schools and education establishments able to provide display space for a variety of 2D and 3D art works. Policy is to enhance and encourage the work of children and adults in the area by providing mutual source of reference, enrichment and stimulus.

Northamptonshire Libraries

[Pa][Ph][Pr][Cr][Sc] ✔

Encourages and supports work in the visual arts and crafts by giving artists and makers opportunity to show and sell their work in an informal and sympathetic environment.

Northamptonshire Libraries & Information Service, PO Box 259, 27 Guildhall Road, Northampton NN1 1DE, tel: 01604 20262
Contact: Janet Walls, Acting Marketing Officer
Details: Main display libraries are: Brackley, Corby, Daventry, Kettering, Rothwell, Towcester, Wellingborough and Weston Favell (see entries for each of these). Also at Hunsbury. Of these following are considered by Northamptonshire Libraries to have particularly good facilities and therefore higher commission rates apply: Daventry, Hunsbury, Rothwell and Towcester. No hire fee for space. Exhibitors apply to each library direct for booking form plus details of space available/opening times.

Onsight Gallery

[Pa][Ph][Pr][Cr][Sc][LA] ✔

Airy exhibition space showing visual arts as part of multi-purpose arts venue for young people.

The Roadmender, 1 Lady's Lane, Northampton NN1 3AH, tel: 01604 604603, fax: 01604 603166
Contact: Mark Brown, Arts Co-ordinator, The Roadmender
Open: Mon-Fri 10-5 and evenings; Sat 12-4
Space: 2 galleries with 56 lin m hanging space plus 5 lin m on screens and 65 sq m floor space
Exhibitions: 12 a year all originated
Details: Challenging exhibitions of work by young artists presented to interest a young audience. Aims to provide workshop or seminar for each exhibition. Particularly welcomes applications from artists working with contemporary youth issues. Day-lit gallery with high ceilings. Sales not priority.

University Centre Northampton

[Pa][Ph][Pr] ✔ ♿

Common Room space for informal but well-lit exhibitions with an adult education audience.

Barrack Road, Northampton NN2 6AF, tel: 01604 30084
Contact: Alan Caine, Exhibition Organiser
Open: (Term-time) Mon-Fri 9am-9pm; some Saturdays
Space: 1 gallery with 18 lin m hanging space
Exhibitions: 5 a year all originated
Details: Housed in the Department of Adult Education of the University, running day and evening classes. Policy is to provide space for local and non-local artists to display their work. Sale of work not a primary aim.

Weston Favell Library

[Pa][Ph][Pr][Cr][Sc] ✔

Library exhibition space.

Weston Favell Shopping Centre, Northampton NN3 4JZ, tel: 01604 413327
Contact: Shaun Smith
Details: See Northamptonshire Libraries.

Norwich
NORFOLK EA

Advice Arcade Gallery

[Pa][Pr][Sc] ✔ ⊘♿

Policy of showing works of contemporary art from artists with a local connection.

Advice Arcade, 4 Guildhall Hill, Norwich NR2 1JH, tel: 01603 665755, fax: 01603 625250
Contact: Maran McKay, Advice Arcade Manager
Open: Mon-Fri 10-5
Space: 4 galleries with 55 lin m hanging space
Exhibitions: 4 a year
Details: Advice centre utilising first-floor space as an art gallery. City council has a policy of displaying works of art in public buildings to encourage appreciation of art as part of everyday life. The Gallery Group commissions work from participating artists to hang in public buildings. Offers artists the opportunity to show larger works not normally accepted by commercial galleries. Quarterly exhibitions plus special events show.

Assembly House *

[Pa][Ph][Pr][Cr][Sc] ✔

Arts centre and meeting place, including cinema and cafeteria.

Theatre Street, Norwich NR2 1RG, tel: 01603 626402
Contact: Ben Russell-Fish, Manager
Space: 3 galleries
Exhibitions: 109 a year all originated
Details: Georgian building administered by arts trust with charitable status. Exhibitors selected to encourage public to use the building , and add interest for visitors. Shows living artists almost exclusively.

Contact Gallery

[A] [Pa][Ph][Pr][Cr][Sc][LA] ✔ ⊘♿

Artist-run gallery presenting monthly exhibitions of work by less established artists in open exhibitions, exchanges, thematic, solo and two-person shows.

56 St Benedict's Street, Norwich NR2 4AR, tel: 01603 760219
Contact: Ada Lee Harrop, Gallery Administrator
Open: Tues-Sat 10-5
Space: 1 gallery with 45 lin m hanging space and 93 sq m floor space
Exhibitions: 11 a year all originated
Details: Light, spacious, yet intimate glass-fronted gallery. Commitment to community outreach and education aims at widening the audience for contemporary art. Sales are not gallery's primary concern.

Glasshouse Gallery

[Pa][Pr] ✔

Gallery showing and selling mainly East Anglian scenes.

11 Wensum Street, Elm Hill, Norwich NR3 1LA, tel: 01603 763751
Contact: T. Beck
Details: Specialises in watercolours, oils and etchings. Some week-long individual exhibitions but mainly changing display of work. Modern-style etchings, silkscreen, watercolours and oils by living artists, predominantly representational work.

King of Hearts

[Pa][Ph][Pr][Sc] ✔ ♿

Gallery in C16th merchant's house with mixed programme of solo and group shows of contemporary work and aiming to help young and inexperienced artists.

13-15 Fye Bridge Street, Norwich NR3 1LJ, tel: 01603 766129
Contact: Mike Power, Manager
Open: Tues-Sat 9-5
Space: 1 gallery with 18 lin m hanging space plus 40 lin m on screens and 80 sq m floor space
Exhibitions: 10 a year all originated
Details: Gallery is a hall 30'x18' with white walls and gallery lighting. Charitable trust. Promotes the work of living artists, local and national, bringing contemporary art to Norwich and providing high quality exhibition space for artist and public. Aim to help young and inexperienced artists, often mounting their first solo show. Selection panel of six which sees applications twice a year. Selling work not considered gallery's main function.

Maddermarket Theatre

[Pa][Ph][Pr][Cr][Sc][LA] ✔ [H] ♿ [4]

Theatre with exhibition space.

St John's Alley, Norwich, tel: 01603 626560
Contact: Jane Rutherford, Artistic Director
Open: Mon-Sat 10-5; and during performances
Space: 1 gallery with 20 lin m hanging space and 100 sq m floor space
Exhibitions: 14 a year all on a hire basis
Details: Shows artistic work of acceptable

quality. Mixed and one-person exhibitions. Sale of work is gallery's primary role.

Mandells Gallery

Commercial art gallery specialises in C20th and contemporary representational art.
Elm Hill, Norwich NR3, tel: 01603 626892/629180, fax: 01603 767471
Contact: Mr G. Allen, Exhibition Organiser
Space: 3 galleries
Details: Some solo exhibitions, mainly by gallery artists.

Norfolk County Council Libraries & Information Service

Initial contact point for exhibitions in Norfolk libraries of small- to medium-scale 2D works.
County Hall, Martineau Lane, Norwich NR1 2DH, tel: 01603 223000
Contact: Hilary Hammond, Director of Arts & Libraries
Details: Selected public libraries in Norfolk display art and craft work by living Norfolk artists in order to stimulate interest in, and income for, these artists. Facilities and access will vary according to library.

Norwich Arts Centre *

Photographic centre for Norfolk and Suffolk. Exhibits work from regional, national and international practitioners.
Reeves Yard, St Benedicts Street, Norwich NR2 4PG, tel: 01603 660352
Contact: Peter Kent, Photography Coordinator
Space: 1 gallery with 30 lin m hanging space
Exhibitions: 11 a year of which 6 originated, 5 touring
Details: Exhibition space is housed within a large cafe/bar area which services the main venue. Audience from across the region.

Norwich Castle Museum

Exhibition space used to promote access to and interest in a range of different disciplines represented by the museum's collections, one of which is contemporary art.
Norwich NR1 3JU, tel: 01603 223624, fax: 01603 765651
Contact: Heather Guthrie, Assistant Keeper of Art (Exhibitions)
Open: Mon-Sat 10-5; Sun 2-5; closed Christmas, New Year and Good Friday
Space: 2 galleries with 340 lin m hanging space plus 32 lin m on screens and 320 sq m floor space

Exhibitions: 5 a year of which 2 originated, 3 touring
Details: Run by Norfolk County Council as the centre of their museums service. Aims to make museums more accessible to the general public, with emphasis on educational and children's events. Strong permanent collection of Norwich School painters, archaeology, natural history, social history, etc. Exhibitions fall into three categories: national touring exhibitions, those generated from Norfolk Museums Service Collections and others developed with local interest groups.

Norwich Gallery

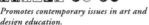

Promotes contemporary issues in art and design education.
Norwich School of Art & Design, St George Street, Norwich NR3 1BB, tel: 01603 610561, fax: 01603 615728
Contact: Lynda Morris, Curator
Open: Mon-Sat 10-5
Space: 2 galleries with 56 lin m hanging space plus 10 lin m on screens and 143 sq m floor space
Exhibitions: 10 a year of which 7 originated, 1 touring
Details: The theme of the contemporary practitioner forms the cornerstone of our policy. Reputation based on researched exhibitions. Committed to equality of opportunity in all aspects of policy and programme.

Sainsbury Centre for Visual Arts

Houses The Robert and Lisa Sainsbury Collection, modern art displayed alongside the art of Africa, the Americas and the Pacific.
University of East Anglia, Norwich NR4 7TJ, tel: 01603 592468, fax: 01603 259401
Contact: William Jeffett, Assistant Keeper
Open: Tues-Sun 12-5
Space: 2 galleries with 700 sq m floor space
Exhibitions: 3 a year of which 2 originated, 1 touring
Details: Exhibition programme includes modern and contemporary art & design as well as non-western art. Three exhibitions each year.

St Gregory's Arts Centre

Redundant mediaeval church used as arts centre, specialising in amateur artists and musicians.
Pottergate, Norwich NR2 1DS
Contact: Ms Frances Hardy, Administrator, Saint Gregory's Trust, 15 Pottergate, Norwich, NR2 1DS, tel: 01603 628777
Open: Mon-Sat 10-4

Space: 1 gallery with 26 lin m hanging space plus 10 lin m on screens
Exhibitions: 12 a year all on a hire basis
Details: Has a magnificent mediaeval wall painting, itself a tourist attraction. Exhibitions are of an appropriate nature for a listed building. Exhibitors must be aware of the needs of other regular users of the centre who are involved in other art forms. Exhibitors are required to supervise their exhibitions.

Take 5

Space in cinema bar and restaurant charging nominal fee to encourage first-time exhibitors as well as established artists.
Cinema City, St Andrews Street, Norwich NR2 4AD, tel: 01603 614210, fax: 01603 767838
Contact: N. Barton, Partner
Open: 11am-11pm
Space: 1 gallery with 7 lin m hanging space and 25 sq m floor space
Exhibitions: 30 a year of which 5 originated, 25 on a hire basis
Details: Café/restaurant with bar for cinema patrons situated in grade 1 listed C14th building in city centre in area of high tourist interest, with adjacent arts cinema and concert hall. Throughput of visitors has been calculated at approx 200,000pa. Policy is to have variety of exhibitions, charging a nominal flat fee, free to charities, good causes, disadvantaged artists, etc. Selling work is not main function of space.

Theatre Royal Condon Gallery

Gallery open to theatre goers and public.
Theatre Street, Norwich NR2 1RL, tel: 01603 623562 ext 26
Contact: Renee Cooper, Deputy House Manager
Open: Mon-Sat 9.30am-11pm; Sun 5.30-10.30 on performance days
Space: 1 gallery with 15 lin m hanging space and 60 sq m floor space
Exhibitions: 22 a year of which 4 originated, 2 touring, 16 on a hire basis
Details: Weekly one-person/group shows presenting variety of work by local/nationally known artists. Aims to create relaxed and informal atmosphere in which theatre goers and public can enjoy viewing and hopefully buy work. Small commission taken on sales.

Nottingham
NOTTINGHAMSHIRE EMA

Angel Row Gallery

Pd Ph Pr Cr Se A ✓①H ⊙We4

One of the leading venues for contemporary art in the East Midlands, the gallery is centrally located and well-used.
Central Library Building, 3 Angel Row, Nottingham NG1 6HP, tel: 0115 947 6334, fax: 0115 950 6743
Contact: Barry Prothero, Visual Arts Officer
Open: Mon, Tues, Thurs-Sat 11-6; Wed 11-8
Space: 4 galleries
Exhibitions: 20 a year of which 10 originated, 10 on a hire basis
Details: Contemporary visual art made up of a third regional artists and rest national/international artists. Four galleries plus foyer and stairs spaces. Large carpeted front space with good natural and track lighting, back space with wood floor and track lighting. Division between two rooms can be removed to create one large area. Workshop space adjacent to gallery. Some exhibitions are originated, some hired and some result of collaboration. Sales not a priority.

Arnold Library

Pd Ph Pr Cr Se ✓ ⊙

Open-plan exhibition area within busy urban library.
Front Street, Arnold, Nottingham NG5 7EE, tel: 0115 920 2247
Contact: Senior Librarian
Open: Mon, Tues, Thurs, Fri 9.30-8; Wed 9.30-1; Sat 9-1
Space: 12 lin m hanging space plus 9 lin m on screens and 37 sq m floor space
Exhibitions: 10 a year all originated
Details: Sale of work not gallery's primary role.

Bonington Gallery

Pd Ph Pr Cr Se A ✓① ⊙We

Large exhibition space specialising in contemporary art and design, as well as a programme of performance and dance events.
Bonington Building, Nottingham Trent University, Dryden Street, Nottingham NG1 4FX, tel: 0115 948 6443, fax: 0115 948 6403
Contact: Stella Couloutbanis, Exhibitions Organiser
Open: Mon-Thurs 10-5; Sat 10-5; Fri 10-4
Space: 1 gallery with 51 lin m hanging space and 186 sq m floor space
Exhibitions: 10 a year of which 8 originated, 2 touring
Details: Space is ideal for installation, sculpture, performance and dance. Programme is contemporary visual arts,

craft and design. Audience student, staff, general public and schools. Welcomes site-specific proposals. Artwork sold but sales not a primary aim.

Broadway Media Centre

Ph ✓ ⊙We

Situated in the café bar of a lively cinema, the gallery is dedicated to photographic exhibitions.
14 Broad Street, Nottingham NG1 3AL, tel: 0115 952 6600
Contact: Head of Front of House
Open: Mon-Fri 5-11; Sat 10am-11pm; Sun 12-10.30
Space: 1 gallery with 19 lin m hanging space
Exhibitions: 4 a year of which 2 originated, 2 touring
Details: Monthly photographic exhibitions held presenting a combination of work by local photographers, specially commissioned shows and touring exhibitions. Priority is given to local photographers. Aims to create a visually stimulating environment and to increase public awareness and appreciation of photography. Sales welcomed (20% commission taken) but not a high priority.

Byard Gallery

Pd Ph Pr Cr Se ✓H ⊗

Small commercial gallery specialising in framed two-dimensional work.
9 Byard Lane, Nottingham NG1 2GJ, tel: 0115 950 0434
Contact: Juliet Burgess
Open: Tues-Sat 10.30-3.30
Space: 1 gallery with 24 lin m hanging space and 84 sq m floor space
Exhibitions: 8 a year of which 6 originated, 2 on a hire basis
Details: Gallery opened December 1993. Exhibitions last 4-6 weeks and are themed with a selection of 2D work, craft and/or sculpture. Gallery aims to increase public awareness of art and shows a diversity of work to please a wide audience.

Carlton Library

Pd Se ✓H ⊙

Wall space in library entrance corridor used to display work by local artists and art departments of local secondary schools.
Manor Road, Carlton, Nottingham NG4 3AY, tel: 0115 987 0276
Contact: Miss J Birchmore, Area Librarian
Open: Mon, Tues, Thurs, Fri 9.30-7.30; Wed 9.30-1; Sat 9-1
Space: 1 gallery with 5 lin m hanging space plus 2 lin m on screens
Exhibitions: 9 a year all on a hire basis
Details: Aims to provide a platform to local artists and to provide access for the public to as wide a range as possible of visual arts within the constraints of the building. Wall space for hanging 5 ft high. Limited space

for free-standing boards. At present (Dec 1994) there is no hire fee for space, but this may change. Sales of work not a priority.

Castle Museum & Art Gallery

Pd Ph Pr Cr Se A ✓① ⊙We4

Two large galleries within museum to exhibit wide range of contemporary and historical visual art.
The Castle, Nottingham NG1 6EL, tel: 0115 948 3504, fax: 0115 935 0988
Contact: Janis Britland/Kate Stoddart, Exhibition Officers
Open: Daily 10-5; seasonally adjusted
Space: 2 galleries with 100 lin m hanging space plus 20 lin m on screens
Exhibitions: 6 a year of which 2 originated, 4 touring
Details: Exhibition galleries on first floor. Lift access to all floors. Sales not main role of gallery.

Djanogly Art Gallery

Pd Ph Pr Cr Se A ✓ ⊙We

Gallery dedicated to mounting temporary exhibitions on both historical and contemporary subjects.
The Arts Centre, University of Nottingham, University Park, Nottingham NG7 2RD, tel: 0115 951 3192, fax: 0115 951 3194
Contact: Joanne Wright, Director
Open: Mon-Fri 10-6; Sat 11-6; Sun & BH 2-5
Space: 2 galleries with 72 lin m hanging space plus 20 lin m on screens and 212 sq m floor space
Exhibitions: 7 a year of which 5 originated, 2 touring
Details: Two exhibition spaces with high environmental and security provision. Exhibitions range from those organised by the gallery to touring shows of contemporary and historical art. Programme of educational activities, cafe, art bookshop and visitors' centre. Sales not a priority.

EMACA Visual Arts

Pd Ph Pr Cr Se ✓① ⊙We

Small multi-media exhibition space promoting contemporary and cultural images by African Caribbean artists from a local, regional and national perspective.
ACFF Education Centre, 28 Beaconsfield Street, Hyson Green, Nottingham NG7 6FD, tel: 0115 924 4611
Contact: Beverley Sterling/Hezrene McKenzie, Visual Arts Officer/Touring Education Officer
Open: Daily 10-6
Space: 1 gallery with 4 lin m hanging space and 59 sq m floor space
Exhibitions: 6 a year of which 3 originated
Details: Aims to create awareness of African/Caribbean artists in the region.

Exhibitions usually last one month. Include film and video as well as other media as indicated. Education programme; workshops accompany all exhibitions. Touring exhibitions available. Some works for sale.

Focus Gallery

Pr Cr Sc

Commercial crafts gallery.
108 Derby Road, Nottingham NG1 5FB, tel: 0115 941 7913
Contact: Director
Space: 2 galleries with 70 lin m hanging space plus 20 lin m on screens and 200 sq m floor space
Details: Commercial, non-grant-aided crafts gallery with permanent exhibitions (for immediate sale) of ceramics, jewellery, wood-carvings, free-blown glass, metal sculpture, original prints – all by leading artists and craftsmen from whom all work is bought outright. Its audience is from every section of society.

Hart Gallery

Pa Pr Cr Sc ✓

Commercial gallery showing contemporary art and ceramics.
23 Main Street, Linby, Nottingham NG15 8AE, tel: 0115 963 8707
Contact: John or Katherine Hart
Space: 1 gallery with 37 lin m hanging space and 184 sq m floor space
Exhibitions: 4 a year all originated
Details: Exhibitions usually consist of one artist and one ceramicist. Emphasis on high quality and encouraging people to obtain original artwork for their own enjoyment and enrichment.

Longdale Gallery

Pa Pr Cr ✓ &

Gallery and restaurant gallery in crafts centre showing contemporary and traditional arts and crafts.
Longdale Craft Centre, Longdale Lane, Ravenshead, Nottingham NG15 9AH, tel: 01623 794858
Contact: Janet Purcell, Manager
Open: Gallery daily 9-6; Restaurant gallery Tues-Sat 9.30-6
Space: 2 galleries with 28 lin m hanging space and 56 sq m floor space
Exhibitions: 12 a year all originated
Details: Exhibitions are selected by panel of resident artists and craftspeople. Craft workshops run. Sales not high priority but encouraged to assist artists.

Nottingham Community Arts

Pa Ph Pr Cr Sc ✓ &

Vibrant and welcoming community orientated arts centre.

39 Gregory Boulevard, Hyson Green, Nottingham NG7 6BE, tel: 0115 978 2463
Contact: David Gilbert, Exhibitions Organiser
Open: Tues, Wed & Fri 9.30-5.30; Thurs 2-8
Space: 2 galleries with 32 lin m hanging space
Exhibitions: 6 a year of which 2 originated, 4 touring
Details: Runs courses and provides facilities for textiles, photography, video and printing. Exhibitions include small-scale touring exhibitions, local artists, and work produced in the centre. Preference for issue-based work, providing positive images. Workshops arranged with exhibitions. Selling work not a priority. Adapted toilets for wheelchair users from mid-1995. Access for wheelchair users upstairs with assistance.

Nottingham Playhouse

Pa Ph Pr Cr Sc LA ✓ & WA

A wide variety of shows are staged in the foyer of the theatre.
Wellington Circus, Nottingham NG1 5AF, tel: 0115 947 4361, fax: 0115 947 5759
Contact: Daniel Slater, Associate Director
Space: 1 gallery with 43 lin m hanging space plus 6 lin m on screens and 56 sq m floor space
Exhibitions: 10 a year all originated
Details: Half solo exhibitions. Programme includes local and regional artists as well as national touring exhibitions. The theatre is planning to make showcases available to makers for selling crafts.

Nottingham Society of Artists

Pa Ph Pr Cr Sc H ⊘

Private gallery used exclusively by gallery members or invited artists and not for regular hire.
St Lukes House, 71 Friar Lane, Nottingham NG1 6DH, tel: 0115 948 0476
Contact: Margaret Spencer, Hon. Secretary
Open: Sat & Sun 10-4.30; daily during major exhibitions
Space: 2 galleries with 55 lin m hanging space and 134 sq m floor space
Exhibitions: 10 a year of which 8 originated, 2 on a hire basis
Details: Currently organising shows of work by members only. Planning to widen its scope to invite students and other artists. Open schools exhibition being considered. Selling work is not gallery's main aim.

Ravenshead Library

Pa Ph Cr Sc ✓ &

Library exhibition space.

Milton Court, Ravenshead, Nottingham NG15 9BD, tel: 01623 794634
Contact: Mrs A Prince, Senior Library Assistant
Open: Mon, Thurs & Fri 9.30-12, 2-7; Tues 9.30-12, 2-5.30; Sat 9.30-12
Space: 1 gallery with 7 lin m hanging space

St Mary's Exhibition Centre

Pa Ph Pr Cr Sc LA ✓ & ◻

Large light area at back of oldest perpendicular church in Nottingham.
St Mary's Church, Lace Market, Nottingham NG1 1HF, tel: 0115 981 2478/ 947 2476
Contact: Revd Jean Lamb, Church of England, 13 Melbourne Road, West Bridgford, Nottingham, NG2 5BG, tel: 0115 981 2478
Open: Tues-Sun 9-5
Space: 1 gallery with 17 lin m hanging space and 63 sq m floor space
Exhibitions: 12 a year all originated
Details: Space suitable for display of 2- or 3-dimensional work and performance. Aims to provide contemporary visual exchange between artists and many visitors to ancient parish church. Work exhibited is compatible with active church community and by artists whose work reflects understanding of spirituality. Sales not primary role.

Nuneaton
WARWICKSHIRE WMA

Nuneaton Museum & Art Gallery

Pa Ph Pr Cr Sc LA ✓ H & WA

Gallery which tries to achieve a balance with exhibitions of gallery's own pictures, local art society/artists' work and touring shows.
Riversley Park, Nuneaton CV11 5TU, tel: 01203 376158
Contact: Gina Quant, Curator
Open: Tues-Sat 10.30-4.30; Sun 2-4.30
Space: 1 gallery with plus 25 lin m on screens and 110 sq m floor space
Exhibitions: 20 a year of which 10 originated, 5 touring, 5 on a hire basis
Details: Especially keen on introducing contemporary work which is fun, and does not alienate audiences not used to contemporary work. Park setting useful for outdoor events.Sales not primary concern.10% commission plus VAT on sales.

Ockley
SURREY SEA

Hannah Peschar Gallery and Sculpture Garden

⊡⊡ ✓ &

Six acres of landscaped water gardens featuring architectural plants used for showing contemporary sculpture and ceramics.
Black and White Cottage, Standon Lane, Ockley RH5 5QR, tel: 01306 679269, fax: 01306 679662
Contact: Mrs Hannah Peschar, Director
Open: Fri & Sat 11-5; Sun & BH 2-5; Tues, Wed & Thurs by appointment
Space: 2 galleries
Exhibitions: 5 a year all originated
Details: Programme runs May to October. Outdoor sculpture garden is on the Crafts Council's selected list. Specialises in showing sculpture and large-scale ceramic pots and urns. Aims to show how well original work can look outdoors. Shows last 6-8 weeks. Mainly British artists are promoted with range of styles, sizes and materials. Small reception gallery space (56 sq metres) in addition to 6 acre outdoor space. Guided tours for visitors and lectures for students. Sales a priority and commission taken.

Okehampton
DEVON SWA

Salar Gallery

⊡⊡⊡⊡ ✓⊞ &

Arts and crafts shop in small market town with room for hire for exhibitions.
20 Bridge Street, Hatherleigh, Okehampton EX20 3HY, tel: 01837 810940
Contact: Sally Ann Vick, Owner
Open: Mon, Wed & Sat 10-1; Tues, Thurs & Fri 10-5; (Jan-March) closed Mon
Space: 2 galleries with 28 sq m floor space
Details: Commercial gallery with work taken on sale or return basis from Devonshire artists and makers. Mainly paintings and wooden items (carvings and furniture). Also carved stone sculpture and some photography. Promotes Devonshire artists and involved with 'Green Tourism', encouraging responsible tourism and local produce. Smaller room available for hire. Frames available. Applications from Devonshire artists only.

Old Harlow
ESSEX EA

St John's Art & Recreation Centre

⊡⊡⊡⊡⊡ ✓ ⊞⊞

Exhibition space in busy arts/community centre.
St John's Walk, Market Street, Old Harlow CM17 0AJ, tel: 01279 442447
Contact: Jane Quinton, Administrator
Open: Daily 10-5
Space: 1 gallery with 89 sq m floor space
Exhibitions: 6 a year all originated
Details: Promotes local and particularly young artists, amateurs and professionals. Intention is to add interest to the centre which is constantly used for music, performance and group classes. Committed to promoting the pursuit of education; arts and recreational subjects. Sales not a priority. 10% commission on sales taken.

Oldham
LANCASHIRE NWA

Artisan

⊡⊡⊡

Craft gallery.
3 King Street, Delph, Oldham OL3 5DL, tel: 01457 874506
Contact: Anne Hamlett
Details: Showing pottery, ceramic sculpture, glass and wood. "I have regular craftspeople who place their work with me and sometimes feature new-comers' work rather than a full exhibition." Prints and original paintings sold on a sale or return basis. Pottery made on the premises.

John McCombs Gallery

⊡⊡

Gallery exhibits mostly representative work in the form of paintings, drawings, prints, and sculpture.
12 King Street, Delph, Oldham OL3 5DQ, tel: 01457 874705
Contact: John McCombs
Open: Mon-Sat 9.30-4.30; Sun 1-4.30
Space: 1 gallery with 16 lin m hanging space and 18 sq m floor space
Exhibitions: 5 a year all originated
Details: Quite a small space taking between 45 & 50 average-size works. Has a spring, summer, autumn, Christmas and winter show for invited artists. Also small group shows now and then. Audience mostly from Oldham, the Greater Manchester area and West Yorkshire.

Oldham Art Gallery

⊡⊡⊡⊡⊡⊡ ✓⊞

Municipal gallery showing contemporary shows alongside collections.
Union Street, Oldham OL1 1DN, tel: 0161 911 4653, fax: 0161 627 1025
Contact: Tessa Gudgeon, Senior Art Gallery Officer
Open: Tues 10-1; Wed-Sat 10-5; Sun 1-5
Space: 6 galleries with 220 lin m hanging space and 520 sq m floor space
Exhibitions: 10 a year of which 6 originated, 4 touring
Details: Lively space aimed at a local and national audience. All types of contemporary art forms and works from the permanent collection of C19th and C20th paintings, drawings, and prints. Includes North West's only Craft and Design Gallery opened July 1993. Programming meetings held approximately every eight weeks. Artists are encouraged to send in slides and proposals. Regularly holds exhibitions and events in collaboration with other galleries and organisations.

Ombersley
HEREFORD & WORCESTER WMA

Ombersley Gallery

⊡⊡⊡ ✓

Private gallery aiming to appeal to collectors and visitors with a selection of work.
Church Terrace, Ombersley WR9 0EP, tel: 01905 620655
Contact: Carole Pimm, Exhibition Organiser
Space: 3 galleries
Exhibitions: 4 a year all originated
Details: Mixed and solo exhibitions. Changing display of work for sale. Tea room.

Oswestry
SHROPSHIRE WMA

Oswestry Heritage and Exhibition Centre

⊡⊡⊡⊡ ✓ ⊞

C15th building housing local history artifacts and providing regional centre for arts and crafts.
2 Church Terrace, Oswestry SY11 2TE, tel: 01691 671323
Contact: Gill Avery, Exhibition Co-ordinator
Open: (Easter-Oct) Mon-Sat 9.30-5; (Oct-Easter) Mon-Sat 9.30-5; closed Thurs; occassional Sun opening
Space: 2 galleries
Exhibitions: 30 a year
Details: Monthly exhibitions by local artists and craftspeople. Cabinet space. Details of space available on request. Craft demonstrations. Encourages local community involvement in Centre from schools, clubs, societies, etc. Aims to create

relaxed, informal atmosphere for local residents and tourists. Entrance to gallery through tearoom. Building also houses Tourist Information Centre. Sales welcome. 14% commission taken.

Oundle
NORTHAMPTONSHIRE EMA

Yarrow Gallery

Gallery within a school, aimed at the school and local community.
Oundle School, Oundle PE8 4EN, tel: 01832 274034, fax: 01832 273564
Contact: Roger Page
Space: 1 gallery with 70 lin m hanging space and 240 sq m floor space
Exhibitions: 5 a year
Details: School-sponsored exhibitions and available for hire.

Oxford
OXFORDSHIRE SA

Ashmolean Museum (McAlpine Gallery)

McAlpine Gallery shows temporary exhibitions, some of contemporary art.
Beaumont Street, Oxford OX1 2PH, tel: 01865 278041, fax: 01865 278056
Contact: Timothy Wilson, Keeper of Western Art
Exhibitions: 3 a year
Details: Collections of European and Oriental art and antiquities. Departments of Western Art, Eastern Art, Antiquities. Coin room. Mounts loan exhibitions often directly related to collections. At least one exhibition a year devoted to work of living artist or artists. Small exhibition gallery in Department of Eastern Art. Department of Western Art can't consider exhibitions of work of living artists unless they are funded from outside.

Bampton Arts Centre

Arts centre upstairs in old town hall offering local and well-established artists a generously sized, well-lit space.
West Oxfordshire Arts Association, Town Hall, Bampton, Oxford, tel: 01993 850137
Contact: Sarah Edwards
Space: 1 gallery with 25 lin m hanging space plus 10 lin m on screens
Exhibitions: 9 a year all originated
Details: Tends to hold group shows on a common theme. Members of the Association given preferential rate of commission.

Bloomin Arts

Two small temporary exhibition spaces for work which reflects involvement in community-based projects.
Princes Street, Oxford OX4 1DD, tel: 01865 245735, fax: 01865 724317
Contact: Gill Breeze/Al Cane/Chris Townsend
Open: Mon-Wed & Fri 10-5; Thurs 2-5
Space: 2 galleries
Exhibitions: 12 a year of which 10 originated, 2 touring
Details: Work exhibited is usually produced in-house by Community Arts Resource projects. Other shows occasionally taken from outside arts projects. Sometimes new artists given opportunity to present work. Particular interest in photography, computer art, copy art, scrap culture. Selling work not main purpose of gallery.

CCA Galleries (Oxford)

One of a network of commercial galleries in South of England specialising in original prints.
90 High Street, Oxford OX1 4BJ, tel: 01865 202818, fax: 01865 202819
Contact: Alice Pargeter, Manager
Open: Mon-Sat 9-5.30
Space: 2 galleries with 34 lin m hanging space and 93 sq m floor space
Exhibitions: 12 a year all originated
Details: CCA Galleries in a leading publisher of original limited edition prints, with other galleries in London, Farnham, Bath and Cambridge (see separate entries for each). Each gallery selects its own work. Primary aim is to promote hand-made prints by CCA artists.

Christ Church Picture Gallery

Main purpose is to house permanent collections but aim to show exciting contemporary exhibitions alongside these or integrated with them.
Christ Church, Oxford OX1 1DP, tel: 01865 276172
Contact: Brigid Cleaver, Exhibitions Officer
Open: Mon-Sat 10.30-4.30 or 5.30 (closed 1-2); Sun 2-4.30 or 5.30
Space: 1 gallery with 30 lin m hanging space and 66 sq m floor space
Exhibitions: 2 a year both originated
Details: Important collection of old master paintings and drawings. Apart from exhibitions based on the drawings collection, there are often temporary exhibitions of modern art and photography. The gallery's audience consists of academics and art lovers of all ages from all over the

world. The temporary exhibition space is restricted to artists from Christ Church, Oxford University, Oxford and Oxfordshire. Sales not a priority.

Computer Corridor *

Corridor exhibition space within university showing wide range of exhibitions.
Oxford Brookes University, Headington, Oxford OX3 0BP, tel: 01865 819460, fax: 01865 819073
Contact: Geoff Olsen, Head of Visual Arts
Space: 2 galleries with 40 lin m hanging space plus 45 lin m on screens
Exhibitions: 5 a year all originated
Details: Exhibitions seen by students, staff and the public, ranging from painting to avant-garde in print. Local artists show during Oxfordshire Artweek and at other times of the year, also exhibitions from abroad, the school of architecture and students. Run for three weeks on average. Permanent collection of work bought from final-year students.

Freud's

Monthly or bi-monthly exhibitions/ residencies in a renovated Neoclassical style church, now a café and one of Oxford's largest live entertainment venues.
Walton Street, Oxford OX2 6AH, tel: 01865 311171
Contact: Pat Thomas, Freud's Cafe, Bar, Gallery HQ, 36 Great James Street, London, WC1N 3HB, tel: 0171 831 8641, fax: 0171 831 3062**
Open: Sun-Tues 11am-12 midnight; Wed & Sat 11-2
Space: 1 gallery
Exhibitions: 8 a year all originated
Details: Its mural, attributed to the Pre-Raphaelite painter Holman Hunt, lofty ceilings and magnificent stained glass windows create a dramatic setting for the display of a wide range of artworks. Interesting mix of the academic, the creative and the arts oriented.

Museum of Modern Art

Five galleries showing temporary exhibitions of C20th and contemporary art, including historical surveys and major shows of international contemporary artists.
30 Pembroke Street, Oxford OX1 1BP, tel: 01865 722733
Contact: David Elliott, Director
Open: Tues-Sat 10-6; Thurs 10-9; Sun 2-6; Mon closed
Space: 6 galleries with 230 lin m hanging space plus 200 lin m on screens and 421 sq m floor space
Exhibitions: 12 a year all originated
Details: International reputation for innovative exhibitions of recent modern art.

Actively engaged in creating a larger, more heterogeneous audience for contemporary art. Frames new viewpoints which counteract ethnocentricity and presents new work, not previously seen or valued. Strong educational programme. Community programme fosters an approach to culture that is non-competitive and emphasises enjoyment and fulfilment of participants. Selling work not a priority.

Museum of Oxford

Pa Ph Pr Sc A ● H ● 4

Through temporary exhibitions aims to create a larger and more heterogeneous audience for contemporary art.
St Aldates, Oxford OX1 1DZ, tel: 01865 815539
Contact: Mrs P.A. O'Neill, Administrator
Open: Tues-Fri 10-4; Sat 10-5
Space: 2 galleries
Exhibitions: 15 a year of which 4 originated, 11 on a hire basis
Details: A strong educational and community programme foster an approach to culture that is non-competitive and enjoyable. One exhibition room has 10 linear metres hanging space plus facilities for lectures; other room has hanging space plus secure display cases. Sales not a priority. Charges are made for facilities.

Old Fire Station Theatre

Pa Ph Pr Sc A ● H

Community theatre and large gallery available to regional artists.
40 George Street, Oxford OX1 2AQ, tel: 01865 794494, fax: 01865 794491
Contact: Glynnis Rolston
Open: Mon-Sat 10-6; Sun 10-4
Space: 1 gallery
Exhibitions: 12 a year all on a hire basis
Details: Run jointly by Apollo Leisure and Oxford City Council. 25% commission on sales.

Oxford Gallery

Pa Ph Pr Cr ●

To provide exhibition space for Britain's best contemporary makers and national and international printmakers.
23 High Street, Oxford OX1 4AH, tel: 01865 242731
Contact: Deborah Elliott, Lindsey Hoole, Valerie Stewart and Kristina Mason, Directors
Open: Mon-Sat 10-5
Space: 1 gallery with 20 lin m hanging space and 56 sq m floor space
Exhibitions: 10 a year all originated
Details: Specialises in contemporary fine and applied art including ceramics, glass, wood, textiles, jewellery and an international collection of limited edition prints. Exhibition programme usually includes two major painting shows, two solo ceramic shows and occasional group

shows. Selling work is gallery's primary role.

Photography Workshop *

Ph ●

Gallery is an integral part of workshop with extensive darkrooms and studio for hire.
103/104 St Mary's Road, Cowley, Oxford OX4 1QD, tel: 01865 246 027
Contact: Keith Barnes, Exhibition Organiser
Space: 230 lin m hanging space
Exhibitions: 12 a year all originated
Details: Aims to provide interest and attract photographers and artists to the workshop not only to sell work, but to further visual awareness.

Rainyday Gallery

Cross Street, Penzance TR18 2EY, tel: 01736 66077

St Giles' Church *

Pa Pr Sc ●

Exhibition space in city centre mediaeval church, with active participation in music and the arts.
10 Woodstock Road, Oxford OX1 3LU
Contact: Carolyn Llewelyn, Organiser of Exhibitions, St Giles' Church, 53 Blenheim Drive, Oxford, OX2 8DL
Exhibitions: 18 a year all originated
Details: North and South aisles (attractive blind arches) for showing work. Takes part in Oxford Artweek. Variety of exhibitions staged in the last 3 years. Effort made to link appropriate exhibitions with the Church calendar, eg Candlemas, Lent, Passiontide. Audience: local and tourist.

Par
CORNWALL SWA

Mid-Cornwall Galleries

Pa Ph Cr ●

Large well-lit space showing and selling fine contemporary paintings and crafts.
St Blazey Gate, Par PL24 2EG, tel: 01726 812131
Contact: Mrs Gould, Exhibition Organiser
Open: Mon-Sat 10-5
Space: 70 lin m hanging space and 150 sq m floor space
Exhibitions: 89 a year all originated
Details: A commercial gallery showing mixed exhibitions featuring work from national South West people. Artists' and makers' group shows of three to twelve people. Aims to sell high-quality painting, prints, craft work, etc. Annual exhibition of ceramics from Craft Potters Association. Coffee served.

Penrith
CUMBRIA NA

Beck Mill Gallery

Pa Ph Pr Cr ● ●

Commercial gallery in converted barn 2 miles outside Penrith.
Langwathby, Penrith CA10 1NY, tel: 01768 881371
Contact: John MacDonald, Owner
Open: Tues-Sat 10-5.30; BH; closed Feb
Space: 3 galleries
Exhibitions: 89 a year all originated
Details: Gallery, annex and room upstairs for prints. 3-4 one-person shows per year plus mixed shows. Exhibits work by professional artists only – local and national. Shows furniture and lighting as well as fine art and craft. Owner selects work according to own notions of quality. 33% commission on sales.

Isis Gallery

Pa Ph Pr Cr ● ●

Converted barn in rural location on fringe of Lake District promoting contemporary art and original prints by established and emerging artists.
Melmerby, Penrith CA10 1HN, tel: 01768 881508
Contact: Irene Faith
Open: Wed-Sun 11-6
Space: 25 lin m hanging space and 65 sq m floor space
Exhibitions: 10 a year all originated
Details: Shows solo and group exhibitions predominantly of northern artists. Temporary exhibitions changing once per month. Audience predominantly tourists. Applications are invited through slides or photographs and CV. Willing to consider touring exhibitions. Selling work is not gallery's primary function.

Laburnum Ceramics

Pa Ph Cr Sc ●

Small rural studio-gallery devoted to mainly Cumbrian contemporary ceramics with Sunderland glass.
Yanwath, Penrith CA10 2LF, tel: 01768 864842
Contact: Viv and Arne Rumbold
Open: (Mar-Dec) Wed-Sun 10.30-4.30; (Jan-Feb) please ring
Space: 4 galleries with 12 lin m hanging space and 23 sq m floor space
Exhibitions: 8 a year all originated
Details: In addition to galleries also cottage garden for sculptures. Varied programme of one-person or theme exhibitions with some live events. Oral and visual interpretation of artists and works. Aims to encourage appreciation of innovative work. Selling exhibitions promote work of 40 mainly Cumbrian ceramicists and Sunderland/

Northern glass artists. 33% commission taken on sales.

Penzance
CORNWALL SW A

Contemporary Gallery

Commercial gallery with spaces for continuous changing display and specific exhibitions.
The Art & Design Building, 46 Queen Street, Penzance TR18 4BQ, tel: 01736 62396, fax: 01736 331794
Contact: Wayne Hesketh, Owner
Open: Mon-Sat 9-5
Space: 2 galleries with 56 sq m floor space
Exhibitions: 6 a year all originated
Details: Mainly shows contemporary figurative paintings by local artists but do show work by artists from outside region. Gallery promotes shows with posters. Commission taken on sales. Would be prepared to hire out gallery.

Jamieson Library

Dedicated exhibition space within library to promote and support the sale of contemporary arts and crafts by women.
The Hive, The Old Post Office, Newmill, Penzance TR20 4XN, tel: 01736 60549, fax: 01736 330704
Contact: Melissa Hardie/Philip Budden, Directors
Open: (Easter week + 3 seven-day slots throughout summer) Mon-Fri 10-5
Space: 2 galleries with 60 sq m floor space
Exhibitions: 4 a year all originated
Details: Gallery within specialist library. Study collection of books and art objects on the subject of women, with over 10,000 books and items held. Shows visual art and craft work by women artists in ten-day exhibitions each with a preview. Also the base for Patten Press. Sale of work not primary role of gallery.

Newlyn Art Gallery

Main purpose is to implement a programme reflecting quality and diversity of local, national and international contemporary art practice.
New Road, Newlyn, Penzance TR18 5PZ, tel: 01736 63715, fax: 01736 331578
Contact: Emily Ash, Director
Open: Mon-Sat 10-5 incl BH
Space: 2 galleries with 72 lin m hanging space and 154 sq m floor space
Exhibitions: 9 a year of which 7 originated, 2 touring
Details: Wide cross section of artforms shown; from painting and sculpture to installation and work involving new technologies. Aims for balanced programme involving locally-based artists as represented by the Newlyn Society of Artists together with artists from across the UK and abroad. Gallery has recently had a major internal refurbishment.

Victoria Studios

Exhibition space in studios which are headquarters of society with about 50 artist members.
Victoria Place, Morrab Road, Penzance, tel: 01736 62228
Contact: Colin Scott, Director, 4 South Parade, Penzance, TR18 4DJ
Open: Throughout the year, opening times vary
Space: 1 gallery with 21 lin m hanging space plus 9 lin m on screens and 42 sq m floor space
Exhibitions: 8 a year all originated
Details: Society members range from beginners to professional artists. Life drawing classes, talks, lectures, slide shows etc. Exhibition space on one long wall, 8ft high plus movable screens. Shows local artists' work mainly but new work generally. Students encouraged to use space at modest cost. Selling work isn't gallery's main purpose.

Wolf at the Door

Commercial gallery showing known and unknown artists.
Bread Street, Penzance TR18 6EQ, tel: 01736 60573
Contact: Lu Simmons/Anne Hearle, Directors
Space: 2 galleries with 40 lin m hanging space and 128 sq m floor space
Exhibitions: 11 a year all originated
Details: 'A funky little gallery down in Penzance.' Tries to be lively and honest. Aims to generate some energy and enthusiasm about art. Upstairs gallery has monthly changing exhibitions. Always on the look out for new (or old) interesting artists. Downstairs gallery has continuous show of paintings, sculpture and applied arts.

Peterborough
CAMBRIDGESHIRE EA

David Holmes Contemporary art

Small commercial gallery specialising in work of major contemporary British artists.
12 Eastfield Road, Peterborough PE1 4AN, tel: 01733 51152
Contact: David Holmes
Open: Tues-Sat 10.30-5.30

Space: 1 gallery with 21 lin m hanging space and 20 sq m floor space
Exhibitions: 6 a year of which 5 originated, 1 touring
Details: Biennial partnership with Peterborough Art Gallery in presenting 'National Pacesetters' exhibition. Private press books exhibited. Gallery owner is printer/constructionist/printmaker and works in open studio in gallery.

Orton District Library *

Exhibition space in a public library foyer with display cases and screens tends to be used by the local community.
Bushfield, Orton Goldhay, Peterborough PE2 0RQ, tel: 01733 234448, fax: 01733 361242
Contact: District Librarian
Space: 1 gallery with plus 22 lin m on screens and 19 sq m floor space
Exhibitions: 10 a year
Details: Continual rotation of exhibitions throughout the year. Is available for hire and applications from outside the area are welcome.

Peterborough Art Gallery

Municipal gallery with mixed programme of visual arts.
Priestgate, Peterborough PE1 1LF, tel: 01733 343329, fax: 01733
Contact: Ian Duckworth, Assistant Curator Exhibitions & Fine Art
Open: Tues-Sat 10-5
Space: 3 galleries with 120 lin m hanging space and 240 sq m floor space
Exhibitions: 10 a year of which 3 originated, 5 touring, 2 on a hire basis
Details: Overhead natural light controlled by blinds, fluorescent and track lighting. Most exhibitions are hired in from other galleries but applications from others by slides and supporting information are welcomed.

Peterborough Arts Centre

Gallery space, darkroom and media workshop enable programme of photography temporary exhibitions.
Goldhay Way, Orton Goldhay, Peterborough PE2 5JQ, tel: 01733 237073, fax: 01733 235462
Contact: Clifton Stewart, Media Coordinator
Exhibitions: 12 a year
Details: Emphasis on photography. Where possible, presents workshops linked to exhibitions. Annual touring exhibition in early summer for schools (not photography).

Peterborough Central Library

Pa Ph Pr Gr Sc ● 🅔🆆4

Exhibition space in public library.
Broadway, Peterborough, tel: 01733
348343, fax: 01733 555277
Contact: Linda Jubb, Marketing Assistant
Open: Mon-Fri 9.30-7; Sat 9.30-5
Space: 3 galleries with 14 lin m hanging
space and 8 sq m floor space
Details: Space made available for
exhibitions mounted by individuals or
organisations which contribute to the
Service's values as information and leisure
service.

Petersfield
HAMPSHIRE SA

Bedales Gallery

Pa Ph Pr Gr Sc ● 🅖🆆

School-based, purpose-built gallery.
Bedales School, Steep, Petersfield GU32
2DG, tel: 01730 263286, fax: 01730
267411
Contact: John Barker, Gallery
Administrator
Open: Mon-Fri 2-5; Sat 10-1
Space: 1 gallery with 43 lin m hanging
space and 93 sq m floor space
Exhibitions: 8 a year of which 4 originated
Details: Opened 1990. All exhibitions
advertised and open to general public.
Provides a balanced programme in fine art,
craft and product design for the art and
design department and an ever-increasing
number of visitors. Limited opportunities
to display work from any one discipline in a
particular year owing to gallery's wide brief.
Booked twelve months ahead.

Pickering
NORTH YORKSHIRE YHA

Green Man Gallery *

Pa Pr Gr IA ●

Private arts and crafts gallery.
The Old Drill Hall, Southgate, Pickering
YO18 7LB, tel: 01751 72380
Contact: Nathan Orme
Space: 1 gallery with 218 lin m hanging
space and 25 sq m floor space.
Details: Shows and sells contemporary arts
and crafts. The gallery is situated in one of
the most visited North Yorkshire market
towns, providing a wide range of
customers. There is also a keen interest
generally in the arts and crafts.

Plymouth
DEVON SWA

Barbican Theatre

Pa Ph Pr Sc IA ● 🅧

*A youth arts and theatre venue in heart of
historic Barbican area of Plymouth.*
Castle Street, Plymouth PL1 2NJ, tel:
01752 267131
Contact: Adminstrator
Open: Mon-Fri 10-4; Mon-Sat 4-10
during performances; Sun by arrangement
Space: 1 gallery with 16 lin m hanging
space and 4 sq m floor space
Exhibitions: 12 a year all originated
Details: Space available free, particularly to
young artists, women and people who have
never exhibited before. Seek contemporary,
new work that challenges its audience either
through form or content. Artist's Guide to
the Gallery available. Exhibitions viewed by
varied theatre audience, mainly young
people. Selling work not gallery's primary
role.

Plymouth Arts Centre

Pa Ph Pr Gr Sc IA ● 🅕 🅖🆆4

*Three galleries in arts centre with cinema
and extensive education programme.*
38 Looe Street, Plymouth PL4 0EB, tel:
01752 660060, fax: 01752 250101
Contact: Bernard Samuels, Director
Open: Mon 10-5; Tues-Sat 10-8; Sun 5-8
Space: 3 galleries with 58 lin m hanging
space and 132 sq m floor space
Exhibitions: 20 a year of which 17
originated, 3 touring
Details: Galleries show broad range of
exhibitions by local and nationally-known
artists, including touring exhibitions, solo
and thematic group shows. Provides
opportunity to see work produced outside
area as well as support for artists working in
the region.

Plymouth City Museum & Art Gallery

Pa Ph Pr Gr Sc ● 🅕 🆆4

*Run by City Museums and Heritage Service
with collections of fine and decorative art,
natural and human history and regular
temporary exhibitions across all disciplines.*
Drake Circus, Plymouth PL4 8AJ, tel:
01752 264878, fax: 01752 264959
Contact: Exhibitions Officer
Open: Tues-Fri 10-5.30; Sat 10-5; BH 10-5
Space: 3 galleries with 136 lin m hanging
space plus 32 lin m on screens and 368 sq
m floor space
Exhibitions: 13 a year of which 8
originated, 5 touring
Details: Exhibits a broad range including
historical exhibitions and work by
contemporary artists in all media and from
different cultures. The chance for
collaborative exhibitions is encouraged. An

excellent venue for 3D works. Sale of work
not a priority.

Plymouth Theatre Royal

Pa Ph Pr Gr Sc ● 🅗 🅔🆆

*Theatre first-floor display area for changing
exhibitions of 2D work and craft.*
Royal Parade, Plymouth PL1 2TR, tel:
01752 668282, fax: 01752 671179
Contact: Jackie Lugger, House Manager,
Francis Mallett, White Lane Gallery, The
Barbican, Plymouth, PL1 2LP, tel: 01752
221450
Open: Mon-Sat 10am-11pm
Space: 1 gallery with 8 lin m hanging space
Exhibitions: 15 a year all originated
Details: Programme mostly solo
exhibitions of artists living and working in
the West Country, Devon and Cornwall.
Work is small to medium between £50 and
£500 with emphasis on the easily accessible.
Aim is to expose contemporary artists' work
to a wide audience. Exhibitions loosely tied
to the theatre productions. Most work for
sale but selling not primary role.

White Lane Gallery

Pa Gr ● 🅧

*Gallery showing one-person and mixed
exhibitions of paintings and ceramics with
a broad cross section of contemporary styles.*
1 White Lane, The Barbican, Plymouth
PL1 2LP, tel: 01752 221450
Contact: Francis Mallett
Opens: Mon 12-4; Tues-Sat 10-5
**30 lin m hanging space and 70 sq m
floor space**
Contact: 12 a year all originated
Open: The gallery aims to present a diverse
exhibition programme by leading and up
and coming South West artists. Styles
ranges from figurative to abstract. Sales a
priority.

Polperro
CORNWALL SWA

Peak Rock Artists' Studios & Gallery

Pa Ph Pr ● 🅧

*Gallery exhibits diverse selection of work by
local artists.*
The Harbour, Polperro PL13 2QY, tel:
01503 72490
Contact: Tony Tewfik
Open: (Summer) daily 9.30am-9pm;
(Winter) Mon-Fri 9.30-5, Sat 10-1
Space: 1 gallery with 42 lin m hanging
space and 98 sq m floor space
Details: Permanent exhibition with
individual exhibits frequently rotated.
Regular life drawing classes and tuition in
painting and drawing for local people and
visitors. Artists' studio space available. Sale
of work is considered gallery's primary role.
Only access to gallery up flight of stairs.

Poole
DORSET SA

Bournemouth University Gallery

Pa Ph Pr Cr Sc LA ✔ ⓔ Ⓗ Ⓕ ⓦ

Small gallery for staff and student viewing during term time and available for private hire during vacations.
Fern Barrow, Poole BH20 5BB, tel: 01202 595469, fax: 01202 595034
Contact: Sarah Hughes, Marketing Officer
Open: Mon-Fri 9-6
Space: 1 gallery with plus 12 lin m on screens and 12 sq m floor space
Exhibitions: 9 a year of which 4 originated, 3 touring, 2 on a hire basis
Details: Gallery's audience is university staff and students. Hopes to attract wider audience from local area as gallery gains reputation. Sales not gallery's primary function.

Poole Arts Centre (Seldown Gallery)

Pa Pr Cr ✔ Ⓗ Ⓕ ⓦ

Purpose-built gallery in performance-orientated art centre with monthly exhibitions.
21 Kingland Road, Poole BH15 1UG, tel: 01202 670521
Contact: Anthony Covell, Director
Open: Mon-Sat 10-6
Exhibitions: 10 a year of which 4 touring, 6 on a hire basis
Details: Work by local artists and groups shown. Some 3D work. Adaptable space with good lighting facilities. Integral part of PAC which has concert hall, theatre, cinema, workshops, function rooms and dance studio. Sales not priority.

Upstairs Gallery

Pa Ph Pr Cr Sc ✔ Ⓧ

Gallery primarily showing contemporary and historical crafts within Scaplen's Court Museum.
Scaplen's Court Museum, High Street, Poole BH15 1BW, tel: 01202 683138
Contact: Jocelyn Glanfield, Craft Development Officer, Poole Museum Service, 4 High Street, Poole BH15 1BW, tel: 01202 683138, fax: 01202 660896
Open: Mon-Sat 10-5; Sun 2-5
Space: 1 gallery with 20 lin m hanging space and 63 sq m floor space
Exhibitions: 8 a year of which 4 originated, 4 touring
Details: Exhibitions are of contemporary and historical crafts with emphasis on links between the two. Half are selling exhibitions. Space available for individual artists whose work relates to local and domestic issues. A contemporary craft shop within Scaplen's Court Museum complements gallery programme.

Exhibition and education officers work together to run comprehensive education programme.

Waterfront Museum

Pa Ph Sc ✔ Ⓔ ⓦ

Two exhibition spaces; mezzanine space in mediaeval town cellars and fourth-floor gallery; both within museum.
4 High Street, Poole BH15 1BW, tel: 01202 683138, fax: 01202 660896
Contact: Exhibitions Officer
Open: Mon-Sat 10-5; Sun 2-5
Space: 2 galleries with 50 lin m hanging space and 68 sq m floor space
Exhibitions: 5 a year of which 4 originated, 1 touring
Details: Mezzanine exhibition space in cellars shows work that reflects historical and maritime themes. Artist-in-Residence scheme envisaged in line with strong educational resource. Fourth-floor gallery exhibitions based on museum collection and local history; mainly 2D and small 3D exhibitions. Sales not a priority.

Portland
DORSET SWA

Chesil Gallery *

Pa Ph Pr Sc LA ✔ Ⓗ

Hire gallery in an old stone building on Chesil beach.
Chiswell, Portland DT5 1AW, tel: 01305 822738
Contact: Margaret Somerville, Chesil Gallery, Hilfield, Dorchester, DT2 7BD, tel: 0196321 0200
Space: 3 galleries with 274 lin m hanging space and 84 sq m floor space
Exhibitions: 6 a year of which 2 originated, 1 touring, 3 on a hire basis
Details: Residential (2 flats). Runs six summer exhibitions, a community exhibition, a South Bank Touring exhibition, sometimes a local exhibition and the rest are visiting artists who live at the gallery, pay a rent, exhibit and work on the island. Specialises in sculptors and painters.

Portsmouth
HAMPSHIRE SA

Aspex Gallery

Pa Ph Pr Cr Sc LA Ⓔ Ⓧ

Gallery part of Aspex Visual Arts Trust, charitable company promoting visual arts.
27 Brougham Road, Portsmouth PO5 4PA, tel: 01705 812121
Contact: Les Buckingham, Director
Space: 1 gallery with 50 lin m hanging space and 186 sq m floor space
Exhibitions: 7 a year of which 5 originated, 2 touring

Details: Shows new work by living artists and runs educational programme with local community. Exhibitions from 4-6 weeks. Application current for major improvements to access.

Portsmouth Arts Centre

Pa Ph Pr Cr Sc ✔ Ⓗ Ⓔ ⓦ

Area alongside studio theatre entrance with bar, open 2 nights a week on average and accessible throughout the day.
Reginald Road, Southsea, Portsmouth PO4 9HN, tel: 01705 732236, fax: 01705 734424
Contact: Nicolas Young, Director
Open: Mon-Fri 10-10; Sat 10-5
Space: 1 gallery with 12 lin m hanging space and 60 sq m floor space
Exhibitions: 9 a year
Details: Gallery within an arts centre. Shows a mixture of professional, amateur and community-based work. Aims to offer a wide and interesting exhibition programme linking to participatory activities wherever possible. Craft-based visual work is particularly prominent. Sales not a priority.

Portsmouth City Museum

Pa Ph Cr Sc ✔ Ⓔ ⓦ

Temporary exhibitions to broaden appeal of permanent collections of local history, fine and decorative art.
Museum Road, Portsmouth PO1 2LJ, tel: 01705 827261, fax: 01705 875276
Contact: Ian Chappell, Exhibitions & Display Officer
Open: Daily 10.30-5.30
Space: 1 gallery with 108 lin m hanging space plus 9 lin m on screens and 112 sq m floor space
Exhibitions: 4 a year of which 3 originated, 1 touring
Details: Museum with emphasis on history of Portsmouth. Exhibition programme aims to provide variety throughout the year with 1 large in-house exhibition of major local interest running for 3-4 months and approximately 8 other exhibitions running for about 1 month. Mix of photography, fine art, decorative art, contemporary crafts, local and natural history. Where possible activities for all ages are arranged in conjunction with exhibitions. Sales not a priority.

Prestbury
CHESHIRE NWA

Artizana

Pa Cr

Selling gallery specialising in contemporary British crafts and contemporary British furniture.
The Village, Prestbury SK10 4DG, tel: 01625 827582

Contact: Mr R. Ghazoul
Open: Mon-Sat 10.30-5.30; Sun 2-5.30; Furniture section closed Sun & Mon
Space: 2 galleries with 20 lin m hanging space and 250 sq m floor space
Exhibitions: 2 a year both originated
Details: Comprises two separate gallery sections of approximately equal areas; the first dedicated to crafts with emphasis on studio glass and ceramics and the second dedicated to furniture with examples of some fifty designer-makers in permanently changing display. Sales a priority.

Preston
LANCASHIRE NWA

Brook Gallery

Original work by contemporary local artists exhibited in a domestic setting.
Brook Farm, Broadith Lane, Goosnargh, Preston PR3 2EJ, tel: 01772 861780
Contact: Mrs Rosemary Owen
Open: Please telephone for opening times.
Space: 1 gallery with 14 lin m hanging space and 25 sq m floor space
Details: Gallery part of old farm house showing a permanent exhibition of original work in a variety of styles. Concentrates on giving local artists a well-lit exhibition space to show smaller paintings and prints including two shows a year (summer and winter) for selected artists. Sales a priority.

Harris Museum & Art Gallery

Permanent collections of fine and decorative arts plus a varied and livley exhibition programme.
Market Square, Preston PR1 2PP, tel: 01772 258248, fax: 01772 886764
Contact: Alexandra Walker, Museum & Art Officer
Space: 3 galleries with 109 lin m hanging space and 315 sq m floor space
Exhibitions: 12 a year
Details: Temporary exhibitions programme organises and tours national and international contemporary art. promotes a wide range of art practice including work influenced by non-Western cultures. Education department seeks to encourage access to, and involvement in, art for all people.

Samlesbury Hall

Hall with variety of exhibition areas and over 100 exhibitions a year 1-3 weeks long as well as continuous displays.
Preston New Road, Samlesbury, Preston PR5 0UP, tel: 01254 812010
Contact: Diana Birnie, Exhibition Coordinator

Space: 4 galleries with 1001 lin m hanging space and 176 sq m floor space
Exhibitions: 100 a year all originated
Details: Admission; adults £2 , children 80p.

Vernon Gallery

Gallery, belonging to University of Central Lancashire, gives exhibition opportunities to artists who might otherwise not be given the chance.
Moor Lane, Preston PR1 3PQ, tel: 01772 59383, fax: 01772 201378
Contact: C.V. Lloyd, Architect Associate, University of Central Lancashire, Vernon Street, Moor Lane, Preston, PR1 3PQ
Open: Mon-Fri 9-5.30
Space: 1 gallery with 66 lin m hanging space and 100 sq m floor space
Exhibitions: 12 a year all originated
Details: Has an associated meeting hall/ music performance space. No commission taken on any sales made.

Victoria Building

Gallery's main purpose is to provide contemporary exhibitions for students & staff who use the building.
University of Central Lancashire, Faculty of Design & Technology, Preston PR1 2TQ, tel: 01772 893201
Contact: Nigel Lewis, Exhibition Officer
Open: Mon-Fri 9-5; Tues-Thurs 9-9
Space: 2 galleries with 40 lin m hanging space
Exhibitions: 9 a year
Details: Used by students – fine art, ceramics, glass, graphics, fashion. Artists from the community are also encouraged to exhibit. Audience from local area, staff and students, and visitors. Exhibition frames of various sizes available. Sales not a priority.

Princetown
DEVON SWA

Dartmoor Gallery

Gallery in visitor centre showing exhibitions with relevance to Dartmoor, landscape and conservation generally.
High Moorland Visitor Centre, Old Duchy Hotel, Tavistock Road, Princetown, tel: 01822 890414
Contact: John Weir, Head of Communications, Dartmoor National Park Authority, Parke, Haytor Road, Bovey Tracey, TQ13 9JQ, tel: 01626 832093, fax: 01626 834684
Open: Daily 10-5; closed Christmas
Space: 2 galleries with 18 lin m hanging space and 46 sq m floor space
Exhibitions: 12 a year of which 7 originated, 2 touring

Details: Gallery aims to increase public awareness of the area and conservation purposes and appreciation of art generally. Work chosen on basis of relevance to visiting and local community. 200,000 visitors a year to Visitor Centre. Displays by local groups and schools included in programme. Sales welcome (20% commission taken) but not high priority.

Ramsgate
KENT SEA

Addington Street Studio & Gallery

Showing owner's work in permanent display alongside programme of mixed and solo exhibitions.
49 Addington Street, Ramsgate CT11 9JJ, tel: 0184 359 7405
Contact: Pat Castle, Exhibition Organiser
Space: 2 galleries with 100 lin m hanging space and 32 sq m floor space
Exhibitions: 4 a year all originated
Details: Attached to Pat Castle's studio and living space and shows artist/owner's own work as well as that of other artists in exhibitions. Also hosts poetry readings, meetings and other small-scale events and takes active part in local community activities such as theatre workshops and street fairs. Sale of work is considered the gallery's primary role.

Ramsgate Library Gallery

Varied programme of exhibitions in library gallery on top floor of listed Andrew Carnegie building.
Guildford Lawn, Ramsgate CT11 9AY, tel: 01843 593532
Contact: Sheena Watson, Arts Promotion Officer, Thanet Group, KCC Arts & Libraries Department, c/o Margate Library, Cecil Square, Margate, CT9 1RE, tel: 01843 223626, fax: 01843 293015
Open: Mon Thurs 9.30 6; Fri 9.30 7; Sat 9.30-5
Space: 1 gallery with 44 lin m hanging space and 149 sq m floor space
Exhibitions: 11 a year
Details: Broad-based exhibitions by contemporary visual artists and makers, many with links to the South East, as well as national and regional touring shows. All work by professional artists. Audience drawn from schools, colleges, clubs and general public. Humidifier, controlled temperature, dimmer lights. Permanently staffed when open to the public. Sales not gallery's primary aim. Commission taken on sales.

Raveningham
NORFOLK EA

Frederick Gallery

[Pa] [Sc] ⬤

Large airy gallery with informal friendly atmosphere including special exhibitions area comprising approx one quarter of overall gallery space exhibiting works by East Anglian artists.
Raveningham Centre, Beccles Road, Raveningham, tel: 01508 548688, fax: 01508 548958
Contact: Adrian Woodard, Proprietor
Open: Daily 10-6
Space: 1 gallery with 60 lin m hanging space and 200 sq m floor space
Exhibitions: 10 a year all originated
Details: Works by East Anglian artists ranging from traditional to abstract. Sales a priority.

Reading
BERKSHIRE SA

Gallery 28

[Pa] [Ph] [Pr] [Sc] [LA] ⬤ ⬤ ⬤

Gallery aims to show interesting and challenging work that could not be shown in commercial galleries in Reading.
The Rising Sun Institute, 30 Silver Street, Reading RG1 2ST, tel: 01734 866788
Contact: Exhibitions Committee
Open: Mon-Fri 1-2; Sat 1-3
Space: 3 galleries with 39 lin m hanging space and 42 sq m floor space
Exhibitions: 12 a year
Details: Gallery and studios in converted terraced house close to Reading town centre. Open to applications from exhibitors, ideally suited to small works or installations. Regular workshops. 10% commission. £15 monthly room hire and approx £20 publicity costs. Part of the Rising Sun Institute, a community arts centre set up by local people on a voluntary basis (see separate entry). Sales not a priority.

Hexagon

[Pa] [Ph] [Pr] ⬤

Two exhibition spaces located in the well-used public areas of the theatre: lower foyer and choir corridor.
Queens Walk, Reading RG1 7UA, tel: 01734 390390, fax: 01734 390028
Contact: Mrs A Jeffery, Senior House Manager
Space: 2 galleries with 55 lin m hanging space
Exhibitions: 18 a year
Details: Programme reflects the diversity of visitors by including a wide spectrum work by both professional and amateur artists.

Jelly Leg'd Chicken Arts Gallery

[A] [Pa] [Ph] [Pr] [Sc] ⬤ ⬤ ⬤

Artist-run space in town centre committed to showing wide variety of work, particularly innovative or quirky.
35 Minster Street, Reading RG1 2JB, tel: 01734 507926
Contact: Suzanne Stallard & Andrew Lord
Open: Mon-Sat 10.30-6; Sun 12-3
Space: 1 gallery with 39 lin m hanging space and 88 sq m floor space
Exhibitions: 26 a year all originated
Details: Exhibits contemporary work by artists from all regions. Gallery is busy with high media profile. No commission taken on sales.

Open Space

[A] [Pa] [Ph] [Pr] [Sc] [LA] ⬤ ⬤

Artist-run gallery exhibiting contemporary fine art.
Open Hand Studios, 571 Oxford Road, Reading RG3 1HL, tel: 01734 597752
Contact: Exhibition Organiser
Open: Sat & Sun 11-6; weekdays by appointment.
Space: 1 gallery with 17 lin m hanging space and 32 sq m floor space
Exhibitions: 6 a year all originated
Details: Open space within an artists' studio complex. Shows work that raises issues and challenges stereotypes – an attitude reflected in the diversity of media on show, including video, performance, and installation. Programme augmented by artists' talks and slide shows. A purpose-built gallery is being developed and will open during 1995/96. This will have disabled access. Sale of work not gallery's primary role.

Rising Sun Institute

[Pa] [Ph] [Cr] [Sc] ⬤ ⬤ ⬤

Aims to show contemporary 2D artwork of interest to the many users of this busy arts centre.
30 Silver Street, Reading RG1 2ST, tel: 01734 866788
Contact: Exhibitions Committee
Open: Mon-Sat 12-4; Thurs, Fri & Sat evenings for events
Space: 2 galleries with 49 lin m hanging space and 112 sq m floor space
Exhibitions: 12 a year
Details: Exhibition space in café room, lounge/meeting room and corridors. Regular workshops. 10% commission taken. £15 monthly room hire fee and about £20 publicity costs charged. The Rising Sun Institute is a community arts centre set up by local people on a voluntary basis. Sales not a priority. Gallery 28 in the same building has a separate entrance and is programmed independently (see separate entry).

Town Hall

[Pa] [Ph] [Cr] [Sc] ⬤ ⬤ ⬤ ⬤ [4]

Exhibition spaces, used predominantly for meetings/conferences, for hire.
Blagrave Street, Reading RG1 1QH, tel: 01734 575911, fax: 01734 566719
Contact: Laura Milner/Christine Johnson, Town Hall Manager/Assistant Town Hall Manager
Open: Mon-Sat 10-11; and by arrangement
Space: 3 galleries with plus 9 lin m on screens and 285 sq m floor space
Exhibitions: 3 a year of which 1 originated, 2 on a hire basis
Details: 3 rooms available: the 'Victoria Hall', 'Waterhouse Chamber' and 'Studio Gallery'. Artists must arrange own hanging system. One week each year designated Reading & Visual Arts Week attracts a variety of visitors in addition to public who attend meetings conferences etc.

Redcar
CLEVELAND NA

Kirkleatham Old Hall Museum

[Pa] [Ph] [Cr] [Sc] [LA] ⬤ ⬤ ⬤ ⬤ ⬤ [4]

Displays the story of Langbaurgh, past and present with the temporary exhibitions promoting local artists' work.
Kirkleatham Village, Redcar TS10 5NW, tel: 01642 479500, fax: 01642 474199
Contact: Mr P. Philo, Curator
Open: Tues-Sun 10-5
Space: 6 galleries with 100 lin m hanging space plus 50 lin m on screens and 80 sq m floor space
Exhibitions: 5 a year of which 3 originated, 1 touring, 1 on a hire basis
Details: Galleries include displays on the industry, maritime history, history of the village, museum and surrounding area, commerce, sea-rescue, local photographs and artists. The audience is mixed with mainly family groups at weekends. Selling work is not gallery's primary function.

Redditch
HEREFORD & WORCESTER WMA

Redditch Library

[Pa] [Cr] [Sc] ⬤ ⬤

Exhibition space showcasing local artists' work in library.
15 Market Place, Redditch B98 8AR, tel: 01527 63291, fax: 01527 68571
Contact: Librarian
Open: Mon, Thurs, Fri 10-7; Tues 10-5; Sat 10-4
Space: 1 gallery with 16 lin m hanging space plus 15 lin m on screens and 18 sq m floor space

Exhibitions: 18 a year all originated
Details: Exhibition space along landing leading to upper floor. Hessian-covered pinboard with hanging rail for showing work by local non-professional artists. Not accessible to wheelchair users. 20% taken on any sales made. See also entry for Hereford & Worcester Libraries & Arts Department, Worcester.

Redruth
CORNWALL SWA

Camborne School of Mines

Pa Ph Pr ✪ ⊕ ♿ Wc

Exhibition area on balcony of Geological Museum free to local artists usually for one person shows with mixture of emerging and established artists.
Geological Museum and Gallery, Pool, Redruth TR15 3SE, tel: 01209 714866, fax: 01209 716977
Contact: Dr R Lesley Atkinson
Open: Mon-Fri 9-5; closed BH
Space: 1 gallery with 40 lin m hanging space plus 3 lin m on screens and 6 sq m floor space
Exhibitions: 12 a year all on a hire basis
Details: Exhibitions are usually of work by Cornish artists, both established and emerging. Exhibitions form a back-drop for displays of mineral and rock collected from all over the world. School parties are encouraged to view art exhibitions and science displays in the gallery. Sale of work not gallery's primary role.

Rickmansworth
HERTFORDSHIRE EA

Watersmeet

Pa ✪ ♿ Wc

Foyer space in multi-purpose arts centre not used principally for selling work.
High Street, Rickmansworth WD3 1HJ, tel: 01923 771542, fax: 01923 710121
Contact: David Chance, Manager

Ringwood
HAMPSHIRE SA

Bettles Gallery

Pa Cr ✪ ♿

Small privately-run gallery specialising in contemporary ceramics and pictures.
80 Christchurch Road, Ringwood BH24 1DR, tel: 01425 470410, fax: 01425 479002
Contact: Gill Bettle
Open: Tues-Fri 10-5; Sat 10-1
Space: 1 gallery with 30 lin m hanging space and 48 sq m floor space
Exhibitions: 9 a year all originated
Details: Ceramics by leading British potters

held in stock, plus regular solo and group exhibitions. Advertised in specialist publications and large circulation of private view invitations. Exhibition area on ground floor of 300 year old building. Alcoves, movable podiums, wall space and shelving units for display of ceramics. Sales a priority.

Ripley
NORTH YORKSHIRE YHA

Chantry House Gallery

Pa Pr ✪ ♿

Commercial gallery providing show place for established and establishing artists working in variety of media.
Main Street, Ripley HG3 3AY, tel: 01423 771011
Contact: Georgina Logan, Exhibition Organiser
Open: (Apr-Oct) Tues-Sat 10-5, Sun 12-5; (Nov-Mar) Wed-Sat 10-4, Sun 12-4
Space: 1 gallery with 28 lin m hanging space and 53 sq m floor space
Exhibitions: 4 a year
Details: Specialises in painting and prints by British contemporary and leading Yorkshire artists. Changing display of work. Exhibitions aim to provide high quality work whilst catering for variety of tastes and interests.

Rochdale
LANCASHIRE NWA

Rochdale Art Gallery

Pa Ph Pr Sc ✪ £ ♿ Wc

Part of Esplanade Arts & Heritage Centre; the gallery's exhibition programme aims to reflect diversity, innovation and debate through historical, contemporary and multi-cultural themes.
Esplanade, Rochdale OL16 1AQ, tel: 01706 342154
Contact: Penny Thompson, Art Gallery Officer
Open: Tues-Sat 10-4.30
Space: 3 galleries with 153 lin m hanging space and 130 sq m floor space
Exhibitions: 6 a year of which 3 originated, 3 touring
Details: Municipal gallery committed to improving quality of life for visitors, promoting equal opportunities and showing historical and contemporary art. Founded in 1901. Supports new work believing that public in Rochdale deserves local, national and international perspective on visual arts. Sales not priority.

Rochester
KENT SEA

Gallery, Kent Institute of Art & Design at Rochester

Pa Ph Sc ✪ ♿

Gallery in main foyer features exhibitions of 2 and 3D works, often in collaboration with other European colleges.
Kent Institute of Art & Design, Fort Pitt, Rochester ME1 1DZ, tel: 01634 829461
Contact: Christine Gist, Exhibitions Officer, KIAD at Canterbury, New Dover Road, Canterbury, CT1 3AN, tel: 01227 769371 ext 240, fax: 01227 451320
Open: Mon-Fri 10-5
Space: 1 gallery with 19 lin m hanging space
Exhibitions: 5 a year all originated
Details: Exhibitions are closely linked to studio practice; photography, ceramics, spatial design, model making, etc. Considers its specialisms as photography and ceramic and architectural based work. The college works closely with the local council and community, curating exhibitions for sites within the city. Wall mounted display cases available. Sales not gallery's primary function.

Medway Gallery *

Pa Ph Pr Cr ✪ ⊕

Housed in an adult education centre with a student attendance in excess of 4000 per week thus giving immediate exposure for all exhibitions.
Medway Adult Education Centre, Eastgate, Rochester ME1 1EW, tel: 01634 845359/ 407782
Contact: Gary Bassett, Head of Arts
Space: 1 gallery with 28 lin m hanging space and 130 sq m floor space
Exhibitions: 8 a year of which 7 originated, 1 on a hire basis
Details: Exhibition programme is mainly derived from the large art & craft department of the centre & area, but also welcomes local artists. All works should if possible be under glass as the area is also used as a refectory.

Strood Library Gallery

Pa Ph Pr Cr Sc ✪ ♿ Wc ♿

Gallery and arts centre, housed in library building, presenting a broad programme of contemporary exhibitions.
Strood Library, 32 Bryant Road, Strood, Rochester ME2 3EP, tel: 01634 718161
Contact: Jim Shean, Arts Promotion Officer
Open: Mon-Wed & Fri 9.30-7; Sat 9.30-5
Space: 1 gallery with 20 lin m hanging space plus 12 lin m on screens and 52 sq m floor space
Exhibitions: 15 a year of which 7 originated, 8 touring

Details: All library users must pass through the gallery to reach other areas. Programme is a mix of local and outside artists, mainly wall hung work, or cabinet displays. Regularly booked up to 18 months in advance. Keen to promote group and thematic shows. Sales not main function.

Romford
ESSEX EA

Central Gallery
[Pa][Ph][Pr][Cr][Sc] ✔ [H] ♿

Well-lit spacious first-floor room with painted hessian walls and movable screens.
Central Library, St Edwards Way, Romford RM1 3AR, tel: 01708 772382, fax: 01708 772391
Contact: Chris Cole, Arts Officer
Open: Mon, Tues, Wed, Fri, 9.30-8; Sat 9.30-4
Space: 1 gallery with 6 lin m hanging space plus 31 lin m on screens and 9 sq m floor space
Exhibitions: 22 a year of which 2 originated, 20 on a hire basis
Details: Shows a diverse selection of temporary exhibitions including work by local artists. Exhibition space hired out free to exhibitors who then responsible for hanging exhibition etc. Sales not a priority.

Ross on Wye
HEREFORD & WORCESTER WMA

Man of Ross Gallery
[Pa][LA] ✔ 🚫♿

Studio gallery above permanent gallery exhibiting work by artist in residence.
1 Eddie Cross Street, Ross on Wye HR9 7BZ, tel: 01989 768118
Contact: Anthony J Avery, Artist in Residence
Open: Thurs, Fri, Sat 10.30-5
Space: 1 gallery with 15 lin m hanging space and 16 sq m floor space
Details: Informal exhibition policy sets out to encourage and give new artists opportunity to display work in any medium and on any subject.

Rossendale
LANCASHIRE NWA

Haslingden Library
[Pa][Ph][Pr][Cr] ✔ [H]

Library exhibition space attempting to cater for all types of art and craft exhibitions.
Higher Deardengate, Haslingden, Rossendale BB4 5QJ, tel: 01706 215690
Contact: Victor Marcinkiewicz, Senior Librarian, 172 Napier Street, Nelson, BB9 0RA, tel: 01282 697003
Space: 26 lin m hanging space and 169 sq m floor space
Exhibitions: 11 a year all on a hire basis
Details: Lack of security and showcases present a problem in some instances. Also used for craft and drama workshops, public meetings and local society functions.

Rossendale Museum
[Pa][Ph][Pr][Cr] ✔ 🚫♿

Museum with varied exhibition programme which includes contemporary work, mainly of local and regional artists.
Whitaker Park, Rawtenstall, Rossendale BB4 6RE, tel: 01706 217777 ext 335
Contact: S. Cruise, Curator
Space: 1 gallery with 150 sq m floor space
Exhibitions: 3 a year all originated
Details: Visitors are predominantly local. Sale of work is not the gallery's primary concern.

Rothbury
NORTHUMBERLAND NA

Coquetdale Gallery
[Pa][Cr] ✔ [H]

Charitable trust set up to promote and encourage interest in arts and crafts in Northumberland.
Church House, Rothbury NE65 7UP
Contact: Malcolm Lowther, Gallery Organiser
Space: 3 galleries with 45 lin m hanging space
Exhibitions: 9 a year all on a hire basis
Details: Upstairs rooms in a Victorian house, with a friendly atmosphere and attracting mainly tourists. Normally has 40 Northumbrian artists exhibiting their work, together with a one-person exhibition. Because of the size of the three gallery rooms, large pieces of work cannot be satisfactorily hung or viewed. Gallery only open between Easter and end of September.

Rotherham
SOUTH YORKSHIRE YHA

Central Library Arts Centre
[Pa][Ph][Cr][LA] ✔

Dedicated exhibition space within library building with varied programme.
Walker Place, Rotherham S65 1AW, tel: 01709 823641, fax: 01709 823638
Contact: Roman Stachiw, Arts Assistant, Civic Theatre Annexe, Catherine Street, Rotherham, S65 1EB, tel: 01709 823641, fax: 01709 823638
Open: Mon-Sat 8.30am-9pm
Space: 1 gallery
Exhibitions: 36 a year
Details: Monthly one-person exhibitions by local artists in display case, corridor or photographic space.

Rotherham Art Gallery
[Pa][Ph][Pr][Cr] ✔ ♿ [WC]

Arts centre including gallery, workshops, studios, other community resources.
Central Library and Arts Centre, Walker Place, Rotherham S65 1JH, tel: 0109 382121 ext 3624
Contact: Keeper of Fine and Applied Art
Open: Tues-Sat 10-5; closed BH
Space: 1 gallery with 40 lin m hanging space plus 50 lin m on screens and 200 sq m floor space
Details: About ten exhibitions a year reflecting culture of locality and region, some bought in. Encourages local talent by mounting exhibitions by regional artists and societies. Staff and students of local colleges and schools stage frequent exhibitions.

Rotherham College of Arts & Technology Gallery
[Pa][Ph][Pr][Cr][Sc] ✔ ♿ [WC]

Exhibition space primarily for students on range of courses, mostly art and design.
Eastwood Lane, Rotherham S65 1EG, tel: 01709 362111 ext 2762, fax: 01709 360765
Contact: Terry Gregory, Head of Department of Creative Studies
Open: Mon-Fri 9-9 during academic year
Space: 1 gallery with 18 lin m hanging space plus 8 lin m on screens and 216 sq m floor space
Exhibitions: 1 a year originated
Details: Exhibitions held in foyer of main college building. Usually run for two weeks. Student exhibitions are a priority but artists from outside the college are occasionally shown. Selling work is not gallery's primary role.

Royston
HERTFORDSHIRE EA

Royston Museum *
[Pa][Ph][Pr][Cr][Sc] ✔

Temporary exhibitions and applications welcomed from local artists.
Lower King Street, Royston SG8 5AL, tel: 01763 242587
Contact: Mrs Vincent, Curator
Space: 1 gallery with 36 lin m hanging space
Exhibitions: 6 a year all originated
Details: Exhibitions change every four to five weeks. Excellent loan collection of late C19th and C20th ceramics and glass. Programme booked until 1994.

Rugby
WARWICKSHIRE WMA

Rugby Exhibition Gallery

Pa Ph Pr Cr Sc LA ✔ 🅷 ⊘

Separate exhibition gallery within library building mainly for hire by artists and groups.
Rugby Library, St Matthews Street, Rugby CV21 3BZ, tel: 01788 535348
Contact: Brian Ashley, Area Manager
Open: Mon & Thurs 9.30-8; Tues & Fri 9.30-5; Wed 9.30-1; Sat 9.30-4; Sat 9.30-4
Space: 1 gallery with 37 lin m hanging space and 73 sq m floor space
Exhibitions: 19 a year of which 3 originated, 16 on a hire basis
Details: Gallery available for hire by local artists and groups. No active commissioning/selection is carried out at present.

Runcorn
CHESHIRE NWA

Norton Priory Museum & Gardens

Sc ✔ Wc

Permanent outdoor sculpture exhibition and indoor space for exhibitions by local artists and craftspeople.
Tudor Road, Manor Park, Runcorn WA7 1SX, tel: 01928 569895
Contact: Jon Marrow, Senior Keeper
Space: 1 gallery with 12 lin m hanging space plus 10 lin m on screens and 55 sq m floor space
Exhibitions: 1 a year originated
Details: The sculpture exhibition is a permanent outdoor display of work by artists working in the north west. Works sited in woodland gardens and C18th walled garden. One work of art is commissioned each year. The artist runs sculpture workshops for the museum's visitors in August. Audience – non-specialist.

Runcorn Shopping City Library

Pa Ph Pr Cr Sc LA ✔

Library showing exhibitions and displays many from local people, both amateur and professional.
Runcorn Shopping City, Runcorn WA7 2PF, tel: 01928 715351, fax: 01928 790221
Contact: Gill Birch, Library Exhibition Department
Space: 3 galleries
Exhibitions: 8 a year of which 7 originated, 1 touring
Details: As learning centre, aims to broaden people's experience and awareness of different art and craft forms, to stimulate and encourage regular use of library facilities. No specific exhibition policy, but will look carefully at exhibitions on contentious issues as these often thought to reflect library views.

Rutland
LEICESTERSHIRE EMA

Goldmark Gallery *

Pa Pr Sc

Commercial gallery showing and selling C20th British art.
Orange Street, Uppingham, Rutland LE15 9SQ, tel: 01572 821424, fax: 01572 821503
Contact: Mike Goldmark, Exhibition Organiser
Space: 2 galleries with 23 lin m hanging space plus 12 lin m on screens and 200 sq m floor space
Exhibitions: 4 a year all originated

Rutland County Museum

Pa Ph Pr Cr Sc ✔ Wc

Variable space for temporary exhibitions within museum rural life displays.
Catmos Street, Oakham, Rutland LE15 6HW, tel: 01572 723654, fax: 01572 757576
Contact: T.H. McK. Clough, Keeper
Open: (Apr-Oct) Mon-Sat 10-5, Sun 2-5; (Nov-Mar) Mon-Sat 10-5, Sun 2-4
Space: 1 gallery
Exhibitions: 4 a year all originated
Details: Museum of rural life of Rutland with area for temporary exhibition use, including art exhibitions which are generated within Museums Service. Housed in 1794 indoor riding school building. 20% commission. Exhibitions include local art society shows and local artists' work. Workshops can be arranged. Selling work not main function of exhibitions.

Ryde
ISLE OF WIGHT SA

Ryde Gallery

Pa Ph Pr Cr Sc ✔

Library gallery.
George Street, Ryde PO33 2JE, tel: 01983 62170
Contact: A D Payne, Head of Libraries & Arts, Cultural and Leisure Services Directorate, I.W. County Council, Cultural Services Dept., Parkhurst Road, Newport, PO30 1TY, tel: 01983 823822, fax: 01983 823841
Open: Mon-Sat library opening hours
Space: 1 gallery with 40 lin m hanging space and 95 sq m floor space
Exhibitions: 12 a year all originated
Details: Four-sided space above lending library. Professional and amateur individual artists and groups. Island population and seasonal visitors. No hanging or commission fee. Payment by picture donation.

Rye
EAST SUSSEX SEA

Easton Rooms, Rye Art Gallery

Pa Ph Pr Cr Sc ✔

Exhibits broad spectrum of contemporary visual arts and crafts, with emphasis on high quality.
107 High Street, Rye TN31 7JE, tel: 01797 222433
Contact: Miranda Leonard, Manager
Open: Mon, Wed-Sun 10.30-12, 2-5
Exhibitions: 9 a year of which 7 originated
Details: Exhibits work by the best artists and makers living in the South. Continuous selection of paintings, prints and crafts on display and for sale. Organises talks, outings and films for Friends of Rye Art Galleries. (See also Stormont Studio, Rye Art Gallery.)

Stormont Studio, Rye Art Gallery

Pa Ph Pr Cr Sc

Gallery with permanent collection predominantly concerned with exhibiting work of cultural interest and historical importance.
Ockman Lane, East Street, Rye TN31 7JE, tel: 01797 223218
Contact: Miranda Leonard, Manager
Open: Daily 10.30-5
Details: Collection includes Edward Burra, Duncan Grant, Ivon Hitchens. About five shows a year by living artists and makers, with exhibitions lasting four to six weeks. Exhibitions aimed at wide audience in the hope of introducing arts to those unused to gallery activities and to remove intimidation. (See also Easton Rooms, Rye Art Gallery).

Saffron Walden
ESSEX EA

Exchange Gallery

Pa Ph Pr Cr Sc ✔ 🅷 Wc

Gallery on mezzanine floor of library/arts centre used to show work of local artists together with some invited professionals.
Saffron Walden Library & Arts Centre, 2 King Street, Saffron Walden CB10 1ES, tel: 01799 523178, fax: 01799 513642
Contact: Janet Crofts, Arts Director
Open: Mon-Tues, Thurs-Fri 9-7; Sat 9-5
Space: 1 gallery with 17 lin m hanging space plus 1 lin m on screens
Exhibitions: 19 a year of which 2 originated, 17 on a hire basis

Details: Shares space with a public library, and as such attracts interest from library users as well as those simply interested in art. Exhibitors tend to be local, usually with some formal art training. Normal waiting list 2 years. Hanging is onto 7 8'x4' exhibition boards. Sales not a priority.

Fry Public Art Gallery

[Pa] [Ph] ♿

Gallery dedicated to changing display of work by C20th North West Essex artists.
Bridge End Gardens, Castle Street, Saffron Walden CB10 1BD
Contact: Hon. Sec., Fry Art Gallery Society.
Open: (Easter Sun – end Oct) weekend & BH 2.45-5.30
Space: 2 galleries
Exhibitions: 2 a year both originated
Details: Demonstrates work by C20th local artists including Eric Ravilious, Edward Bawden and Michael Rothenstein. Permanent exhibition plus two exhibitions during each year by North West Essex artists who have made 'a significant contribution' in their field. Exhibition by invitation. Sales not primary role of gallery.

Saffron Walden Museum

♿ [WC] [4]

General non-fine art museum with permanent galleries plus programme of exhibitions including decorative arts and crafts.
Museum Street, Saffron Walden CM10 1JL, tel: 01799 510333
Contact: Len Pole, Curator
Open: (Nov-Feb) Mon-Sat 11-4, Sun 2.30-4.30; (Mar-Oct) Mon-Sat 10-5, Sun & BH 2.30-5; closed 24 & 25 Dec.
Space: 2 galleries with 62 lin m hanging space plus 10 lin m on screens
Exhibitions: 1 a year originated
Details: Permanent collections of archaeology, natural history, ethnography, geology, local history, ceramics, glass, and costume alongside temporary exhibitions; of which one a year is an art exhibition. Commission is charged and occasionally touring shows organised. Sale of work not a priority.

St Albans
HERTFORDSHIRE EA

C.R.A. Gallery

[Pa] [Ph] [Cr] [SC] ✔ [H] ♿ [4]

Three exhibition spaces for artists and exhibitors to show and sell their work.
13-15 Victoria Street, St Albans AL1 3JJ, tel: 01727 811575, fax: 01727 811508
Contact: Sarah Jackson, Exhibition Co-ordinator
Open: Mon-Sat 9-5
Space: 3 galleries with 82 lin m hanging space and 419 sq m floor space
Exhibitions: 12 a year of which 6 originated, 6 on a hire basis
Details: Gallery aims to promote local artists and their work. When space is hired out to artists this is on a first-come-first-served basis with policy to balance the work to provide variety of subject matter and technique on display. When space is hired artists hang their own work. Sales a priority and commission taken.

Museum of St Albans

[Pa] [Ph] [Pr] [Cr] [SC] ✔ £ ♿ [WC] [4]

Small gallery with varied programme of in house and artists' exhibitions.
Hatfield Road, St Albans AL1 3RR, tel: 01727 819340, fax: 01727 859919
Contact: David Curry, Keeper of Natural Science
Open: Mon-Sat 10-5; Sun 2-5
Space: 1 gallery with 34 lin m hanging space and 63 sq m floor space
Exhibitions: 4 a year of which 3 originated, 1 touring
Details: Old Victorian building which has many windows and no actual wall space. Professional and amateur artists may use ground floor mezzanine to display work on a series of adjustable screens. 30% commission on sales.

St Albans Central Library

[Pa] [Ph] [Cr] [SC] ✔ [H] ♿ [WC]

Dedicated exhibition space within library offering local artists and community organisations an opportunity to promote their work.
The Maltings, St Albans AL1 3JQ, tel: 01727 868100/860000, fax: 01727 848613
Contact: Pat Love, Library Manager
Open: Mon ,Wed, Fri 9.30-7.30; Tues 9.30-5.30; Thurs 9.30-1; Sat 9-4
Space: 1 gallery with 17 lin m hanging space plus 9 lin m on screens and 111 sq m floor space
Exhibitions: 39 a year of which 3 originated, 2 touring, 34 on a hire basis
Details: Offers exhibition space for professional and amateur artists. Most exhibitors are local but also regular national touring exhibitions. Contact library for details of current charges.

St Albans Town Hall

[Pa] ✔ [H] 🚫♿ [WC]

Large light assembly room on first floor of old town hall used for a variety of events.
Market Place, St Albans AL3 5DJ, tel: 01727 811084
Contact: Brenda Webb, Bookings Administrator
Open: As required by hirer.
Space: 1 gallery with 200 sq m floor space
Exhibitions: 1 a year on a hire basis.

St Austell
CORNWALL SWA

St Austell Arts Centre

[Pa] [Ph] [Pr] ✔ 🚫♿

Gallery offering artists based in South West means to display and sell their work.
87 Truro Road, St Austell PL25 5HJ, tel: 01726 73949
Contact: Phil Webb, Development Director, Restormel Arts, 14 High Cross Street, St Austell, PL25 4AN, tel: 01726 68532
Open: Mon-Fri 10-4
Space: 1 gallery with 39 lin m hanging space
Exhibitions: 11 a year
Details: Aims to encourage and support talented artists based in South West by providing them exhibition space. Gallery on first floor. Sales not priority for gallery.

St Austell Library

[Pa] ✔ ♿

Exhibition space in gallery showing work by local artists.
Carlyon Road, St Austell PL25 4LD, tel: 01726 64634
Contact: John Farmer, County Librarian, Libraries & Arts Department, County Library Headquarters, Old County Hall, Station Road, Truro, TR1 3UW
Open: Mon, Wed, Thurs & Fri 9.30-5; Tues 9.30-7; Sat 9.30-12.30
Space: 1 gallery with 7 lin m hanging space
Exhibitions: 4 a year all originated

St Helens
MERSEYSIDE NWA

Citadel Arts Centre *

[Pa] [Ph] [Pr] [SC] [LA] ✔ [H]

An arts resource for young people with exhibition spaces in café area, first-floor rehearsal and exhibition room.
Waterloo Street, St Helens WA10 1PX, tel: 01744 35436
Contact: Mario Clarke, Executive Director
Space: 2 galleries with 80 lin m hanging space and 800 sq m floor space
Exhibitions: 8 a year of which 5 originated, 3 on a hire basis
Details: Emphasis on young people, and aims to make a major contribution to cultural life of the town. Primary purpose to enable young people to devise and invent forms of leisure/self-expression, and give a positive and satisfying range of activities that are easily accessible. Promotes performing and visual arts and operates a non-sexist, non-racist, non-commercial policy.

Pilkington Glass Museum

Pa Ph Pr Cr Se ● ⓖ We

Permanent exhibition of history of glass, process and current uses and temporary exhibitions.
Prescot Road, St Helens WA10 3TT, tel: 01744 692499/692014, fax: 01744 693738
Contact: Ian Burgoyne, Curator
Open: Mon-Fri 10-5, Sat, Sun 2-4; BH 2-4.30
Space: 1 gallery
Exhibitions: 7 a year of which 1 originated, 6 touring
Details: Temporary exhibitions of historical and contemporary work on glass-related themes, plus other crafts and paintings from North West Museum and Art Gallery Service. Also exhibitions initiated by local artists and groups. Exhibition room also used for lectures/videos so only the perimeter of 3 sides is available for exhibitions.

St Helens Museum & Art Gallery

Pa Ph Pr Cr Se ● ⓖ We

Municipal museum and art gallery with varied programme of art and museum exhibitions and also monthly exhibitions of work by local artists.
College Street, St Helens WA10 1TW, tel: 01744 456961
Contact: Roger Hart, Museum Officer
Open: Tues-Fri 10-5; Sat 10-4
Space: 1 gallery with 43 lin m hanging space plus 15 lin m on screens and 78 sq m floor space
Exhibitions: 15 a year all originated
Details: Also features touring displays and an annual selection of the permanent collection of fine and decorative art of the C19th and C20th. Sale of work not considered gallery's primary role.

St Ives
CAMBRIDGESHIRE EA

L'Bidi Studio

Pa Pr Cr Se ●

Commercial gallery showing and selling mainly contemporary and representational work.
40 The Broadway, St Ives PE17 4BN, tel: 01480 466886
Contact: Lindsay Beedie, 81 High Street, Buckden, Huntingdon, PE18 9TA, tel: 01480 810545
Open: Mon-Sat 10-5.30; Thurs closed; (May-Aug) Sun 2-5
Exhibitions: 5 a year all originated
Details: Gallery linked to L'Bidi Studio in Buckden, Huntingdon. Exhibition and sale of good-quality watercolours, pastels, oil paintings, sculpture, prints and hand-made craft items. Exhibitions 2-3 weeks, both

group and solo. Between exhibitions there is a changing display of work.

St Ives
CORNWALL SWA

New Craftsman

Pa Pr Cr Se ●

Crafts Council selected gallery showing work by Cornish artists as well as crafts by leading English makers.
24 Fore Street, St Ives TR26 1HE, tel: 01736 795652
Contact: Janet Leach/Mary Redgrave, Partners
Space: 2 galleries with 75 lin m hanging space and 163 sq m floor space
Details: Pottery, weaving, jewellery, etc. Also paintings, prints and sculpture from artists living and working in Cornwall. Permanent collection of Cornish art from 1939-46 and rotating exhibition of contemporary work for sale.

Penwith Galleries

Pa Pr Cr Se ●

Exhibitions of members' work throughout the year.
Back Road West, St Ives TR26 1NL, tel: 01736 795579
Contact: Kathleen Watkins, Curator
Open: Tues-Sat 10-1, 2.30-5
Space: 3 galleries
Details: Exhibitions of members' work throughout the year. Also one person and "featured" exhibitions of work by artists from Cornwall and elsewhere. Gallery's main aim is "the furtherance of the arts in Cornwall".

Plumbline Gallery

2 Barnoon Hill, St Ives TR26 1AD, tel: 01736 797771

Salthouse Gallery *

Pa Pr Cr Se LA ●

Policy of promoting young and little-known artists as well as showing work by the more established.
Norway Square, St Ives TR26 1NA, tel: 01736 795003
Contact: Bob Devereux, Director
Space: 3 galleries with 45 lin m hanging space and 84 sq m floor space
Exhibitions: 10 a year all originated
Details: Deals primarily with contemporary art. Two exhibitions a year devoted to the work of artists outside the region. Gallery spaces are intimate and informal. Established since 1979. Stages a literature festival annually in September.

Tate Gallery St Ives

Pa Ph Pr Cr Se ● ⓔ ⓖ We

Continuing displays of work by invited contemporary artists are presented in addition to changing displays drawn from the Tate's national collection of British and Modern Art.
Porthmeor Beach, St Ives TR26 1TG, tel: 01736 796226, fax: 01736 794480
Contact: Michael Tooby, Curator
Open: (Apr-Oct) Mon, Wed, Fri & Sat 11-7, Tues & Thurs 11-9, Sun 11-5; (Nov-Mar) Tues-Sun 11-5
Exhibitions: 3 a year all originated
Details: Galleries are used for the collection. Non-gallery areas (entrance, stairwell, courtyard, restaurant, roof terrace) are used for displays resulting from artists' projects. Invited artists are encouraged to produce site specific work, usually linked to a study display which focuses on a particular artist or theme in the collection. Artist in Education policy involves the chosen artist in the gallery's broad range of activities. Fees paid but vary depending on the project. Sale of work is not a priority.

Salford
GREATER
MANCHESTER NWA

Chapman Gallery

Pa Ph Pr Se ● ⓔ ⓧ

Small but flexible university gallery space providing exhibitions relevant to university courses and regional audience.
University of Salford, The Crescent, Salford M5 4WT, tel: 0161 745 5241
Contact: Arts Administrator, University of Salford, Crescent & Campus Joint Arts Programme, Chapman Building, The Crescent, Salford, M5 4WT
Open: Mon-Fri 9.30-5.30
Space: 1 gallery with 50 lin m hanging space plus 60 lin m on screens and 200 sq m floor space
Exhibitions: 8 a year all originated
Details: First-floor gallery promoting young artists from the region as part of a broader arts programme in Salford aimed at students, staff and the public. Sales not a priority.

City of Salford Cultural Services

Pa Ph Pr Cr Se ● ⓔ

Department managing number of exhibition spaces including those in galleries, museums and libraries.
Vulcan House, Albion Place, Salford M5 4NL, tel: 0161 736 9448, fax: 0161 745 7806
Contact: Royston Futter, Arts & Leisure Manager

Space: 3 galleries
Exhibitions: 20 a year
Details: Four separate gallery spaces; one dedicated to works of L.S. Lowry, one a Victorian art collection, two showing temporary exhibitions of contemporary or C20th work. Also manages the Viewpoint Photography Gallery (see separate entry). Arts and Leisure Department has number of libraries which show contemporary exhibitions. The Buile Hill Mining Museum also shows exhibitions of painting and photography related to mining and miners.

Glass Box Gallery

Pa Gr IA ● ⓔ ● We

University gallery promoting variety of work by North West artists chosen for relevance to university courses.
University of Salford, Frederick Road, Salford M6 6PU
Contact: Arts Administrator, Crescent & Campus Joint Arts Programme, Salford University, The Crescent, Salford, M5 4WT
Open: Mon-Fri 9.30-5.30
Space: 1 gallery with 36 sq m floor space
Exhibitions: 8 a year all originated
Details: Exhibition space for installation, live art, sculpture and 3D work. Monthly exhibitions October-July each year. Sales not a priority.

Salford Museum & Art Gallery

Pa Ph Pr Gr SC ● ● We ④

Museum with permanent displays for Victorian art and L S Lowry and varied temporary exhibition programme showing contemporary and historical work.
Peel Park, Salford M5 4WU, tel: 0161 736 2649, fax: 0161 745 9490
Contact: Sheena MacFarlane, Senior Museums Officer
Open: Mon-Fri 10-4.45; Sun 2-5
Space: 2 galleries with 64 lin m hanging space and 152 sq m floor space
Exhibitions: 13 a year of which 9 originated, 4 touring
Details: Temporary exhibitions programme includes contemporary art, craft, social history, fine art. City gallery with large percentage of visitors coming in organised parties – schools, community groups, etc. Sales not a priority.

Viewpoint Photography Gallery

Ph Pr SC IA ●ⓔⒽ ● We

Dedicated photography exhibition space with publishing, education and outreach programmes.
The Old Fire Station, The Crescent, Salford M5 4NZ, tel: 0161 737 1040, fax: 0161 736 0429

Contact: Simon Grennan, Viewpoint Art Base Manager
Open: Mon-Fri 9.30-5; Sun 2-5
Space: 1 gallery with 400 lin m hanging space plus 50 lin m on screens
Exhibitions: 13 a year of which 9 originated, 1 touring, 3 on a hire basis
Details: Modern exhibition space, housed in converted Fire Station. Aims to educate and stimulate debate, excite the imagination and entertain. Shows and promotes North West photographers as well as national and international work. Encourages commission and exhibition of new work by photographers in North West. Sales not a priority.

Salisbury
WILTSHIRE SA

Bill Toop Gallery

Pa Ph Pr Gr ● ●

Showcase for work of established printmakers and ceramicists as well as owner/artist's own watercolour work.
5 St John's Street, Salisbury SP1 2SB, tel: 01722 320916
Contact: Bill and Elizabeth Toop, Exhibition Organiser, 2 The Crescent, Hillview Road, Salisbury, SP1 1HY, tel: 01722 324201
Open: Mon, Tues, Thurs & Fri 10-2, 2.30-5.30; Sat 10.30-5.30
Space: 2 galleries with 31 lin m hanging space plus 10 lin m on screens and 37 sq m floor space
Exhibitions: 5 a year all originated
Details: Ceramics by range of British makers. Cards and prints also sold. Framing service. Occasional exhibitions of work by well-known artists, potters & printmakers. Permanent changing exhibition of work by members of Royal Institute of Painters in Watercolours. Selling work is gallery's primary role. Downstairs gallery fully accessible.

Fisherton Mill

108 Fisherton Street, Salisbury SP2 7QY, tel: 01722 415121

Salisbury Arts Centre

Pa Ph Pr Gr SC IA ● ⒺWe

Arts centre with exhibition policy to show contemporary, community art and craft.
Bedwin Street, Salisbury SP1 3UT, tel: 01722 321744
Contact: Jill Low, Director
Space: 2 galleries with 37 lin m hanging space
Exhibitions: 9 a year
Details: Arts centre for performance, music and visual arts with some arts and craft workshops. Exhibitions usually run for one month.

Salisbury Playhouse Gallery

Pa Ph Pr ● ● We ④

Wall space of theatre foyer, lobbies and bar showing work by contemporary artists with smaller exhibitions in meetings room.
Malthouse Lane, Salisbury SP2 7RA, tel: 01722 320117, fax: 01722 421991
Contact: Exhibitions Officer
Open: Mon-Sat 10-late
Space: 2 galleries with 37 lin m hanging space
Exhibitions: 9 a year all originated
Details: Selection of exhibitions is based on standard of work and/or relevance to area. Local artists are encouraged and exhibitions of their work is interspersed with that of nationally known painters. Work is seen by wide section of theatre and gallery going public. Sales encouraged and commission taken.

Salisbury & South Wiltshire Museum

Pa Ph Gr SC ● Ⓔ We ④

Print Room designed to display pictures from museum's collections and exhibitions by artists with local connection or theme reflecting collections or region.
The King's House, 65 The Close, Salisbury SP1 2EN, tel: 01722 332151
Contact: Curator
Open: Mon-Sat 10-7; Sun during Jul & Aug & Salisbury Festival 2-5
Space: 1 gallery with 19 lin m hanging space and 70 sq m floor space
Exhibitions: 4 a year all originated
Details: Aims to give local people opportunity to view art from the community and region which might otherwise not be available to them. Two other larger galleries occasionally used for contemporary exhibitions. Sales not a priority.

Saltash
CORNWALL SWA

Cotehele Quay Gallery

Pa Pr SC Ⓔ We

Small exhibition space in old carpenter's workshop run by The National Trust to promote work by local artists/makers.
National Trust, Cotehele Quay, St Dominick, Saltash PL12 6TA, tel: 01579 51494
Contact: Rebecca Coombes, Gallery Organiser,
Open: (Easter-mid Nov) daily 12-5; (Nov-Christmas) Wed-Sun 11-4
Space: 1 gallery with 10 lin m hanging space
Exhibitions: 5 a year
Details: Shows work of professional makers principally from Cornwall and Devon.

Artists invited to submit work to themed exhibitions. Floor space in gallery filled by large table to exhibit smaller crafts. Sales important.

Sandbeach
CHESHIRE NWA

Dukes Oak Gallery
Pa Ph Pr Cr Sc ✓ ⓛ

Small commercial gallery in converted barn with varied programme of exhibitions and events.
Brereton, Sandbeach CW11 9SD, tel: 014775 32337
Contact: Ruth Foster
Open: Tues-Sun 10-5.30
Space: 1 gallery with 15 lin m hanging space and 84 sq m floor space
Exhibitions: 9 a year all originated
Details: Art and craft exhibitions by known and unknown artists. Also large outdoor sculpture garden. Occasional workshops held for local communities indoors and in sculpture garden. Also gallery shop selling variety of contemporary art and craft. Sales priority and commission taken.

Sandwich
KENT SEA

Hunt Gallery
33 Strand Street, Sandwich CT13 9DS, tel: 01892 525525

Saxmundham
SUFFOLK EA

Gallery (The)
Pa Ph Cr ✓ ⓛ Wc

Exhibition space available for hire alongside continuing mixed exhibition and sale of paintings and artists' prints in selling gallery.
Snape Maltings, Snape, Saxmundham IP17 1SR, tel: 01728 688305, **fax:** 01728 688930
Contact: Jonathon Gooderham
Open: (Summer) daily 10-6 ; (Winter) daily 10-5; closed 25 & 26 Dec
Space: 2 galleries with 43 lin m hanging space plus 61 lin m on screens and 140 sq m floor space
Exhibitions: 4 a year all originated
Details: Selling work main role of gallery.

Yoxford Gallery
Pa Pr Cr Sc ✓ ⓗ

Private gallery with changing exhibitions of contemporary work in all media through Summer.
Yoxford Gallery, Yoxford, Saxmundham IP17 3EP, tel: 01728 668327
Contact: Deborah Ardizzone, Organiser

Open: (May-end Sept) Thurs-Sun 11-1, 2.30-5; or by arrangement
Space: 2 galleries with 30 lin m hanging space and 91 sq m floor space
Exhibitions: 3 a year all originated
Details: Walled garden sometimes used for displaying sculpture. Two rooms with beamed ceilings and period brick floors. Natural lighting and the scale to show domestic works to advantage. Small gallery often used for exhibitions of textiles and fibre art. Galleries can be hired by arrangement.

Scarborough
NORTH YORKSHIRE YHA

Crescent Arts Workshop
Pa Ph Pr Cr Sc ✓ ⓛ

Arts centre with gallery space, artists' studios and open access workshop areas.
The Crescent, Scarborough YO11 2PW, tel: 01723 351461
Contact: Rachel Welford, Exhibitions Officer
Open: Tues-Sat 10-1, 2-5
Space: 3 galleries with 37 lin m hanging space and 44 sq m floor space
Exhibitions: 7 a year all originated
Details: Presents broad and balanced exhibition programme with both one-person and group shows. Craft showcase displays mini exhibitions of craft items Strong education programme; slide talks and workshops run by exhibiting artists. Varied lecture programme, workshops and activities for all ages throughout the year, run by resident and invited artists. Outreach service regularly provides artists for workshops in schools and with community groups, etc.

Scarborough Art Gallery
Pa Ph Pr Sc ✓

Collection of Victorian art and changing exhibition programme of contemporary art.
The Crescent, Scarborough YO11 2PW, tel: 01723 374753, **fax:** 01723 376941
Contact: Josie Adams, Curator
Open: (End Oct-End May) Fri, Sat, Sun 11-4; (End May-End Oct) Tues-Sun 10-5
Space: 3 galleries with 72 lin m hanging space plus 10 lin m on screens and 113 sq m floor space
Exhibitions: 10 a year all originated
Details: Aims to cover most sections of visual arts with no particular specialisation, although painting tends to dominate. Annual open for local artists and Yorkshire artists biennial for artists living and working in region. Benefits from tourist trade. Eleven exhibitions a year each lasting four weeks. Both solo and group shows.

Scunthorpe
HUMBERSIDE YHA

Scunthorpe Museum & Art Gallery
Pa Ph Pr Cr Sc ✓ ⓗ ⓗ ⓛ Wc

Archaeology, natural sciences, social history and visual arts presented in local authority museum and art gallery.
Oswald Road, Scunthorpe DN15 7BD, tel: 01724 843533, **fax:** 01724 270474
Contact: Paul Gover, Museums & Arts Officer
Open: Mon-Sat 10-4; Sun 2-5
Space: 3 galleries with 89 lin m hanging space and 165 sq m floor space
Exhibitions: 12 a year of which 6 originated, 4 touring, 2 on a hire basis
Details: Visual art exhibitions given same high professional status, expert administration, handling and interpretation as other subjects presented. Quality and size of temporary exhibition galleries are good. Government-approved security and controlled environment. Aims to be innovative and diverse yet maintain high levels of display and interpretation.

Thomas Sumpter Comprehensive School
Pa Ph Pr Cr Sc ✓ ⓛ ⓛ

Comprehensive school showing exhibitions as an educational resource.
Chandos Road, Scunthorpe DN17 1HA, tel: 01724 868666
Contact: Andy James, Hed of Art and Design
Open: Mon-Fri 9-5
Space: 1 gallery with 40 lin m hanging space plus 10 lin m on screens
Exhibitions: 2 a year both touring
Details: Stretches of large uninterrupted wall space; three separate areas aim to integrate visual arts into the school and local community. Programme includes workshops by exhibiting artists, sometimes combined with creative writing workshops. Sale of work not a priority.

Seaford
EAST SUSSEX SEA

Crypt Gallery
Pa Ph Pr Cr Sc ✓ ⓛ Wc

Gallery built around restored mediaeval crypt with exhibitions of work by locally-based and nationally established artists and craftspeople.
off Church Street, Seaford, tel: 01323 891461
Contact: Carole Buchan, Arts Officer, Lewes District Council, Lewes House, 32 High Street, Lewes, BN7 2LX, **tel:** 01273 484167, **fax:** 01273 484166

Open: Tues-Sat 10.30-5 (during exhibitions); some Sundays and late nights
Space: 1 gallery with 27 lin m hanging space
Exhibitions: 13 a year of which 10 originated
Details: Contemporary exhibition programme with emphasis on ceramics and sculpture. Most shows originated by gallery. Showcase for younger artists. Workshops linked to exhibitions where possible plus educational links between exhibiting artists and local schools. Sales of work not primary role of gallery. Between 25% and 30% commission taken on sales made.

Settle
NORTH YORKSHIRE YHA

Linton Court Gallery

Gallery in converted hay loft in centre of Settle showing work of well-established and up-and-coming artists.
Duke Street, Settle BD27, tel: 01729 822695
Contact: Ann Carr, Exhibition Organiser
Open: variable
Space: 1 gallery with 31 lin m hanging space and 56 sq m floor space
Exhibitions: 7 a year all originated
Details: Specialises in contemporary art exhibitions with a permanent collection of watercolours, prints and ceramics. Selling work is not gallery's primary role.

Sevenoaks
KENT SEA

Bank Street Gallery

Ground- and first-floor conversion of C17th-C18th building, showing exclusively contemporary paintings for sale.
3-5 Bank Street, Sevenoaks TN13 1UW, tel: 01732 458063
Contact: Fay Leighton
Open: Mon-Sat 9.30-5.30
Space: 2 galleries with 76 sq m floor space
Exhibitions: 4 a year all originated
Details: Contemporary figurative painting, landscapes and still lives in a programme of five exhibitions a year. Includes a range of artists from established RA's to new graduates. Always looking for new painters but asks artists not to pay unsolicited visits. Ground-floor only accessible to wheelchair users.

Pratt Contemporary Art

Gallery, print workshop and studio run by the Pratt Contemporary Art/Pratt Editions

The Gallery, Ightham, Sevenoaks TN15 9HH, tel: 01732 882326, fax: 01732 885502
Contact: Bernard Pratt/Susan Pratt
Space: 1 gallery with 25 lin m hanging space and 37 sq m floor space
Details: Limited edition screen prints, etchings published by Pratt Contemporary Art, paintings, drawings and sculpture. The gallery exclusively represents and promotes its own artists.

Sevenoaks Library Gallery

Dedicated exhibition space in library.
Buckhurst Lane, Sevenoaks TN13 1LQ, tel: 01732 453118/452384, fax: 01732 742682
Contact: Amber Baylis, Arts & Heritage Officer
Open: Mon, Tues, Wed, Fri 9.30-5.30; Thurs 9.30-8; Sat 9-5
Space: 1 gallery with 25 lin m hanging space plus 2 lin m on screens and 48 sq m floor space
Exhibitions: 17 a year of which 16 originated, 1 touring
Details: Aims to provide balanced and varied programme of visual arts. Encourages local artists and clubs to exhibit. This balanced by input of exhibitions from outside region. Gallery programme for calendar year is set preceding summer; programme leaflet produced every 6 months. White walls and spotlights. Height of hanging space 2.35 M. 20% commission taken on sales.

Shaftesbury
DORSET SWA

Shaftesbury Arts Centre

Small well-lit gallery for displaying centre's painting and photography and exhibitions of individual artists' work.
13 Bell Street, Shaftesbury SP7 8RN, tel: 01747 854321
Contact: Ronald Homes, Exhibition Secretary, 69 Linden Park, Shaftesbury, tel: 01747 852727
Open: Mon-Sat 10.30-12.30; other times as organised by exhibitors.
Space: 1 gallery with 12 lin m hanging space plus 5 lin m on screens and 31 sq m floor space
Exhibitions: 16 a year of which 5 originated, 11 on a hire basis
Details: Gallery provides exhibition space to promote activities of the centre and to show work of local artists with the occasional exhibition of school work. Selling work is considered a primary function.

Shebbear
DEVON SWA

Shebbear College (Little Gallery)

Provides a community link encouraging support for artists and craftsmen amongst North Devon rural communities.
Shebbear EX20 5HJ, tel: 01409 281228, fax: 01409 281784
Contact: Mr John Scotney
Open: 10-6 during term-time
Space: 1 gallery with 9 lin m hanging space plus 8 lin m on screens and 60 sq m floor space
Exhibitions: 6 a year all originated
Details: Displays are arranged to coincide with major college functions to ensure a good audience for exhibitors. Hosts an annual Art Workshop for Preparatory Schools in the South West and offers an art scholarship.

Sheffield
SOUTH YORKSHIRE YHA

Bishops' House Museum

Exhibitions primarily social history-based but applications welcome from artists working locally.
Meersbrook Park, Norton Lees Lane, Sheffield S8 9BE, tel: 0114 255 7701
Contact: Ms Kim Streets, Assistant Keeper, Social History, Kelham Island Ind Museum, Alma Street, Sheffield, S3 8RY, tel: 0114 272 2106
Space: 1 gallery with 16 lin m hanging space and 30 sq m floor space
Exhibitions: 1 a year originated
Details: C16th Tudor house in Meersbrook Park. 3 rooms contain a permanent Tudor & Stuart exhibition. Given local audience, exhibitions should shown to Sheffield's past and future.

Crucible Theatre Gallery

Exhibitions held in foyer area of theatre which, if possible, tie in with stage production.
Norfolk Street, Sheffield S1 1DA, tel: 0114 276 0621, fax: 0114 275 5088
Contact: Margot Williams, Exhibition Organiser
Open: Mon-Sat 10-11 depending on theatre programme
Space: 2 galleries with plus 28 lin m on screens
Exhibitions: 14 a year of which 13 originated, 1 touring
Details: Exhibitions last 4 weeks and, if possible, tie in with stage production, eg a portfolio of photographs of present day

farmworkers to coincide with a production of 'Cider with Rosie'. Only the studio gallery affords good disabled access. Selling work not a primary function.

Cupola

A small commercial gallery
178a Middlewood Road, Hillsborough, Sheffield S6 1TD, tel: 0114 285 2665, fax: 0114 285 3150
Contact: Karen Sherwood, Managing Director
Open: Mon-Sat 9.30-5.30; late opening by appointment
Space: 1 gallery with 12 lin m hanging space and 16 sq m floor space
Exhibitions: 11 a year all originated
Details: Gallery wants to encourage interest and enthusiasm for art generally and visual art specifically. Aims to create friendly and visually exciting atmosphere, where people feel comfortable buying or simply looking at work. Sale of work is considered a priority and 12 months interest free credit scheme is operated. Also shop unit promoting and selling contemporary art and crafts. Picture framing.

Darnall Library

Exhibition/activities room with hanging space within library.
Brittania Road, Sheffield S9 5JG, tel: 0114 273 4280
Contact: Angela Hall or Sue Rowan, Display Organisers
Open: Mon, Tues & Fri 9.30-5; Thurs 9.30-12.30; Wed 9.30-7.30; Sat 9.30-1; Sat 9.30-1
Space: 1 gallery with 13 lin m hanging space
Exhibitions: 20 a year of which 10 originated, 10 touring
Details: Broad selection policy. Will consider any proposals not political or racist in origin. Sales not priority.

Graves Art Gallery

Municipal gallery with collection of European art and changing exhibition programme of both contemporary and historical art.
Surrey Street, Sheffield S1 1XZ, tel: 0114 273 4781, fax: 0114 273 5994
Contact: Anne Goodchild, Exhibitions Organiser
Open: Mon-Sat 10-5
Space: 7 galleries with 200 lin m hanging space and 760 sq m floor space
Details: Shows a broad range of exhibitions divided between displays using permanent collection and work by living artists and makers hired in or originated by the gallery. Also historical exhibitions.

Mappin Art Gallery

Municipal gallery exhibiting a wide range of art, historical and contemporary.
Weston Park, Western Bank, Sheffield S10 2TP, tel: 0114 272 6281, fax: 0114 275 0957
Contact: Tim Whitten, Acting Keeper
Open: Tues-Sat 10-5; Sun 11-4
Space: 5 galleries
Exhibitions: 6 a year of which 2 originated, 4 touring
Details: Aims to show challenging contemporary work of national significance. Education programme seen as of primary importance. Mappin Art Workshops run 6 days a week for children & adults in studio space alongside gallery. Includes classes about basic skills/techniques to activities based around exhibitions. Employs artists to run workshops. Sale of work not a priority.

Ora Gallery *

Gives contemporary craft makers from Greece and Britain an opportunity to show ceramics, glassware, jewellery, prints and painting.
239 Sharrowvale Road, Sheffield S11 8ZE, tel: 0114 266 1444
Contact: Michael and Jane Sofos
Space: 2 galleries with 24 lin m hanging space and 70 sq m floor space
Details: Also an ongoing mixed show of work by young designers and graduates. Gallery building has two floors equipped with spotlighting, wall screens, plinths and display cases for craftwork and some sculpture. All art exhibited on a sale or return basis. Commission on sales.

Ruskin Craft Gallery

Contemporary crafts gallery showing exhibitions often with educational emphasis.
101 Norfolk Street, Sheffield S1 2JE, tel: 0114 273 5299, fax: 0114 273 5994
Contact: Principal Keeper
Open: Mon-Sat 10-5
Space: 1 gallery with 144 lin m hanging space and 39 sq m floor space
Exhibitions: 7 a year all originated
Details: Exhibitions range from one-person shows to mixed thematic exhibitions to selling shows. Sometimes linked to historical displays in the Ruskin Gallery (adjoining gallery in same building) to highlight contemporary and historical context. Selection made from local, regional and national artists/craftspeople on basis of media or thematic criteria. Sales not high priority.

Sheffield City Art Galleries Touring Exhibitions Service

Origination of small-scale touring exhibitions to venues around Sheffield, plus support for artists and venues.
Mappin Art Gallery, Weston Park, Western Bank, Sheffield S10 2TP, tel: 0114 276 5619
Contact: Mike Hodson/Viv Sillar, Education/Projects Officers
Exhibitions: 8 a year
Details: Offers guidance and support to artists, craftspeople and venues wishing to show work in community and non-gallery venues in Sheffield. Small number of touring shows and projects taken to libraries, community and adult education centres and groups. Facilities and access vary according to venue. Sales not a priority. Local directory of exhibition spaces 'Show It' published.

Sheffield Hallam University Gallery

Showcase for students' work and annual degree shows; aims to show work by artists which promotes discussion and debate.
Psalter Lane, Sheffield S11 8UZ, tel: 0114 255 6101, fax: 0114 253 2603
Contact: Steve Dutton, Exhibition Organiser
Space: 1 gallery with 49 lin m hanging space and 17 sq m floor space
Exhibitions: 3 a year of which 2 originated, 1 touring
Details: Provides a forum for contemporary art within the college. Exhibitions last for 2-4 weeks and artists are invited to talk about the work on show. Space is also being developed as a venue for performances.

Site Gallery

Formerly Untitled Gallery, photography and media centre with galleries, darkrooms, shop and café.
1 Brown Street, Sheffield S1 2BS, tel: 0114 272 5947
Contact: Carol Maund, Director
Open: Tues-Sat 11-5
Space: 3 galleries with 210 lin m hanging space and 400 sq m floor space
Exhibitions: 8 a year
Details: Emphasis on broadening definition of the programme to include all lens-based media, photography, film and video, installation and work using new technology. Balance of originated, collaborative projects and hired-in shows presented. Policy to present innovative, challenging and creative work addressing contemporary debates and issues taking advantage of scale of exhibition space.

Promotes emerging artists on regional, national and international level. Education programme, courses and events.

Star Works Café

 ✓

Space for small exhibitions, particularly for local artists.
Star Works, Darnall Road, Sheffield S9 5AF, tel: 0114 243 4490, fax: 0114 244 4067
Contact: A. Piesold, Development Worker
Open: Mon-Fri 10-4
Space: 1 gallery with 12 lin m hanging space and 120 sq m floor space
Exhibitions: 1 a year touring
Details: Community café in a local neighbourhood centre in the east end of Sheffield.

Stocksbridge Library

✓

Facilities in downstairs meeting room for local artists, groups, or Sheffield based projects to exhibit work.
Manchester Road, Stocksbridge, Sheffield S30 5DH, tel: 0114 273 4205
Contact: Librarian
Space: 1 gallery with 15 lin m hanging space and 59 sq m floor space
Exhibitions: 2 a year both originated
Details: Additional screens can be used with available wall space. Shows last maximum 2 weeks.

University of Sheffield (Library Exhibition Area) *

✓

Exhibition area within the library programmed by the University's Fine Art Society for exhibitions of members' work, to display the library's rare books or special collections and to show work of other artists (mainly local).
Main Library, Western Park, Sheffield S10 2TN, tel: 0114 276 8555, fax: 0114 273 9826
Contact: David Jones, Sub Librarian (Services and Collection Development)
Space: 1 gallery with 15 lin m hanging space plus 15 lin m on screens and 165 sq m floor space
Exhibitions: 7 a year of which 6 originated, 1 touring
Details: Aims to bring contemporary work on to the campus.

Walkley Centre

✓

Adult education centre aiming to generate interest in the visual arts in the local community, both by showing touring exhibitions and encouraging local artists to exhibit.
South Road, Walkley, Sheffield S6 36A, tel: 0114 233 0360

Contact: Pat Gregory
Open: Mon & Wed 9-4, 6-9; Tues & Thurs Fri 9-4
Space: 1 gallery with 37 sq m floor space
Exhibitions: 8 a year of which 5 originated, 3 touring
Details: Tries to provide a programme of exhibitions by artists working in a variety of media. Strong links with the Mappin Gallery, Sheffield, who organise touring exhibitions and workshops here.

Waterhope Library

✓ ❋

Exhibition area for use by art and community groups and shop area for display of craftwork within library.
1-3 Peak Square, Crystal Peaks Shopping Centre, Sheffield S19 6HZ, tel: 0114 248 1127
Contact: Sue Walker, Community Arts Assistant
Open: Mon & Fri 9-7.30; Tues & Thurs 9-5.30; Sat 9-12.30 & 1.30-4.30
Space: 2 galleries with 11 lin m hanging space and 13 sq m floor space
Exhibitions: 50 a year of which 7 originated, 43 on a hire basis
Details: Length of exhibitions vary; community exhibitions up to 3 weeks, craft exhibitions change weekly, originated exhibitions last 4 weeks. Policy is to encourage local members of the public to become involved. 10% commission taken on work sold but sales not a primary role. Shop space appropriate for craftspeople with glass counter and fitted shelves.

Woodhouse Community Education Centre *

✓ ❋

Exhibition space in a community centre.
Station Road, Woodhouse, Sheffield S13 7RD, tel: 0114 269 4464
Contact: D. Bryan, Head of Centre
Space: 1 gallery with 15 lin m hanging space
Exhibitions: 6 a year of which 2 originated, 4 on a hire basis
Details: Room also used as a coffee lounge – only space therefore for 2D exhibits. Used by local community. Around 500 people per week. Exhibitions are either local artists, local groups or those sponsored by Sheffield Arts Department.

Yorkshire Artspace Society

✓ ❋

Well-lit gallery within artists' studio group, for use by members and for hire to other artists and craftspeople.
Sydney Works, 111 Matilda Street, Sheffield S1 4QF, tel: 0114 276 1769
Contact: Exhibition Organiser
Open: Mon-Fri 10-12.30, 1.30-4; and by arrangement.

Space: 1 gallery with 31 lin m hanging space and 74 sq m floor space
Exhibitions: 5 a year of which 1 originated, 4 on a hire basis
Details: One room gallery within Artspace in Sheffield's cultural industries quarter. Current hire rates around £25 a day, £65 a week, £200 a month. Space can also be hired for seminars and workshops. Sales not gallery's main aim.

Sherborne
DORSET SWA

Alpha House Gallery

✓

Selling gallery with exhibitions of mainly figurative contemporary art.
South Street, Sherborne DT9 3LU, tel: 01935 814944, fax: 01935 816717
Contact: Tony Birks, Director
Open: Tues-Sat 10-5; otherwise by appointment
Space: 100 lin m hanging space and 150 sq m floor space
Exhibitions: 10 a year all originated
Details: Modern well-lit gallery with exhibition space on two floors. Solo or two-person shows by invitation only. Tables for display of sculpture and ceramics. Audience made up of collectors of contemporary work, artists and museums. Only ground-floor gallery fully accessible.

Melbury Gallery

✓

Permanent display of work by leading artists and makers usually from South West.
Half Moon Street, Sherborne DT9, tel: 01935 814027
Contact: Thelma Drabik
Open: Mon-Fri 9.30-5.30; Sat 9.30-5; closed Sun
Space: 1 gallery with 100 sq m floor space
Details: Variety of work on offer; sculpture, etchings, jewellery, ceramics. 'Shop front' for stable of artists whose work on permanent display.

Shoreham by Sea
WEST SUSSEX SEA

Marlipins Museum Gallery

✓ ⊘

Gallery of topographical paintings and maps.
Shoreham High Street, Shoreham by Sea, tel: 01273 462994
Contact: David Rudkin, Curator, Fishbourne Roman Palace, Salthill Road, Fishbourne, Chichester, PO19 3QR, tel: 01243 785859, fax: 01243 539266
Open: (May-Sept) Tues-Sat 10-1, 2-4.30, Sun 2-4.30

Space: 1 gallery with 23 lin m hanging space and 50 sq m floor space
Exhibitions: 1 a year originated
Details: Exhibitions relevant to museum's collections or to area. Unrelated contemporary art exhibitions can be held outside normal museum season. Education policy to foster interest in history & archaeology through displays, exhibitions and school visits. Sales not priority.

Shrewsbury
SHROPSHIRE WMA

Gateway Galleries

Three small well-lit spaces in busy education & arts centre.
The Gateway Education & Arts Centre, Chester Street, Shrewsbury SY1 1NB, tel: 01743 355159/ 361120, fax: 01743 358951
Contact: Elizabeth Perkins, Exhibitions Organiser
Open: Mon-Fri 10-9 (except Aug 10-4.30); Sat 10-4
Space: 3 galleries with 34 lin m hanging space plus 14 lin m on screens and 60 sq m floor space
Exhibitions: 28 a year of which 26 originated, 2 touring
Details: Very varied programme including both amateur and professional artists'/craftspeoples' work. 4 major exhibitions and 24 small exhibitions a year. Audience very variable, right across age range but probably more older than younger. Monthly turn-about of exhibitions run on a shoe-string. New craft cases selling high quality small to medium scale pieces on sale or return basis. Selling work not gallery's primary role.

Music Hall Photographic Gallery

Gallery offering range of photographic exhibitions of all types.
The Music Hall, The Square, Shrewsbury SY1 1LH, tel: 01743 352019, fax: 01743 358 780
Contact: Janet Flynn, Gallery Co-ordinator
Open: Mon-Sat 10-8
Space: 1 gallery with 17 lin m hanging space and 32 sq m floor space
Exhibitions: 12 a year of which 10 originated, 2 touring
Details: Wide range of types of photographic work exhibited. Aims to increase public awareness of the medium and hope in future to hold courses and classes. Sales not high priority. 20% commission taken on sales made.

Parade Shops

Gallery occupies shop unit suitable for artists to use as gallery or window display.
St Mary's Place, Shrewsbury SY1 1DL
Contact: Philip Freeman, Director, PSC (Shrewsbury) Ltd, Pimley Manor, Sundorne Road, Shrewsbury, SY4 4SD, tel: 01743 343178, fax: 01743 352429
Open: Mon-Sat 9-5; closed BH, Christmas, Boxing & New Year
Space: 1 gallery with 23 lin m hanging space plus 7 lin m on screens and 48 sq m floor space
Exhibitions: 12 a year all on a hire basis
Details: Provides informal exhibition facility for artists and craftspeople to display for minimum period of a week. If opening the shop as a gallery artists must staff the unit themselves. Town centre location. Sales of work primary function.

Rowley's House Museum

Varied temporary exhibition programme.
Barker Street, Shrewsbury SY1 1QH, tel: 01743 361196
Contact: Mary White, Marketing and education officer
Space: 20 lin m hanging space and 60 sq m floor space
Details: Mixture of museum collections based, touring and contemporary exhibitions. All work subject to selection. Annual craft show. Proposals for exhibitions welcomed.

Shropshire County Library

Network of exhibition and display facilities in 33 branch libraries throughout Shropshire.
Shropshire County Library Headquarters, Column House, 7 London Road, Shrewsbury SY2 6NW, tel: 01743 253666, fax: 01743 253678
Contact: Tim Williams, County Librarian
Space: 10 galleries
Exhibitions: 30 a year of which 5 originated, 25 on a hire basis
Details: Artists encouraged to use the premises, especially those who have never exhibited before. Over 50% of the population of Shropshire visit libraries so there is great potential for artists to have their work seen.

Tower Gallery

Compact exhibition area for local amateur and professional artists in a busy town centre area available for hire.
St Julians Craft Centre for Shropshire, Shrewsbury SY1 1UH, tel: 01743 353516
Contact: A.G.B. Wright (Mrs), Organiser
Open: Mon-Sat 10-5; closed most Thurs

Space: 1 gallery with 7 lin m hanging space and 9 sq m floor space
Exhibitions: 24 a year all on a hire basis
Details: Situated in the C12th tower of the former town centre church now a 14-year-old thriving craft centre with several thousand visitors each week. Taste tends to be conservative but appreciate good quality water colours or embroidered pictures. Exhibitors need to be present on Saturdays, on other days exhibition will be manned. Sale of work is gallery's primary role.

Skelmersdale
LANCASHIRE NWA

Skelmersdale Arts Centre

Gallery serves the region with variety of exhibitions ranging from social history to contemporary art.
Central Library, Southway, Skelmersdale WN8 6NL, tel: 01695 20312
Contact: Eddie Ohren, Arts Coordinator
Space: 1 gallery with 74 lin m hanging space plus 26 lin m on screens and 540 sq m floor space
Exhibitions: 9 a year of which 6 originated, 3 touring
Details: Aims to show a varied and interesting exhibition programme covering all aspects of the visual and performing arts. Takes some Arts Council touring shows. Lectures, workshops and demonstrations are organised alongside exhibitions.

St Thomas the Apostle RC High School *

Foyer and corridors of school, used for visual arts and crafts displays by artists from the region.
Glenburn Road, Skelmersdale WN8 6JW, tel: 01695 25635, fax: 01695 556046
Contact: Roger O'Connor, Deputy Headteacher
Space: 3 galleries with 50 lin m hanging space and 1000 sq m floor space
Exhibitions: 1 a year originated
Details: Aims to bring visual arts and crafts to the young people of Skelmersdale and to be used as a resource by local educational establishments and the community.

Solihull
WEST MIDLANDS WMA

Solihull Arts Complex

Small formal gallery and large exhibition Hall, part of theatre complex with bar, coffee lounge and Tourist Information Centre attached to central library.

Homer Road, Solihull B91 3RG, tel:
0121 704 6961, fax: 0121 704 6991
Contact: Martin Collett, Arts Complex
Manager
Open: Mon-Wed 9.30-5.30; Thurs & Fri
9.30-8.00; Sat 9.30-5.00
Space: 2 galleries with 187 lin m hanging
space plus 300 lin m on screens and 272 sq
m floor space
Exhibitions: 51 a year of which 1 touring,
50 on a hire basis
Details: Exhibition hall – versatile space
opening onto landscaped courtyard. High
ceiling at one end allows for large
sculptures/paintings. Ideal for larger single
exhibitor or consortia of artists. Art gallery
– formal gallery showing 2D work by local
artists. Selling work not gallery's primary
role.

South Shields
TYNE & WEAR NA

Customs House Art Gallery

Po Ph Pr Cr Sc IA ✓ ⓔ ⓑ ⓦ ④

L-shaped gallery in arts complex within
renovated Customs House showing work by
artists based within the region alongside
international artists.
**The Customs House, Mill Dam, South
Shields NE33 1ES, tel: 0191 454 1234,
fax: 0191 456 5979**
Contact: Liz White, Arts Development
Officer
Open: Mon-Sat 10-9; Sun 12-9
Space: 1 gallery
Exhibitions: 9 a year all originated
Details: Opened 1994. Work in
exhibitions to date, whether by local or
international artists, has been either
relevant to area or in direct response to
gallery/building and its history/
surroundings. In addition to main gallery
two spaces for showing work by schools and
residents of South Tyneside. Working
closely with LEA to develop outreach/
education facility. Events, including
performance, planned for outside building.
Customs House is responsible for South
Tyneside's Local Arts Development
Agency. Some selling exhibitions but
generally work sold but not a priority

South Shields Museum & Art Gallery

Po Ph Pr Cr Sc ✓ ⓑ ⓦ

Gallery on first-floor of museum presenting
temporary exhibitions covering a wide
variety of themes and subject areas.
**Ocean Road, South Shields NE33 2A, tel:
0191 456 8740**
Contact: John Wilkes, Curator
Open: Tues-Fri 10-5.30; Sat 10-4.30; Sun
2-5
Space: 1 gallery with 37 lin m hanging

space plus 18 lin m on screens and 119 sq
m floor space
Exhibitions: 4 a year of which 3
originated, 1 touring
Details: Rectangular gallery with flexible
screening system showing exhibitions
concerned with local history and some
other exhibitions. Annual show of work by
local artists. Building also houses Catherine
Cookson Museum, which attracts visitors
from all over region and rest of country.

Southampton
HAMPSHIRE SA

First Gallery

Po Ph Pr Cr Sc ⊗

Gallery displaying pictures, pots and
sculpture for sale but primarily concerned
with people, positive values, mutual
enjoyment and warmth within a household.
**1 Burnham Chase, Bitterne,
Southampton SO18 5DG, tel: 01703
462723**
Contact: Margery Clarke, Director
Open: At any time by telephone
appointment; set hours during exhibitions
Space: 1 gallery with 15 lin m hanging
space plus 6 lin m on screens and 26 sq m
floor space
Exhibitions: 4 a year all originated
Details: Unusual self-financing exhibition
space in owner's house, open to the public,
with permanent changing display of
pictures, ceramics and other contemporary
craft; part of house transforms for
exhibitions plus small patio and lawn for
occasional exhibits. Emphasises that art is
part of everyday life. Aims for high
professional standards. Initiates touring
exhibitions. Sales not primary role but
necessary.

Gantry (The)

Po Ph IA ✓ ⓔ

Part of a multi-arts centre viewed by many
members of the public.
**Off Blechynden Terrace, Southampton
SO15 1GW, tel: 01703 330729/ 229319,
fax: 01703 332804**
Contact: Andrew Buchanan, Director
Open: Tues-Fri 10-5; Sat 12-5
Space: 1 gallery with 40 lin m hanging
space and 45 sq m floor space
Exhibitions: 10 a year of which 6
originated, 4 touring
Details: Mixed programme of work. Open
to public during other events, especially
evenings. Floor space restricted due to
permanent wall down middle of gallery. As
such, not particularly suitable for sculpture.

Gutteridges

Po Ph Cr Sc ✓ ⓑ

Part of architects' premises holding
occasional exhibitions with aim of
encouraging incorporation of art into the
built environment.
**45 Westwood Road, Southampton SO9
2RA, tel: 01703 671712, fax: 01703
584086**
Contact: Robert Chambers, Director
Open: Mon-Fri 8.30-5
Space: 2 galleries with 2530 lin m hanging
space
Details: Art in the Office/Art in the
Working Environment encourages clients/
consultants etc to consider a wide range of
art and craft, including stained glass, for
incorporation within buildings. Encourages
commissions on practice's own
architectural projects. Direct sales of work
displayed not a priority.

John Hansard Gallery

Po Ph Pr Sc ✓ ⓔ ⓑ ⓦ

Gallery mounts exhibitions that encourage
inter-disciplinary debate with emphasis on
challenging new work and site-specific or
installation-based work relating to unique
shape and history of building.
**University of Southampton, Highfield,
Southampton SO17 1BJ, tel: 01703
592158, fax: 01703 593939**
Contact: Stephen Foster, Director
Open: Tues-Sat 10.30-5.30
Space: 1 gallery with 69 lin m hanging
space plus 37 lin m on screens and 1127 sq
m floor space
Exhibitions: 7 a year of which 4
originated, 3 touring
Details: Gallery often works with other
university departments. Talks or seminars
putting the exhibitions into a wider context
are part of the programme. Shop sells
catalogues, magazines, posters and cards.
Selling work is not primary function.

Lordshill Library

Po Ph Pr Cr ✓ ⓗ ⓑ

Branch library showing work by local
artists groups, photographers, etc.
**District Centre, Lordshill, Southampton
SO1 8HY, tel: 01703 732845**
Contact: Miss R Beadle, Senior Librarian
Open: Tues-Fri 10-7; Sat 10-4
Space: 1 gallery with 9 lin m hanging space
and 27 sq m floor space
Exhibitions: 8 a year all on a hire basis
Details: Also welcome work by people
from other areas, but do not have funds for
transport etc. A main wall 9m long and
2.5m high on hessian-covered board.
Picture rail. Track spotlighting. Display
case also available. 10% commission on
sales.

Nuffield Theatre Restaurant

Restaurant gallery with exhibitions to create relaxed atmosphere for theatre goers.
University Road, Southampton SO17 1TR, tel: 01703 315500, fax: 01703 315511
Contact: Lori Dorman, House Manager
Open: Mon-Sat 10.30am-11pm
Space: 1 gallery with 20 lin m hanging space
Exhibitions: 6 a year of which 1 touring, 5 on a hire basis
Details: Exhibition space showcases work by local artists and offering opportunities for sales. 20% commission taken. Variety of work encouraged.

On Line Gallery

76 Bedford Place, Southampton, tel: 01703 330660
Contact: Exhibitions Organiser

Southampton City Art Gallery

Municipal gallery with growing permanent collection of historic and contemporary work and programme of historic and contemporary exhibitions.
Civic Centre, Southampton SO14 7LP, tel: 01703 832743, fax: 01703 832153
Contact: Margot Heller, Keeper of Art & Exhibitions
Open: Tues, Wed & Fri 10-5; Thurs 10-8; Sat 10-4; Sun 2-5
Space: 5 galleries
Exhibitions: 12 a year of which 8 originated, 4 touring
Details: Two or three major contemporary exhibitions a year. Aims to show work by both established and emerging artists, of regional, national and international significance and across full media range. In addition series of approximately 6 modest showcase exhibitions in foyer area. Work shown in foyer tends to be by regional artists. Education programme. Sale of work not a priority.

Starlight Gallery

Specialises in the support of new, up-and-coming artists, particularly those doing abstract work.
27 Bellevue Road, Southampton SO15 2AX, tel: 01703 366122
Contact: Caz Hale, Senior Partner
Space: 1 gallery with 18 lin m hanging space and 28 sq m floor space
Details: Opened 1995 and intends to stage shows on the basis of hiring out space to exhibitors at £4 per item per week for works up to 30"x30" regardless of medium.

Quote given for larger sizes. 10% of sales will go to Disability Arts Magazine.

Visage *

Exhibits fairly unusual range of contemporary work by national and local artists.
7 Manor Farm Road, Bitterne Park, Southampton SO2 4NN, tel: 01703 582202
Contact: Mr Newton
Space: 1 gallery with 38 sq m floor space
Exhibitions: 5 a year all originated
Details: Programme includes variety of solo and mixed shows, including mixed summer show. Specialist framing service. Exhibitions last 2 weeks.

Southend on Sea
ESSEX EA

Focal Point Gallery

Gallery dedicated to promoting photographic arts.
Southend Central Library, Victoria Avenue, Southend on Sea SS2 6EX, tel: 01702 612621, fax: 01702 469241
Contact: Ronnie Simpson, Gallery Director
Space: 1 gallery with 90 lin m hanging space
Exhibitions: 18 a year of which 9 originated, 9 touring
Details: Modern space within Southend's Central Library. Complemented by a lecture theatre, video arts resource, meeting rooms and largest collection of art periodicals in Essex. Programme and audience wide ranging. Fully wheelchair accessible.

Southport
MERSEYSIDE NWA

Atkinson Art Gallery

Principal forum for visual arts in Sefton, with regularly changing displays from permanent collection and busy programme of temporary exhibitions.
Lord Street, Southport PR8 1DH, tel: 01704 33133 ext 2111
Contact: Anthony K Wray, Keeper of Art Galleries and Museums
Space: 2 galleries with 114 lin m hanging space plus 20 lin m on screens
Exhibitions: 8 a year all originated
Details: Aims to provide visitors with insight into wide range of artistic practice, embracing past and present, tradition and experimentation. Permanent collection from C18th, C19th and C20th and is building up its range of contemporary

work. Picture hire scheme ensures that items from collection are used and enjoyed by people in own homes. Two temporary exhibitions almost every month, great majority featuring work of living artists.

Birkdale Branch Library

Library space shows mainly amateur work and occasional touring exhibitions.
244-246 Liverpool Road, Southport PR8 4PD, tel: 01704 67380
Contact: Miss D R Draper, Branch Librarian
Space: 1 gallery
Exhibitions: 12 a year all on a hire basis
Details: 25,000 regular users. Exhibitions all of work by living artists. Charges of 20% commission on sales, or £20 per week.

Southwold
SUFFOLK EA

Great Eastern Craft Co-operative *

Run by co-operative of ten makers as outlet for their own work and limited number of non-members.
10 Market Place, Southwold IP18 6EE
Contact: Kate O'Halloran, Secretary, Bell Cottage, Walpole, Halesworth, IP19 9AP
Exhibitions: 4 a year all originated

Portland Studio *

Commercial gallery supplies art to offices with space available for hire by artists.
Portland House, High Street, Southwold IP18 6AB, tel: 01502 723652
Contact: Melanie Strank, Exhibition Officer
Space: 1 gallery with 215 lin m hanging space and 60 sq m floor space
Exhibitions: 1 a year originated
Details: Specialises in sale of original prints, although exhibitions of paintings, drawings and sculpture staged.

Spalding
LINCOLNSHIRE EA

Lincolnshire gallery

Beck Bank Nursery, Beck Bank, West Pinchbeck, Spalding PE11 3QN

South Holland Centre

Dedicated exhibition gallery in busy multi-purpose arts and leisure building.
Market Place, Spalding PE11 1SS, tel: 01775 725031, fax: 01775 711253
Contact: Nigel Hawkins, Arts Officer, South Holland District Council, Priory

Road, Spalding, PE11 2XE, tel: 01775
761161, fax: 01775 711253
Open: Mon-Fri 9.30-5; Sat 9.30-12; closed
BH
Space: 1 gallery with 47 lin m hanging
space and 67 sq m floor space
Exhibitions: 10 a year of which 1
originated, 2 touring, 1 on a hire basis
Details: Aims to provide varied
contemporary arts programme of
professional artists' work. Sales not a
priority.

Wills Lane Gallery *

Pa Pr Sc ✓

*Small commercial gallery with programme
of mixed and solo shows, mainly abstract
work.*
**Wills Lane, St Ives TR26 1AF, tel: 01736
795723**
Contact: Henry Gilbert, Director
Space: 74 sq m floor space
Details: British artists whose work is shown
include Hepworth, Hilton and Nicholson
alongside work by young contemporary
artists.

Stafford
STAFFORDSHIRE WMA

Shire Hall Gallery

Pa Ph Pr Cr Sc ✓ H & wc 4

*Gallery shows exhibitions of fine art, craft
and photography.*
**Market Square, Stafford ST16 2LD, tel:
01785 278345, fax: 01785 278327**
Contact: Hilary Foxley, Gallery Manager
Open: Tues-Sat 10-5
Space: 1 gallery with 72 lin m hanging
space and 105 sq m floor space
Exhibitions: 16 a year of which 13
originated, 3 touring
Details: Objectives of the gallery are to
present a balanced programme of
exhibitions and related events of
contemporary and historical visual arts and
crafts for all.

Staines
SURREY SEA

Old Town Hall Arts Centre

Pa Ph Pr ✓ & wc 4

Arts centre opened February 1994.
**Market Square, Staines TW18 4RH, tel:
01784 461565, fax: 01784 449861**
Contact: Richard Crowe, Artistic Co-
ordinator
Open: Mon-Sat 10-5.30
Space: 1 gallery with 20 lin m hanging
space
Details: Arts centre with theatre anticipates
holding 20 exhibitions a year. Sales
important.

Stalybridge
CHESHIRE NWA

Astley Cheetham Art Gallery

Pa Ph Pr Cr ✓

*Municipal gallery with contemporary
exhibitions alongside collections.*
**Trinity Street, Stalybridge SK15 2BN,
tel: 0161 338 2708/ 3831**
Contact: Museums Officer, Portland Basin
Heritage Centre, Portland Street South,
Ashton-under-Lyne, OL6 7SY, tel: 0161
308 3374
Open: Mon-Wed, Fri 1-7.30; Sat 9-4
Space: 1 gallery with 45 lin m hanging
space and 200 sq m floor space
Exhibitions: 10 a year
Details: Houses Cheetham Collection
which includes diverse selection of
paintings ranging from C14th Italian to
Burne-Jones. Contemporary arts, crafts and
photography exhibitions including work by
schools.

Stamford
LINCOLNSHIRE EA

Stamford Arts Centre

Pa Ph Pr Cr Sc ✓ £ H & wc

*Self-contained gallery space, programmed to
complement other aspects of arts centre's
programme.*
**27 St Mary's Street, Stamford PE9 2DL,
tel: 01780 63203, fax: 01780 66690**
Contact: Celia Frisby, Manager
Open: Mon-Sat 9.30-5
Space: 1 gallery with 34 lin m hanging
space and 79 sq m floor space
Exhibitions: 14 a year of which 7
originated, 3 touring, 4 on a hire basis
Details: Committed to exhibiting work by
young artists and by local schools. When
the gallery is hired this is by local groups
only. Exhibitions are planned
approximately one year in advance and are
by invitation. Selling work is not gallery's
primary role.

Stamford Museum

Pa ✓ H &

*Temporary exhibitions aim to expand the
scope of a local history/archaeology museum
by exploring themes outside its collecting
range.*
**Broad Street, Stamford PE9 1PJ, tel:
01780 66317, fax: 01780 480363**
Contact: Mr J.F. Smith, Curator &
Manager, Stamford & Grantham Museums
Open: (Apr-Sep) Mon-Sat 10-5, Sun 2-5;
(Oct-Mar) Mon-Sat 10-5
Space: 1 gallery with 20 lin m hanging
space plus 15 lin m on screens and 37 sq m
floor space

Exhibitions: 2 a year of which 1 touring, 1
on a hire basis
Details: Hanging onto boarded walls with
movable boards and display cases available.
Caters for local audience, plus large tourist
element. Sales not a priority but 20%
commission taken on any sales made.

Torkington Gallery

Pa Pr Cr Sc ✓

*Commercial gallery specialises in
contemporary craftwork.*
**38 St Peters Street, Stamford PE9 2PF,
tel: 01780 62281**
Contact: Will & Christine Illsley,
Directors
Space: 1 gallery with 22 lin m hanging
space and 56 sq m floor space
Exhibitions: 3 a year all originated
Details: Paintings (figurative and
representational), prints (etchings and
lithographs), ceramics and textiles with
emphasis on hand-painted silks. Shows
selection of work by owners. Aims to
promote range of contemporary work, local
and national, through combination of
regularly changing displays and four annual
thematic group shows, occasional solo and
two-person shows. Commission charged.

Stanley
CO DURHAM NA

Stanley Civic Hall

Pa Ph Pr Cr Sc ✓ & wc 4

*Exhibition space in reception area and
theatre bar.*
Civic Hall, Stanley, tel: 01207 281144
Contact: Marin Weston, Arts Development
Officer, Louisa centre, Front Street,
Stanley, tel: 01207 232164
Space: 3 galleries with 18 lin m hanging
space plus 15 lin m on screens and 233 sq
m floor space
Details: Exhibition areas (movable
mounting boards) in foyer and theatre bar
(wall hanging space only) for free usage by
individuals and organisations who take
responsibility for hanging and invigilation
of work. Negotiable fee charged on sales.
Main auditorium of 233 sq metres on fee
basis and requires advanced notice.

Stevenage
HERTFORDSHIRE EA

Boxfield Gallery

Pa Ph Pr Cr Sc ✓ & wc

*Open-plan purpose-built gallery, bringing
wide spectrum of art to general public.*
**Stevenage Arts & Leisure Centre, Lytton
Way, Stevenage SG1 1LZ, tel: 01438
766877**
Contact: George Cass, Arts & Crafts
Officer

Space: 1 gallery with 36 lin m hanging space and 54 sq m floor space
Exhibitions: 3 a year all originated
Details: Exhibitions run for one month. Gallery aims to increase public awareness and appreciation of art in general and make gallery a welcoming and popular place. Selling work not gallery's main aim.

Stevenage Library

Pa Ph Cr Sc ✔ ⊗

Area within public library showing work by local individual artists and potters.
Southgate, Stevenage SG1 1HD, tel: 01438 369441, fax: 01438 365144
Contact: Ann Jansz, Town Librarian
Open: Mon-Thurs 9.30-8; Fri 9.30-5; Sat 9.30-4
Space: 1 gallery
Details: Exhibitions changed every 3 weeks. Exhibition area of descending steps suitable for wall-mounted displays only. Not secure area. Free standing units (bring your own) can be accommodated to rear of library. Lighting by spots and fluorescent tubes. 10% + VAT sales commission if exhibitor handles sales; 20% + VAT if library handles sales. Exhibitor hangs own work. Outreach, educational activities, talks and workshops organised by library.

Stockbridge
HAMPSHIRE SA

Courcoux & Courcoux *

Pa Cr Sc

Gallery represents established and new generation sculptors, painters and potters.
Hatchett's Barn, Nether Wallop, Stockbridge SO20 8ET, tel: 01264 872456
Contact: Ian Courcoux, Exhibition Organiser
Space: 1 gallery with 80 lin m hanging space and 1100 sq m floor space
Exhibitions: 10 a year all originated
Details: Artists/sculptors/makers represented include Elisabeth Frink, Sophie Ryder, Eva Drewett, Philip Sutton, Lesley Main, John Emanuel, John Ward, David Roberts. Gallery garden. Crafts Council selected list.

Stockport
GREATER MANCHESTER NWA

Bramall Hall Café Gallery

Pa Ph ✔ ⊕

Displays the work of local artists in a café environment.
Bramall Hall, Bramhall, Stockport SK7 3NX
Contact: Jan Harrap, Duty Officer
Open: Daily 10-4

Space: 1 gallery
Exhibitions: 4 a year all on a hire basis
Details: No hire fee payable by exhibitors for space. 25% commission taken on sales made.

Bramhall Library

Pa Ph Pr Cr ✔ ⊕

Exhibition space in library.
Bramhall Lane South, Bramhall, Stockport SK7 2DU, tel: 0161 439 6067
Contact: Senior Library Assistant
Open: Mon, Thurs, Fri 9-8; Tues 9-5; Sat 9-12
Space: 1 gallery
Exhibitions: 12 a year all on a hire basis
Details: Wall mounted display boards for exhibitions of art and craft work by individuals and groups in the local community. No hire fee payable by exhibitors; 20% commission taken on sales made.

Bredbury Library Gallery

Pa Ph Sc ✔ ⊕

Exhibition space in library.
George Lane, Bredbury, Stockport SK6 1DJ, tel: 0161 474 4545
Contact: Senior Library Assistant
Open: Mon, Tues, Fri 9-8; Wed 9-5; Sat 9-12
Space: 1 gallery
Exhibitions: 12 a year all on a hire basis
Details: Display space available to individuals and groups from the community to exhibit art work. No hire fee payable by exhibitors for space but 20% commission taken on sales made.

Brinnington Library Gallery

Pa Ph Pr ✔ ⊕

Exhibition space in library.
The Arcade, Taunton Avenue, Brinnington, Stockport SK5 8LP, tel: 0161 430 3909
Contact: Senior Library Assistant
Open: Mon, Fri 9-8; Tues, Thurs 9-5; Sat 9-12
Space: 1 gallery
Exhibitions: 12 a year all on a hire basis
Details: Display space for the use of individuals and groups from the community to exhibit artwork. No hire fee payable. 20% commission taken on any sales made.

Cheadle Library Gallery

Pa Ph Pr Cr ✔ ⊕

Purpose-built exhibitions space in library.
Ashfield Road, Cheadle, Stockport SK8 1BB, tel: 0161 428 7169
Contact: Senior Library Assistant
Open: Mon, Thurs, Fri 9-8; Tues 9-5; Sat 9-12
Space: 1 gallery

Exhibitions: 12 a year all on a hire basis
Details: Exhibition space for individuals and groups from the community to display art and craft work. No hire fee payable by exhibitors; 20% commission taken on sales made.

Dialstone Library

Pa Ph Pr ✔ ⊕ ⊛

Exhibition space in library for display of 2D work.
Dialstone Centre, Lisburne Lane, Offerton, Stockport, tel: 0161 474 2255
Contact: Senior Library Assistant
Open: Mon, Thurs 2-5, 6-8; Tues, Fri 2-5; Sat 9-12
Space: 1 gallery
Exhibitions: 12 a year all on a hire basis
Details: Wall mounted display panels for the use of individuals and groups to exhibit 2D art work of local interest. No hire fee payable by exhibitors. 20% commission taken on sales made.

Heatons Library Gallery

Pa Ph Pr ✔ ⊕ ⊛ ⊛

L-shaped space for display of artwork, photography, etc from individuals and groups from the local community.
Thornfield Road, Heaton Moor, Stockport SK4 3JT
Contact: Senior Library Assistant
Open: Mon, Tues, Fri 9-8; Wed 9-5; Sat 9-12
Space: 1 gallery
Exhibitions: 12 a year all on a hire basis
Details: No hire fee to exhibit in space. 20% commission taken on sales made.

Marple Library

Pa Ph Sc ✔ ⊕

Exhibition room in Marple Library for displaying 2D artworks of local interest and display space in lending library itself.
Memorial Park, Marple, Stockport SK3 6BA, tel: 0161 427 3236
Contact: Andy Firth, Exhibition Officer, Stockport Art, Wellington Road South, Marple, Stockport, SK3 8AB, tel: 0161 474 4453
Open: Mon, Tues, Fri 9-8; Wed 9-5; Sat 9-12
Space: 2 galleries
Exhibitions: 10 a year all on a hire basis
Details: Exhibition room (Marple Library Gallery) – wall and standing boards available. No fee for 'hiring' space; 30% commission taken on sales. Contact Andy Firth for enquiries about exhibitions in gallery. Also floor-standing display board in library for individuals and groups from the local community to exhibit artwork, photography and works of local interest. Contact Senior Library Assistant at library regarding this space.

Stockport Art Gallery

Pa Ph Pr Cr SC LA ✔ ⓕ ⓔ Wc

Monthly exhibitions of local or national importance based on relevance to workshop and national curriculum.
Wellington Road South, Stockport SK3 8AB, tel: 0161 474 4453, fax: 0161 480 4960
Contact: Andrew Firth, Exhibitions Officer
Open: Mon-Fri 11-5; Wed 11-7; Sat 10-5
Space: 3 galleries with 101 lin m hanging space and 302 sq m floor space
Exhibitions: 22 a year
Details: Three galleries all showing temporary exhibitions, each lasting 3-4 weeks. 2 galleries each 68 sq meters, 1 gallery 166 sq meters. Full education programme is organised to complement exhibitions. Ground-floor only fully accessible. Sales not primary role of gallery.

Stockport Central Library

Pa Ph Pr Cr ✔ ⓗ

Exhibition space in library.
Wellington Road South, Stockport SK1 3RS, tel: 0161 474 4540
Open: Mon, Tues, Fri 9-8; Wed 9-5; Sat 9-4
Space: 1 gallery
Exhibitions: 12 a year all on a hire basis
Details: Display cases and wall-mounted boards for use of individuals and groups from the community to exhibit art and craft work. No hire fee; organised on basis of 20% commission taken on sales made.

Stocksfield
NORTHUMBERLAND NA

Bewick Studios

 Ph ✔ ⓔ

Large open print workshop/working museum of engraving and etching with exhibition space on back wall.
Mickley Square, Stocksfield NE43 7BL, tel: 01661 844055
Contact: Christopher Bacon, Owner
Open: Tues-Sat 10-12, 1-5.30; closed Christmas and New Year's Day
Space: 1 gallery with 10 lin m hanging space
Details: Owner passionate about printing, especially traditional processes. Keen to help other printmakers and suggests any printmaker interested in an exhibition should call in or ring. No definite philosophy but needs to be some dialogue/understanding of each other's aims and ways of working. 33.3 % commission taken, sale or return.

Stockton on Tees
CLEVELAND NA

Dovecot Arts Centre

Pa Ph Pr SC ✔ ⓔ Wc

Ground-floor gallery in arts centre, open to street, exhibiting work by local national and international artists.
Dovecot Street, Stockton on Tees TS18 1LL, tel: 01642 611625, fax: 01642 613425
Contact: Paul Mellor, Film/Photography/Gallery Officer
Open: Tues-Sat 10-10.30; Sun-Mon 7-10
Space: 1 gallery with 35 lin m hanging space and 94 sq m floor space
Exhibitions: 12 a year of which 11 originated, 1 touring
Details: Arts centre containing, gallery, theatre, cinema, darkroom, bar and restaurant.

Stoke on Trent
STAFFORDSHIRE WMA

Edge City Gallery

Edge City Complex, Foundry Street, Hanley, Stoke on Trent, tel: 01782 274885

Flaxman Gallery

Pa Ph Pr Cr SC ✔ ⓔ Wc 4

Purpose-built gallery space with wide range of exhibitions, mainly promoting living artists and designers.
Staffordshire University, College Road, Stoke on Trent ST4 2DE, tel: 01782 294000/ 294955, fax: 01782 744035
Contact: J G Skinner, Curator
Open: Mon-Sat 10-6; film evenings 6-8
Space: 1 gallery with 30 lin m hanging space plus 20 lin m on screens and 82 sq m floor space
Exhibitions: 12 a year
Details: Not all exhibitions are originated by the gallery which does occasionally take touring shows. Selling work is not considered gallery's primary function.

Stoke on Trent City Museum & Art Gallery

Pa Ph Pr Cr SC LA ✔ ⓕ ⓔ Wc 4

Local authority museum with large temporary exhibition space and a sculpture court.
Bethesda Street, Hanley, Stoke on Trent ST1 3DE, tel: 01782 202173, fax: 01782 205033
Contact: Lucien Cooper/Ian Vines, Assistant Exhibitions Officers
Open: Mon-Sat 10-5; Sun 2-5
Space: 3 galleries with 176 lin m hanging space plus 92 lin m on screens and 489 sq m floor space

Exhibitions: 12 a year of which 8 originated, 4 touring
Details: Wide programme aiming to increase the audience's awareness and understanding of art and craft. Shows work by local, national and international artists in solo or group exhibitions. Programme by invitation and application. One installation of new work and one residency are organised each year. Extensive educational activities are an integral part of the exhibition programme. 230,000 visitors per year.

Stratford upon Avon
WARWICKSHIRE WMA

Gallery (The)

Pa Cr SC ✔ ⓔ Wc

Commercial gallery exhibiting contemporary art and craft.
Windsor Street, Stratford upon Avon, tel: 01788 720270
Contact: Igor Kolodotschko, Color Art Galleries, The Moat House, Dorsington, Stratford upon Avon, CV37 8AX, tel: 01789 720270, fax: 01789 720988
Open: Daily 10-6
Space: 1 gallery with 288 lin m hanging space plus 79 lin m on screens and 295 sq m floor space
Details: The gallery divides into two spaces; front gallery for changing exhibitions, rear gallery for permanent display. Opened May1995 and anticipates holding 10 shows a year. Sales of work a priority.

Montpellier Gallery

Pa Cr

Private gallery representing work by variety of contemporary artists and craftspeople.
8 Chapel Street, Stratford upon Avon CV37 3EP, tel: 01789 261161
Contact: Linda Burridge
Space: 3 galleries with 25 lin m hanging space and 59 sq m floor space
Exhibitions: 5 a year
Details: Both new and established artists/craftspeople represented. Paintings, original etchings and sculpture, studio ceramics, glass, and designer jewellery endorsed by the Crafts Council. Exhibitions are either one-person or thematic. Also monthly changing displays.

Shakespeare Centre

Pa Ph Pr Cr SC ✔ ⓗ

Mix of historical/contemporary exhibitions on themes relating to William Shakespeare and his works, history of Stratford upon Avon and theatre.
Henley Street, Stratford upon Avon CV37 6QW, tel: 01789 204016, fax: 01789 296083
Contact: Roger Pringle, Director

Open: Mon-Fri 10-5; Sat 9.30-12.30
Space: 1 gallery with 19 lin m hanging space
Exhibitions: 4 a year of which 3 originated, 1 on a hire basis
Details: Display equipment includes movable screens, picture suspension system, secure display cases, UV filtration and alarms. Complementary education programme. Sales welcome but not priority. 25% commission taken.

Stroud
GLOUCESTERSHIRE SWA

Yew Tree Gallery

Pa Ph Pr Cr ✓ &

Exhibitions of contemporary fine art and craft in five rooms of Cotswold house.
Holly House, Steanbridge Lane, Slad , Stroud GL6 7QE, tel: 01452 813601
Contact: Gill Wyatt Smith
Open: Tues-Sat 10.30-5.30 ; Sun 2-5 during exhibition
Space: 5 galleries with 34 lin m hanging space and 97 sq m floor space
Exhibitions: 2 a year both originated
Details: Variety of contemporary British craft and paintings. Shelving and cabinets for display of 3D work. Sales considered primary role of gallery. Commissions arranged.

Sudbury
SUFFOLK EA

Gainsborough's House

Pa Ph Pr Cr SC ✓ ① & W

Independent museum with permanent collection, temporary exhibitions and open-access print workshop is both national memorial to Gainsborough and a regional centre for contemporary art.
46 Gainsborough Street, Sudbury CO10 6EU, tel: 01787 372958
Contact: Andrew Hunter, Assistant Curator
Open: Tues-Sat 10-5; Sun & BH 2-5; (Oct-Easter) closes at 4
Space: 2 galleries with 48 lin m hanging space and 93 sq m floor space
Exhibitions: 12 a year of which 10 originated, 2 touring
Details: Birthplace of Thomas Gainsborough, half the house is hung with a collection of his work. Temporary exhibition galleries overlook the garden which is used for sculpture shows. Programme includes a biennial drawing competition. Strong craft presence. Welcomes speculative submissions from artists. Committee meets twice a year to plan the programme. Sales not a priority.

Quay Theatre Gallery

Pa Ph Pr SC ✓ &

Gallery provides forum for wide variety of monthly exhibitions, primarily to contribute funds towards theatre activities.
The Quay at Sudbury, Quay Lane, Sudbury CO10 6AN, tel: 01787 374745
Contact: John Culverwelll & John Everrett, Joint Gallery Managers
Space: 1 gallery with 24 lin m hanging space and 70 sq m floor space
Exhibitions: 11 a year all originated
Details: Performing arts theatre, with a small restaurant, bar. The walls in foyer, stairs and bar are all used as exhibition space. Most work shown by professional artists with proven sales record but flexible approach is maintained. Gallery under new management since March 1994 and is now following more commercially orientated policy to benefit both artists and theatre. Sales therefore a priority. Access for wheelchair users to most of exhibition space but some display on stairways.

Sunderland
TYNE & WEAR NA

City Library and Arts Centre

Pa Ph Pr Cr SC LA ✓ ① & W

New gallery complex for touring exhibitions of international contemporary art & craft, year-round programme of events, education and outreach, artists in residence and craft shop.
Fawcett Street, Sunderland, tel: 0191 514 1235, fax: 0191 514 8444
Contact: Niki Braithwaite, Exhibitions Officer
Open: Mon & Wed 9.30-7.30; Tues, Thurs, Fri 9.30-5; Sat 9.30-4; closed BH
Space: 1 gallery with 137 lin m hanging space plus 73 lin m on screens and 604 sq m floor space
Exhibitions: 12 a year of which 7 originated, 5 touring
Details: Programme of exhibition and interpretation of contemporary visual art & craft that will engage and challenge perceptions of audiences inside and outside the Northern region. Promotes the best of the region's contemporary visual artists and craftspeople as part of its overall aim of developing work of national and international significance. Sales not a priority.

Reg Vardy Arts Foundation Gallery

Pa Ph Pr Cr SC LA ✓ ①

University gallery showing contemporary and historical art with a local, national and international perspective.

University of Sunderland, School of Arts, Design & Communications, Ashburne House, Ryhope Road, Sunderland SR2 7EF, tel: 0191 515 2128, fax: 0191 515 2132
Contact: John Davidson, Arts Development Officer
Open: Mon-Fri 10-5
Space: 2 galleries with 54 lin m hanging space and 115 sq m floor space
Exhibitions: 9 a year of which 3 originated, 6 touring
Details: Open to the public, showing a range of work in different media, which reflects the teaching of the University. Committed to broadening access to and awareness of issues within the art community.

Sunderland Museum & Art Gallery

Pa Ph Pr Cr SC ✓ ① & W 4

Founded in 1846, the museum (run by Tyne and Wear Museums) has wide-ranging permanent collections and presents a varied programme of temporary exhibitions.
Borough Road, Sunderland SR1 1PP, tel: 0191 565 0723, fax: 0191 565 0713
Contact: Neil Sinclair, Senior Curator
Open: Mon-Fri 10-5; Sat 10-4.30; Sun 2-5
Space: 1 gallery with 48 lin m hanging space plus 15 lin m on screens and 212 sq m floor space
Exhibitions: 2 a year of which 1 originated, 1 touring
Details: Temporary exhibitions cover; contemporary and historical fine and applied art, craft, history and natural history. Accompanying programme of talks, workshops and demonstrations aimed at children, family groups as well as schools and a wide general audience. Specific emphasis on involving people with disabilities. Sale of work is not gallery's primary concern.

Sutton Coldfield
WEST MIDLANDS WMA

Artifex

Pr Cr ✓ ⊗

Upstairs gallery space in craft centre that is a converted barn.
Unit 7, Hungry Horse Craft Centre, Weeford Road, Sutton Coldfield B75 6NA, tel: 0121 3233776
Contact: Nigel Bates, Manager
Open: Wed-Sun 10-5
Space: 1 gallery with 56 sq m floor space
Exhibitions: 6 a year all originated
Details: Range of craft shows; themed, group shows and one person shows. Selling work is considered primary function of gallery.

Swanage
DORSET SWA

Alpha Gallery *
[Pa][Sc] ✔ [H][4]

Commercial Road, Swanage, tel: 01929 423692
Contact: Jill Mirza/Nick Harris
Space: 1 gallery with 31 lin m hanging space and 38 sq m floor space
Exhibitions: 9 a year all originated
Details: Shows painting and sculpture, usually small scale. Range of artists broad. Programme mixture of group and solo shows. Mixed shows each Winter and Summer present up to 30 artists.

Swindon
WILTSHIRE SA

Swindon Arts Centre
[Pa][Ph][Pr] ✔ ♿

Exhibition space in small-scale theatre café/bar area displaying community generated exhibitions.
Devizes Road, Swindon SN1 4BJ, tel: 01793 614837, fax: 01793 541685
Contact: Celia Yeoman, Visual Arts Development Officer, Thamesdown Borough Council
Open: Mon-Fri 10.30-5; Sat 10-12; during performances
Space: 1 gallery with 15 lin m hanging space and 72 sq m floor space
Exhibitions: 15 a year all originated
Details: To provide varied experience of range of visual arts and opportunities for all to participate in exhibition process; amateur and established professional artists. Sales not main function of gallery.

Wyvern Theatre
[Pa][Ph][Pr] ✔ [WC][4]

Exhibition spaces in theatre foyer and bar area showing wide range of 2D work by amateur and professional artists.
Theatre Square, Swindon SN1 1QN, tel: 01793 535534, fax: 01793 480278
Contact: Celia Yeoman, Visual Arts Development Officer, Thamesdown Borough Council, Arts Centre, Devizes Road, Swindon, SN1 4BJ, tel: 01793 614837
Open: (Harlequin Bar) daily 9-2 & 6-9; (foyer) daily 9-7 & during performances
Space: 2 galleries with 55 lin m hanging space and 140 sq m floor space
Exhibitions: 15 a year all originated
Details: Two exhibition spaces; Harlequin Bar and large foyer area providing varied programme of shows to people of all ages and interests. Independent access for wheelchair users to bar, not possible to reach foyer. Work sold; commission taken.

Tamworth
STAFFORDSHIRE WMA

Palace Gallery *
[Pa][Ph][Pr][Cr][Sc][LA] ✔

Exhibition space in Tamworth's media centre.
Palace Media Centre, Lower Gungate, Tamworth B79 7AW, tel: 01827 57100
Contact: David Mulcahy
Space: 1 gallery with 11 lin m hanging space plus 11 lin m on screens and 110 sq m floor space
Exhibitions: 2 a year both originated
Details: A publicly-funded project aimed at giving opportunities for training in use of high-technology. Supports the broadly educational aims of the Centre. Temporary exhibitions will focus on the following: black & white and colour photography (individual, documentary and commercial), graphic design, 3D design, prints, tape/slash slide material, video projection and installation. 2D design should be supplied ready framed. Supports EPR in principle, although no funding currently available to enable this policy.

Palace Media Centre
Lower Gungate, Tamworth

Tamworth Arts Centre
[Pa][Pr][Cr][LA] ✔[£] 🚫♿

Offers visitors a space to view and purchase a wide variety of quality contemporary applied art through regular temporary exhibitions.
Church Street, Tamworth B79 7BX, tel: 01827 53092
Contact: David Kreps, Manager
Open: Mon-Fri 11.30-4
Space: 2 galleries with 21 lin m hanging space plus 4 lin m on screens and 36 sq m floor space
Exhibitions: 12 a year
Details: Listed C18th building which houses top-floor gallery with elevated ceiling and four arched windows. Plenty of natural light. Policy to promote 2D, 3D and live work which demonstrates links with literature, in particular myth-making. Sales not primary role of gallery.

Tamworth Central Library
[Pa][Ph][Pr][Cr][Sc] ✔

Exhibition space in library aims to be a focal point for town's cultural activities.
Corporation Street, Tamworth B79 7DN, tel: 01827 52244
Contact: E Rees-Jones, Group Librarian
Space: 1 gallery with 21 lin m hanging space and 128 sq m floor space
Exhibitions: 24 a year all originated
Details: Exhibitions of local interest, or by local artists/makers shown.

Taunton
SOMERSET SWA

Albermarle Centre Gallery
[Pa][Ph][Sc] ✔ ♿[WC][4]

Gallery providing exhibition space for local artists, including disabled artists, at low cost.
Albermarle Centre, Taunton TA1 1BA, tel: 01823 252945
Contact: Cleve Lott, Centre Manager
Space: 1 gallery with 22 lin m hanging space and 40 sq m floor space
Exhibitions: 6 a year all originated
Details: Gallery open to all local artists to exhibit. Sales considered a priority.

Brewhouse Gallery
[Pa][Ph][Pr][Cr][Sc] ✔ ♿[WC]

Three exhibition spaces within arts centre.
Brewhouse Theatre & Arts Centre, Coal Orchard, Taunton TA1 1JL, tel: 01823 274608, fax: 01823 323116
Contact: Louise Baker, Visual Arts Co-ordinator
Open: Mon 12-5.30; Tues-Sat 10-5.30; performance evenings till 9.30
Space: 3 galleries with 70 lin m hanging space and 30 sq m floor space
Exhibitions: 19 a year of which 16 originated, 3 touring
Details: Programme of one-person and groups shows often giving lesser-known artists their first exhibition. Range of artforms but only one exhibition space can be used for free-standing work due to theatre fire regulations. White walls. Spot lights. Sales not primary role; 25% commission taken.

Byram Gallery
[Pa][Pr][Sc][LA] ✔[H] ♿[WC][4]

Large, high-ceilinged neutral space suited to large contemporary work.
Somerset College of Arts & Technology, Wellington Road, Taunton TA1 5AX, tel: 01823 283403
Contact: Bill Wier, Head of Art Dept
Space: 1 gallery with 350 sq m floor space
Exhibitions: 16 a year of which 12 originated, 4 on a hire basis
Details: Gallery floor with large main 'industrial' space and additional mezzanine level. Also exhibition space in art and design foyer. Main gallery shows work by artists from around country; particularly innovative large-scale work, eg installation pieces. Committed to promoting and supporting artists. Lighting by tracks and spots. Artists often asked to give talks. Degree shows also shown. 20% commission taken on sales but selling work not primary function. Prepared to hire gallery out. Independent access for wheelchair users to main exhibition space.

Makers

Makers' co-operative with occasional exhibitions by non-members.
7a Bath Place, Taunton TA1 4ER, tel: 01823 251121
Contact: Holly Webb, Secretary, 3 Ducks Corner, Thorney, Langport, tel: 01458 252701
Exhibitions: 1 a year originated
Details: Co-operative with 12 members whose work is shown in the gallery. We welcome new members. Craft person always in the gallery.

Telford
SHROPSHIRE WMA

Elton Gallery

Permanent display of C18th and C19th industrial art with temporary exhibitions space.
Museum of Iron , Ironbridge Gorge Museum, Coalbrookdale, Telford TF8 7AW, tel: 01952 433418
Contact: David de Hoan, Senior Curator
Open: Daily 10-5
Space: 1 gallery with 25 lin m hanging space and 75 sq m floor space
Details: Collection of paintngs, prints and drawings, commemorative ceramics and decorative castings. Temporary exhibitions with content linking art with industry.

Gallery at Madeley Court School

Public exhibition space within school art department used as teaching resource for Shropshire schools/colleges.
Madeley Court School, Court Street, Telford TF7 5DZ, tel: 01952 680306
Contact: Ian Warburton/Meabh Warburton, Co-ordinators
Open: (Term-time) weekdays 10-4
Space: 1 gallery with 24 lin m hanging space
Exhibitions: 8 a year all originated
Details: Gallery is housed in the busy art department of a comprehensive school with full public access. Opened in February 1993 it aims to hold eight exhibitions a year of a wide range of fine and applied art. It is linked to the art department of the school and is used as a teaching resource for pupils as well as being open to the public. Plinths available. Track lighting, white walls. Workshops are linked to exhibitions and exhibitors should be prepared to run these with wide range of students (primary to tertiary age groups). Sales not a priority.

New College Gallery

Gallery on two levels offering variety of different art forms mainly for interest and information of student body.
King Street, Wellington, Telford TF1 1NY, tel: 01952 641892, fax: 01952 243564
Contact: Roger Turner, Head of Art Department
Open: (College term-time) Mon-Fri 8.30-5.30
Space: 1 gallery with 17 lin m hanging space and 80 sq m floor space
Exhibitions: 10 a year of which 2 originated, 8 touring
Details: Policy is to enable students to meet contemporary art, inform them about the artists and their motivations and to offer as wide a range of media, materials and imagery as possible. Artists exhibited usually live and work in West Midlands area. Hired shows often from Ikon Gallery, Craftspace and Shropshire Visual Arts Trust. Easy access to lower level from inside and outside building. Sales not a priority.

Spout Farm House Gallery

Varied programme of national touring exhibitions, theme and open exhibitions, including the work of local artists.
Telford Town Park, Telford, tel: 01952 202579, fax: 01952 290628
Contact: Helen Papasodaro, Arts & Entertainments Assistant, Wrekin Council, PO Box 211, Civic Offices, Telford, TF3 4LA, tel: 01952 202579, fax: 01952 290628
Open: Daily 12-4; other hours by arrangement.
Space: 1 gallery with 16 lin m hanging space plus 22 lin m on screens and 80 sq m floor space
Exhibitions: 12 a year of which 2 originated, 10 touring
Details: Workshops and lectures organised to complement programme where appropriate. Sales not a priority.

Tenbury Wells
HEREFORD & WORCESTER WMA

Tenbury Library

Exhibition room in library where main aim is to entertain and inform the public.
24 Teme Street, Tenbury Wells WR15 8BA, tel: 01584 810285
Contact: Miss S Matthews, Librarian
Open: Mon 9.30-1, 2-4; Tues & Thurs 9.30-1, 2-5.30; Fri 9.30-1, 2-7; Sat 9.30-1
Space: 1 gallery with 2 lin m hanging space

plus 13 lin m on screens and 30 sq m floor space
Exhibitions: 1 a year originated
Details: Displays of information for the public and local history as well as art exhibitions held. Access to exhibition room by staircase only but chair lift currently being installed. 3 fixed lockable glass-fronted cabinets available. Space available for hire. Exhibitor to provide insurance, transport, display the work, produce publicity if necessary and provide list of prices. 20% commission + VAT on sales made. See also entry for Hereford & Worcester Libraries & Arts Department, Worcester.

Tetbury
GLOUCESTERSHIRE SWA

Gumstool Gallery *

Artist-run gallery with studios and workshops.
8 Gumstool Hill, Tetbury GL8 8DG, tel: 01666 503710
Contact: Pamela Cox, Artist/Owner
Space: 2 galleries with 28 lin m hanging space
Exhibitions: 3 a year all originated
Details: Shows work of three or four artists for a period of time in continuous mixed exhibitions. This enables visitors to take away purchased work. Contemporary work is shown in all media. Abstract and figurative, mainly domestic size.

Thame
OXFORDSHIRE SA

Thame Sports & Arts Centre

Space showing one-person/group exhibitions aimed at giving enjoyment and stimulation to the many centre users.
Oxford Road, Thame OX9 2BB, tel: 01844 215607, fax: 01844 216927
Contact: Ray Boulton, Manager
Open: Daily 9am-10pm
Space: 2 galleries with / lin m hanging space plus 3 lin m on screens and 13 sq m floor space
Exhibitions: 10 a year of which 2 originated, 8 on a hire basis
Details: Exhibitions last about a month. Hanging space and lockable display cases available. Evening preview events very popular. Sales not considered primary role. 10% commission on sales. Independent access for wheelchair users to lower gallery only.

Thetford
NORFOLK EA

Thetford Art Gallery
Small voluntary-run gallery with varied programme of temporary exhibitions.
Upstairs in the Guildhall, Market Square, Thetford IP24 2AP, tel: 01842 766599
Contact: J. Pilling, Administrator
Open: Mon, Wed 10-1; Tues, Thurs, Fri, Sat 10-3.30
Space: 1 gallery with 30 lin m hanging space plus 10 lin m on screens and 130 sq m floor space
Exhibitions: 18 a year all originated
Details: Programme includes open art competition and photographic competition. Each exhibition is previewed. Relaxed atmosphere. Tea & coffee facilities. Aims to give the amateur artist the experience of exhibiting. No charges made for exhibition, publicity, preview, etc. Sales a priority.

Thirsk
NORTH YORKSHIRE YHA

Zillah Bell Contemporary Art
Gallery with five rooms showing a wide range of artists, styles and media.
15 Kirkgate, Thirsk YO7 1PQ, tel: 01845 522479, fax: 01845 526558
Contact: Pauline Stoker or J Bell
Open: Mon-Sat 10-5.30
Space: 5 galleries with 72 lin m hanging space and 115 sq m floor space
Exhibitions: 12 a year
Details: Gallery is keen to promote work by talented, less-known artists as well as the more established ones. Each month it concentrates on a featured artist and in addition 2 major exhibitions held a year. Sale of work is not gallery's primary role.

Thornton
WEST YORKSHIRE YHA

South Square Gallery

Gallery with main room for exhibitions of contemporary art and sculpture and community gallery for mainly local group exhibitions.
South Square, Thornton BD13 3LD, tel: 01274 834747
Contact: Patricia Calver, Exhibition Organiser
Open: Tues-Sat 10.30-5; Sun 1-4.30
Space: 2 galleries with 47 lin m hanging space and 57 sq m floor space
Exhibitions: 12 a year all originated

Details: Gallery in artists' studio complex mixing regional and national artists and makers with those from outside Britain. Majority of exhibitions are local group ones. Community gallery is used by disabled and other groups. Stair lift. Sales not a priority.

Thornton Cleveleys
LANCASHIRE NWA

Wryreside Ecology Centre
River Road, Stanah, Thornton Cleveleys FY5 5LR
Contact: Centre Manager

Tiverton
DEVON SWA

Angel Gallery

Gallery attached to vegetarian café/restaurant providing space to show 'unusual' work by contemporary national and international artists.
1 Angel Terrace, Tiverton EX16 6PD, tel: 01884 254778
Contact: Carola Buhse, Proprietor
Open: Mon-Thurs 10-5; Fri & Sat 10-10
Space: 1 gallery with 20 lin m hanging space and 18 sq m floor space
Exhibitions: 4 a year all originated
Details: Visitors invited to discuss exhibition and work in relaxed and open atmosphere in café. 20% commission on sales but selling work not primary function of gallery.

Todmorden
WEST YORKSHIRE YHA

Red Water Arts
Small rural barn gallery and garden for display of sculpture at arts centre.
Back Rough Farm, Coalclough Road, Todmorden OL14 8NU, tel: 01706 815328
Contact: Mike Pemsel, Joint Co-ordinator
Open: Wed-Sun 10-5
Space: 1 gallery with 19 lin m hanging space and 42 sq m floor space
Exhibitions: 3 a year all originated
Details: Exhibitions May – November. Work by established and little-known artists. Open days organised in conjunction with workshops. Also provides a resource for arts activities at the centre and in community. Work sold not a priority but encouraged.

Tonbridge
KENT SEA

Angel Leisure Centre
Exhibitions held in main foyer of sports and leisure centre.
Angel Lane, Tonbridge TN9 1SF, tel: 0173 235 9966
Contact: G Littlejohn, Operations Manager
Open: Mon-Sun 9-11
Exhibitions: 2 a year
Details: Space available for any form of exhibition or display but mostly group shows. Policy is to ensure balanced programme based on demand. Talks and slide-shows arranged occasionally when applicable to event. Apart from annual art exhibition, most shows last two or three days only. Sales not main reason showing work.

Tonbridge Library Gallery
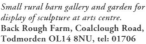
Exhibition space situated between entrance foyer and lending library ensures it is visited by almost everybody using lending facilities.
Avebury Avenue, Tonbridge TN9 1TG, tel: 01732 352754, fax: 01732 358300
Contact: Hilary Streeter, Arts & Libraries Officer
Open: Mon, Tues, Thurs 9.30-7; Wed, Fri 9.30-6; Sat 9.30-5
Space: 1 gallery with 8 lin m hanging space plus 5 lin m on screens
Exhibitions: 17 a year all on a hire basis
Details: Shows primarily work of locally-based artists, but touring exhibitions also shown. Part of Kent County Council Arts & Libraries Department. Programme intended to promote work of living artists working locally and show exhibitions which would not otherwise be seen in the area. Sales not a priority. Artists hang their own exhibition.

Torquay
DEVON SWA

Torre Abbey Historic House & Gallery
Torbay's most historic building, containing period room settings and extensive art galleries set in gardens and parklands.
The Kings Drive, Torquay TQ2 5JX, tel: 01803 293593
Contact: Dr Michael Rhodes, Principal Curator, Borough of Torbay
Open: (Easter-Oct) daily 9.30-6
Space: 2 galleries with 100 lin m hanging space plus 28 lin m on screens and 264 sq m floor space

Exhibitions: 7 a year of which 1 originated, 6 on a hire basis
Details: Stately home owned by Torbay Borough Council. Majority of exhibitions organised by local art and/or craft societies or local professional artists. Some touring exhibitions are shown from Area Museums Council and other institutions. Sales not a priority.

Torrington
DEVON SWA

Plough Gallery

Pa Ph Pr Gr Sc ☯ ⊕ ⓑ ⊛ ④

Large gallery in multi-purpose arts centre specialising in contemporary arts and crafts, mainly by local artists.
Plough Arts Centre, The High Street, Torrington EX38 8HQ, tel: 01805 622552, fax: 01805 624624
Contact: Peter Stiles, Visual Arts Co-ordinator
Open: Wed-Sat 10am-10.30pm
Space: 2 galleries with 37 lin m hanging space
Exhibitions: 12 a year of which 10 originated, 1 touring, 1 on a hire basis
Details: Promotes work by local artists, especially painting, craft and photography. One large main gallery on first floor and additional space in mezzanine and stair areas. Occasionally plays host to touring exhibitions from Arts Council of England etc. Collection of photographs from Beaford Archive available for tour. Attracts cross section of North Devon public. Sale of work is gallery's primary role.

Totnes
DEVON SWA

Dartington Arts Gallery

Pa Ph Pr Gr Sc LA ☯ ⊕ ⓑ

Gallery's purpose is to promote a wide range of visual arts by amateur and professional artists.
Dartington Hall, Totnes TQ9 6DE, tel: 01803 867068/ 865864, fax: 01803 868108
Contact: Marcus Davey, Exhibitions Programmer/Arts Manager
Open: Mon-Fri 10.30-5; Sat & Sun 2-5
Space: 1 gallery with 36 lin m hanging space plus 5 lin m on screens and 86 sq m floor space
Exhibitions: 20 a year of which 19 originated, 1 on a hire basis
Details: Aims to promote the widest possible range of arts and artists and involve participation in the arts by people of all ages and abilities. Work by local, national and international artists is programmed. Suitable for one-person or small group exhibitions. Aims to develop audiences for

specialist and innovative work. Sales not a priority.

Dartington Cider Press Centre

Gr Sc ☯

Commercial gallery stocking local and British craftwork, open all year.
Shinners Bridge, Dartington, Totnes TQ9 6TQ, tel: 01803 864171
Contact: Sales Director
Open: Mon-Sat 9.30-5.30
Space: 100 lin m hanging space plus 50 lin m on screens and 245 sq m floor space
Exhibitions: 6 a year all originated
Details: Mainstream work not avant garde, and appropriate price structure to mainstream sales.

Marshall Arts Gallery *

Pa Pr Gr Sc

Small commercial gallery.
3 Warland, The Plains, Totnes TQ9 5EL, tel: 01803 863533
Contact: Exhibition Organiser
Space: 1 gallery with 23 sq m floor space
Exhibitions: 4 a year all originated
Details: Specialises in individual works by West-Country artists and makers of jewellery, ceramics and turned-wood items.

Seymour Gallery

Pa Ph Pr Gr Sc ☯ ⊕ ⓑ

Gallery with four rooms showing and selling contemporary work for local and national artists.
10 High Street, Totnes TQ9 5RY, tel: 01803 864200
Contact: Shirley Seymour, Gallery owner
Open: Tues-Sat 10.30-4.30
Space: 4 galleries with 100 sq m floor space
Exhibitions: 12 a year of which 10 originated, 1 touring, 1 on a hire basis
Details: Selling gallery aiming to show interesting middle of the road artwork but occasionally something controversial. Two rooms downstairs and two rooms upstairs plus landing and stairs. Wall height 10'.

Towcester
NORTHAMPTONSHIRE EMA

Blakesley Gallery

Pa Gr Sc ☯

Rural commercial gallery housed in 400 year old barn.
Barton House, Blakesley, Towcester NN12 8RE, tel: 01327 860282
Contact: George or Romayne Wisner
Space: 2 galleries with 34 lin m hanging space and 50 sq m floor space
Exhibitions: 4 a year all originated
Details: Mixed exhibitions featuring painting, mostly watercolour, prints, ceramics, glass, sculpture, jewellery and

textiles. Mailing list of 1500. Customers from 30 mile radius.

Towcester Library *

Pa Ph Pr Gr Sc ☯

Library exhibition space.
Richmond Road, Towcester NN12 7EX, tel: 01327 350794
Contact: Community Services Librarian, Brackley Library, Manor Road, Brackley, tel: 01280 703455
Details: See Northamptonshire Libraries, Northampton.

Truro
CORNWALL SWA

Gallery Portscatho

Pa Gr ⓑ

Gallery specialising in work by Newlyn, St Ives artists and modern British art as well as representing selected Cornwall-based artists.
nr St Mawes, Truro TR2 5HQ, tel: 01872 580719
Contact: Christine Insoll, Exhibition Organiser
Open: Mon-Tues, Thurs-Sat 10-12.30, 2-5.30; and by appointment
Space: 2 galleries
Exhibitions: 12 a year all originated
Details: Artists' co-operative which exhibits work by members who work together regularly, usually outside. Applications welcomed from artists willing to work alongside existing members. Gallery helps support a number of artists. No commission taken on members' exhibitions. Sales important but not top priority. Studio above gallery in use all year and open to public on request. Gallery also exhibits and sells locally-acquired collectors' pictures.

Royal Cornwall Museum Galleries

Pa Ph Pr Gr Sc ☯ ⓔ ⓑ ⓦ ④

Permanent display of Cornish, British and European fine and decorative arts and ceramics and temporary exhibitions ranging from major contemporary art to community projects.
River Street, Truro TR1 2SJ, tel: 01872 72205
Contact: Hazel Berriman, Curator of Art & Exhibitions
Open: Mon-Sat 10-5
Space: 2 galleries with 90 lin m hanging space plus 14 lin m on screens and 325 sq m floor space
Exhibitions: 12 a year of which 6 originated, 6 touring
Details: Two exhibition spaces: Theatre Gallery houses community-based and contemporary shows by local artists and also a café; Upper Chapel Gallery used for wide variety of touring & gallery-generated shows of longer duration, including

contemporary art, craft and photography. Audience local throughout year with additional summer tourist trade. Sales not a priority.

Tidelines

Pa Ph Gr ● ④

Gallery/shop with strong coastal theme.
33 St Pirans Road, Perranporth, Truro TR6 0BH, tel: 01872 571302
Contact: Stuart Thorn/Barbara Tremewan
Open: (Summer) Mon-Sat 10-5 & 2-5; (Winter) Thurs-Sat 10-1 & 2-4
Space: 1 gallery with 12 lin m hanging space and 15 sq m floor space
Exhibitions: 4 a year all originated
Details: Exhibitions are held during winter and spring featuring art and craft work with specific local interest. Aims to provide variety of artistic experiences and a showcase for established and younger artists.

Trelissick Gallery

Pa Pr Gr SÉ

Gallery showing and selling work by members of the Cornwall Crafts Association.
Trelissick Gardens, King Harry Ferry, Truro, tel: 01872 864084
Contact: Lynne King, Exhibition Organiser, Cornwall Crafts Association
Details: See also details on Cornwall Crafts Association at Pencarrow, Bodmin and Cornwall Crafts Association at Trellowarren, Helston.

Tunbridge Wells
KENT SEA

Clare Gallery *

Pa SÉ ●

Private gallery.
21 High Street, Tunbridge Wells TN1 1UT, tel: 01892 538717, fax: 01323 29588
Contact: M Ettinger, Exhibition Organiser

Fairfax Gallery

23 The Pantiles, Tunbridge Wells TN2 5TD, tel: 01892 525525
Contact: A Scrutton

Trinity Gallery

Pa Ph Pr Gr SÉ LA ● ④ ④ ⑩

Independent gallery presents work of young, unknown and avant-garde artists.
Trinity Arts Centre, Church Road, Tunbridge Wells TN1 1JP, tel: 01892 525111
Contact: Lesley Bates, Gallery Organiser
Open: Daily 10-12.30
Space: 1 gallery with 10 lin m hanging space and 17 sq m floor space
Exhibitions: 11 a year all on a hire basis

Details: Aims to provide year round accessibility to wide range of high quality contemporary arts and crafts, by exhibiting the work of professional artists demonstrating a diversity of techniques. So hopes to further establish the Trinity Gallery as serious exhibitor of local importance and stimulating the artforms by appealing to a broad audience base, both locally and regionally.

Tunbridge Wells Museum and Art Gallery

Pa Ph Pr Gr SÉ ● ④ ④

Versatile municipal gallery showing wide range of art and craft exhibitions.
Civic Centre, Mount Pleasant, Tunbridge Wells TN1 1JN, tel: 01892 526121/ 547221
Contact: Dr M. Rowlands, Museum Curator
Open: Mon-Sat 9.30-5; closed BH & Easter Sat
Space: 1 gallery with 41 lin m hanging space plus 20 lin m on screens and 92 sq m floor space
Exhibitions: 20 a year of which 6 originated, 2 touring, 12 on a hire basis
Details: Stages a varied programme of work including art and craft of local societies and artists, touring exhibitions from the national galleries, and works from the reserve collection. Sales not primary role but welcomed.

Uley
GLOUCESTERSHIRE SWA

Prema Arts Centre *

Pa Ph Pr SÉ LA ● ④

Rural arts centre showing solo exhibitions of living, working, innovative artists.
South Street, Uley GL11 5SS, tel: 01453 860703, fax: 01453 860123
Contact: Alan Whiteley
Space: 3 galleries
Exhibitions: 12 a year of which 6 originated, 5 touring, 1 on a hire basis
Details: Based in a converted chapel. Programme of classes, workshops, theatre, dance, music, and exhibitions.

Ulverston
CUMBRIA NA

Welfare State International

Pr Gr SÉ LA ● ④ ④ ⑩

The landscaped garden at the company's HQ has been designated a "sculpture park" providing open and intimate places complemented by working studios and interior exhibition spaces.
The Ellers, Ulverston LA12 0AA, tel: 01229 581127, fax: 01229 581232

Contact: David Haley and Sue Gill, General Manager and Education Co-ordinator
Open: Mon-Fri 10-6; plus special events
Space: 1 gallery with 10 lin m hanging space plus 10 lin m on screens and 80 sq m floor space
Exhibitions: 4 a year all originated
Details: First-floor exhibition space with chair lift access and landscaped garden which features local stone, flowing water and installations in oak and hazel. Interior and exterior premises used for wide range of education and training courses also used as sites for performances, gatherings and installations. Individuals and organisations are welcome to use these spaces. Degree of access for wheelchair users varies around site.

Uppermill
GREATER MANCHESTER NWA

Saddleworth Museum & Art Gallery

Pa Ph Gr SÉ ● ④ ④ ⑩

Canal-side gallery in small independent museum displaying mainly North West and Pennine artists.
High Street, Uppermill OL3 6HS, tel: 01457 874093/870336
Contact: Sue Latimer, Curator
Open: (Mar-Oct) Mon-Sat 10-5, Sun 12-5; (Nov-Feb) Mon-Sun 1-4
Space: 1 gallery with 30 lin m hanging space
Exhibitions: 9 a year all on a hire basis
Details: Exhibitions last about 3 weeks. Aims to encourage visitors to enjoy art, and occasionally to provoke. Sale of work is important to Museum funds but new artists encouraged over winter quiet period. Visitors pay admission charge to gallery as part of museum charge.

Ventnor
ISLE OF WIGHT SA

Ventnor Library

Pa Ph Pr Gr ● ④

Pictures hung on walls of lending library.
High Street, Ventnor PO38 1LZ, tel: 01983 852039
Contact: A D Payne, Head of Libraries & Arts, Cultural & Leisure Services Directorate, I.W. County Council, The Guildhall, High Street, Newport, PO30 5TX, tel: 01983 823822, fax: 01983 823841
Exhibitions: 12 a year all on a hire basis
Details: Professional and amateur individual artists and groups. Island population and seasonal visitors. No hanging or commission fee – payment by

picture donation or 10% of sales at discretion.

Wakefield
WEST YORKSHIRE YHA

Bothy Shop/Gallery
Yorkshire Sculpture Park, West Bretton, Wakefield WF4 4LG, tel: 01924 830125
Contact: Dee Barnes

Elizabethan Exhibition Gallery
Po Ph Pr Cr Se ✓ 🖼️4

Municipal gallery with varied programme of temporary exhibitions and range of activities.
Brook Street, Wakefield, tel: 01924 295797, fax: 01924 380299
Contact: Bill Manwaring, Exhibitions Officer, Wakefield Art Gallery, Wentworth Terrace, Wakefield, WF1 3QW, tel: 01924 375402, fax: 01942 380299
Open: (During exhibitions only) Mon-Sat 10.30-5; Sun 2.30-5
Space: 1 gallery with 40 lin m hanging space plus 39 lin m on screens and 123 sq m floor space
Exhibitions: 6 a year of which 3 originated
Details: Maintaina a varied programme of temporary exhibitions, as well as educational and outreach work to local communities and disadvantaged groups. Aims to improve access to all groups and widen audiences and support contemporary artists working locally and regionally. Sales of work not a priority.

Lawrence Batley Centre
Po Ph Pr Cr Se ✓ 🖼️

Gallery/exhibition space featuring work of artists in art and education in order to increase public awareness and to foster an appreciation of art in general.
Bretton Hall, West Bretton, Wakefield WF4 4LG, tel: 01924 830261, fax: 01924 832043
Contact: Leonard Bartle, Centre Administrator
Open: Mon-Fri 9-5; closed BH
Space: 1 gallery with 14 lin m hanging space plus 35 lin m on screens and 61 sq m floor space
Exhibitions: 12 a year
Details: Open-plan foyer, exhibition area and adaptable studio/performance area, incorporating full tailor-made flexible exhibition system with display and performance lighting. Exhibitions of established and younger artists and designers, archive art and education exhibitions. Sales not a priority.

Marie Jordan Gallery *
Po Ph Pr Cr Se ✓

Gallery specialising in domestic-scale works and large bronzes for gardens for sale to discerning customers.
659 Barnsley Road, Wakefield WF2 6HJ, tel: 01924 255419
Contact: Marie Jordan, Exhibition Organiser
Space: 1 gallery with 8 sq m floor space
Exhibitions: 4 a year all originated
Details: Three different floor areas including a balcony area. Changing displays of work for sale and four exhibitions a year. Contemporary work with the accent on quality, prices vary but range from £10-£1000. Exhibitions last for 4-6 weeks and favour solo promotions or group shows.

Wakefield Art Gallery
Po Ph Pr Cr Se ✓ 🖼️

Municipal gallery housing important collection of British modern art with related programme of temporary exhibitions.
Wentworth Terrace, Wakefield WF1 3QW, tel: 01924 295796, fax: 01924 380299
Contact: Antonino Vella, Keeper of Art
Open: Mon-Sat 10.30-5; Sun 2.30-5; closed Christmas & New Year
Space: 3 galleries with 50 lin m hanging space and 80 sq m floor space
Exhibitions: 2 a year both originated
Details: Of six temporary exhibitions held a year, usually 2 are contemporary shows originated by gallery. In selecting exhibitions priority is given too regional artists/craftspeople. Education and outreach an important part of exhibitions programme.

Wakefield College Arts Centre
Po Ph Pr Cr Se ✓

Margaret Street, Wakefield WF1 2DH, tel: 01924 810339
Contact: Pete Morton, Exhibitions Officer
Space: 4 galleries with 280 lin m hanging space
Exhibitions: 12 a year all originated
Details: Shows mainly young and upcoming artists. Also making room for established artists.

Yorkshire Sculpture Park
Pr Cr 💷 🖼️4

One of Europe's leading open air sculpture galleries with extensive programme of temporary national and international exhibitions.
Bretton Hall, West Bretton, Wakefield WF4 4LG, tel: 01924 830579, fax: 01924 830044
Contact: Clare Lilley, Art Coordinator
Open: Galleries: (Winter) daily 11-4,

(Summer) daily 11-5; Park: (Winter) daily 10-4, (Summer) daily 10-6
Space: 2 galleries with 73 lin m hanging space and 205 sq m floor space
Exhibitions: 13 a year of which 11 originated, 2 touring
Details: 100 acres of C18th parkland. Programme of temporary exhibitions and projects. Collection includes Rodin, Hepworth, Paladino, Le Witt, Nash, Serra. Permanent display of large sculptures by Henry Moore in adjoining 96 acre country park. Sculpture purchased and commissioning consultancy service. Bursary and residency programme. Education programme includes master classes and environmental work. Access Sculpture Trail designed for people with disabilities. Free booster scooters for those who have difficulty walking. Large print leaflet, free audio tapes. Café and book/craft shop. Selling work not a priority.

Walberswick
SUFFOLK EA

Parish Lantern
Po Ph Cr Se ✓ 🇭 🖼️

Shop selling local crafts with tea garden and gallery upstairs; also Lantern Gallery available for hire by artists.
Village Green, Walberswick IP18 6TT, tel: 01502 723173
Contact: Mary Allen, Owner
Open: (Apr – Christmas Eve) daily; (Jan, Feb, Mar) Fri, Sat & Sun
Space: 2 galleries
Exhibitions: 20 a year of which 6 originated, 14 on a hire basis
Details: First-floor gallery above shop available to artists for exhibiting work. Commission taken on work sold. Owner also runs Lantern Gallery next door but one; this space for hire to artists on weekly rental basis. At Lantern Gallery artists organise all aspects of exhibition and invigilation. Opening hours therefore at hirer's discretion. Independent access for wheelchair users to Lantern Gallery.

Wallingford
OXFORDSHIRE SA

Julius Gottlieb Gallery
Po Ph Pr Cr Se ✓ 🖼️

Large open space on 3 levels showing contemporary work in wide variety of media.
Carmel College, Wallingford OX10 8BT, tel: 01491 837505, fax: 01491 825305
Contact: Hilary Campbell, Gallery Administrator
Open: Sun-Fri 10-1 & 2-4
Space: 1 gallery with 60 lin m hanging space plus 30 lin m on screens and 93 sq m floor space

Exhibitions: 6 a year all originated
Details: Unique setting on the banks of the river Thames. A pyramid designed by Basil Spence. Aims to show a wide variety of contemporary artists both for the general public and the college students who use the gallery in their studies. Selling work is not gallery's primary role.

Wallsend
TYNE & WEAR NA

Buddle (The)

Exhibitions of contemporary work biased towards women though annual open exhibition is more traditional and varied.
258b Station Road, Wallsend NE28 8RH, tel: 0191 262 4276, fax: 0191 295 1947
Contact: Carol Alevroyianni, Arts Development Officer
Open: Tues-Fri 10-5; occasional evenings
Space: 1 gallery with 50 lin m hanging space and 80 sq m floor space
Exhibitions: 7 a year all originated
Details: Particularly interested in showing work which celebrates a theme. Photographic exhibitions both documentary and experimental are a major part of the programme. Annual Open Art Exhibition (Nov-Dec) attracts a wide variety of work and is a selling exhibition. Audience comprises visitors to the building for other reasons as well as schools, disabled groups, colleges and both performance and visual artists. Selling work not primary function of gallery.

Walsall
WEST MIDLANDS WMA

Walsall Museum & Art Gallery

Gallery aiming to increase audiences for contemporary art by showing range of work with innovative approaches to presentation and interpretation.
Lichfield Street, Walsall WS1 1TR, tel: 01922 653116/ 653196, fax: 01922 32824
Contact: Deborah Robinson, Senior Exhibitions Officer
Open: Tues-Sat 10 5; Sun 2-5
Space: 2 galleries with 75 lin m hanging space plus 28 lin m on screens and 199 sq m floor space
Exhibitions: 12 a year of which 9 originated, 3 touring
Details: Particularly committed to creating new audiences for contemporary visual arts and C20th developments. Large percentage of audience local, many attend frequently.

Audience reflects the cultural diversity of region. Selling work not gallery's main aim.

Waltham Abbey
ESSEX EA

Epping Forest District Museum

Wide range of temporary exhibitions ranging from historical subjects to contemporary arts and crafts.
39/41 Sun Street, Waltham Abbey EN9 1EL, tel: 01992 716882, fax: 01992 700427
Contact: Kate Carver, Museum Officer
Open: Fri-Mon 2-5; Tues 12-5; party bookings on Wed & Thurs by appointment.
Space: 2 galleries with 30 lin m hanging space plus 12 lin m on screens and 104 sq m floor space
Exhibitions: 10 a year of which 8 originated, 2 touring
Details: As part of exhibitions programme runs county-wide biennial open exhibition 'Artists in Essex'. Work sold from temporary exhibitions. Applications welcome but programme booked up to 18-24 months ahead. Extensive education programme runs in tandem with temporary exhibition programme. Many activities for children and adults. Sales not a priority.

Walton on Thames
SURREY SEA

Boathouse Gallery

The Towpath, Manor Road, Walton on Thames KT12 2PG, tel: 01932 242718
Contact: Bernard Clark
Open: Mon-Sat 10-5
Space: 1 gallery with 49 lin m hanging space and 27 sq m floor space
Exhibitions: 12 a year all originated
Details: Sited between two excellent hostelries, right next to riverbank. Has as much to offer inside as out. Contemporary artists in watercolour, oil and pastels form programme of monthly exhibitions. More occasional shows of photography and print. Most exhibitions group shows of local artists as well as artists from further afield.

Ware
HERTFORDSHIRE EA

Trading Places Gallery

Contemporary gallery encouraging the emerging and established artist to sell and display.

11 New Road, Ware SG12 7BS, tel: 01920 469620, fax: 01920 463003
Contact: Mrs K Walden, Exhibition Organiser
Open: Tues & Sat 11.30-4.30; or by arrangement
Space: 1 gallery with 152 lin m hanging space plus 3 lin m on screens
Exhibitions: 4 a year all on a hire basis
Details: Specialises in contemporary British oil and watercolour paintings, studio ceramics, blown & kiln formed glass, bronzes, designer jewellery and tapestries. Gallery has showcases in various hotels. Aims to bring together new craft design work by both established and emerging artists. Available for hire by individuals or groups of professional artists. Sales a priority.

Wareham
DORSET SWA

Peter Hedley Gallery

10 South Street, Wareham BH20 4LT, tel: 01929 551777
Contact: Peter Hedley
Open: Mon-Sat, 9.30-5.30
Space: 2 galleries with 60 sq m floor space
Exhibitions: 7 a year all originated
Details: Well-established contemporary art gallery showing mainly figurative paintings and sculpture. Programme includes mixture of solo and mixed shows which attract visitors from all over region and rest of country.

Trinity Art Gallery *

Commercial gallery in converted church.
32a South Street, Wareham BH20 4LU, tel: 01929 556541
Contact: Douglas Chaffey, Exhibition Organiser
Space: 2 galleries with 191 sq m floor space
Details: Ever changing exhibition of paintings and sculpture. Encourage known and unknown artists.

Warminster
WILTSHIRE SA

Athenaeum *

Theatre, cinema and coffee bar gallery.
High Street, Warminster BA12 9AE, tel: 01985 218519/ 213891
Contact: Amanda Harper, Administrator
Space: 1 gallery
Exhibitions: 8 a year all originated
Details: Encourages participation in, and enjoyment of, range of arts activities by all ages and abilities. Presents varied selection of art work – photography, paintings,

drawings – by both professional and amateur artists, in informal setting. Encourages casual visitors to coffee lounge, and theatre-goers to look at and enjoy work on walls.

Warrington
CHESHIRE NWA

Warrington Museum and Art Gallery

Municipal museum providing exhibitions having both national and regional appeal.
Bold Street, Warrington WA1 1JG, tel: 01925 442392
Contact: Alan Leigh, Curator
Details: Founded in 1848. Collections of C18th and C19th fine art. Temporary exhibitions includes historic and contemporary material to stimulate interest in art, past and present. Within limitations of the building, all visual art forms encouraged. Solo shows restricted to professional artists. Promotes public involvement with exhibitions through activities organised by the education department. One space has been redesignated a community gallery.

Warwick
WARWICKSHIRE WMA

Mill Gallery

Two galleries in crafts village showing work by professional and amateur artists and makers.
Hatton Country World, Dark Lane, Hatton, Warwick CV35 8XA, tel: 01926 842436
Contact: Peter Maylor-Yates, Exhibitions Organiser
Open: Mon-Sun 10.30-5.30; times vary so check first.
Space: 2 galleries
Exhibitions: 12 a year of which 6 originated, 6 on a hire basis
Details: Large main gallery with specialist lighting, brick walls and beams and smaller gallery used for classes. Space generally hired to artists but quality considered important and work is screened. Gallery forms nucleus and meeting place for people interested in art. Classes run from basic to advanced. Sale of work not gallery's primary role. Gallery flexible about sales and can take work on sale or return basis if they like it.

Warwick Gallery

Gallery specialising in contemporary work by established and emerging British artists and craftspeople.

12/14 Smith Street, Warwick CV34 4HH, tel: 01926 495880
Contact: Peter Forde
Open: Mon-Sat 9.30-5
Space: 1 gallery
Exhibitions: 1 a year originated
Details: One exhibition held a year, usually by one of artists/craftspeople already displaying work in gallery/shop. Remainder of year gallery/shop holds continuous changing display of ceramics, jewellery, wood, studio glass, prints and watercolours. Sales very important.

Warwickshire Museum

Small ground-floor gallery with exposed timbers, stone floor and pillars, within the Warwickshire Museums Market Hall.
Market Place, Warwick CV34 4SA, tel: 01926 412500, fax: 01926 419840
Contact: Catherine Roberts, Museum Designer
Open: (Oct-April) Mon-Sat 10-5.30; (May-Sept) Mon-Sat 10-5.30, Sun 2.30-5
Space: 1 gallery with 27 lin m hanging space and 43 sq m floor space
Exhibitions: 6 a year of which 2 touring, 4 on a hire basis
Details: The majority of Warwickshire Museums' 72,000 visitors per year will visit the temporary exhibition gallery. The gallery has Museum & Galleries Commission approved security. Controllable lux levels.

Washington
TYNE & WEAR NA

Arts Centre (Washington)

Gallery in an arts centre which aims to increase public awareness and appreciation of art.
Biddick Lane, Fatfield, District 7, Washington NE38 8AB, tel: 0191 416 6440, fax: 0191 415 7662
Contact: Helen Gordon-Hogg, Manager
Open: Mon 9-5; Tues-Sat 9-7.30; later depending on programme
Space: 1 gallery with 30 lin m hanging space plus 12 lin m on screens and 350 sq m floor space
Exhibitions: 12 a year all originated
Details: Policy to show work of local artists and work reflecting local culture, as well as quality art and craft from further afield. Exhibitions often integrated with other arts activities: music, dance, theatre etc. Exhibitions also tend towards combined ventures, eg local schools exhibitions, disabled artists exhibitions. Sales not a priority.

Watford
HERTFORDSHIRE EA

Oxhey Library

Separate exhibition room in public library with hessian walls and screens for wide variety of displays.
Bridlington Road, South Oxhey, Watford WD1 6AG, tel: 0181 428 2868
Contact: Miss Lee Abraham, Librarian
Open: Mon & Fri 10-6; Tues & Thurs 10-7.30; Sat 9.30-1
Space: 1 gallery with 28 sq m floor space
Details: Exhibition room available for free hire for 3-week periods. Work by local artists and art groups shown. Lighting by spots on tracks and hanging by mirror plates and picture hooks. Screens available. 5% + VAT commission on sales. Artist to arrange publicity. No library staff available to invigilate. Library organises educational activities, talks, etc.

Watford Central Library

Exhibition room on first floor within library showing work by local artists and craftspeople.
Hempstead Road, Watford WD1 3EU, tel: 01923 226230
Contact: Andrew Bignell, Town Librarian
Open: Mon, Tues, Thurs, Fri 9.30-8; Wed 9.30-1; Sat 9.30-4
Space: 1 gallery with 96 sq m floor space
Exhibitions: 12 a year all originated
Details: Programme put together by invitation and application. Special exhibitions mounted occasionally and out of area exhibitions considered. Fluorescent lighting and daylight. Two large double-fronted display cases available but no plinths. Hanging onto peg boards with clips. No hire charge. 5% + VAT commission if exhibitor handles sales; 20% + VAT if library handles sales. Library staff may be able to help with installation. Library promote exhibitions by posters, press and radio if shows organised by library.

Watford Museum

Two designated temporary exhibition galleries within local history museum run by Watford Council.
194 High Street, Watford WD1 2HG, tel: 01923 232297, fax: 01923 249729
Contact: Andrew Lewis, Manager, Culture, Museum & Arts
Open: Mon-Fri 10-5; Sat 10-1, 2-5; closed BH
Space: 2 galleries with 48 lin m hanging space plus 4 lin m on screens and 270 sq m floor space

Exhibitions: 8 a year of which 5 originated, 1 touring, 2 on a hire basis
Details: Exhibitions aimed at complementing & enhancing permanent displays. Also used to attract repeat visits and non-users. Exhibitions of local artists and art societies. Each show lasts 4 weeks. Touring exhibitions and Herts Open Art Exhibition. Collection of painting & sculpture on permanent display. Sales are welcome (35% commission) but not a priority. Independent access for wheelchair users to one gallery; other gallery only with assistance.

Wednesbury
WEST MIDLANDS WMA

Wednesbury Museum & Art Gallery

Pa Ph Pr Gr Sc ●

Permanent collection and temporary exhibition programme of local and regional artists and craftspeople.
Holyhead Road, Wednesbury WS10 7DF, tel: 0121 556 0683, fax: 0121 505 1625
Contact: Martin Senior, Keeper of Museums
Space: 2 galleries with 44 lin m hanging space plus 8 lin m on screens and 102 sq m floor space
Exhibitions: 12 a year of which 6 originated, 6 touring
Details: Showing a wide variety of work including touring exhibitions from Ikon Gallery, the Arts Council and work by local artists. There are two rooms available, the smaller one on a no cost basis.

Wellingborough
NORTHAMPTONSHIRE EMA

Gallery (The) *

Pa Pr Sc ● ⊕

Commercial gallery aims to show diversity of approach and to break down elitist attitudes to art.
108 Midland Road, Wellingborough NN8 1NB, tel: 01933 274215
Contact: John Black, Exhibition Organiser
Space: 700 lin m hanging space
Exhibitions: 12 a year all originated
Details: Holds monthly exhibitions of paintings, with an opening on the first Sunday of each month with a musical recital. No 'house style'. Space also available for hire.

Wellingborough Library *

Pa Ph Pr Gr Sc ● ⊕

Library exhibition space available for hire.
Pebble Lane, Wellingborough NN8 1AS, tel: 01933 225365, fax: 01933 442060

Contact: Derrick Bond/Dominica Jones, Assistant County Librarian (East)
Space: 1 gallery with 14 lin m hanging space and 42 sq m floor space
Exhibitions: 12 a year of which 1 originated, 11 on a hire basis
Details: (See also Northamptonshire Libraries.) Workshops and demonstrations arranged.

Wellington
SOMERSET SWA

Pitminster Studio

Pa Ph Pr ● ●

Exhibition space within courtyard of converted stone barns.
Budleigh Farm, West Buckland, Wellington TA21 9LW, tel: 01823 42710
Contact: Tim or Karen Everett, Partners
Open: By appointment; Daily 10-5 during exhibitions
Space: 2 galleries with 46 lin m hanging space and 105 sq m floor space
Exhibitions: 3 a year all originated
Details: Selling work is gallery's primary function.

Wells next the Sea
NORFOLK EA

Holkham Art Gallery

Pa Ph Pr Sc ● ⊘

Four first-floor cottage-size rooms in 1680 building, exhibiting contemporary paintings in wide range of styles and prices.
The Ancient House, Holkham Village, Wells next the Sea NR23 1RS, tel: 01328 710783
Contact: Margaret Melicharova, Gallery Organiser, Stable Cottage, Creake Road, Burnham Thorpe, Kings Lynn, PE31 8HW, tel: 01328 738 625
Open: (Good Friday-Nov) Mon-Sun 10-1, 2-5; (Nov-Dec) Sat-Sun 10-1, 2-5; (Christmas-Easter) closed
Space: 4 galleries with 60 lin m hanging space and 900 sq m floor space
Exhibitions: 5 a year all originated
Details: Four rooms on first floor of The Ancient House in Holkham Village, close to the sea and to Holkham Park. Café and giftshop on ground floor. Permanent (but changing) exhibition of paintings and prints by leading local artists, and occasional solo exhibitions. All work is contemporary. Varies from traditional to avant-garde, figurative to abstract. Prices from £40 to £1000 with commission and VAT charged on sales made. Sales a priority.

School House Gallery *

Pa Pr Gr Sc

Regular exhibitions of selected contemporary paintings, watercolours, drawings and limited edition prints – both national and international.
Wighton, Wells Next The Sea NR23 1AL, tel: 01328 820457
Contact: Diana Cohen, Director
Space: 1 gallery with 50 lin m hanging space
Exhibitions: 6 a year all originated
Details: Work of the foremost modern East Anglian artists always in stock. Annually, during August and September, a mixed exhibition of some of the best and most lively work to be found in the region.

Westcliff on Sea
ESSEX EA

Beecroft Art Gallery

Pa Ph Pr Gr Sc ● ⊕

Functions as a focus for visual arts displaying works by local and British artists.
Station Road, Westcliff on Sea SS0 7RA, tel: 01702 347418
Contact: Mrs M Maton, Assistant Keeper Human History (Art)
Open: Tues-Sat 9.30-5
Space: 8 galleries with 173 lin m hanging space and 229 sq m floor space
Exhibitions: 16 a year all originated
Details: Permanent collection of works from the C16th-C20th. C17th Dutch and Flemish paintings and some fine watercolours. Hires out studio space to teachers in various media. Encourages art groups to meet on premises. Programme of exhibitions includes major selected exhibition for Essex artists each summer. Two other annual events are Southend Schools Exhibition and Southend Art Club Exhibition.

Whitby
NORTH YORKSHIRE YHA

Montage Studio Gallery

Pa Ph Gr Sc ● ⊘

Selling gallery showing original contemporary art in variety of media.
12 Church Street, Castleton, Whitby YO21 2EQ, tel: 01287 660159
Contact: Jean Freer, Proprietor
Open: (Easter-Christmas) Tues-Sat 10-5, Sun 2-5; (Christmas-Easter) Thurs-Sat 10-4.30
Space: 3 galleries with 24 lin m hanging space and 33 sq m floor space
Exhibitions: 18 a year all originated
Details: Exhibitions held fortnightly Easter-Christmas. Artists have free range to use space as they wish. Talks and courses by

artists, photographers, ceramicists etc in the studio. Sales a priority.

Whitehaven
CUMBRIA NA

Beacon (The)
Po Ph Pr Cr Sc ✓ ♿ wc

Centre opening mid-1995, replacing Whitehaven Museum and Art Gallery.
South Beach, Whitehaven CA28 7SH
Contact: Barbara Barnes, Manager
Space: 1 gallery with 30 lin m hanging space plus 20 lin m on screens and 92 sq m floor space
Details: Centre has exhibition room specifically for temporary exhibitions of national importance. Also has additional space for smaller exhibitions, one-person or groups, preferably based in the region.

Foyer Gallery
Po Ph Pr Cr ✓ ♿

Exhibition space within theatre available for local amateur and professional artists.
Rosehill Theatre, Moresby, Whitehaven CA28 6SE, tel: 01946 692422
Contact: Jennifer Woodward, Administrator
Space: 1 gallery with 10 lin m hanging space plus 59 sq m floor space
Exhibitions: 4 a year all originated
Details: Primary motive is that the work will be seen by theatre audiences.

Whitstable
KENT SEA

Whitstable Museum & Gallery
Po Ph Pr Cr Sc ✓ ♿ 4

Varied exhibition programme of art and historical shows.
Oxford Street, Whitstable CT5 1DB, tel: 01227 276998
Contact: Manda Gifford
Open: Mon, Tues, Thurs-Sat 10.30-1, 2-4
Space: 1 gallery with 25 lin m hanging space plus 12 lin m on screens and 36 sq m floor space
Exhibitions: 2 a year both originated
Details: Exploration of unique coastal community and seafaring traditions. Exhibitions relating to Whitstable and surrounding area, coast and wildlife. Also some touring exhibitions. Selling work not gallery's main aim.

Whittlesford
CAMBRIDGESHIRE EA

Peppin Brown Gallery
Po Ph Pr Cr Sc ✓ ♨ ♿

Hanging space incorporated within busy framing and restoration business.
The Old School, High Street, Whittlesford, tel: 01223 836394
Contact: Darryl Nantais, Proprietor
Open: Mon, Wed-Fri 9.30-6; Tues 9.30-9; Sat 9.45-5.30; other times by appointment
Space: 1 gallery with 20 lin m hanging space plus 4 lin m on screens and 270 sq m floor space
Exhibitions: 6 a year of which 3 originated, 3 on a hire basis
Details: Exhibitions last two weeks with organised previews for collectors and regular clients. Gallery exhibits only work it considers of a high standard.

Wickford
ESSEX EA

Wickford Library *
Po Pr Cr Sc ✓ ♨

Exhibition space in public gallery, available for hire.
Market Road, Wickford SS12 0AG, tel: 01268 732354
Contact: Joanne Cullen, Library Manager
Space: 1 gallery
Exhibitions: 8 a year of which 1 originated, 7 on a hire basis
Details: Exhibitions of an educational or cultural nature, arts and craft exhibitions with or without sale of work, exhibitions nominated by other bodies including industrial and commercial organisations.

Wigan
LANCASHIRE NWA

Drumcroon Art Centre
Po Ph Pr Cr Sc ✓ ℰ

Edwardian doctor's house and surgery. Has operated for past twelve years as education art centre.
2 Parsons Walk, Wigan WN1 1RS, tel: 01942 321840/ 33303
Contact: Curriculum Adviser for Art
Open: Mon-Fri 9-5
Space: 5 galleries with 73 lin m hanging space and 79 sq m floor space
Exhibitions: 5 a year all originated
Details: Exhibition spaces, coffee lounge, library, resident artists' studios, workshop areas etc. 5 exhibitions per year covering art, craft and design, 2D, 3D and textiles media. Extensive education programme used daily by schools, colleges, private individuals.

Metropolitan Borough of Wigan
Po Ph Pr Cr Sc LA

Co-ordinates exhibitions in local authority buildings in Wigan, including libraries.
Leisure Services Department, Trencherfield Mill, Wallgate, Wigan WN3 4EF, tel: 01942 828536, fax: 01942 828540
Contact: Stephen Ruffley
Details: Exhibition space available in the following buildings in the Wigan area: Golborne Library, Ashton Library, Parlour at the Pier, Shevington Library, Standish Library and Wigan Library. See also entry for Turnpike Gallery, Leigh.

Wimborne
DORSET SWA

Walford Mill Craft Centre
Ph Pr Cr ♿ wc

Accessible ground-floor gallery within a converted C18th mill, showing a wide range of contemporary crafts.
Stone Lane, Wimborne BH21 1NL, tel: 01202 841400
Contact: Margaret Woodhead, Director
Open: (Easter-Xmas) Mon-Sun 10-5; Closed Christmas, Boxing and New Year's Day; (New Year-Easter) Tues-Sun 10-5
Space: 1 gallery with plus 30 lin m on screens and 70 sq m floor space
Exhibitions: 6 a year of which 4 originated, 2 touring
Details: Exhibitions held adjacent to craft shop selling contemporary work. Balanced programme aiming to show best in contemporary craft and design. High-educational, interpretational content. Venue for medium-scale touring shows. Very little permanent hanging space. Large number of windows/limited wall space. Best for 3D work. Some screens available, plus numerous plinths and boxes. Lux levels problematic. Sale of work not gallery's primary concern.

Winchester
HAMPSHIRE SA

Circle Bar Gallery
Po Pr ✓ ♨ ♿

Small commercial gallery exhibiting stimulating work by, mostly, Hampshire artists.
Theatre Royal, Jewry Street, Winchester SO23 8SB, tel: 01962 843434/ 842123/ 842122, fax: 01962 840039
Contact: Gillian Lovegrove, Gallery Manager
Open: Mon-Sat 10-5 via Box Office & during theatre hours
Space: 1 gallery with 17 lin m hanging space and 34 sq m floor space

Exhibitions: 11 a year of which 10 originated, 1 on a hire basis
Details: Gallery introduces visual arts into theatre experience. Gallery shows broad range of work from amateur and professional artists, mostly one-person exhibitions. Good attendance during day as well as theatre going audience. Wall-hung work only. Sale of work very important as 40% commission helps maintain theatre.

Guildhall Gallery

Pa Ph Pr Cr SS ○ H ○ We

Gallery aims to promote local artists' and groups' work although not all work exhibited is by local artists.
The Broadway, Winchester SO23 9LJ, tel: 01962 848289, fax: 01962 841365
Contact: Christopher Wardman Bradbury, Keeper of Exhibitions, Winchester Museums Service, Hyde Historic Resources Centre, 75 Hyde Street, Winchester, SO23 7DW, tel: 01962 848296, fax: 01962 841365
Open: (Oct-Mar) Tues-Sat 10-5, Sun 2-5; (Apr-Sept) Tues-Sat 10-5, Sun & Mon 2-5
Space: 2 galleries with 72 lin m hanging space plus 28 lin m on screens and 108 sq m floor space
Exhibitions: 22 a year of which 21 originated, 1 on a hire basis
Details: Sited on the first-floor of Guildhall above tourist information centre. Exhibitions include paintings, sculpture, crafts, photography, etc. One exhibition per year – part of the city's topographical collection. Audience: locals, tourists, all year round. Schools exhibit if work submitted to museums service. Most of work for sale although sales not primary role of gallery.

Hampshire County Council Museums Service

Pa Ph Pr Cr SS ○ ①

Aims to provide stimulating, lively and relevant programme of temporary exhibitions in eight of its museums.
Chilcomb House, Chilcomb Lane, Winchester SO23 8RD, tel: 01962 846334, fax: 01962 869836
Contact: Carol Littlefair, Exhibitions Officer
Details: Exhibitions held at Allen Gallery, Andover Museum, Willis Museum, Red House Museum and gardens, Eastleigh Museum, Westbury Manor Museum, Gosport Museum and Havant Museum (see separate entries for each). Programme includes contemporary and historical art & craft as well as social and natural history, costume & textiles, etc. Provides access to council collections not normally on display. Educational programme. Sales not high priority. 20% commission. Well used by local audiences.

Winchester Gallery

Pa Ph Pr Cr SS ○ ① ① ○ We

Part of Winchester School of Art, so mainly contemporary art and design shows, with growing emphasis on selected, mixed exhibitions.
Park Avenue, Winchester SO23 8DL, tel: 01962 852500, fax: 01962 842496
Contact: John Gillett, Director
Open: Tues-Fri 10-4.30
Space: 2 galleries
Exhibitions: 17 a year of which 16 originated, 1 touring
Details: Naturally lit through roof over 20' high. Operating base for Southern Arts Touring Exhibition Service. Slide submissions received from the gallery programme are also viewed with the touring programme in mind.

Windsor
BERKSHIRE SA

Old Court Gallery

Pa Ph Pr Cr SS ○ ⊗

Arts centre with well lit and pleasant gallery aiming to serve local community with varied and stimulating programme.
Windsor Arts Centre, St Leonard's Road, Windsor SL4 3DB, tel: 01753 859421
Contact: Jenny Joyce, Arts Centre Coordinator
Open: Mon 4-11; Tues-Fri 9.30-11; Sat 9.30-3, 7-11; Sun 7-10.30; Sun 7-10.30
Space: 1 gallery with 34 lin m hanging space and 60 sq m floor space
Exhibitions: 8 a year all originated
Details: Gallery on first floor and while relatively small and high, is well lit. Encourages sales but prime purpose is to promote new work. No charge to hire the gallery but takes 20% commission on sales. Gallery run by volunteers so input is required from artists to help publicise and display their work. Unsupervised during open hours but there is CCTV system in operation. Gallery not accessible to wheelchair users but ground-floor theatre is (live art, films concerts, etc).

Winsford
CHESHIRE NWA

Vale Royal Community Arts Centre

Pa Ph Pr Cr SS ⒧ ○ ① We ④

Gallery space within multi-functional room aims to present a mixture of styles and media to users of arts centre.
Dene Drive, Winsford CW7 1AU, tel: 01606 863988
Contact: Sally Probert, Centre Adminstrator
Open: Mon-Fri 10-4

Space: 1 gallery with 15 lin m hanging space and 19 sq m floor space
Exhibitions: 10 a year all originated
Details: About 4 shows a year are of contemporary work. Exhibits artists from North West and work of local groups. Aims to promote diverse range of work within the community to challenge any preconceived notions of art.

Woodford Visual Art Centre

Pa Ph Pr Cr SS ⒧ ○ H

Educational gallery to display pupils' and students' work and allow them to study work of professional contemporary artists.
Woodford Lane West, Winsford CW7 4EH, tel: 01606 557328, fax: 01606 862113
Contact: David J. Firmstone, County Senior Art Adviser
Open: (Term-time only) Mon-Fri 9-4.30
Space: 1 gallery with 140 lin m hanging space plus 82 lin m on screens and 475 sq m floor space
Exhibitions: 4 a year of which 3 originated, 1 on a hire basis
Details: Exists primarily for Cheshire schools and colleges. Usually four three-month exhibitions a year, open to schools and the public. Workshop area with teacher/staff member in attendance during school time.

Winslow
BUCKINGHAMSHIRE SA

Redfield Exhibition Gallery

Pa Ph Pr Cr SS ○ ⊗ We

Exhibition/studio space in converted Victorian stable block, run with open attitude towards contemporary art, new experimental art, multi-media work and crafts.
Redfield, Buckingham Road, Winslow MK18 3LZ, tel: 01296 713661, fax: 01296 714983
Contact: Gallery Co-ordinator
Open: By arrangement
Space: 1 gallery with 25 lin m hanging space plus 25 lin m on screens and 85 sq m floor space
Details: Encourages exhibitions on eco-political themes. Gallery itself is within a large community which will consider using its land and facilities in conjunction with the gallery. Artists' contribution to exhibition costs negotiable. Sale of work not gallery's primary consideration.

Wirksworth
DERBYSHIRE EMA

Howard Gallery

🄿🄿🄿🄶 ✔ &

Selling gallery promoting professionally trained artists, printmakers and nationally-known studio potters.
4 West End, Wirksworth DE4 4EG, tel:
01629 823557
Contact: M.W.R. & M.M.C. Howard
Space: 40 lin m hanging space plus 50 lin m on screens
Exhibitions: 2 a year both originated
Details: Housed on the ground floor of a C16th town house of great character. Two main exhibitions per year. One in May and one in November. Interested in artists who are able to produce good quality watercolours, particularly of Derbyshire.

Modern Print Gallery *

🄿

Commercial gallery set up to promote prints and printmaking.
25 Market Place, Wirksworth DE4 4ET,
tel: 01629 824525
Space: 2 galleries with 20 lin m hanging space and 37 sq m floor space
Exhibitions: 3 a year all originated
Details: Shows modern and contemporary prints through solo and thematic exhibitions.

Wisbech
CAMBRIDGESHIRE EA

Angles Centre

🄿🄿🄿🄸 ✔🄷 &

Small area in bar/foyer hired out.
Alexandra Road, Wisbech PE13 1HQ,
tel: 01945 585587
Contact: Ida Jones, Administrator
Open: Mon-Sat 10-11
Space: 1 gallery with 11 lin m hanging space
Exhibitions: 26 a year of which 13 originated, 13 on a hire basis
Details: Houses 112 seat theatre, large and small studio.Children's arts activities, pottery, drama clubs, youth theatre, workshops, live theatre (amateur and professional). Exhibitions usually run on a two-weekly basis. Artists seeking exhibition space are charged a hanging fee.

Hudson Gallery

🄿🄿🄿🄶🅂 ✔🄷 ⊘

Gallery available for exhibitions and/or lectures.
Wisbech & Fenland Museum, Museum Square, Wisbech PE13 1ES, tel: 01945 583817
Contact: David C. Devenish, BA, AMA

Open: (Summer) Tues-Sat 10-5; (Winter) Tues-Sat 10-4
Space: 1 gallery with 15 lin m hanging space plus 21 lin m on screens and 100 sq m floor space
Exhibitions: 14 a year of which 11 originated, 3 on a hire basis
Details: Fixed screens along two sides, windows along another. Movable screens across fourth side or in centre. Exhibitions include: artists' work for sale (20% commission); exhibitions of items not for sale, accepted on a no cost basis; exhibitions organised by the Museum using part of permanent collection. Entrance free to the public.

Skylark Studios

🄿🄿🄿🄶 ✔ &

Gallery housed in converted barn.
Hannarth Road, Tydd Gote, Wisbech PE13 5ND, tel: 01945 420403
Contact: Louise Williams
Open: Wed-Fri 10-5; Sat 11-5; Sun 11-4
Space: 1 gallery with 15 lin m hanging space and 30 sq m floor space
Exhibitions: 12 a year all originated
Details: Varied programme of one-person and group shows lasting about 1 month each. Also permanent display of jewellery, ceramics, wood, print bins and handmade cards. Workshop area with variety of arts events for the community. Sales from gallery not a priority.

Witham
ESSEX EA

Witham Library

🄿🄿🄶🅂 ✔🄷 🄐🅆

Exhibition space in library aims to provide focal point for the local community.
18 Newland Street, Witham CM8 2AQ,
tel: 01376 519625, fax: 01376 501913
Contact: Jane Richardson, Library Manager
Open: Mon, Tues, Thurs, Fri 9-7; Sat 9-5
Space: 1 gallery with plus 31 lin m on screens and 17 sq m floor space
Exhibitions: 8 a year all on a hire basis
Details: Exhibitions are viewed by library users and art work is often purchased although sale of work is not primary role of venue.

Witney
OXFORDSHIRE SA

We Three Kings

🄶

Contemporary jewllery, ceramics, wood and glass.
19 Bridge Street, Witney OX8 6DA, tel:
01993 775399
Open: Tues-Sat 10-4; Thurs 10-2

Woburn
BEDFORDSHIRE EA

Clifford Gallery *

🄿🅂 ✔

Retail gallery specialising in sporting and wildlife subjects.
11 Market Place, Woburn MK17 9P3,
tel: 01525 290355
Contact: Gordon Williams, Owner
Exhibitions: 4 a year all originated

Wolverhampton
WEST MIDLANDS WMA

Eagle Works

🄿🄿🄿🅂 ✔&🄷

Independent group studio with gallery space offering an immediate and inexpensive venue to artists wishing to show their work.
Alexandra Street, Wolverhampton WV3 0TE, tel: 01902 25958
Contact: Gallery Organiser
Space: 1 gallery with 30 lin m hanging space and 30 sq m floor space
Exhibitions: 6 a year of which 5 originated, 1 on a hire basis
Details: Promotes exciting new work in all areas of fine art, and brings it to as wide a public as possible – local press, art organisations, schools, colleges, gallery curators, and local public. Also used for public workshops.

Lighthouse Media Centre

🄿🄿🄿🄶🅂🄸 ✔⊘

Particularly interested in work linked with cinema and contemporary issues.
Chubb Building, Fryer Street, Wolverhampton WV1 1HT, tel: 01902 716044
Contact: Evelyn Wilson
Space: 3 galleries
Exhibitions: 11 a year of which 6 originated, 5 touring
Details: Two main galleries and a covered glass atrium which is very large and adaptable to different uses. The building is an old converted factory and exhibitions take place beside 2 cinemas and video production facilities. The spaces are used for the exhibition of photography and new media specifically. Regular events and symposia take place around new media/new media techniques, etc.

University of Wolverhampton

🄿🄿🄿🄶🅂🄸 ✔

Foyer space and purpose-built gallery in Fine Art Department.
School of Art & Design, Molineux Street, Wolverhampton WV1 1DT, tel: 01902 321000

Contact: Knighton Koskins, Head of Painting
Open: (Term-time) Mon-Fri 10-5
Space: 1 gallery with 167 sq m floor space
Exhibitions: 4 a year all originated
Details: Wide range of exhibitions from regional sources, staff and students. Open selection, showing painting, sculpture, graphics, ceramics, film, video, live art. Artists may be charged a rental fee for gallery space. Not available for touring shows.

Wolverhampton Museum & Art Gallery *

Pa Ph Pr Gr Sc LA ✓

Municipal gallery with temporary exhibition programme often of national significance.
Lichfield Street, Wolverhampton WV1 1DU, tel: 01902 312032, fax: 01902 715582
Contact: Martin Jones, Keeper of Fine Art
Space: 4 galleries with 194 lin m hanging space plus 10 lin m on screens and 547 sq m floor space
Exhibitions: 8 a year of which 4 originated, 4 touring
Details: Permanent collection contains British painting from the C18th and C19th and American pop art, photo-realism and contemporary painting and sculpture. Majority of exhibitions solo shows. Includes shows to interest minority audiences and broader section of community.

Woodbridge
SUFFOLK EA

Butley Pottery Barn Gallery

Pa Ph Pr Gr Sc ✓ ● Wc 4

Gallery promoting contemporary work covering wide range, figurative and non-figurative and specialist ceramics showroom.
Mill Lane, Butley, Woodbridge IP12 3PA, tel: 01394 450843
Contact: Graham Hussey, Owner
Open: Daily 10.30-5
Space: 2 galleries
Exhibitions: 10 a year all originated
Details: Gallery in converted thatched barn with daylight at one end. Pottery attached. Tearoom/restaurant also in complex. Applications from artists working in wide range of media welcomed and from those living outside region. In pottery showroom only contemporary ceramics shown. Sales encouraged and commission taken. Gallery available for hire. Short courses offered in variety of media.

Denis Taplin Gallery

Pa Pr Sc ✓

Commercial gallery with 'special' exhibitions interspersed with mixed exhibitions of work by 'gallery artists'.
68 Thoroughfare, Woodbridge IP12 1AL, tel: 01394 386603
Contact: Denis Taplin
Open: Mon, Tues, Thurs-Sat 9.30-1, 2.30-5.30
Space: 1 gallery with 18 lin m hanging space and 32 sq m floor space
Exhibitions: 7 a year all originated

Fraser Gallery

Pa Ph Pr ✓ ●

Gallery with continuous exhibition of fine art prints and occasional exhibitions of work by mainly local artists in variety of media.
62a New Street, Woodbridge IP12 1DX, tel: 013943 87535
Contact: Rosemary Mitchell, Proprietor
Open: Mon-Thurs 10-5; Fri 10-5; Sat 10-1
Space: 1 gallery with 27 lin m hanging space plus 5 lin m on screens and 67 sq m floor space
Exhibitions: 2 a year both originated
Details: Mainly etchings, lithos, screen, etc. Fine art cards and postcards. Antique maps and prints also in keeping with print media theme of gallery. Solo or two-person shows when suitable artists appear. Undertakes exhibition framing and restoration of paintings. Sales a priority.

Woodstock
OXFORDSHIRE SA

Oxfordshire County Museum

Pa Ph Pr Gr Sc LA ✓ H ●

Run by Oxfordshire County Council's Leisure and Arts Department the Museum offers variety of exhibition spaces for showing work of artists and craftspeople.
Fletchers House, Park Street, Woodstock OX20 1SN, tel: 01993 811456, fax: 01993 813239
Contact: Carol Anderson, Senior Museums Officer
Open: (May-Sept) Tues-Sat 10-5, Sun 2-5; (Oct-Apr) Tues-Sat 10-4, Sun 2 5
Space: 3 galleries with 21 lin m hanging space plus 30 lin m on screens and 35 sq m floor space
Exhibitions: 18 a year of which 4 originated, 14 on a hire basis
Details: Coffee bar: 11 exhibitions a year of work of local artists or artists whose work reflects aspects of Oxfordshire. Main gallery: approx 7 exhibitions a year with emphasis on work of Oxfordshire artists, photographers and craftspeople but including work with broader background. Sales not primary function.

Worcester
HEREFORD & WORCESTER WMA

Framed

Pa Ph Pr ✓ ●

Commercial contemporary fine art gallery with original work by national and local artists.
46 Friar Street, Worcester WR1 2NA, tel: 01905 28836
Contact: David Birtwhistle, Partner
Open: Mon-Wed, Fri & Sat 10.30-4.30; Thurs 10.30-1.30
Space: 5 galleries with 80 lin m hanging space and 96 sq m floor space
Exhibitions: 10 a year all originated
Details: Commercial gallery and framers showing variety of work from local, regional and national sources. General collection displayed alongside series of special exhibitions. Independent access to ground-floor gallery only; first and second-floor gallery not possible.

Hereford & Worcester Libraries & Arts Department

Department co-ordinates some touring exhibitions into branch libraries.
County Hall, Spetchley Road, Worcester WR5 2NP, tel: 01905 763763, fax: 01905 763000
Contact: Tim Porter
Details: Department's policy is to encourage use of its public spaces for the display of visual arts. Initial contact for enquiries about appropriate space or about showing work in a number of libraries. If interested in showing work in specific library, contact that library direct. Facilities vary but all following have dedicated exhibition areas/rooms; see separate entries for libraries at Malvern, Droitwich, Evesham, Leominster, Redditch &Tenbury and Hartlebury County Museum. Also spaces at Pershore and Bewdley.

John Noott Galleries

Pa Pr Sc ✓

Gallery on two floors showing predominantly small-scale and figurative works.
14 Cotswold Court, Broadway, Worcester WR12 7AA, tel: 01386 858969/ 852787
Contact: John Noott
Space: 2 galleries
Exhibitions: 4 a year all originated
Details: Audience attracted jointly by extensive mailing list and gallery's location in a popular tourist area.

Swan Theatre *

Exhibitions held in restaurant and back of auditorium of theatre.
The Moors, Worcester WR1 3EF, tel: 01886 888762
Contact: Angela Hill, Hon Sec, WSA, The Laurels, Martley, Worcester, WR6 6QA
Space: 2 galleries
Exhibitions: 9 a year all originated
Details: Monthly exhibitions organised by Worcester Society of Artists, mostly local artists work.

Worcester Arts Workshop

Informal gallery space staffed by volunteers with coffee bar, set within a small local arts centre.
21 Sansome Street, Worcester WR1 1UH, tel: 01905 21095
Contact: John Denton, Director
Open: Mon-Sat 10-1; other times by prior arrangement.
Space: 1 gallery with 14 lin m hanging space
Exhibitions: 12 a year of which 9 originated, 1 touring, 2 on a hire basis
Details: Available for use by individual local and regional artists, local groups of artists, community groups, schools and colleges. However the workshop is being re-structured and will not be inviting exhibition applications before Autumn 1995. For details of new arrangements and priorities, contact the Director after July 1995.

Worcester City Museum & Art Gallery

Municipal gallery showing work from local, regional and national sources, both contemporary and historical, and embracing a wide variety of media.
Foregate Street, Worcester WR1 1DT, tel: 01905 25371
Contact: Deborah Dean, Gallery and Exhibitions Officer
Open: Mon-Wed & Fri 9.30-6; Sat 9.30-5
Space: 2 galleries with 43 lin m hanging space and 84 sq m floor space
Exhibitions: 12 a year of which 9 originated, 3 touring
Details: Exhibitions accompanied by educational events and some shows intended to target specific sections of community. 'Craftcase' showing contemporary craft. Gallery covers transport, insurance, publicity and preview costs.

Workington
CUMBRIA NA

Carnegie Theatre & Arts Centre

Displays professional photographic exhibitions and local crafts.
Finkle Street, Workington CA14 2BD, tel: 01900 602122, fax: 01900 67143
Contact: Bryony Flanagan, Administrator, Carnegie Theatre & Arts Centre
Open: Mon-Sat 9.30-5
Space: 1 gallery with 26 lin m hanging space plus 20 lin m on screens
Exhibitions: 14 a year of which 8 originated, 6 touring
Details: Centre is well used by elderly groups and disabled people and is particularly interested in exhibitions which may promote wider understanding of problems associated with various disabilities. We try to look at educational possibilities when setting up exhibitions.

Worksop
NOTTINGHAMSHIRE EMA

Harley Gallery

Commercial gallery set up to show continuity between art and craft of past with present.
Welbeck, Worksop S80 3LW, tel: 01909 501700
Contact: Steve Abbott
Open: (May-Oct) Fri, Sat, Sun & BH Mon 12-5
Space: 3 galleries with 67 lin m hanging space and 230 sq m floor space
Exhibitions: 4 a year all originated
Details: Programme runs end of April to end of October. Exhibitions last 6 weeks. Work selected via committee and Harley Foundation trustees. Emphasis is on well-crafted work whether 2D or 3D. Commission charged on sales.

Priory Gatehouse

Small independent non profit making gallery funded by district & county showing contemporary 2D and 3D work.
Cheapside, Worksop S80 2HX, tel: 01909 474173
Contact: Karen Bell, Administrator, Arts Alive
Open: (Apr-mid Oct) Wed-Sat 10-5, Sun 2-5; (Mid Oct-Mar) Wed-Fri 10-5, Sat 10-4
Space: 1 gallery with 21 lin m hanging space plus 2 lin m on screens and 81 sq m floor space
Exhibitions: 12 a year of which 8 originated, 4 on a hire basis

Details: Gallery in building of historical interest. Exhibitions focus on local, regional and some national work. Art and craft exhibitions shown. Outreach work complements exhibitions and provides relevance for local community and assists audience development. Selling work not high priority but member of RAB interest free credit scheme. Small tearoom.

Worthing
WEST SUSSEX SEA

Northbrook Photography Gallery and theatre

Documentary/constructed image photography shown on walls of Northbrook Theatre bar/foyer.
Northbrook College, Littlehampton Road, Goring-by-Sea, Worthing, tel: 01903 830057 x253
Contact: Dave Yorath/Jim Cooke
Open: (Term-time) Mon-Fri 10-5
Space: 1 gallery
Exhibitions: 9 a year all originated
Details: Exhibitions programme forms part of service provided by integrated arts, exhibition, entertainment and training unit. A new venue for regional photographers to exhibit and promote their work. Most exhibitions feature work by leading British photographers; occasional shows of non-contemporary photographers/movements. Series of open lectures, workshops, summer schools planned. Commitment to showing European and non-European photographers and encouraging cultural exchange. Sale of work from exhibitions not a priority.

Terrace Gallery

Gallery dealing in contemporary art and crafts.
7 Liverpool Terrace, Worthing BN11 1TA, tel: 01903 212926
Contact: Margrit Avon, Director
Open: Tues-Fri 10.30-4.30; Sat 11-2 during exhibitions; closed in between shows.
Space: 2 galleries with 24 lin m hanging space and 50 sq m floor space
Exhibitions: 6 a year all originated
Details: Shows a wide variety of contemporary work by established artists and new talent, and advises companies and individuals on their art requirements.

Worthing Museum and Art Gallery

Galleries used to display broad range of work by local and non-local artists as well as material from the collections.

Chapel Road, Worthing BN11 1HD, tel:
01903 239999 ext 2528
Contact: Dr Sally White, Principal Curator
Open: (Apr-Sept) Mon-Sat 10-6; (Oct-March) 10-5
Space: 2 galleries with 86 lin m hanging
space and 203 sq m floor space
Exhibitions: 10 a year of which 6
originated
Details: One space has full glass ceiling
making a quality facility for temporary
exhibitions. Shows more group than solo,
booked up to 2 years ahead. Gallery charges
small commission. Garden used for outdoor
sculpture displays. Sales not gallery's
primary concern.

Yeovil
SOMERSET SWA

Yeovil Community Arts Centre

Pa Ph Pr Cr Sc H &

*Galleries and coffee shop committed to
bringing experience of visual arts to the
community.*
80 South Street, Yeovil BA20 1QH, tel:
01935 32132
Contact: Eleanor McLaghlin, Exhibitions
Organiser, Yeovil Community Arts
Association, 80 South Street, Yeovil, BA20
1QH
Open: Mon-Fri 10-4.30; Sat 10-1.30;
closed BH
Space: 2 galleries with 56 lin m hanging
space plus 6 lin m on screens and 6 sq m
floor space
Exhibitions: 23 a year of which 5
originated, 2 touring, 16 on a hire basis
Details: Yeovil Community Arts
Association is a registered charity that aims
to provide high-quality exhibitions and
reach as wide an audience as possible.
Classes and talks organised. Involvement
with schools. Curates touring exhibitions
and organises residencies in schools and
colleges. Sales not priority.

York
NORTH YORKSHIRE YHA

AD Gallery

A Pa Pr Cr Sc

*Private gallery showing work by co-op artist
members from Yorkshire area.*
73 Micklegate, York YO1 1OJ, tel:
01904 658230
Contact: Olga Roebuck or Glenys Brooks,
Secretary
Space: 1 gallery
Exhibitions: 6 a year
Details: Artists living in area are welcome
to join the group which currently has about
30 professional and semi-professional
members. Plenty of local support for the

gallery and a number of tourists and visitors
to York. 15% commission on sales.

Burton Stone Community Centre *

Pa Ph Pr Cr LA ✓

*Provides wide range of art and sport
activities catering for educational and
social needs of wide section of community.*
Evelyn Crescent, York YO3 6DR, tel:
01904 645816
Contact: Manager
Details: Looking to encourage community
and fringe artists to bring work to display at
the centre and to run workshops.
Particularly interested in artists whose work
is relevant to community. Focus on
community art events, fashion and drawing
displays, photographic and print
demonstrations. Have been no solo shows.
Exhibitions last from one day to one year.

Impressions Gallery

Ph Sc ✓ £ ⊘

*Gallery housed in listed building in central
York displays photographic exhibitions on
contemporary cultural issues.*
29 Castlegate, Castlewalk, York YO1
1RN, tel: 01904 654724, fax: 01904
651509
Contact: Director
Open: Daily 9.30-5.30
Space: 4 galleries with 70 lin m hanging
space and 110 sq m floor space
Exhibitions: 8 a year of which 6
originated, 2 touring
Details: Shows photographic work.
Exhibitions focus on a theme or idea, and
include work from many sources: fine art,
documentary, photojournalism, scientific
and advertising. Historical and
contemporary work is exhibited together.
Exhibits work produced by new
technologies. Due to location in the centre
of York has a very broad audience range.
Sales not a priority.

Kentmere House Gallery

Pa Ph Cr ✓ & 4

*Independent gallery in owner's Edwardian
home, showing both established names and
talented newcomers working in
representational tradition.*
53 Scarcroft Hill, York YO2 1DF, tel:
01904 656507
Contact: Ann Petherick, Gallery Owner
Open: Thurs 6-9; first weekend of month
11-5; also any time by appointment
Space: 3 galleries with 48 lin m hanging
space and 59 sq m floor space
Exhibitions: 8 a year all originated
Details: Shows work of living British
artists. A 'featured artist' each month.
Work is contemporary without being
avant-garde. Aims to banish elitism and
broaden the market for contemporary
work. Sells work.

New York Gallery (The)

Pa Pr Sc ✓ H &

*Gallery consists of two well-lit ground floor
rooms and its main purpose is to sell
contemporary paintings by up-and-coming
artists.*
8 Franklin's Yard, Fossgate, York YO1
2TN, tel: 01904 610345
Contact: David Hair, Proprietor
Open: Tues-Thurs 10-4.30; Fri & Sat 10-5
Space: 2 galleries with 30 lin m hanging
space and 54 sq m floor space
Exhibitions: 6 a year of which 4
originated, 2 on a hire basis
Details: Through exhibitions gallery aims
to make the general public more aware of
the diverse styles in contemporary painting.

Priory Street Centre

Pa Ph Sc ✓ & Wc

*Free wall space for exhibitions in busy café
environment.*
15-17 Priory Street, York YO1 1EY, tel:
01904 639968
Contact: Wendy Epstein, Manager
Space: 1 gallery with 10 lin m hanging
space plus 8 lin m on screens and 30 sq m
floor space
Exhibitions: 3 a year all originated
Details: Artists have free use for one month
to display any work which may be attached
to walls, ie pictures, textiles. Exhibitions
seen by wide range of people. Sales of work
not of major importance.

Pyramid Gallery

Pr Cr Sc ✓ ⊘

*Commercial gallery above shop specialising
in contemporary craft, ceramics, jewellery
and prints in pedestrian street near York
Minster.*
43 Stonegate, York YO1 2AW, tel: 01904
641187
Contact: Tery Brett, Proprietor
Open: Mon-Sat 10-5; some Sundays
Space: 2 galleries with 50 lin m hanging
space and 27 sq m floor space
Exhibitions: 8 a year all originated
Details: Gallery exhibits work that would
not normally be stocked in shop, to give
visitors opportunity to appreciate
contemporary art, craft, glass & ceramics.
Sale of work is a priority but not essential.

Robert Feather Gallery

Cr ✓ &

*Commercial gallery specialising in modern
jewellery with work by over 40 jewellers.*
10 Gillygate, York YO3 7EQ, tel: 01904
632025
Contact: Robert Feather
Open: Mon-Sat 9.30-5.30
Details: As well as jewellery gallery also
shows and sells wood and glass craft
objects.

Shandy Hall

Gallery in restored granary above barn holding exhibitions in summer months.
Coxwold, York YO6 4AD, tel: 01347 868465
Contact: Mrs J Monkman, Hon Secretary, Laurence Sterne Trust
Open: (Jun-Sep) Mon-Fri & Sun 11-4.30
Space: 1 gallery with 32 lin m hanging space plus 5 lin m on screens and 59 sq m floor space
Exhibitions: 2 a year both originated
Details: Aim is to encourage interest in Shandy Hall and its surroundings and, through sales, to raise money for Laurence Stern Trust. Encourages local art societies and individual artists to exhibit. Sales good to summer visitors.

Stonegate Gallery

Selling gallery on ground floor of mediaeval building in centre of York showing mostly, but not solely, work by local artists.
52A Stonegate, York YO1 2AS, tel: 01904 35141
Contact: Alan Hitchcock, Owner, 30 Main Street, Heslington, YO1 5EG, tel: 01904 411038
Open: (Apr-Dec) Tues-Sat 10.30-5; closed between exhibitions
Space: 1 gallery with 27 lin m hanging space and 40 sq m floor space
Exhibitions: 8 a year all originated
Details: Specialises in contemporary painting by local and national artists. Saleability a consideration, but not the prime reason for selection – "I will only show work which I like." Solo and group shows, each exhibition lasts three weeks.

Wentworth Exhibition Area

Conference area with good lighting used for two exhibitions a year; one of work by students and one featuring an outside artist.
Wentworth College, University of York, York YO1 5DD, tel: 01904 433025, fax: 01904 433433
Contact: Maria Maddej, Tutor in Art
Space: 1 gallery with 20 lin m hanging space
Exhibitions: 2 a year both originated
Details: One exhibition a year of students' Arts Society; one exhibition featuring outside artist chosen for innovative, often issue-based work. Audience mainly university students and staff but public welcomed and encouraged. Help with frames available. Not principally a selling space but 10% commission taken. Only wall hung work can be shown.

York Arts Centre

Various exhibition spaces for hire within arts centre.
Micklegate, York YO1 1JG, tel: 01904 642 582
Contact: Martin Pople, Fundraising Officer
Space: 2 galleries with 55 lin m hanging space and 40 sq m floor space
Exhibitions: 20 a year all on a hire basis
Details: Foyer/box office area: hanging and free standing displays, £15 per week. Café/bar area: hanging space only, £15 per week. Private viewings can be organised on Sunday/Monday evenings, £40.

York City Art Gallery

Municipal gallery with permanent displays reflecting the past seven hundred years of Western European art and a varied programme of temporary exhibitions.
Exhibition Square, York YO1 2EW, tel: 01904 551861, fax: 01904 551866
Contact: Helen Grundy, Exhibitions Officer
Open: Mon-Sat 10-5; Sun 2.30-5; closed 1 Jan, Good Friday, 25 & 26 Dec
Space: 1 gallery with 150 lin m hanging space and 150 sq m floor space
Exhibitions: 10 a year of which 5 originated, 5 touring
Details: Wide-ranging programme includes annual exhibitions of work by York school children and local artists, historical and contemporary shows. Educational activities support permanent displays and temporary exhibition programme. Sale of work not gallery's primary function.

The Factory Gallery, Belfast

"Through having worked in London with the architects Nicholas Grimshaw & Partners for several years both as marketing manager and senior architect I have been responsible for the commissioning of many public art works on behalf of client bodies therefore I have good contacts with much of the contemporary art world and I sincerely hope to be able to host important and possibly controversial works in Northern Ireland by overseas artists as well as work by local artists." Simon Templeton

Northern Ireland

Antrim
CO ANTRIM

Clotworthy House Arts Centre

Pₐ Pʰ Pr Gr ⬤ ⬤ 🅷 ⬤ 🅦

Two galleries within arts centre showing work of artists from Northern Ireland and further afield (one gallery dedicated to photography).
Randalstown Road, Antrim BT41 4LH, tel: 01849 428000, fax: 01849 460360
Contact: Nick Livingston, Arts & Heritage Officer
Open: Mon-Fri 9.30-4.30
Space: 2 galleries with 62 lin m hanging space plus 22 lin m on screens and 154 sq m floor space
Exhibitions: 30 a year of which 16 originated, 12 touring, 2 on a hire basis
Details: Exhibitions organised along with theatre, music, courses, lectures and various community events. Providing varied experiences of the visual arts and making arts accessible to the widest possible public. Takes Arts Council touring exhibitions and organises lectures, talks and demonstrations for schools and others. Sales not a priority. Independent access for wheelchair users to Main Gallery; not Photography Gallery which is on first floor.

Armagh
CO ARMAGH

Adam Gallery

Shows mainly work by Irish artists in group or one-person exhibitions.
28 Linenhall Street, Armagh, tel: 01861 526908
Contact: WGI and GM Wilson, Directors
Open: (During exhibitions) Mon, Tues, Thurs-Sat 11-5
Exhibitions: 5 a year

Armagh County Museum

Pₐ Pʰ Pr Gr SC ⬤ ⊗

Community museum showing history of Co Armagh with temporary exhibitions of art, craft, natural history, etc.
The Mall East, Armagh BT61 9BE, tel: 01861 523070, fax: 01861 522631
Contact: Catherine McCullough, BA Dip Man, Curator
Open: Mon-Fri 10-5; Sat 10-1, 2-5
Space: 1 gallery with 62 lin m hanging space plus 9 lin m on screens and 118 sq m floor space
Exhibitions: 8 a year of which 5 originated, 3 touring
Details: Programme attempts to provide a breadth of temporary exhibitions covering art, craft, natural history, and exhibitions for school children using the National Curriculum as a guide. The audience is mainly local of all ages, but also many tourists. Sales not a priority.

Ballymena
CO ANTRIM

North Eastern Education & Library Board

Pₐ Pr SC ⬤

Administrative centre for all branch libraries in its jurisdiction.
NEELB Library Service, Area Library, Demesne Avenue, Ballymena BT43 7BG, tel: 01266 41531/2/3
Contact: Chief Librarian
Details: Contact Chief Librarian for details of branch libraries in Antrim, Ballymena, Ballymoney, Carrickfergus, Coleraine, Larne, Maghera, Magherafelt, Newtownabbey, Portrush, Portstewart, Whitehead and smaller towns and villages. Libraries display a wide range of arts, crafts and other objects, often accompanied by books from stock.

Bangor
CO DOWN

North Down Visitors and Heritage Centre

Heritage Centre which occasionally holds exhibitions of work by regional professional and amateur artists and photographers.
Town Hall, Castle Park Avenue, Bangor BT20 4BT, tel: 01247 270371 ext 275, fax: 01247 271370
Contact: Ian Wilson, Manager
Open: Tues-Sat 10.30-4.30; Sun 2-4.30; BH Mons

Belfast
CO ANTRIM

Belfast Public Libraries

Pₐ Pʰ Pr SC ⬤ ④

Exhibition space available in the foyer of the Central Library
Belfast Central Library, Royal Avenue, Belfast BT1 1EA, tel: 01232 243233, fax: 01232 332819
Contact: J. Montgomery, Chief Librarian
Open: Mon & Thurs 9.30-8; Tues, Wed, Fri 9.30-5.30; Sat 9.30-1
Space: 1 gallery with 13 lin m hanging space plus 16 lin m on screens and 150 sq m floor space
Exhibitions: 3 a year
Details: Administrative centre for all branch libraries in Belfast. Contact Chief Librarian for details of branch libraries. Exhibitions changed monthly. Full access should be available summer 1995.

Bell Gallery

Gallery dealing in C18th, C19th and C20th Irish art with continuous display and one-person shows.
13 Adelaide Park, Malone Road, Belfast BT9 6FX, tel: 01232 662998, fax: 01232 381524
Contact: James Nelson Bell, Director
Open: Mon-Fri 9-5; Sat by appointment
Exhibitions: 7 a year

Catalyst Arts

🅐

Studios and exhibition space in artist-run centre.
5 Exchange Place, Belfast BT1 2NA, tel: 0232 313303
Contact: Síofra Campbell, Director
Open: Mon-Sat 10-6

Cavehill Gallery

Pₐ Pr SC ⬤

Gallery run from the home of the owners, mainly specialising in contemporary Irish artists.
18 Old Cavehill Road, Belfast BT15 5GT, tel: 01232 776784
Contact: Catherine & Joe McWilliams, Exhibition Organisers
Open: Tues-Sat 1-6; closed Jan, Feb, Jul & Aug
Space: 2 galleries with 14 lin m hanging space
Exhibitions: 6 a year all originated
Details: Situated off gallery circuit in North Belfast. Hopes to encourage mid-career artists who are under-exposed as well as a small number of younger artists. Six exhibitions shown a year; 4 two-person shows, mixed Summer and Christmas shows. Exhibitions last for two and a half weeks and tend towards the figurative with abstract expressionist qualities.

Crescent Arts Centre

Centre showing Irish and international artists through group and one-person exhibitions, exchanges and collaborations.
2-4 University Road, Belfast BT7 1NT, tel: 01232 242338
Contact: Rhoda MacManus, Administrator
Open: Mon-Fri 10-5, Sat 11-5
Exhibitions: 12 a year

Factory Gallery

Pₐ SC LA ⬤ ⊗④

Part of large Victorian warehouse with cast iron columns and access hatch suitable for large scale paintings or installations.
52 Hill Street, Belfast BT1 2LB, tel & fax: 01232 244000
Contact: Simon Templeton
Space: 2 galleries with 36 lin m hanging space and 200 sq m floor space
Exhibitions: 2 a year both originated
Details: Keen tp promote irish artists, or to

import top level UK originated shows. The space is unique and artists have enjoyed reacting to it in installation or performance pieces. Wheelchair access possible to ground floor showroom but not first floor gallery.

Fenderesky Gallery at Queen's

Gallery promoting work by Irish contemporary artists, usually through one-person shows.
5-6 Upper Crescent, Belfast, tel: 01232 235245
Contact: Dr Jamshid Mirfenderesky, Director
Open: Tues-Fri 11.30-5.30; Sat 12-5
Exhibitions: 15 a year

Gallery (The)

Pa Ph Pr Cr SC IA ✓ € &

Public gallery run by an independent trust which aims to promote both Irish and international art.
56-60 Dublin Road, Belfast BT2 7HP, tel: 01232 321402, fax: 01232 312232
Contact: Lisa Irvine, Gallery Manager
Open: Tues-Sat 10-6
Space: 2 galleries with 109 lin m hanging space and 250 sq m floor space
Exhibitions: 14 a year
Details: Pprovides a platform for artists based in Northern Ireland and exhibits a range of touring shows curated by other galleries and exhibition spaces. Exhibitions take the form of solo, two-person or group shows. Sales not a priority.

Linen Hall Library

Independent library occasionally hosts exhibitions being toured by other organisations.
17 Donegall Square North, Belfast BT1 5GD, tel: 01232 321707, fax: 01232 438586
Contact: Jennifer Campbell, Public Relations Officer
Open: Mon-Fri 9.30-5.30; Thurs 9.30-8.30; Sat 9.30-4
Exhibitions: 3 a year

Magee Gallery

Pa Pr ✓ ⊘

First-floor gallery showing original works by Irish, British and continental artists as well as framed reproductions.
455-457 Ormeau Road, Belfast BT7 3GQ, tel: 01232 693830, fax: 01232 491009
Contact: RR Miller, Managing Director
Open: Mon-Sat 9-5
Space: 1 gallery with 61 lin m hanging space and 58 sq m floor space
Exhibitions: 4 a year all originated
Details: Selling work is considered the gallery's primary role.

Old Museum Arts Centre

Ph SC IA ✓ € &

Gallery with commitment to exhibiting photographic and lens-based media work.
7 College Square, Belfast BT1 6AR, tel: 01232 235053, fax: 01232 322912
Contact: Una McCarthy, Director
Open: Mon-Sat 10-5
Space: 2 galleries with 40 lin m hanging space and 50 sq m floor space
Exhibitions: 15 a year of which 8 originated, 7 touring
Details: Commissions site specific work, eg installations, as well as exhibiting photographic and video work. Developing education /outreach programme. Sales not a priority.

One Oxford Street

Gallery holding monthly exhibitions of work by young and more established artists.
1 Oxford Street, Belfast BT1 3LA, tel: 01232 310400, fax: 01232 310444
Contact: J Lesley McKeown, Owner
Open: Mon-Fri 10-4; occasional Sat mornings

Ormeau Baths Gallery

Pa Ph Pr Cr SC IA ✓ € & Wc 4

An independent major new modern and contemporary art venue in Belfast.
18a Ormeau Avenue, Belfast BT2 8HS, tel: 01232 321402, fax: 01232 312232
Contact: Ms Noreen O'Hare, Gallery Director
Space: 4 galleries with 177 lin m hanging space and 607 sq m floor space
Exhibitions: 25 a year
Details: Aims to establish Belfast as a truly European city with a thriving artistic community.

Orpheus Gallery *

Pa Ph Pr SC IA ✓

Programme includes contemporary Irish and international art with an emphasis on innovative installation work.
Orpheus Building, York Street, Belfast BT15 1AA, tel: 01232 246259, fax: 01232 660145
Contact: Liam Kelly, Exhibitions Director
Space: 1 gallery with 33 lin m hanging space and 66 sq m floor space
Exhibitions: 10 a year of which 8 originated, 2 touring
Details: Located in North Belfast. Funded by the Arts Council of Northern Ireland. The street aspect of the gallery has provided artists with an opportunity to engage with a passing audience. Gallery has also developed community outreach projects and lectures and seminars are organised periodically.

Tom Caldwell Galleries

Pa Cr SC

Commercial gallery promoting a number of contemporary Irish artists.
40/42 Bradbury Place, Belfast BT7 1RT, tel: 01232 323226, fax: 01232 233437
Contact: Tom Caldwell, Exhibitions Organiser
Exhibitions: 8 a year all originated
Details: Eight exhibitions a year on average, two of which are usually the work of young emerging artists. Does not hire out gallery space.

Ulster Arts Club Gallery

Pa Ph Pr Cr SC ✓ &

Gallery based in large Victorian terraced house showing work by new and established artists to benefit club and community.
56 Elmwood Avenue, Belfast BT9 6AG, tel: 01232 660644
Contact: Mrs Doreen Corcoran, Gallery Administrator
Open: Tues-Fri 11-4
Space: 1 gallery with 58 sq m floor space
Exhibitions: 12 a year of which 11 originated, 1 touring
Details: Programme features both solo and group shows, and previews held every month. Majority of exhibitions of work by local artists but some international exhibitions. Walls clad brick with pale grey surface. Hanging by rods. Spot lights on track. 25% commission taken on sales but sales not gallery's primary role. Hopes to increase visits of school parties. Poetry readings, music recitals, lectures.

Ulster Museum

Pa Ph Pr Cr SC

National museum with extensive art collection and exhibitions.
Botanic Gardens, Belfast BT9 5AB, tel: 01232 381251, fax: 01232 665510
Contact: Anne Stewart, Exhibitions Officer
Open: Mon-Fri 10-5; Sat 1-5; Sun 2-5
Space: 2 galleries with 198 lin m hanging space plus 270 lin m on screens and 700 sq m floor space
Exhibitions: 6 a year of which 1 originated, 5 touring
Details: Important collection of Irish art (C16th – present day), Old Masters, British and International C20th painting and sculpture, watercolours, prints, drawings, costume, ceramics, glass and silver.

Coleraine
CO DERRY

Town House Gallery

Selling gallery which exhibits work by artists from Ireland or abroad, selected by the owner.
45 Milburn Road, Coleraine BT52 1QT, tel: 01265 44869

Contact: Dale Cuthbert, Owner
Open: Mon-Sat 9.30-5.30

University of Ulster (Riverside Gallery)

Pa Ph Pr ✓ & wc 4

University-run gallery in main foyer of Riverside Theatre which specialises in first exhibitions by young graduates.
Riverside Theatre, Coleraine BT52 1SA, tel: 01265 44141 ext 4430, fax: 01265 324924
Contact: Jeremy Lewis, University Arts Administrator
Open: Mon-Fri 9-6; when theatre is open
Space: 1 gallery with 33 lin m hanging space
Exhibitions: 9 a year all originated
Details: Mounts first exhibitions in any media; firstly to Coleraine graduates, next to other art and applied art graduates in Ireland, and then to similar graduates from Britain. Local established artists also considered. Brick walls, grey carpet. Lighting by rail and rods. Limited natural light, adjustable spots. PA, audio equipment, display cases and slide projector available. Targets its publicity at schools and students. Captive audience for exhibitions as theatre patrons have to pass the work on display. Sales a priority, 20% commission taken. Award won for accessibility.

Comber
CO DOWN

Castle Espie Gallery

Exhibitions shown are relevant to the concerns of the Wildfowl and Wetlands Trust who are based in the building.
78 Ballydrain Road, Comber, tel: 01247 872517
Contact: Patrick Mackie
Open: Mon-Sat 10.30-5; Sun 2-5
Exhibitions: 4 a year

Salem Gallery

Gallery holds group exhibitions of work by Irish artists, both established and less well known.
29 Mill Street, Comber, tel: 01247 874455
Contact: WL Morrison, Owner
Exhibitions: 12 a year

Craigavon
CO ARMAGH

Brownlow Library Gallery

Pa Ph Pr ✓ H &

Established library exhibition wall.
Brownlow Branch Library, Brownlow Road, Legahory, Craigavon BT65 5DP, tel: 01762 341946
Contact: Branch Librarian

Open: Mon & Wed 10-5.30; Tues & Thurs 10-8; Fri-Sat 10-5
Space: 1 gallery with 25 lin m hanging space
Exhibitions: 3 a year all on a hire basis
Details: Hessian wall covering, light oatmeal colour/texture. Around 2.5m high. Photography, paintings, creative writings, crafts. Audience: local community, especially public library users. Two banks of spotlighting on main display areas.

Pinebank House Arts Centre (Peacock Gallery)

Pa Ph Pr Cr Sc ✓ & wc

Municipal gallery run by Craigavon Borough Council with changing monthly exhibitions featuring a wide variety of artforms.
Tullygally Road, Craigavon BT65 5BY, tel: 01762 341618, fax: 01762 342402
Contact: Rosaleen McMullan, Arts Development Officer
Open: Mon-Fri, 10-5
Space: 2 galleries with 24 lin m hanging space and 247 sq m floor space
Exhibitions: 12 a year
Details: Exhibitions mainly by young artists from Northern Ireland. Wide variety of contemporary sculpture, painting and mixed-media exhibitions especially by artists recently graduated from art college. Regular lectures and seminars held in conjunction with exhibitions. Group visits arranged, if possible with the artist in attendance. Large courtyard adjacent to gallery can be used for outdoor sculpture. Sometimes used for public meetings. Sale of work not gallery's primary concern.

Demesne
CO ARMAGH

Hayloft Gallery

Shows exhibitions to appeal to visitors to the heritage centre.
Palace Stables Heritage Centre, The Palace, Demesne BT60 4EL, tel: 01861 522519, fax: 01861 524246
Contact: The Supervisor
Open: (Apr-Sep) Mon-Sat 10-7, Sun 1-7; (Oct-Mar) Mon-Sat 10-5, Sun 2-5

Derry
CO DERRY

Context Gallery

Gallery in Playhouse theatre complex showing work by both established and emerging artists.
The Playhouse, 5-7 Artillery Street, Derry, tel: 01504 264481, fax: 01504 261884
Contact: Hugh Mulholland, Exhibition Organiser
Open: Tues-Sat 9.30-4.30

Foyle Arts Centre

Arts centre with developing exhibition programme aims to promote the arts at a local, national and international level.
Lawrence Hill, Derry, tel: 01504 266657, fax: 01504 365419
Contact: Finola O'Doherty, Exhibition Organiser
Open: Mon-Fri 9-5; evening opening possible

Gordon Galleries

Fine and applied arts by well established artists; most of them Irish.
7 London Street, Derry BT48 6RQ, tel: 01504 374044
Contact: Nat Gordon and Richard Gordon, Directors
Open: Tues-Sat 11-5.30
Exhibitions: 12 a year

Orchard Gallery

Pa Ph Pr Cr Sc IA ✓ & 4

Derry City Council's primary venue for contemporary visual arts and associated community liaison and education programmes.
Orchard Street, Derry BT48 6EG, tel: 01504 269675, fax: 01504 267273
Contact: Noreen O'Hare, Organiser
Open: Tues-Sat 10-6
Space: 5 galleries with 114 lin m hanging space plus 30 lin m on screens and 218 sq m floor space
Exhibitions: 18 a year of which 14 originated, 4 touring
Details: Subsidised by the Arts Council of Northern Ireland and Derry City Council. Contemporary exhibitions from Ireland and abroad, including performance, film, installations and video. Exhibitions reflect current activity in art internationally, nationally, regionally and locally; most are contemporary with occasional historical/ retrospective exhibitions. Collaborates regularly with other galleries to instigate major shows. Organises a varied programme of public art projects. Sales not gallery's primary concern.

Donaghadee
CO DOWN ACI

Cleft Art Gallery

Pa Pr ✓ & wc

Commercial gallery specialising in watercolour and oil paintings.
3 Market House, New Street, Donaghadee, tel: 01247 888502
Contact: WL Morrison, Director
Open: Mon-Sat 11-5
Space: 1 gallery with 30 lin m hanging space and 33 sq m floor space
Exhibitions: 4 a year all originated

Details: Exhibitions in gallery all year round, with four special exhibitions each year. Work is mainly traditional representational landscape paintings. Sale of work is a priority.

Downpatrick
CO DOWN

Down Arts Centre

Pa Ph Pr Gr Sc ⬤H ⬤vc

Contemporary art exhibitions balancing both local and outside work, professional and amateur.
2-6 Irish Street, Downpatrick BT30 6BN, tel: 01396 615283, fax: 01396 612390
Contact: Belinda Loftus/Christina Hurson, Arts & Cultural Development Officer/Arts Assistant
Open: (Term-time) Mon, Fri, Sat10-4.30, Tues-Thurs 10am-10pm; (Holidays) Mon-Sat 10-4.30
Space: 1 gallery with 36 lin m hanging space plus 16 lin m on screens and 118 sq m floor space
Exhibitions: 18 a year of which 12 originated, 2 touring, 4 on a hire basis
Details: White-walled space with full-length windows down one side. Excellent backup track lighting system. Floor: grey vinyl enabling wide range of sculpture installations. Applications from outside Ireland welcome. Attendances average 550 for a 3 week show. Where appropriate workshops and talks organised in conjunction with exhibition programme. Sales not a priority.

Enniskillen
CO FERMANAGH

Ardhowen Photographic Gallery

Ph Sc LA ⬤£ ⬤vc4

Theatre foyer area exhibiting photographic work from within local area as well as nationally and internationally.
Ardhowen Theatre, Dublin Road,, Enniskillen BT74 6BR, tel: 01365 323 233, fax: 01365 327102
Contact: Eamonn Bradley, Manager & Artistic Director
Open: Mon-Sat 11-4
Space: 1 gallery with 10 lin m hanging space plus 20 lin m on screens and 100 sq m floor space
Exhibitions: 12 a year of which 2 originated, 10 touring
Details: Theatre foyer and restaurant area. Appeals to wide range of audience types and has the advantage of being viewed in the evening when performances are on. Sale of work not a priority.

Enniskillen Castle

Pa Ph Pr Gr Sc ⬤ ⬤vc4

Collections of local history and archaeology and temporary exhibitions of history, art, craft natural history, folklife and local photography.
Castle Barracks, Enniskillen, tel: 01 365 325000, fax: 01 365 322024
Contact: Helen Lanigan Wood, Curator
Open: Mon 2-5; Tues-Fri 10-5; (May-Sept) Sat 2-5; (Jul-Aug) Sun 2-5; open BH 10-5
Space: 2 galleries with 21 lin m hanging space plus 7 lin m on screens and 82 sq m floor space
Exhibitions: 5 a year of which 2 originated, 3 touring
Details: Specialises in museological exhibitions. Temporary exhibitions last six weeks, accompanied by talks and lectures, demonstrations and craft displays for school groups and general public. Walls of galleries 2.3 m high. Sales not a priority.

Hillsborough
CO DOWN

Shambles Gallery *

Pa Sc

Commercial gallery specialising in the work of contemporary Irish painters and sculptors.
Inns Court Park Lane, Dromore Road, Hillsborough BT26, tel: 01232 667528
Contact: Sheelagh Flanagan
Space: 5 galleries
Details: Converted Georgian stables, part of the Hillsborough Arts Centre. Although exhibition policy is currently under review, presently concentrating on exhibitions by appointment for commercial firms and private individuals. Acts as art agent for a stable of Irish artists. There are a number of exhibition areas including an indoor gallery, two enclosed outdoor spaces, a green area and a small cobbled area.

Holywood
CO DOWN

Priory Art Gallery

Gallery shows and sells work by local artists/craftspeople from continuous exhibition with special one-person or group shows of work by Irish and international artists.
10 Shore Road, Holywood BT18 9HX, tel: 01232 428173
Contact: Elizabeth Ballard
Open: Mon, Tues, Thurs-Sat 10-4
Exhibitions: 6 a year

Lisburn
CO ANTRIM

Harmony Hill Arts Centre

Pa Ph Pr Gr Sc LA ⬤H ⬤vc

Gallery in attractive mature gardens showcasing Irish artists of all disciplines.
Clonmore House, 54 Harmony Hill, Lisburn BT27 4ES, tel: 01846 678219, fax: 01846 662679
Contact: Bertha A Walker, Art Centre Organiser
Open: Mon-Fri 9am-9pm; Sat (by arrangement) 10-4
Space: 2 galleries with 24 lin m hanging space and 65 sq m floor space
Exhibitions: 20 a year of which 14 originated, 4 touring, 2 on a hire basis
Details: Exhibitions with emphasis on contemporary artists from Ireland and further afield. Well-lit with good natural light. Walls throughout the arts centre also utilised. Audience mainly local. Very well-attended. Mature gardens may be used for education workshops. Gallery talks organised.

Seymour Galleries

Gallery aims to promote young artists and to exhibit the best in traditional art forms.
20 Seymour Street, Lisburn01232 662685
Contact: Joan Kirk, Director
Open: Mon-Fri 9-1, 2-5; Sat 10-12
Exhibitions: 6 a year

Lurgan
CO ARMAGH

Corridor Gallery

Pa Ph Pr Gr Sc LA ⬤ ⬤vc

Community gallery supporting local talent as well as national and international artists.
Upper Bann Institute of Further and Higher Education, Kitchen Hill, Lurgan BT66 6AZ, tel: 01762 326135, fax: 01762 322762
Contact: Gallery Committee
Open: Mon-Fri 9-5
Space: 2 galleries with 40 lin m hanging space and 200 sq m floor space
Exhibitions: 12 a year all originated
Details: Originally concentrated on photography but expanded to include mixed media, painting, sculpture. Gallery organises regular lectures and seminars by exhibiting artists, critics, gallery directors etc. Grounds around college also available for shows. Occasional touring shows.

Newcastle
CO DOWN

Grant Fine Art

Commercial gallery showing and selling work by mainly Irish artists with some special one-person or group exhibitions.
87c Bryansford Road, Newcastle, tel: 013967 22349
Contact: Margaret Grant, Owner
Exhibitions: 4 a year

Newcastle Art Gallery

Gallery selling work from permanent exhibition with special one-person or group exhibitions each lasting two weeks.
18-22 Main Street, Newcastle, tel: 013967 23555
Contact: Denis Murphy, Proprietor
Open: Mon-Fri 12-5.30; Sat 12-6; Sun 3-6
Exhibitions: 6 a year

Newcastle Centre

Pa Ph Pr Cr Sc ✓

Exhibition space in foyer of local leisure centre.
Central Promenade, Newcastle, tel: 01396 722222
Contact: Belinda Loftus/Christina Hurson, Arts & Cultural Development Officer/Arts Assistant, Down Arts Centre, 2-6 Irish Street, Downpatrick, BT30 6BN, tel: 01396 615283
Space: 1 gallery with 5 lin m hanging space plus 20 lin m on screens and 20 sq m floor space
Exhibitions: 3 a year all originated
Details: Aims to bring wide range of contemporary visual arts to local viewers and those from outside the district. Features work by professional and amateur, traditional and avant garde, student and established artists from district, Ireland and elsewhere.

Newry
CO DOWN

Carroll

Pa Ph Pr Cr Sc LA ✓ H &

Newry Arts Centre, 1A Bank Parade, Newry BT35 6HP, tel: 01693 66232, fax: 01693 65513
Contact: Paula Clamp, Arts & Museums Officer,
Open: Mon-Fri 11-10; Sat 11-1
Space: 3 galleries with 12 lin m hanging space
Exhibitions: 20 a year of which 10 originated, 5 touring, 5 on a hire basis
Details: Galleries are large and of Georgian structure, which impose a degree of formality on exhibitions. We attempt to overcome this when possible.

Newtownards
CO DOWN

Ards Arts Centre

Pa Ph Pr Cr Sc ✓

Exhibition space in local authority town hall used by amateur and professional artists.
Town Hall, Conway Square, Newtownards BT23 4BD, tel: 01247 810803, fax: 01247 823131
Contact: Maureen Armstrong, Arts Officer
Space: 1 gallery with 3 lin m hanging space plus 26 lin m on screens and 12 sq m floor space
Exhibitions: 11 a year of which 6 originated, 5 touring
Details: Run by local authority through arts sub-committee responsible for on and off-site promotions. Aims to widen appeal of arts and crafts amongst local community. Exhibitions mostly drawn from professional and semi-professional artists within area. Art classes run on regular basis for schools and members of public. Sales not primary role of gallery.

Portadown
CO ARMAGH

Roy Edwards Fine Arts

Pa

Specialises in traditional Irish landscape painting with occasional solo exhibitions.
Mahon Road, Portadown BT62 3EH, tel: 01762 339116, fax: 01762 350179
Contact: Roy Woolsey/Edward Cassidy, Directors
Space: 65 lin m hanging space and 600 sq m floor space
Details: Continuous display of oils and watercolours which are purchased from the artist outright. Exhibitions last three to four weeks organised in conjunction with the continuous programme. Main outlets-private houses, presentation gifts, etc.

Portrush
CO ANTRIM

Portrush Gallery

Pa ✓ &

Commercial ground-floor gallery with continuous exhibition of oil and watercolour paintings.
93-95 Main Street, Portrush BT56 8DA, tel: 01265 823739
Contact: Gabrielle Orok
Open: Mon-Tues & Thurs-Sat 10-6
Space: 3 galleries with 36 lin m hanging space and 42 sq m floor space
Details: Gallery specialising in marine and landscape painting with continuous display of works by Irish and English artists. Keen to encourage younger artists who work in a realistic manner. Most works exhibited on a sale or return basis with a commission of 25% on sales.

Portstewart
CO DERRY

Flowerfield Arts Centre *

Pa Ph Pr Cr Sc ✓

Arts centre widely used for workshops, exhibitions and performances.
185 Coleraine Road, Portstewart BT55 7HU, tel: 01265 833959
Contact: Malcolm Murchison, Arts Organiser
Space: 2 galleries with 33 lin m hanging space plus 10 lin m on screens and 64 sq m floor space
Exhibitions: 12 a year of which 8 originated, 4 touring
Details: 1 large gallery and 1 smaller in Georgian building. Well-lit by natural light and track lighting system. Friendly and homely atmosphere. Gallery spaces used for workshops and performances as well as for exhibitions.

**Model Arts Centre,
The Mall, Sligo**

Installation of **Jack Pakenham's** work at
the Model Arts Centre, Sligo.

Republic
of Ireland

Achill Island
CO MAYO

Western Light Art Gallery

`Po` `Ph` `Pr` `Sc` ● ⓖ

Family-run gallery showing group exhibitions from Easter to October aimed at tourist market.
The Sandybanks, Keel, Achill Island, tel: [00 353] 98 43325
Contact: Seán Cannon, Exhibition Organiser
Open: (Apr-Oct) Daily 10-6; (Nov-Mar) by appointment
Space: 1 gallery with 40 sq m floor space
Details: Exhibits variety of artistic styles and media with distinctive Celtic theme. Emphasis is on landscapes and Irish mythology. Aims to provide friendly, warm atmosphere and exposure for artists to international touring public. Gallery covers exhibition costs. Sales a priority.

Yawl Art Gallery

Group shows presented during summer months.
Dooega, Achill Island [00 353] 98 36137
Contact: Seosamh Ó Dálaigh, Exhibition Organiser
Open: (Summer) Daily 10-5

Ardee
CO LOUTH

Ardee Branch Library

`Po` `Sc`

Library gallery displays work by local artists and craftspeople.
Market Square, Ardee, tel: [00 353] 41 56080
Contact: Austin Vaughan, Exhibition Organiser
Open: Tues 2-5, 6-8; Wed & Sat 10-1; Thurs 6-8; Fri 10-1, 2-5
Exhibitions: 5 a year

Athlone
CO WESTMEATH

Dolan Moore Gallery

Gallery on two floors specialising in Irish contemporary art with most exhibitions of work by established artists.
33 Church Street, Athlone, tel: [00 353] 902 78507
Contact: Amy Moore, Director
Open: Mon-Fri 9.30-6; Sat 10.30-5.30
Exhibitions: 6 a year

Athy
CO KILDARE

Athy Community Library

Library gallery run by Kildare County Library Service exhibiting work by professional artists.
Town Hall, Emily Square, Athy, tel: [00 353] 507 31144
Contact: Monica Corcoran, County Arts Officer, Kildare County Library Service, Athgarvan Road, Newbridge, tel: [00 353] 45 31486, fax: [00 353] 45 32490
Open: Tues & Thurs 10-8; Wed, Fri & Sat 10-5
Exhibitions: 6 a year

Crookstown Mill Heritage Centre

`Po` `Cr` `Sc` ● ⓖ

Restored watermill with milling museum, tea room and gift shop with various exhibitions and fairs throughout the year.
Ballitore, Athy, tel: [00 353] 507 23222
Contact: Jim Maher, Owner
Open: (Apr-Sept) Daily 10-7; (Oct-Mar) Sun 2-5
Space: 140 lin m hanging space and 335 sq m floor space
Details: Exhibitions and fairs are advertised through press and media. Sales from exhibitions and fairs are a priority. Summer schools held.

Ballinasloe
CO GALWAY

Ballinasloe Library

`Po` `Ph` `Cr` ● ⓖ

Exhibition space in reference room of public library.
Fairgreen, Ballinasloe, tel: [00 353] 905 43464
Contact: Mary Dillon, Assistant Librarian
Open: Mon, Wed, Fri & Sat 10-1, 2-5.30; Tues & Thurs 10.30-1, 2-5.30, 6.30-8.30
Space: 1 gallery with 8 lin m hanging space plus 4 lin m on screens and 9 sq m floor space
Exhibitions: 6 a year
Details: Most exhibitions are from locally-based organisations with some from national organisations. However library would like to bring exhibitions of all types to the attention of the public and would welcome proposals for exhibitions in any field of 'the arts'. Sale of work not a primary consideration.

Ballsbridge
CO DUBLIN

Milmo-Penny Fine Art

`Po`

Gallery specialising in Irish impressionists and hosting occasional exhibitions of contemporary artists working in the same style.
55 Ailesbury Road, Ballsbridge 4, tel: [00 353] 1 269 3486, fax: [00 353] 1 283 0414
Contact: Dominic Milmo-Penny, Director
Open: (During exhibitions) daily 11-8; or by appointment

Ballyvaughan
CO CLARE

Dallan Gallery

Gallery exhibits and promotes artists who work in artforms other than painting.
Ballyvaughan, tel: [00 353] 65 77156
Contact: Seamus McGuinness, Proprietor
Open: (Mar-Dec) daily 10-7
Exhibitions: 5 a year

Bantry
CO CORK

Bantry Library

Library display space suitable for small 2D exhibitions, mostly used by local artists and groups.
Bridge Street, Bantry, tel: [00 353] 27 50460
Contact: Noel O'Mahony, Branch Librarian
Open: Tues, Wed, Fri & Sat 10-1, 2.30-6; Thurs 10-6

O'Kane's Green Gallery

Continuous display of work by professional artists living in West Cork with occasional solo or two-person exhibitions.
Glengarriff Road, Bantry, tel: [00 353] 27 50003
Contact: Christine Nicholas, Owner
Open: (Jun-Sept) Mon-Sat 10-6; or by enquiry at next door craftshop.

Birdhill
CO TIPPERARY

Lucy Erridge Gallery

`Po` `Sc`

Gallery exhibits work by mainly Irish artists and craftspeople in one- and two-person shows and thematic exhibitions.
Birdhill, tel: [00 353] 61 379366, fax: [00 353] 61 302459
Contact: Lucy Erridge, Exhibition Organiser

Open: Mon-Sat 10.30-5.30; Sun 1.30-5.30
Exhibitions: 9 a year

Bray
CO WICKLOW

Craft Art Gallery

Gallery showing emerging and established artists in one-person and group exhibitions.
74 Main Street, Bray, tel: [00 353] 1 286 6728
Contact: Jean Colohan, Director
Open: Tues-Sat 10-1, 2-6
Exhibitions: 6 a year

Hangman Gallery

Pa Cr

Converted Victorian house with seven rooms for exhibitions of work by Irish artists and craftspeople.
2 Westbourne Terrace, Quinnsborough Road, Bray, tel: [00 353] 1 286 6208, fax: [00 353] 1 286 6207
Contact: Val Byrne, Owner
Open: Mon-Sat 11-5.30
Exhibitions: 8 a year

Signal Arts Centre

A

Gallery, with studios, run by artists' co-operative and showing work across the artforms selected from applications by committee.
3 Albert Walk, Bray, tel: [00 353] 1 286 4266
Contact: Patrick Verner, Administrator
Open: Mon-Sat 10-5
Exhibitions: 25 a year

Bunclody
CO WEXFORD

Chantry Gallery

Owner invites Irish artists to show work in gallery.
Bunclody, tel: [00 353] 54 77482
Contact: Betty Craig, Owner
Open: By appointment
Exhibitions: 2 a year

Buncrana
CO DONEGAL

Tullyarvan Mill Culture & Exhibition Centre

Pa Cr

Centre in converted mill encouraging local arts and crafts through exhibitions and providing a base for community arts groups which organises workshops.
Buncrana, tel: [00 353] 77 61613
Contact: Francis Crawford
Open: (Jun-Sept) Mon-Sat 10-6, Sun 2-6; or by appointment

Carlingford
CO LOUTH

Artistic Licence

Pa Pr SE ✓ ♿

Gallery on two floors presenting exhibitions with minimum of two hundred works in each show.
The Old Coach House, Dundalk Street, Carlingford, tel: [00 353] 42 73745
Contact: P Mussen, Exhibition Organiser
Open: Mon-Thurs, Sat & Sun noon-dusk
Space: 2 galleries with 152 lin m hanging space and 140 sq m floor space
Exhibitions: 4 a year all originated
Details: Constant group show always in progress featuring work by at least twenty artists. Contemporary and traditional work always stocked. Generally four one-person exhibitions a year offered to established artists. Gallery covers exhibition costs. Sale of work a priority.

Holy Trinity Heritage Centre

Floor space available for free standing exhibitions in centre aimed at providing visitors with knowledge of Carlingford and its history.
Carlingford, tel: [00 353] 42 73454
Contact: Carlingford Lough Heritage Trust
Open: Daily 9.30-5

Carlow
CO CARLOW

Pembroke Studio Gallery

Gallery attached to artist's studio that exhibits work by artists with Carlow connections.
1 Pembroke, Carlow, tel: [00 353] 503 41562
Contact: Bev Carbery, Proprietor
Open: Mon, Wed & Sat 2-6; Tues, Thurs & Fri 10-6

Carrick on Shannon
CO LEITRIM

Old Barrel Store Arts Centre

A

Gallery run by co-operative situated above craft shop.
The Quays, Carrick on Shannon, tel: [00 353] 78 20911
Contact: David Knight and Sandra Vernon, Exhibition Organisers
Open: Daily 10.30-6

Carrick on Suir
CO TIPPERARY

Carrick on Suir Heritage Centre

Ground and first-floor gallery with varied exhibition programme featuring work of mostly local artists.
off Main Street, Carrick on Suir, tel: [00 353] 51 40200
Contact: Patrick Fitzgerald, Exhibition Organiser
Open: Daily 10-1, 2-5

Castlebar
CO MAYO

Castlebar Public Library

Library with exhibition areas enabling local artists to show their work and with the aim of increasing public access to the arts.
The Mall, Castlebar, tel: [00 353] 94 24444, fax: [00 353] 94 23937
Contact: John Coll, County Arts Officer
Open: Tues & Wed 11.30-1, 2-7.30; Thurs-Sat 11.30-1, 2-5
Exhibitions: 12 a year

Kirk Gallery

Gallery presenting and promoting work of professional Irish and European artists.
Lower Charles Street, Castlebar, tel: [00 353] 94 22452, fax: [00 353] 94 21127
Contact: John Dawson-Evans, Exhibition Organiser
Open: Mon-Sat 10-6; or by appointment

Linenhall Arts Centre Company

Pa Ph Pr Cr SE A ✓ ♿ Wc

Gallery on first floor of C18th building showing all forms of contemporary art with a bias towards young professional artists working in the area.
Linenhall Street, Castlebar, tel: [00 353] 94 23733, fax: [00 353] 94 24187
Contact: Marie Farrell, Director
Open: Mon-Fri 10-6; Sat 11-6
Space: 1 gallery with 34 lin m hanging space and 84 sq m floor space
Exhibitions: 14 a year of which 11 originated, 3 touring
Details: Sale of work not considered gallery's primary role.

Castleisland
CO KERRY

Ivyleaf Arts Centre

Pa ⊘

The arts centre which is chiefly devoted to theatre, provides an exhibition area in the foyer.
Old Church Lasne, Castleisland, tel: [00 353] 66 41135

Contact: Jerome Stack, Exhibition Organiser
Open: Mon-Sat 9-6
Space: 1 gallery
Exhibitions: 4 a year all originated
Details: Exhibitions are organised in conjunction with drama productions and run concurrently. They feature work by local artists. Aim is to provide relaxed and informal atmosphere in which theatre goers can enjoy viewing an exhibition. Sales are welcome but not a priority. No commission taken.

Cavan
CO CAVAN

Cavan County Arts Service

Arts service organising exhibitions in three venues in the area.
Cavan County Library, 17 Farnham Street, Cavan, tel: [00 353] 49 31799, fax: [00 353] 49 61565/31384
Contact: Catriona O'Reilly, Arts Orgasiner

Celbridge
CO KILDARE

Celbridge Branch Library

Library gallery on first floor showing mostly work by individual artists and groups from the area.
Celbridge, tel: [00 353] 1 627 2207
Contact: Monica Corcoran, County Arts Officer, Kildare County Library Service, County Library, Athgarvan Road, Newbridge, tel: [00 353] 45 31486, fax: [00 353] 45 32490
Open: Mon & Thurs 2-8.30; Tues 2-5.30; Wed & Fri 10-5.30
Exhibitions: 3 a year

Charleville
CO CORK

Charleville Library

Library exhibition space for groups and individuals who organise and hang their own display.
Main Street, Charleville, tel: [00 353] 63 89769
Contact: Nora O'Flynn, Senior Library Assistant
Open: Mon-Sat 10-1, 2-6

Claremorris
CO MAYO

Claremorris Gallery

Pa Pr Cr SE O H & 4
Gallery in former bank.
James Street, Claremorris, tel: [00 353] 94 71348/21733

Contact: Patricia Noone, Director
Open: (May-Oct) Tues-Sat 11-6; other times during exhibitions only
Space: 2 galleries with 70 lin m hanging space and 85 sq m floor space
Exhibitions: 6 a year of which 4 originated, 1 touring, 1 on a hire basis
Details: Exhibitions of work by mostly established and aspiring artists. Also travelling shows and large theme exhibitions. Occasional community art shows and gallery operates as a community arts centre. Sales not considered gallery's primary function.

Clonmel
CO TIPPERARY

Tipperary South Riding County Museum

Pa Ph Pr SE O Ø

Temporary exhibition gallery in museum in which visiting exhibitions are housed.
Parnell Street, Clonmel, tel: [00 353] 52 21399, fax: [00 353] 52 24355
Contact: Patrick Holland, Curator
Open: Tues-Sat 10-1, 2-5
Space: 1 gallery with 15 lin m hanging space plus 44 lin m on screens and 65 sq m floor space
Exhibitions: 5 a year of which 1 originated, 4 touring
Details: Visiting exhibitions are usually historical, sometimes contemporary art. Gallery has wall boards, stands and display cases. Sales not a priority.

Cobh
CO CORK

Sirius Commemoration Trust

Gallery in building that also houses tourist office where exhibitions are organised in conjunction with Crawford Municipal Art Gallery, Cork.
The Old Yacht Club, Cobh, tel: [00 353] 21 813612, fax: [00 353] 21 811018
Contact: Peter Murray, Exhibition Organiser
Open: Mon-Fri 9-5

Connemara
CO GALWAY

Danlann (An)

Gallery with stock of work by established artists in the area and some special exhibitions.
Casla, Connemara, tel: [00 353] 91 72141
Contact: Marion Nic Con Iomaire, Owner
Open: Mon-Fri 10.30-6; Sat & Sun 1-6

Cork
CO CORK

Art Hive

Committed to provision of arts activity for and in the community and runs varied exhibition and education programmes.
Thompson House, MacCurtain Street, Cork, tel: [00 353] 21 505228
Contact: Sinéad Ní Chionaola & Ian Healy, Visual Arts Directors
Open: Mon-Sat 10-6

Blackcombe Art Gallery

Promotes artists for whom it acts as agent and exhibits work by both Irish and international artists.
44a MacCurtain Street, Cork, tel: [00 353] 21 500040
Contact: Luis Poretta, Director
Open: Mon-Sat 10-6
Exhibitions: 18 a year

Crawford Municipal Art Gallery

Pa Pr SE O & Wc

Provides exhibition space for both historical permanent collections and contemporary exhibitions.
Emmet Place, Cork, tel: [00 353] 21 273377, fax: [00 353] 21 275680
Contact: Peter Murray/Curator, Nuala Fenton/Exhibitions Officer
Open: Mon-Sat 10-5
Space: 6 galleries with 131 lin m hanging space and 500 sq m floor space
Exhibitions: 15 a year of which 7 originated, 8 touring
Details: Gallery holds permanent collection of work by both local and international artists. Visiting artists exhibit on a monthly basis. Tours of exhibitions are organised for local and foreign visitors. Lecture theatre available for talks, concerts, use by drama groups etc. Sale of work not a priority.

Lavitt's Quay Gallery

Gallery run by Cork Arts Society exhibits work by established artists, mostly in one-person shows.
16 Lavitt's Quay, Cork, tel: [00 353] 21 277749
Contact: Charlo Quain, Administrator
Open: Tues-Sat 10.30-2, 3-5.30
Exhibitions: 22 a year

Triskel Arts Centre

Main gallery and two smaller exhibition spaces showing both emerging and established artists; local, national and international.
Tobin Street, Off South Main Street, Cork, tel: [00 353] 21 272022/3, fax: [00 353] 21 275945
Contact: Fiona Cunningham, Visual Arts Co-ordinator

Open: Mon-Sat 10.30-5.30
Exhibitions: 17 a year

University College Cork (Boole Library)

Exhibition space in foyer of Boole Library with exhibitions to encourage students' appreciation of contemporary art.
College Road, Cork, tel: [00 353] 21 276871, fax: [00 353] 21 276647
Contact: William Gallagher, Visual Arts Co-ordinator
Open: (1st term) Mon-Fri 8-10; Sat 10-1, (2nd term)10-6, (3rd term) 10-10
Exhibitions: 10 a year

Dalkey
CO DUBLIN

James Gallery

Gallery with regular exhibitors, Irish artists, whose work forms exhibitions of paintings and sculpture.
7 Railway Road, Dalkey, tel: [00 353] 1 285 8703
Contact: Pat Hopper, Owner
Open: Tues-Fri 3-10; Sat 3-6; Sun 2-6

Dingle
CO KERRY

Simple Pleasures Art Gallery

Gallery presenting one-person exhibitions each lasting two weeks.
The Mall, Dingle, tel: [00 353] 66 51224
Contact: Michael and Julie Hennessy, Directors
Open: (May-Sept) daily 10-10; (Winter) 10.30-6
Exhibitions: 6 a year

Drogheda
CO LOUTH

Droichead Arts Centre

Pa Ph Pr Cr Sc LA ✓ ⊕ & Wc

Well-established exhibition venue, recently moved to first floor of a newly-built arts centre and library.
Stockwell Street, Drogheda, tel: [00 353] 41 33946, fax: [00 353] 41 42055
Contact: Tony Conaghy, Visual Arts Director
Open: Mon-Sat 10-5
Space: 2 galleries with 59 lin m hanging space and 147 sq m floor space
Exhibitions: 19 a year of which 9 originated, 4 touring, 6 on a hire basis
Details: Exhibitions last two weeks and feature contemporary and local art and C20th Irish artists' retrospectives. Workshops run by artists for schools and community groups. Sales of work not gallery's primary role but work is sold and

20% commission taken. Exhibition fee sometimes paid; depends on exhibition.

Dublin
CO DUBLIN

Andrews Lane Theatre

Foyer exhibition space shows and sells work by young painters.
9-17 St Andrew's Lane, Dublin 2, tel: [00 353] 1 679 5720, fax: [00 353] 1 679 7552
Contact: Exhibitions Organiser
Open: Mon-Sat 10.30am-11pm; Sun variable
Exhibitions: 10 a year

Anya Von Gösseln Gallery

2nd Floor, Inside Makullas, 11-13 Suffolk Street, Dublin 2, tel: [00 353] 1 671 4079

Arts Council

Exhibition space in foyer of the Arts Council offering exhibitions to artists who have received an Arts Council grant in previous 12 months.
70 Merrion Square, Dublin 2, tel: [00 353] 1 661 1840, fax: [00 353] 1 676 1302
Contact: Sarah Finlay, Visual Arts Officer
Open: Mon-Fri 9.30-1, 2.15-5.30
Exhibitions: 12 a year

City Arts Centre

Two galleries, recording studios and theatre space in large converted factory.
23-25 Moss Street, Dublin 2, tel: [00 353] 1 677 0643, fax: [00 353] 1 677 0131
Contact: Sandy Fitzgerald, Executive Director
Open: Mon-Fri 11-5; Sun 2-4
Exhibitions: 15 a year

Combridge Fine Arts

Commercial gallery specialising in Irish landscape painting.
Gainsboro House, 24 Suffolk Street, Dublin 2, tel: [00 353] 1 677 4652
Contact: Brian Sibley, Managing Director
Open: Mon-Fri 9.30-5.45; Sat 9.30-5.30
Exhibitions: 4 a year

Crafts Council Gallery

  Cr Sc ✓ ⊘

Aims to set high standards of design and craftsmanship for Ireland's craftworkers, to inform and enthuse the public about craftwork and to place Irish crafts in European and international context.
Powerscourt Town House, South William Street, Dublin 2, tel: [00 353] 1 679 7368, fax: [00 353] 1 679 9197
Contact: Catherine Jordan, Exhibitions Assistant

Open: Mon 10-5; Tues-Sat 10-6
Space: 1 gallery with 20 lin m hanging space plus 15 lin m on screens and 233 sq m floor space
Exhibitions: 7 a year of which 6 originated, 1 touring
Details: Gallery's brief is to challenge Irish makers to use exhibitions to develop new work and ideas, and to make the exhibitions accessible to the general public to increase awareness and appreciation of the crafts. Achieves this through publication of catalogues, encouragement of critical writing and reviewing and through education programme. Council insists on rigorous selection of work for exhibitions to ensure that its objective of showing best of work is achieved. Sales not gallery's primary role.

Davis Gallery

Pa Cr Sc ⅄

Commercial gallery's whose usual policy is to show only artwork and art/craft by artists residing in Ireland.
11 Capel Street, Dublin 1, tel: [00 353] 1 872 6969, fax: [00 353] 1 873 3080
Contact: Gerald Davis, Owner
Open: Mon-Fri 10-5; Sat 11-5
Space: 1 gallery with 33 lin m hanging space and 75 sq m floor space
Exhibitions: 6 a year all originated

Designyard

Cr ⊕ & Wc

Applied arts centre operating over three floors and exhibiting contemporary international jewellery design along with Irish contemporary furniture, glass, ceramics, lighting and objets d'art.
12 Essex Street, Temple Bar, Dublin 2, tel: [00 353] 1 677 8453, fax: [00 353] 1 677 8482
Contact: Cornelia McCarthy, Projects Manager
Open: Mon-Sat 10.30-5.30
Space: 3 galleries with 350 sq m floor space
Exhibitions: 8 a year of which 6 originated, 2 on a hire basis
Details: Shows work of selected craft workers and designers with emphasis on quality in terms of design and manufacture. Acts as link between maker and users (domestic and professional). Special projects include providing furniture to contract market, corporate gifts & encouraging use of craftwork in structure of buildings. Jewellery Gallery has display cases. Furniture Gallery used as showroom; Seminar Room with 26 lin metres for temporary exhibitions. Independent access for wheelchair users to ground floor only.

Douglas Hyde Gallery

One of Dublin's few purpose-built galleries showing major exhibitions by Irish and international artists.
Trinity College, Nassau Street, Dublin 2, tel: [00 353] 1 608 1116, **fax:** [00 353] 1 677 2694 (attn DHG)
Contact: John Hutchinson , Director
Open: Mon-Wed, Fri 11-6; Thurs 11-7; Sat 11-4.45
Space: 1 gallery with 71 lin m hanging space and 158 sq m floor space
Exhibitions: 8 a year of which 7 originated, 1 touring
Details: Gallery committed to exploration of cultural issues that dominate the end of C20th, through work of artists engaged in debates of historical self-definition, identity and transformation. Most forms of fine and time-based art shown with roughly two-thirds of exhibitions presenting work by international artists and one-third Irish. Each show lasts 6 weeks; some exhibitions tour. Active education programme with lectures, gallery tours and artists' talks. Sales not a priority.

Dublin Photographic Centre

Centre devoted to photography showing mainly work of young and up and coming Irish and foreign photographers.
10 Lower Camden Street, Dublin 2, tel: [00 353] 1 660 8513
Contact: Eddie Chandler, President, Dublin Camera Club
Open: (Summer) daily 11-5.30; (rest of year) Sat only, phone for appointment
Space: 1 gallery with 30 lin m hanging space and 80 sq m floor space
Exhibitions: 12 a year all originated
Details: Main aim is to provide a space where young or unknown up and coming photographers may present their work. Gallery is part of Dublin Camera Club which includes provision of dark room and studio flities for member photographers and the organisation of classes in photography. Sale of work not considered gallery's primary role.

Dublin Public Libraries

Exhibition space in Dublin libraries provided for use of local groups with aims of promoting visual arts and encouraging local art activity.
Cumberland House, Fenian Street, Dublin 2, tel: [00 353] 1 661 9000
Contact: Alastair Smeaton, Divisional Librarian, Development Office

Dublin Writers Museum

Museum holds exhibitions of items and artwork that relate to Dublin writers and in particular to the Dublin Writers Museum Collection.
18 Parnell Square, Dublin 1, tel: [00 353] 1 872 2077, **fax:** [00 353] 1 872 2231
Contact: Louise Keogh, Exhibition Organiser
Open: Daily 10-5

Gallery of Photography

Aims toxhibit the best in Irish and international photography.
Meeting House Square, Temple Bar, Dublin, tel: [00 353] 1 671 4654, **fax:** [00 353] 1 670 9293
Contact: Christine Redmond, Director
Open: Mon-Sat 11-6
Space: 3 galleries with 50 lin m hanging space plus 31 lin m on screens and 100 sq m floor space
Exhibitions: 12 a year of which 6 originated, 6 touring
Details: Main concerns of the gallery's exhibition/education programme continues to be the creation of an ever more active, widespread and dynamic photographic culture/dialogue in Ireland. Sale of work not considered gallery's primary concern.

Gorry Gallery

Dealer in C18th, C19th and C20th Irish paintings holding occasional exhibitions of contemporary work.
20 Molesworth Street, Dublin 2, tel: [00 353] 1 679 5319
Contact: James Gorry, Exhibition Organiser
Open: Mon-Fri 10.30-5.30; Sat 10.30-1

Graphic Studio Dublin Gallery

Contemporary print gallery on two levels, owned by Graphic Studio Dublin – the longest established Irish printmaking organisation.
8a Through the Arch, Cope Street, Temple Bar, Dublin 2, tel: [00 353] 1 679 8021
Contact: Catriona Fallon, Administrator
Open: Tues-Fri 10.30-6; Sat 11-5
Space: 1 gallery with 38 lin m hanging space and 106 sq m floor space
Exhibitions: 6 a year all originated
Details: Promotes the knowledge and understanding of fine prints, (etchings, lithographs, relief prints etc). Occasional solo or group exhibitions by both Irish and International artists are held. Works sold. Access with assistance for wheelchair users to ground floor only.

Green on Red Gallery

Shows contemporary art and photography by emerging and established Irish and international artists and promotes its gallery artists.
58 Fitzwilliam Street, Dublin 2, tel: [00 353] 1 661 3881
Contact: Jerome O Drisceoil, Director
Open: Mon-Fri 11-6; Sat 11-3
Exhibitions: 16 a year

Guinness Gallery

Exhibits and sells paintings and designer crafts.
Foxrock Village, Dublin 18, tel: [00 353] 1 289 7955
Contact: Elisabeth Guinness, Director
Open: Mon-Sat 11.30-5.30; Sun 2.30-5.30

Guinness Hop Store

Two large galleries and small bar area providing space to individuals and organisations for variety of exhibitions.
Crane Street, off Thomas Street, Dublin 8, tel: [00 353] 1 453 6700 , **fax:** [00 353] 1 453 3631
Contact: Peter Walsh, Curator
Open: Mon-Fri 10-5
Exhibitions: 8 a year

Hallward Gallery

Shows Irish contemporary fine art, mainly through one-person exhibitions.
64 Merrion Square, Dublin 2, tel: [00 353] 1 662 1482
Contact: Bríd Dukes, Exhibition Organiser
Open: Mon-Fri 10.30-5.30; Sat 11-3; or by appointment

Hugh Lane Municipal Gallery of Modern Art

Temporary exhibition programme of contemporary art is run alongside permanent collection displays of C19th and C20th Irish and international art.
Charlemont House, Parnell Square, Dublin 1, tel: [00 353] 1 741 1903, **fax:** [00 353] 1 872 2182
Contact: Barbara Dawson, Director
Open: Tues-Fri 9.30-6; Sat 9.30-5; Sun 11-5

Irish Life Exhibition Centre

Exhibition space available to visual arts organisations; groups, societies, colleges, etc and run by the Irish Life Arts Policy Committee.
Irish Life Mall, Lower Abbey Street, Dublin 1, tel: [00 353] 1 704 2000, **fax:** [00 353] 1 704 1907
Contact: Jim Mac Cormaic, c/o Arts Policy Committee, Irish Life
Open: Mon-Sat 10-5

Irish Museum of Modern Art

[Sc] [LA] ✔ [£] ♿ [WC]

IMMA is housed in refurbished C17th building and opened in 1991 to represent art of C20th in its temporary exhibition programme and in its collection.
The Royal Hospital, Kilmainham, Dublin 8, tel: [00 353] 1 671 8666, fax: [00 353] 1 671 8695
Contact: Brenda McParland, Curator: Head of Exhibitions
Open: Tues-Sat 10-5.30; Sun 12-5.30
Details: Broad range of exhibitions developed by Education/Community programmes with locally based community groups, schools, colleges, Active Aged groups and people with special needs. Sale of work not gallery's primary function.

Jo Rain

First Floor, 23 Anglesea Street, Temple Bar, Dublin

Kennedy Gallery

[Pa] [Pr] [Cr] [Sc] [H]

Two large Georgian rooms exhibiting work by contemporary artists.
12 Harcourt Street, Dublin 2, tel: [00 353] 1 675 1749, fax: [00 353] 1 675 3851
Contact: Ultan Kennedy, Partner responsible for exhibitions
Open: Mon-Sat 10-5
Exhibitions: 9 a year of which 7 originated, 1 touring, 1 on a hire basis
Details: Group and solo shows by contemporary artists with an emphasis on still life, landscape and figurative. Painting, sculpture and print are shown in 12 exhibitions a year (lasting 3 weeks). Artists may apply to exhibit.

Kerlin Gallery

[Pa] [Ph] [Pr] [Sc]

Gallery shows work by Irish and international established and emerging artists.
Anne's Lane, South Anne Street, Dublin 2, tel: [00 353] 1 677 9179, fax: [00 353] 1 677 9652
Contact: John Kennedy and David Fitzgerald, Directors
Open: Mon-Fri 10-5.45; Sat 11-4.30
Exhibitions: 13 a year
Details: Shows painting, sculpture, print, photography and installation by both established and up and coming artists, promoting their work both in Ireland and abroad (represents its artists at International art fairs). 13-14 shows a year are held, each for 3 weeks, mostly solo, occasionally 2-3 group shows are also held. Artists may apply to exhibit.

Mansion House

Public rooms attached to the Mansion House which are leased to individuals for exhibitions and fairs.
Dawson Street, Dublin 2, tel: [00 353] 1 679 6111 ext 2811, fax: [00 353] 1 679 8159
Contact: Anne Moore, Booking Officer
Open: Daily 10-10

New Apollo Gallery

Commercial gallery which has permanent stock of contemporary Irish art and holds one-person exhibitions.
18 Duke Street, Dublin 2, tel: [00 353] 1 671 2609, fax: [00 353] 1 679 7558
Contact: Hugh Charlton, Owner
Open: Mon-Fri 11-6; Sat 10-6; Sun 12-6
Exhibitions: 8 a year

Oisin Art Gallery (Marino Mart)

Commercial gallery which holds exhibitions mainly of traditional work by Irish artists as well as permanent stock of paintings.
10 Marino Mart, Fairview, Dublin 3, tel: [00 353] 1 833 3456, fax: [00 353] 1 833 5197
Contact: Donal McNeela, Director
Open: Mon-Fri 9-5.30; Sat 10-5.30
Exhibitions: 4 a year

Oisin Art Gallery (Westland Row)

Gallery showing and selling mainly figurative work by contemporary Irish artists.
44 Westland Row, Dublin 2, tel: [00 353] 1 661 1315, fax: [00 353] 1 661 0464
Contact: Rory McNeela, Director
Open: Mon-Fri 9-5.30; Sat 10-5.30
Exhibitions: 6 a year

Oriel Gallery

Gallery with continuous display of C20th traditional Irish paintings and some exhibitions.
17 Clare Street, Dublin 2, tel: [00 353] 1 676 3410
Contact: Oliver Nulty, Director
Open: Mon-Fri 10-5.30; Sat 10.30-1
Exhibitions: 8 a year

Ormond Gallery

[Pa] [Ph] [Pr] [Cr] [Sc] [LA] ✔ [H] ♿ [WC] [4]

City centre gallery in a multi-media centre with monthly shows from both first-time exhibitors and established artists.
16-18 Ormond Quay Lower, Dublin 1, tel: [00 353] 1 872 3500, fax: [00 353] 1 872 3348
Contact: Deirdre Black, Director
Open: Mon-Fri 11-6; Sat by appointment
Exhibitions: 1 gallery with 43 lin m hanging space plus 5 lin m on screens and 223 sq m floor space
Exhibitions: 14 a year of which 13 originated, 1 on a hire basis
Details: Gallery in multi-media centre which contains restaurant open during the day. At weekends becomes part of an alternative performance venue. Applications welcome from artists or groups of artists wishing to exhibit in vibrant environment. Sale of work not considered gallery's primary role. 25% commission taken on any sales made. Extent of exhibitor's contribution to exhibition costs is negotiable and depends on available funds.

Project Arts Centre

Showcase for younger artists and it encourages installation, site-specific and time-based work.
39 East Essex Street, Temple Bar, Dublin 2, tel: [00 353] 1 671 2321, fax: [00 353] 1 671 3327
Contact: Fiach MacConghail, Director
Open: Mon-Sat 11-6

RHA Gallagher Gallery

Royal Hibernian Academy's headquarters' presents broad ranging exhibition programme.
15 Ely Place, Dublin 2, tel: [00 353] 1 661 2558, fax: [00 353] 1 661 0762
Contact: Ciaran MacGonigal, Director
Open: Mon-Wed, Fri & Sat 11-5; Thurs 11-9; Sun 2-5
Exhibitions: 30 a year
Details: Programme includes one-person, group and touring shows of work by Irish and international artists as well as exhibitions by major societies.

Royal Dublin Society

RDS's Visual Arts Committee's policy focuses on hosting exhibitions that encourage and promote excellence in the visual arts.
Ballsbridge, Dublin 4, tel: [00 353] 1 668 0866, fax: [00 353] 1 660 4014
Contact: John Coleman, Chairman Visual Arts Committee
Open: Daily 8.15am-11pm

Rubicon Gallery

Basement gallery presenting mainly one-person shows by both established and emerging artists.
11 Upper Mount Street, Dublin 2, tel: [00 353] 1 676 2331
Contact: Josephine Kelliher & Peter KcKenna, Directors
Open: Mon-Fri 11-6; Sat 11-3
Exhibitions: 13 a year

Solomon Gallery

[Pa] [Pr] [Sc] ✔ ♿

Commercial gallery situated C18th Georgian town house showing Irish and international contemporary painters and sculptors working primarily in representational/figurative style.

Powerscourt Town House, South William Street, Dublin 2, tel: [00 353] 1 679 4237, fax: [00 353] 1 671 5262
Contact: Suzanne Macdougald, Director
Open: Mon-Sat 10-5.30
Space: 2 galleries with 41 lin m hanging space plus 2 lin m on screens and 112 sq m floor space
Exhibitions: 18 a year all originated
Details: Exhibitions are mounted every three weeks with emphasis on one-person exhibitions. Two annual group shows during Christmas and Summer to which all Gallery artists are invited to submit. Work sold on a commission basis. Gallery's aim is to provide a friendly and efficient environment in which individuals and businesses can enjoy viewing and hopefully buy work. Sales a priority.

Taylor Galleries

Commercial gallery specialising in work by established and up and coming Irish artists.
34 Kildare Street, Dublin 2, tel: [00 353] 1 676 6055, fax: [00 353] 1 676 8305
Contact: John Taylor & Patrick Taylor, Directors
Open: Mon-Fri 10-5.30; Sat 11-1
Exhibitions: 16 a year

Temple Bar Gallery & Studios

Thirty artists' studios and gallery exhibiting innovative work and first shows by young promising artists, the majority of which are Irish.
5-9 Temple Bar, Dublin 2, tel: [00 353] 1 671 0073, fax: [00 353] 1 677 7527
Contact: Ruairi o Cuiv, Director
Open: Mon-Sat 10-6; Sun 12-6
Exhibitions: 12 a year

Village Art Gallery

Gallery shows mainly work by established artists based in the area with continuous displays and special exhibitions.
Thomas Hand Street, Skerries, Dublin, tel: [00 353] 1 849 2236
Contact: Emer Mullins, Director
Open: Tues-Sat 10-5.30; Sun 2.30-5.30

Wyvern Gallery

Po Sc ✓ &

Exhibition space on ground floor showing painting and sculpture by established Irish artists with upper floors showing work by gallery artists.
2 Temple Lane, Temple Bar, Dublin 2, tel: [00 353] 1 679 9589
Contact: Terry Carroll, Owner
Open: Mon-Fri 10.30-5.30; Sat 11-5
Space: 2 galleries with 91 lin m hanging space and 158 sq m floor space
Exhibitions: 12 a year all originated
Details: Work shown mainly by artists gallery represents. Touring shows occasionally shown. Sales a priority.

Dun Laoghaire
CO DUBLIN

Bobby Dawson Gallery

Gallery showing wide variety of arts and crafts encouraging young artists in particular.
16 Upper Georges Street, Dun Laoghaire, tel: [00 353] 1 284 3366
Contact: Marjorie Walshe, Exhibition Organiser
Open: Mon-Fri 10-5.30; Sat 10.15-1.15

Dundalk
CO LOUTH

Basement Gallery

Gallery in basement of Town Hall showing architecture and theatre set designs as well as more conventional artforms.
The Town Hall, Dundalk, tel: [00 353] 42 32276, fax: [00 353] 42 36171
Contact: Brian Harten, Arts Organiser
Open: Mon-Fri 10-12.45, 1.45-5; Sat 10-1
Exhibitions: 12 a year

County Museum Dundalk

Museum, exhibition space and library situated together in restored bonded warehouse.
Jocelyn Street, Dundalk, tel: [00 353] 42 27056, fax: [00 353] 42 27058
Contact: Carol Gleeson, Curator
Open: Tues-Sat 10.30-5.30; Sun 2-6

TristAnn's Gallery

Town Hall, Crowe Street, Dundalk, tel: [00 353] 42 2276, fax: [00 353] 42 26777

Ennis
CO CLARE

De Valera Library

Library exhibition space for work by local professional and amateur artists
Harmony Row, Ennis, tel: [00 353] 65 21616, fax: [00 353] 65 28233
Contact: Eugene Crimmins, County Arts Officer
Open: Mon-Thurs 11-5.30; Tues, Wed, Fri 1-8
Exhibitions: 12 a year

Ennistymon
CO CLARE

Ennistymon Branch Library

Library gallery suitable for exhibiting 2D work.
The Square, Ennistymon, tel: [00 353] 65 71245

Contact: Brian Doyle, Senior Library Assistant
Open: Mon, Wed & Fri 11-1, 2.30-5.30 & 7-8.30; Tues & Thurs 11-1, 2.30-5.30

Foxford
CO MAYO

Foxford Exhibition Centre

Po Ph Pr G Sc ✓ & Wc 4

Venue for exhibitions which is used by Irish and foreign professional artists.
St Joseph's Place, Foxford, tel: [00 353] 94 56756, fax: [00 353] 94 56794
Contact: Bernie Byron, Project Manager
Open: Mon-Sat 11-5; Sun 2-6
Space: 1 gallery with 29 lin m hanging space and 76 sq m floor space
Exhibitions: 13 a year all originated
Details: Due to lighting and layout of the Centre, exhibitions taking many forms can be mounted. Primary objective is to promote arts and culture in Mayo among all ages. Exhibition launches are made into public occasions for the celebration of art. Local schools hold annual 'Student Review'. Sale of work and education viewed by gallery as being equally important. 25% commission taken on sales made.

Foynes
CO LIMERICK

Foynes Branch Library

Library with first-floor exhibition space.
Foynes, tel: [00 353] 69 65365
Contact: Irene Kelly, Branch Librarian
Open: Tues & Thurs 10-12.30, 2.30-5; Wed & Fri 10-12.30, 2.30-8.30; Sat 10-12.30
Exhibitions: 12 a year
Details: Welcomes applications to exhibit but particularly from young recently-graduated artists.

Galway
CO GALWAY

Dámhlann Kenny Gallery

An Spidéal, Galway, tel: [00 353] 91 83733, fax: [00 353] 91 83734

Galway Arts Centre

Arts centre promotes and exhibits work by artists living in West of Ireland and hosts some international shows.
47 Dominick Street, Galway, tel: [00 353] 91 65886
Contact: Michael Diskin, Director
Open: Mon-Sat 10-5.30
Exhibitions: 12 a year

Grainstore Gallery

Shows contemporary fine art and craft and specialises in ceramics and works on paper.
Lower Abbeygate Street, Galway, tel: [00 353] 91 66620
Contact: Katie Verling, Gallery Director
Open: Mon-Sat 9.30-5.30

Kenny Gallery

Holds large stock of paintings and presents exhibitions of work in most art and craft forms by mainly Irish artists.
High Street, Galway, tel: [00 353] 91 61014/61021, fax: [00 353] 91 68544
Contact: Tom Kenny & Conor Kenny, Directors
Open: Mon-Sat 9-6
Exhibitions: 15 a year

University College Galway

Gallery available for groups and organisations to organise their own exhibitions.
University Road, Galway, tel: [00 353] 91 24411 Ext 2135, fax: [00 353] 91 25047
Contact: Anne Duggan
Open: Variable depending on exhibitors' requirements and staffing available.
Exhibitions: 10 a year

Gleann Cholm Cille
CO DONEGAL

Foras Cultuir Uladh - Ulster Cultural Centre

Ph Cr   ✓   🌐 ♿ 4

Gallery in centre founded to promote the learning and use of Irish and to foster Irish culture.
Gleann Cholm Cille, tel: [00 353] 73 30248
Contact: Liam O Cuinneagain, Exhibition Organiser
Open: (April-Sept) Daily 10-8
Space: 1 gallery with 12 lin m hanging space and 11 sq m floor space
Exhibitions: 6 a year
Details: Exhibitions of work with Celtic themes or of traditional craft form shown. Sales not a priority.

Gorey
CO WEXFORD

Woodland Arts & Crafts Gallery

Pa Ph Pr Cr Sc   ✓   ♿

A two-storey, open plan gallery with central staircase and adjoining coffee shop in summer months.
Tinnock, Gorey, tel: [00 353] 402 37474
Contact: Michael G Murphy, Artistic Director

Open: Mon-Fri 12-6; Sat 10-6; Sun 2-6; or any time by arrangement
Space: 1 gallery with 61 lin m hanging space and 186 sq m floor space
Exhibitions: 8 a year all originated
Details: The gallery aims to increase public awareness of art and craft. Mixed theme exhibitions are usual. Exhibition programme includes displays of work by local artists and craftspeople. Informal and relaxed atmosphere in woodland setting. Outdoor mixed theme exhibitions in the wood during the summer. Sales are a priority.

Graiguenamanagh
CO KILKENNY

Kilkenny County Library

Library exhibition space.
Convent Road, Graiguenamanagh, tel: [00 353] 56 52699
Contact: Brenda Ward, Librarian
Open: Tues & Thurs 10-8; Wed & Fri 10-5; Sat 10-1.30
Exhibitions: 5 a year

Howth
CO DUBLIN

Howth Harbour Gallery

Gallery overlooking harbour showing variety of 2D work by Irish artists.
6 Abbey Street, Howth, tel: [00 353] 1 839 3366
Contact: Phyllis Ger, Director
Open: Wed-Sun 2-7
Exhibitions: 5 a year

Kenmare
CO KERRY

Iverni Gallery

Pa Pr   ✓   ♿

A selling gallery showing work by artists based in the Beara Peninsula.
Henry Street, Kenmare, tel: [00 353] 64 41720
Contact: Gearoid O'Shea, Owner Director
Open: (Summer) Mon-Sat 10-6; (Winter) closed for 7 weeks & from end of 1st week of Jan to St Patricks holiday.
Exhibitions: 10 a year all originated

Keshcarrigen
CO LEITRIM

Fionn Mc Cumhaill Centre

Exhibition space exhibiting mainly landscape paintings.
Keshcarrigen, tel: [00 353] 78 42098, fax: [00 353] 78 42093
Contact: Sandra Vernon, Exhibition Organiser
Open: Daily 11-7

Kilcar
CO DONEGAL

Ram's Head Gallery

Gallery based in small business complex holding exhibitions and sells work.
Main Street, Kilcar, tel: [00 353] 73 38002, fax: [00 353] 73 38094
Contact: Gilbert Burns, Exhibition Organiser
Open: Daily 11-5

Kilcock
CO KILDARE

Kilcock Art Gallery

Pa Pr Cr Sc   ✓   ♿

Gallery with sculpture yard that also advises collectors (companies and individuals) and acts as artists' agent.
School Street, Kilcock, tel: [00 353] 1 628 7619/8586
Contact: Breda Smyth, Proprietor
Open: Mon-Fri 10-4; Sat 2-5
Space: 3 galleries
Exhibitions: 8 a year all originated
Details: Two rooms with white walls and lighting by spots as well as natural lighting. Artists' talks held. Work sold and 40% commission taken.

Kilkenny
CO KILKENNY

Butler Gallery

Pa Pr Sc   ✓ £   ♿

Gallery with compartmentalised space used to show the best of known and unknown Irish and international artists.
The Castle, Kilkenny, tel: [00 353] 56 61106, fax: [00 353] 56 63448
Contact: Shirley Lanigan, Administrator
Open: (Mid Mar-Sept) daily 10-7; (Sept-Nov) daily 10-5; (Nov-mid Mar) 10-12.45, 2-5
Space: 1 gallery with 80 lin m hanging space
Exhibitions: 10 a year of which 8 originated, 2 touring
Details: Policy is to bring to public attention the work of unknown and known artists whose work attains excellence in the view of the gallery committee. Exhibition fee sometimes paid. Artists applying for an exhibition requested to enclose SAE. Sale of work not gallery's primary function.

Killarney
CO KERRY

Frank Lewis Gallery

Pa Pr Sc   ✓   ♿

Established private gallery presenting a varied programme of exhibitions from

established and emerging artists whom the gallery promotes.
6 Bridewell Lane, Killarney, tel: [00 353] 64 31108/ 34843, fax: [00 353] 64 31570
Contact: Frank Lewis, Proprietor/Principal
Open: Mon-Sat 9-6; Sun by appointment only
Space: 1 gallery with 95 sq m floor space
Exhibitions: 12 a year all originated
Details: Sale of work is considered the gallery's primary role.

Killarney Art Gallery

Commercial gallery with continually changing display and twice-yearly group shows.
52 High Street, Killarney, tel: [00 353] 64 34628
Contact: Declan Mulvany, Proprietor
Open: Mon-Sat 11-1, 2-6; (Apr-Sept) also Mon-Sat 8.30pm-10pm

Killarney Branch Library

PaPhPrCrSc ● ⓖ④

Library gallery showing community and touring exhibitions.
Rock Road, Killarney, tel: [00 353] 64 32972, fax: [00 353] 64 36065
Contact: Liz Culloty/Tommy O'Connor, County Arts Officer/Librarian
Open: Tues-Sat 10.30-5
Space: 1 gallery with 93 sq m floor space
Exhibitions: 6 a year of which 2 originated, 4 touring
Details: Gallery has concrete walls and hanging by nails to wall and hanging rail. Screens and two glass display cases available. Natural lighting, spots and recessed lighting. Library covers costs of transport, handout, invitations. No commission taken on works sold.

Killorglin
CO KERRY

Sheeog Art Gallery

Small gallery aims to show variety of art and craft with emphasis on quality.
Langford Street, Killorglin, tel: [00 353] 66 61220, fax: [00 353] 66 62018
Contact: Marguerite Falvey, Director
Open: (mid Mar-Sept) Mon-Sat 10-6; (Oct-Dec) Mon-Sat 2-6
Exhibitions: 4 a year

Siamsa Tire Theatre/Arts Centre

PaPhPrSc ●Ⓗ ⓖⓌ

Specially-designed areas for visual arts, including sculpture court and artists' studios, within new building which is home to the National Folk Theatre.
Town Park, Killorglin, tel: [00 353] 66 23055, fax: [00 353] 66 27276
Contact: Martin Whelan, General Manager
Open: Mon-Sat 10-6; performance

evenings (approx 250 a year) 7-10.30
Space: 2 galleries with 41 lin m hanging space and 152 sq m floor space
Exhibitions: 14 a year of which 3 originated, 5 touring, 6 on a hire basis
Details: In addition to exhibitions, runs outreach education programme of workshops, talks, seminars and demonstrations organised. Sale of work not considered gallery's primary role.

Kilshanny
CO CLARE

Atlantis Gallery

PaPh Ⓖ

Modern gallery in converted stone barn exhibiting contemporary Irish and international artists with emphasis on abstract work.
Caherkinalla, Kilshanny, tel: [00 353] 65 74270
Contact: Beverley O'Keeffe, Director
Open: (Mar-Oct) Wed-Sun 11-6; or by appointment
Space: 1 gallery with 25 lin m hanging space and 55 sq m floor space
Exhibitions: 4 a year all originated
Details: One- or two-person exhibitions generated by the gallery director. Aims to increase public awareness of abstract works and is only gallery in Co Clare dedicated to this policy. Gallery pays all exhibition costs. Sales a priority. Commission negotiable.

Kinsale
CO CORK

Keane-on-Ceramics

Cr ● Ⓖ

Studio ceramics gallery representing over 30 potters.
Pier Road, Kinsale, tel: [00 353] 21 774553
Contact: Francis Keane, Owner
Open: (Apr-Sep) daily 10-6; (Oct-Mar) most days 10-6; vistors should telephone first during Jan & Feb
Space: 2 galleries with 47 sq m floor space
Exhibitions: 3 a year all originated
Details: Aims to increase awareness of Irish studio ceramics. One-person and group shows. No set education policy. Sale of work is gallery's primary role. Applications for exhibitions welcomed from Irish potters only.

Letterkenny
CO DONEGAL

Cristeph Gallery

Gallery showing work by up and coming and established artists and craftspeople from Donegal, Derry, Tyrone and Fermanagh.

Port Road, Letterkenny, tel: [00 353] 74 26411
Contact: Niall O'Donnell, Proprietor
Open: Mon-Sat 10.30-6

Donegal County Arts Service

Service organises exhibitions in a variety of venues including Central Library and Arts Centre, Letterkennny opening mid 1995.
c/o County Library, Letterkenny, tel: [00 353] 74 21968
Contact: Traolach O Fionnain, Arts Organiser

Donegal County Museum

Museum with permanent collection and running temporary exhibition programme.
High Road, Letterkenny, tel: [00 353] 74 24613
Contact: Curator
Open: Tuesday to Friday 11 to 4.30; Saturday 1 to 4.30
Exhibitions: 6 a year

Glebe House and Gallery

PaPr ● Ⓖ

House and gardens given to the nation by Derek Hill with gallery showing exhibitions from the permanent collection and touring exhibitions
Church Hill, Letterkenny, tel: [00 353] 74 37071, fax: [00 353] 74 37072
Contact: Chris Wilson, Curator
Open: (Easter Week & June-Sept) Mon-Thurs, Sat & Sun 11-6.30
Space: 2 galleries
Exhibitions: 3 a year of which 2 originated, 1 touring
Details: Three temporary exhibitions a year are one-person or group shows of 3-4 weeks duration. Local schools' groups visit gallery and house. No specific education policy. July and August devoted to permanent Derek Hill collection. Sale of work not gallery's primary function.

Port Gallery

Gallery exhibits and sells work mainly by local artists.
86a Upper Main Street, Letterkenny, tel: [00 353] 74 25073
Contact: John O'Connell, Owner
Open: Mon-Sat 10-6
Exhibitions: 5 a year

Limerick
CO LIMERICK

Belltable Arts Centre

PaPhPrSc ●Ⓔ ⓖⓌ

Multi-purpose arts centre which gives preference in its exhibition programme to young emerging artists, either local or national.

69 O'Connell Street, Limerick, tel: [00 353] 61 319709, fax: [00 353] 61 418552
Contact: Mary Coll, Director
Open: Mon-Sat 10-6; theatre until 11pm
Space: 1 gallery with 377 lin m hanging space
Exhibitions: 12 a year of which 10 originated, 2 touring
Details: Proposals welcomed for site-specific installation work. Where possible gallery tries to tour work onwards to other arts centres. Sale of work not gallery's primary role.

Chris Doswell's Gallery

Pr

Gallery promoting printmakers, with permanent collection of prints and one person exhibitions.
The Basement, 28 Mallow Street, Limerick, tel: [00 353] 61 318292
Contact: Chris Doswell, Exhibition Organiser
Open: Mon-Fri 9-5.30; Sat 10.30-2.30
Exhibitions: 6 a year

Dolmen Gallery

Gallery showing art and craft work by both Irish and international artists and makers.
Honan's Quay, Limerick, tel: [00 353] 61 417929
Contact: Helen O'Donnell, Administrator
Open: Mon-Sat 10-6
Exhibitions: 12 a year

Limerick City Gallery of Art

Municipal gallery with temporary exhibition programme of regional, national and international shows, including some touring shows.
Pery Square, Limerick, tel: [00 353] 61 310633, fax: [00 353] 61 415266
Contact: Paul M O'Reilly, Director
Open: Mon-Wed & Fri 10-1, 2-5; Thurs 10-1, 2-7; Sat 10-1
Exhibitions: 35 a year

Muse Gallery

Gallery exhibiting work by up-and-coming and established artists in one-person and group shows.
75 O'Connell Street, Limerick, tel: [00 353] 61 314699
Contact: Gerard Ryan, Proprietor
Open: Mon-Sat 10-5.30; Sun 2.30-5

University of Limerick Gallery

Work by local and national artists shown in small gallery in university buildings.
Plassey Technological Park, Limerick, tel: [00 353] 61 333644, fax: [00 353] 61 330316
Contact: David Lilburn, Exhibition Organiser
Open: 8 am till 10 pm (University Hours)
Exhibitions: 8 a year

Lismore
CO WATERFORD

Lismore Library

Some exhibitions in display area are initiated and organised by library and some are organised by artists.
Lismore, tel: [00 353] 58 54128
Contact: Donal Brady, Librarian
Open: Mon & Fri 11.30-2, 3-6; Tues, Wed & Thurs 1-4.30, 5.30-8

Listowel
CO KERRY

St Johns Arts and Heritage Centre

Pa Ph Pr LA ✿ H ● W 4

Gallery aims to flitate access to and participation in contemporary art, showing work by local, national and international artists with emphasis on youth work.
The Square, Listowel, tel: [00 353] 68 22566, fax: [00 353] 68 22524
Contact: Joe Murphy, Manager
Open: Mon-Fri 10-5; Sat 11-5; Sun 11.30-5
Space: 1 gallery with 30 lin m hanging space plus 12 lin m on screens and 14 sq m floor space
Exhibitions: 12 a year of which 4 originated, 5 touring, 3 on a hire basis
Details: Aims to promote appreciation of and participation in visual arts among the local community, promote local, national and international artists and to engage community and youth in workshops to enhance their creativity and critical awareness. Commercial exhibitions sometimes held when exhibitors contribute to costs; otherwise gallery covers exhibition costs. Sales not a priority.

Longford
CO LONGFORD

Carroll Gallery

Pa Pr SS ✿

Ground-floor space showing the work of established Irish artists with occasional exhibition by new artists.
6 Keons Terrace, Longford, tel: [00 353] 43 41148
Contact: Kevin Carroll, Director
Open: Mon-Fri 9.30-5.30; Sat & Sun by appointment
Space: 2 galleries with 21 lin m hanging space and 51 sq m floor space
Exhibitions: 12 a year all originated
Details: Gallery's policy is to show exhibitions of 'high-quality' Irish art for sale. 10 one-person and 2 group shows per annum. Gallery covers most exhibition costs including private view. Artist pays for

transport only. Commission taken on sales. Separate room for permanent stock by gallery artists.

Louisburgh
CO MAYO

Aimhirgin Gallery

Gallery promotes established and emerging artists through exhibitions.
Bridge Street, Louisburgh, tel: [00 353] 98 66577/66467
Contact: Merle & Austin Bergin, Exhibition Organisers
Exhibitions: 8 a year

Lucan
CO DUBLIN

Phoenix Art Studio

Artist-run gallery with framing service and studio showing art and craft by established local artists and makers.
15 Main Street, Lucan, tel: [00 353] 1 628 2129
Contact: Bernadette Walsh
Open: Tues-Fri 10.30-4.30; Sat 11-4.30

Macroom
CO CORK

Vangard Gallery

Gallery above pottery and ceramics shop showing range of fine art and ceramics.
New Street, Macroom, tel: [00 353] 26 41198
Contact: John Philip Murray, Exhibition Organiser
Open: Mon-Sat 9-6; Sun 2.30-5.30
Exhibitions: 12 a year

Maynooth
CO KILDARE

Maynooth Exhibition Centre

Exhibition area in foyer of college's arts block is used by outside organisations as well as showing annual student show.
St Patrick's College, Maynooth, tel: [00 353] 1 628 5222, fax: [00 353] 1 708 3954
Contact: Dominic McNamara, Exhibition Organiser
Open: Daily 8.30am-11pm
Details: Exhibits local, national and international work.

Monaghan
CO MONAGHAN

Market House Gallery

Group, one-person and thematic exhibitions held in gallery on first floor of Market House built in 1792.
Tourist Office, Market House, Monaghan, tel: [00 353] 47 81122
Contact: Somhairle MacConghail, Monaghan County Council
Open: (Sept-May) Mon-Fri 9-1, 2-5; (June-Aug) Mon-Fri 9-5, Sat 9-1, 2-5
Exhibitions: 7 a year

Monaghan County Museum

Museum with permanent collection and programme of exhibitions showing work by mainly Irish artists.
1-2 Hill Street, Monaghan, tel: [00 353] 47 82928
Contact: Patrick Long, Curator
Open: Tues-Sat 11-1, 2-5
Exhibitions: 7 a year

Mullingar
CO WESTMEATH

Midland Arts Resource Centre

Centre commited to enabling access to, and participation in, the arts; and runs artists-in-residence schemes as well as programme of exhibitions and activities/workshops.
Austin Friars Street, Mullingar, tel: [00 353] 44 43308, fax: [00 353] 44 43533
Contact: Evelyn Gibson, Assistant Administrator
Open: Mon-Fri 10-6; Sat 11-5; and during performances
Exhibitions: 12 a year

Naas
CO KILDARE

Naas Branch Library

First-floor library gallery hosting occasional touring shows und available to individuals and groups for exhibitions.
Naas
Contact: Monica Corcoran, County Arts Officer, Kildare County Library Service, Athgarvan Road, Newbridge, tel: [00 353] 45 31486, fax: [00 353] 45 32490
Open: Tues & Thurs 2-8; Wed, Fri & Sat 11-5

Tuckmill Gallery

Small gallery showing art and some craft by local or Irish artists and makers.
Dublin Road, Naas, tel: [00 353] 45 79761
Contact: Martina Phipps
Open: Mon-Sat 9.30-6
Exhibitions: 2 a year

Navan
CO MEATH

Meath County Library Service

Organises exhibitions, mainly of work by local artists but some touring shows, at Navan Library and at Trim Library.
Navan Library, Railway Street, Navan, tel: [00 353] 46 21134
Contact: Liam Smyth, Exhibition Organiser

Nenagh
CO TIPPERARY

Nenagh District Heritage Centre

Space in heritage centre occasionally showing exhibitions.
Governor's House, Nenagh, tel: [00 353] 67 32633
Contact: Geraldine Malone
Open: (May-Sept) Mon-Fri 10-5, Sun 2.30-5
Exhibitions: 2 a year

Newcastle West
CO LIMERICK

Newcastle West Library

Glass-fronted foyer provides exhibition space in modern library.
Gortboy, Newcastle West, tel: [00 353] 69 62273
Contact: Aileen Dillane, Librarian
Open: Mon-Sat 10-5; Tues-Fri 10-8
Exhibitions: 14 a year

Oughterard
CO GALWAY

West Shore Gallery

Commercial gallery specialising in work by Galway and Connemara-based artists.
Camp Street, Oughterard, tel: [00 353] 91 82562
Contact: Peter Conneely and Kathleen Furey, Exhibition Organisers
Open: Mon-Sat 10-6; (May-Sept) Sun 1-5
Exhibitions: 5 a year

Portlaoise
CO LAOIS

Laois County Hall

Gallery within council office building.
Portlaoise, tel: [00 353] 502 22044, fax: [00 353] 502 22313
Contact: Muireann Ni Chonaill, County Arts Officer
Open: Mon-Fri 9-5
Exhibitions: 10 a year

Riverstown
CO SLIGO

Taylor's Art Gallery

Family-run gallery and framing service showing fine art by mainly Irish artists.
Taunagh, Riverstown, tel: [00 353] 71 65138
Contact: Alec Taylor, Owner
Open: Mon-Fri 10-6; or by appointment

Roscrea
CO TIPPERARY

Roscrea Heritage Centre

Exhibitions covering most artforms held in Heritage Centre where displays are mainly concerned with local social history.
Damer House, Castle Street, Roscrea, tel: [00 353] 505 21850
Contact: Eimear Hughes, Manager
Open: (June-Sept) Daily 9.30-6.30; (Oct-May) Sat & Sun 10-5

Shannon
CO CLARE

Seán Lemass Library

Pa Ph Cr ✓ 🅰 We

Open-plan U-shaped exhibition space at entrance to modern purpose-built library.
Town Centre, Shannon, tel: [00 353] 61 364266
Contact: Librarian
Open: Mon, Wed & Thurs 11-5.30; Tues & Fri 11-8
Exhibitions: 4 a year
Details: Library hosts approximately twelve exhibitions a year including information displays as well as art, photography and craft shows. Each lasts three weeks. These are national, local and occasionally international. Sale of work not considered gallery's primary role.

Skibbereen
CO CORK

West Cork Arts Centre

Pa Ph Pr Cr Sc ✓ 🅰 We 4

Gallery acts as focal point of arts activities in the area.
North Street, Skibbereen, tel: [00 353] 28 22090
Contact: Jackie Butler, Administrator
Open: Mon-Sat 10-6
Space: 2 galleries
Exhibitions: 14 a year of which 12 originated, 2 touring
Details: Gallery shows wide range of fine and applied art in exhibitions which may be one or two person shows, group or touring exhibitions. Applications from artists for exhibitions to be received by 1 Sept each

year. Organises annual "Living Landscapes" exhibition selected by an invited artist/critic. Also annual non-selected members' exhibitions. Education programme of lectures and artists' talks. Work sold but sales not considered gallery's highest priority. Exhibition fee sometimes paid.

Sligo
CO SLIGO

Hawk's Well Theatre

Theatre foyer available for exhibitions from end of 1995 when theatre will reopen after renovations.
Temple Street, Sligo, tel: [00 353] 71 62167
Contact: Maeve McCormack, Administrator

Model Arts Centre

[Pa] [Ph] [Pr] [Cr] [SC] ✔ ♿
Arts centre in converted old building with number of rooms now suitable for temporary exhibitions.
The Mall, Sligo, tel: [00 353] 71 41405, fax: [00 353] 71 44121
Contact: Sheila McSweeney, Administrator
Open: Mon-Fri 10-6; Sat 10-3
Space: 1 gallery with 178 lin m hanging space and 338 sq m floor space
Exhibitions: 14 a year of which 8 originated, 6 touring
Details: Shows contempary work both national and international. "We would like to see a school of painting emerge among the young painters." Aims to provide access for as many community groups as possible, encourages school groups to visit and particpate. Classes, workshops and lectures organised.

Sligo Art Gallery

[Pa] [Ph] [Pr] [Cr] [SC] ✔ [H]
Gallery in former bank organises exhibitions here and in other venues, enabled by the Yeats Society.
Yeats Memorial Building, Hyde Bridge, Sligo, tel: [00 353] 71 45847, fax: [00 353] 71 62301
Contact: Ronan MacEvilly, Director
Open: Mon-Sat 10-5.30
Space: 51 lin m hanging space plus 41 lin m on screens and 770 sq m floor space
Exhibitions: 17 a year of which 15 originated, 2 touring
Details: Exhibitions in gallery and in other community-based venues with main aims to encourage artistic activity within the community and provide exhibition space for contemporary art. Exhibitions from overseas are sometimes shown. Sales not a priority but 30% commission taken on works sold.

Swords
CO DUBLIN

Swords Art and Craft Centre

Centre run by volunteers offering exhibition space free of charge to local artists and craftworkers.
10 North Street, Swords, tel: [00 353] 1 840 8258
Contact: Pauline Langan, Exhibition Organiser
Open: Tues-Sat 10.30-5
Exhibitions: 12 a year

Tallaght
CO DUBLIN

Old Bawn Community School

Exhibition area in school presenting mainly touring shows but artists may also apply.
Old Bawn, Tallaght 24, tel: [00 353] 1 452 0566, fax: [00 353] 1 452 0847
Contact: Mairead Tobin, Exhibition Organiser
Open: (Term-time) Mon, Wed & Fri 9-5, Tues & Thurs 9-9.30

Thomastown
CO KILKENNY

Berkeley Gallery

Gallery set up to promote and exhibit young emerging artists.
Grennan Water Mill, Thomastown, tel: [00 353] 56 62453
Contact: Canice Hogan
Open: Mon-Sat 10-5
Exhibitions: 7 a year

Thurles
CO TIPPERARY

Tipperary County Library Serice

Service aims to promote the arts in the area and organises exhibition programme that covers most artforms.
Castle Avenue, Thurles, tel: [00 353] 504 21555, fax: [00 353] 504 23442
Contact: Martin Maher, County Librarian

Tralee
CO KERRY

Bín Bán Gallery

[Pa] [SC] ✔ 🚫♿
Commercial gallery showing mainly contemporary work by Irish artists.
124 Lower Rock Street, Tralee, tel: [00 353] 66 22520
Contact: Helen Shanahan, Director
Open: Mon-Sat 9.30-6
Space: 1 gallery with 28 lin m hanging space
Exhibitions: 4 a year all originated
Details: Special exhibitions last approx 3-4 weeks. Mixed exhibitions on display periodically. Gallery aims to be a welcoming place where art is accessible to everyone. Sales are a priority and to assist this interest free credit flities are provided. Gallery covers exhibition costs. School groups welcome.

Tralee Library

[Pa] [Ph] [Pr] ✔ ♿ [WC] [4]
Gallery shows work of local groups, professional artists and organises exhibitions relevant to the community.
Moyderwell, Tralee, tel: [00 353] 66 21200, fax: [00 353] 66 22466
Contact: Liz Culloty, County Arts Organiser
Open: Mon-Sat 10.30-5
Space: 2 galleries
Exhibitions: 8 a year of which 4 originated, 4 touring
Details: Library gallery aims to show work mainly of professional artists but also includes exhibitions by local arts groups, community groups and schools. Aims to accompany each exhibition with a lecture/artist's workshop and/or a talk. Library covers exhibitions costs. Work not sold but groups showing can sell work if they provide personnel. No commission on sales. Natural light, spots and fluorescent.

Wellspring Gallery

[Pa] [Ph] [Pr] [Cr] [SC] ✔ ♿
Small commercial gallery showing contemporary fine and applied arts by predominantly Irish artists.
16 Denny Street, Tralee, tel: [00 353] 66 21218, fax: [00 353] 66 23870
Contact: Louise O'Donnell, Owner
Open: Mon-Sat 10-6; or by appointment
Space: 1 gallery with 37 lin m hanging space and 34 sq m floor space
Exhibitions: 10 a year all originated
Details: Mixture of one-person and group shows. Gallery aims to increase general awareness and appreciation of art by making the gallery a relaxed and friendly place to visit. Lighting by adjustable track spots and limited natural light. Gallery generally pays exhibition costs. Sale of work a priority; 30% commission. Visits by school groups are encouraged. Student and adult art classes held.

Tullamore
CO OFFALY

Offaly County Library Service

Service aims to promote arts in its area by holding exhibitions in venues in Tullamore, Birr, Edenderry, Clara, Ferbane, Kilcormac and Banagher.
O'Connor Square, Tullamore, tel: [00 353] 506 21419, fax: [00 353] 506 52769

Waterford
CO WATERFORD

Dyehouse Gallery

Pa Pr Cr Sc ✓

A purpose-built gallery specialising in painting, drawing, print and sculpture.
Dyehouse Lane, Waterford, tel: [00 353] 51 78166, fax: [00 353] 51 50399
Contact: Oliver Dempsey

Garter Lane Arts Centre

Pa Ph Pr Cr Sc LA ✓ £ H & Wc

Annual shows as well as work by individual artists and groups.
22a O'Connell Street, Waterford, tel: [00 353] 51 55038, fax: [00 353] 51 71570
Contact: Anthony Costine/Miranda Cleary, Exhibition Organisers
Open: Mon-Sat 10-6
Space: 1 gallery with 33 lin m hanging space and 105 sq m floor space
Exhibitions: 12 a year of which 3 originated, 3 touring, 6 on a hire basis
Details: White-walled room with hanging rail. As well as Summer/Christmas craft fairs also hosts annual Waterford Art Group Show and 'Newgate Works' – work by tutors from Waterford Regional Technical College Art & Design Dept. Otherwise work for exhibition is selected from proposals. All work for sale although sales not primary role. Local school visits encouraged. Occasional artists' talks. Gallery usually covers all exhibition costs.

Westport
CO MAYO

Westport Pubic Library

Library exhibition space programmed by Castlebar Public Library
Westport, tel: [00 353] 94 24444, fax: [00 353] 94 23937
Contact: John Coll, County Arts Officer
Open: Tues, Wed & Fri 10-1, 2-8; Thurs & Sat 10-1, 2-5.30
Exhibitions: 19 a year

Wexford
CO WEXFORD

Wexford Arts Centre

Pa Ph Cr Sc ✓ & Wc

Arts centre with a large 'drop in' audience as well as a strong tourist audience.
Cornmarket, tel: [00 353] 53 23764/24544
Contact: Denis Collins, Artistic Director
Open: Mon-Sat 10-6
Space: 3 galleries with 52 lin m hanging space plus 8 lin m on screens and 215 sq m floor space
Exhibitions: 30 a year of which 24 originated, 6 touring
Details: The centre aims to provide varied and wide ranging programme of professional, semi-professional and amateur art both from the local community and outside. Main gallery also used for community projects and centre hosts other exhibitions, not in the visual arts, but of interest to local people. The most important exhibitions, are those held during the Wexford Opera Festival. Gallery covers transport, insurance, handout and private view costs. Sales a priority; 20% commission taken (30% during festival).

Wicklow
CO WICKLOW

Renaissance III Gallery

Council offices' foyer designed to display art and showing mainly one-person exhibitions of work by Wicklow's professional artists.
County Buildings, Wicklow, tel: [00 353] 404 67324, fax: [00 353] 404 67792
Contact: Brendan O'Connor, Co-ordinator
Open: Mon-Fri 9-5

Transmission Gallery, Glasgow

Transmission re-invented as the **New Rose Hotel**. Contemporary design and furniture, computer imagery and wall-drawings alter the 'white cube' of the space; work by artists and designers are brought together in this new context. It is envisaged as a transformed environment, at the same time optimistic and pessimistic place to meet and talk, to exchange ideas about our future.

Scotland

Aberdeen
GRAMPIAN

Aberdeen Art Gallery

Pa Ph Pr Cr Sc LA ◐①⊕ ⑥⑩

Municipal art gallery whose temporary exhibition/events programme provides a platform for new and emerging artists.
Schoolhill, Aberdeen AB9 1FQ, tel: 01224 646333, fax: 01224 632133
Contact: Deirdre Grant, Programme Support Officer
Open: Mon-Sat 10-5; Sun 2-5; Thurs 10-8
Space: 4 galleries with 189 lin m hanging space and 434 sq m floor space
Exhibitions: 60 a year of which 14 originated, 45 touring, 1 on a hire basis
Details: Aims "to stimulate and maintain the public's interest in the arts through a rigorous programme of acquisition, conservation, research, interpretation and exhibition with related events based on material from local, Scottish and international sources." Permanent collection of contemporary fine and applied art of 18th, 19th & 20th centuries. Workshops, children's activities & talks held, and artist and craftworker in residence programme organised. Sales of work not a primary role of gallery.

Aberdeen Arts Centre

Pa Ph Pr Cr Sc ◐⊕ ⑥⑩

Small gallery and corridor space showing monthly exhibitions by contemporary artists, mainly local.
33 King Street, Aberdeen AB2 3AA, tel: 01224 635208, fax: 01224 626390
Contact: Arthur Deans, AACA Administrator
Open: Mon-Sat 10-5
Space: 2 galleries with 66 lin m hanging space and 48 sq m floor space
Exhibitions: 14 a year
Details: A 350-seat theatre and a small gallery. Occasional touring exhibitions can be taken but no funds available for hire of exhibitions. Sales not main aim of exhibiting work. 20% commission on sales, otherwise no charge.

Gallery Heinzel

Pa Pr Cr Sc ◐ ⑥

Commercial gallery specialising in contemporary Scottish art.
21 Spa Street, Aberdeen AB1 1PU, tel: 01224 625629, fax: 01224 624101
Contact: Chris Heinzel, Gallery owner
Open: Tues-Sat 10-5.30
Space: 3 galleries with 56 lin m hanging space and 75 sq m floor space
Exhibitions: 6 a year all originated
Details: A programme of painting, sculpture and ceramics. Mostly landscape, with a smaller amount of figurative and abstract art. Monthly programme of

temporary exhibitions run alongside the ongoing stock of 30 gallery artists. New artists are taken on if their work fits the concept of the gallery.

Haddo Arts Trust

Pa Ph Pr Cr Sc LA ◐⊕ ⑥⑩

Multi-purpose arts centre with auditorium used for theatre, music and exhibitions.
The Hall, Haddo Estate, Tarves, Aberdeen AB41 0ER, tel: 01651 851770
Contact: Charles Barron, Arts Director
Open: Mon-Sun 10-4
Space: 1 gallery with 20 lin m hanging space plus 20 lin m on screens and 220 sq m floor space
Exhibitions: 6 a year all on a hire basis
Details: Large Canadian-style hall used as theatre, exhibitions & community venue. Wide range of events and audiences. Small exhibitions in bar/reception area. Sales not primary role of centre.

Lemon Tree

Pa Ph Pr ◐ ⑥⑩

Informal exhibition space within Café Theatre providing platform for 2D work by local and regional artists.
5 West North Street, Aberdeen AB2 3AT, tel: 01224 642230
Contact: Shona Powell, Administrator
Open: Mon-Sat 11-5; Sun 12.30-5; plus during evening events in café
Space: 1 gallery with 16 lin m hanging space
Exhibitions: 10 a year all originated
Details: Promotes work by local and regionally-based artists within busy arts centre space. 75,000 visitors annually to music and theatre events and 25,000 plus visiting for lunch. Brings artists' work to attention of many people who wouldn't otherwise see it. Sales welcome but not priority.

Peacock Printmakers *

Pa Pr Sc

Independent gallery connected to a printmaking workshop showing contemporary Scottish art – particularly from North-East of Scotland.
21 Castle Street, Aberdeen AB42 8DA, tel: 01224 637534
Contact: Arthur Watson
Space: 2 galleries with 65 lin m hanging space and 118 sq m floor space
Exhibitions: 12 a year all originated
Details: The only independent gallery in the city so attracts a wide audience of artists, residents and visitors to the city. Initiate a number of touring exhibitions related to the workshop and also to North-East Scottish artists.

Scottish Sculpture Workshop *

Pa Ph Pr Cr Sc ◐

Open workshop with exhibition space.
1 Main Street, Lumsden, Huntly, Aberdeen AB544JN, tel: 0146 46372, fax: 0146 46550
Contact: Christopher Bailey, Exhibitions Organiser
Space: 1 gallery with 13 lin m hanging space and 37 sq m floor space
Exhibitions: 10 a year all originated
Details: Mainly showing sculpture and related drawings. Applications considered from other disciplines. We cover publicity, mailing and information leaflets. The space has a large window opening onto the main street. Audience local and visitors.

Alloa
CENTRAL

Alloa Museum & Gallery

Pa Ph Pr Cr Sc ◐

Small local museum showing occasional temporary exhibitions.
Speirs Centre, Primrose Street, Alloa FK10 1JJ, tel: 01259 213131
Contact: Jannette Archibald, Exhibition Organiser
Space: 2 galleries
Exhibitions: 3 a year all originated
Details: Programme comprises mostly historical exhibitions; 2-3 contemporary art exhibitions a year. Commission taken.

Arbroath
TAYSIDE

Arbroath Library Art Gallery

Pa Ph Pr Cr Sc ◐

Temporary exhibition programme with mostly one-person exhibitions by local and non-local artists and makers.
Public Library, Hill Terrace, Arbroath DD11 1AH, tel: 01307 72248
Contact: John Stewart, Exhibition Organiser, Meffan Institute, 20 West High Street, Forfar, Angus, DD8 1BB, tel: 01307 68813**
Space: 1 gallery with 104 sq m floor space
Exhibitions: 10 a year all originated
Details: Specialises in local work with large collection of paintings by J W Herald. Occasional group and society exhibitions.

Ayr
STRATHCLYDE

Maclaurin Art Gallery

Po Ph Pr Gr Sc LA ✓ ⓖ

Gallery complex with five exhibition spaces around central courtyard.
Rozelle Park, Monument Road, Ayr KA7 4NQ, tel: 01292 445447/443708, fax: 01292 442065
Contact: Mike Bailey, Curator
Open: Mon-Sat 10-5; (Apr-Oct) Sun 2-5
Space: 5 galleries with 133 lin m hanging space and 264 sq m floor space
Exhibitions: 30 a year of which 12 originated, 18 touring
Details: Programme covers national and international touring exhibitions, local arts groups or individuals in addition to offering facilities to professional artists. Associated spaces in Rozelle House for temporary exhibitions. Extensive programme of workshop activities including life drawing. Sale of work not gallery's primary role. Gallery contributes to some exhibition costs.

Banff
GRAMPIAN

Warehouse Gallery

Po Ph Pr Gr Sc LA ✓ ⓖ

Show broad spectrum of contemporary work, both national and international.
7 Quayside, Banff Harbour, Banff AB45 1HQ, tel: 01261 818048
Contact: Victoria Clarke, Proprietor
Open: Mon-Sat 10-5.30
Space: 1 gallery with 29 lin m hanging space plus 7 lin m on screens and 84 sq m floor space
Exhibitions: 9 a year all originated
Details: Gallery on third floor. Large open rectangular area with central columns and north light. Varied programme aims to create appreciation of art in general. Selling work is important function of gallery.

Bathgate
LOTHIAN

Balbardie Gallery

Po Ph Pr Gr ✓ ⓖ ⓦ

Gallery with monthly changing programme of contemporary fine art.
Bathgate Sports Centre, Balbardie Park of Peace, Bathgate, tel: 01506 843121
Contact: Alison Cutforth, Cultural Services Officer, West Lothian District Council Leisure Services, County Buildings, Linlithgow, EH49 7EZ
Open: Daily from 9
Space: 2 galleries with 56 lin m hanging space

Exhibitions: 12 a year of which 2 originated, 10 touring
Details: Aims to increase public awareness and appreciation of art. Sales not gallery's primary function.

Biggar
BORDERS

Broughton Gallery

Po Ph Pr Gr ✓ ⓖ

Commercial gallery in Broughton Place, a Scottish 'castle' designed in 1938 by Sir Basil Spence.
Broughton Place, Broughton, Biggar ML12 6HJ, tel: 01899 4234
Contact: Graham Buchanan-Dunlop, Director
Open: Mon & Tues, Thurs-Sun 10.30-6; closed part of Nov & Chtismas-Mar.
Space: 3 galleries with 42 lin m hanging space plus 12 lin m on screens and 100 sq m floor space
Exhibitions: 8 a year all originated
Details: Selling exhibitions of paintings, original prints, ceramics, glass, wood, jewellery. Emphasis on representational art. Gardens also open to the public.

Cardenden
FIFE

Arts in Fife

Po Ph Pr 4

As part of Fife Regional Council, a local authority arts organisation placing work and exhibitions in a variety of venues and a travelling gallery.
Tower Block, ASDARC, Woodend Road, Cardenden KY5 0NE, tel: 01592 414714, fax: 01592 414641
Contact: Andrew Neil, Assistant Arts Officer
Open: Varied
Exhibitions: 15 a year of which 5 originated, 5 touring
Details: Arts in Fife organise and tour exhibitions within a travelling gallery and to a variety of venues. Exhibitions are usually small. Access and facilities vary.

Carnoustie
TAYSIDE

Carnoustie Library Art Gallery

Po Ph Pr Gr Sc ✓

Temporary exhibitions programme with one-person and mixed shows from local and non-local artists and makers.
Public Library, High Street, Carnoustie, tel: 01241 859620
Contact: Jake Stewart, Exhibitions Officer, Meffan Museum & Art Gallery, 20 West

High Street, Forfar, DD8 1DD, tel: 01307 468813
Open: During library hours
Space: 1 gallery with 34 lin m hanging space
Exhibitions: 10 a year all originated

Castle Douglas
DUMFRIES & GALLOWAY

Castle Douglas Art Gallery

Po Ph Pr Gr ✓ Ⓗ ⓖ

Purpose-built exhibition gallery run as branch of Stewartry Museum, Kirkcudbright.
Market Street, Castle Douglas DG7 1BE
Contact: D.F. Devereux, Curator, Stewartry District Council, Dept of Env. Health & Leisure Services, Cannonwalls, High Street, Kirkcudbright, DG6 4JG, tel: 01557 331643
Open: Variable, according to exhibition programme
Space: 1 gallery with 30 lin m hanging space and 55 sq m floor space
Exhibitions: 11 a year of which 1 originated, 3 touring, 7 on a hire basis
Details: Programme is varied, covering fine art, craft, printmaking and photography. Exhibitions organised by the museum service hiring in or producing exhibitions, and by local individual artists or art and craft groups. 10,000 visitors, half being tourists. For those wishing to hire the gallery for selling exhibition, no hire charge but 10% commission on sales and these exhibitors pay all exhibition costs. Selling work is not gallery's primary role.

Cleland
STRATHCLYDE

Cleland Arts Schoolhouse *

Po Ph Pr ✓

24 Main Street, Cleland ML1 5QN, tel: 01698 861740, fax: 01698 860144
Contact: Paul Clifford, Arts Coordinator
Space: 1 gallery with 26 lin m hanging space
Exhibitions: 12 a year all originated
Details: Urban-Aid funded project set up to stimulate participation in visual and performing arts. The schoolhouse is a new project with an educational priority. Classes and activities throughout the year for children, youth and adults. Exhibitions held within this community learning context. The nature of the space makes only 2D work appropriate. The centre is funded in part by Strathclyde Regional Council and the Scottish Office Urban Renewal Unit.

Clydebank
STRATHCLYDE

Dalmuir Branch Library
[Pa][Ph][Pr][Cr][Sc] ✔ ♿

Small gallery space used for displaying local art and small touring exhibitions.
3 Lennox Place, Clydebank G81 4HR, tel: 0141 952 3532
Contact: John Hood, District Chief Librarian, Central Library, Dumbarton Road, Clydebank, G81 1XH, tel: 0141 952 8765/1416, fax: 0141 951 8275
Open: Mon, Tues, Thurs 2-8; Wed & Fri 10-5; Sat 10-1
Space: 1 gallery with 30 lin m hanging space and 53 sq m floor space
Exhibitions: 6 a year of which 4 originated, 2 touring
Details: Aims to encourage artists/photographers by providing vehicle for reaching public and media. Preference given to local artists but all will be sympathetically considered. Sales not a priority.

Coatbridge
STRATHCLYDE

Ironworks Gallery
[Pa][Ph][Pr][Cr][Sc] ✔ [£] ♿ [Wc]

Varied exhibition programme balancing fine and applied art, contemporary and historical work in variety of media.
Summerlee Heritage Trust, West Canal Street, Coatbridge ML5 1QD, tel: 01236 431261, fax: 01236 440429
Contact: Jillian Ferrie, Head of Administration & Support Services
Open: Daily 10-5
Space: 1 gallery with 48 lin m hanging space and 122 sq m floor space
Exhibitions: 3 a year of which 1 originated, 2 touring
Details: Series of temporary exhibitions throughout the year with subjects of interest to the local community. Space suitable for any media and dividing wall enables two exhibitions to be shown at the same time. Sales not a priority.

Crieff
TAYSIDE

Strathern Gallery
[Pa][Pr][Cr][Sc] ✔ ♿

Commercial gallery exhibiting work by artists/craftspeople based in Scotland.
32 West High Street, Crieff PH7 4DL, tel: 01764 656100
Contact: Mr and Mrs Maguire
Open: Mon-Sat 10-5; Sun 1-5
Space: 1 gallery with 30 lin m hanging space and 65 sq m floor space
Exhibitions: 5 a year
Details: Gallery opened 1994. Exhibitions held every 2 months. Provides outlet for young artists/craftspeople working in Scotland. Gallery is light and welcoming and attracts about 20,000 visitors a year.

Cumnock
STRATHCLYDE

District History Centre & Baird Institute Museum
[Pa][Ph][Cr][Sc] ✔ [no ♿]

Temporary exhibitions including local photography, local art and crafts and displays from museum's own collections plus touring exhibitions on variety of subjects.
Lugar Street, Cumnock KA18 1AD, tel: 01290 421701, fax: 01290 422461
Contact: Charles Woodward, Museums Officer
Open: Mon, Tues, Thurs, Fri 10-1, 1.30-4.30; Sat 11-1
Space: 2 galleries with 40 lin m hanging space plus 10 lin m on screens and 55 sq m floor space
Exhibitions: 5 a year of which 3 originated, 2 touring
Details: Exhibition Room is flexible space adaptable from all exhibition cases to 25 lin m of hanging space with track lighting. Corridor Gallery has picture rail and rod systems with track lighting where exhibitions from local community are shown. Sales not a priority.

Dalkeith
LOTHIAN

Dalkeith Arts Centre
[Pa][Ph][Pr][Cr][Sc][LA] ✔ [H]

Two gallery areas exhibiting the work of mainly local artists from Autumn to early Summer.
White Hart Street, Dalkeith EH22 1AE, tel: 0131 663 6986
Contact: Mrs Christine Sleater, Secretary, Dalkeith & District Arts Guild, 24 Dalhousie Road, Eskbank, Dalkeith, tel: 0131 663 3872
Open: Wed-Fri 10-3.30; Sat 10-12.30
Space: 2 galleries with 28 lin m hanging space and 111 sq m floor space
Exhibitions: 8 a year all on a hire basis
Details: In addition, a series of monthly musical recitals, concerts, etc. Facilities include a Steinway drawing-room piano. Catering facilities available.

Dumbarton
STRATHCLYDE

Dumbarton Public Library
[Pa][Ph][Sc] ✔ [H] ♿ [Wc]

A small exhibition space designed to exhibit variety of changing exhibitions.
Strathleven Place, Dumbarton G82 1BD, tel: 01389 763129
Contact: Trisha Robins, Exhibitions Officer, Library HQ, Levenford House, Helenslee Road, Dumbarton, G82 4AJ, tel: 01389 765100 ext 330
Open: Mon, Tues, Thurs 10-8; Wed, Fri, Sat 10-5
Space: 1 gallery with 24 lin m hanging space plus 10 lin m on screens and 69 sq m floor space
Exhibitions: 4 a year of which 1 touring, 3 on a hire basis
Details: Museum room exhibits mainly thematic presentations relating to history of the area. Balcony exhibits work by local artists and art clubs. Small touring exhibitions hired in. About ten balcony exhibitions a year. Talks and meetings also held. Sale of work not a priority.

Dumfries
DUMFRIES & GALLOWAY

Gracefield Arts Centre
[Pa][Ph][Pr][Cr][Sc][LA] ✔ [£] [H] ♿ [Wc]

Run by Dumfries and Galloway Regional Council, centre shows extensive range of visual arts and craft.
28 Edinburgh Road, Dumfries DG1 1JQ, tel: 01387 62084, fax: 01387 60453
Contact: John Stewart-Young, Dumfries & Galloway Arts Officer
Open: Tues-Sat10-5; (Apr-Oct) Sun 12-5
Space: 6 galleries with 140 lin m hanging space plus 50 lin m on screens
Exhibitions: 19 a year of which 8 originated, 5 touring, 6 on a hire basis
Details: Temporary exhibitions run alongside permanent collection – large exhibitions can use whole building. Exhibition space devoted to contemporary art. Also printmaking and photography studios used by local groups. Show best work being made both in the region and nationally. Education a priority. Dedicated craft gallery with own programme of 8 shows a year. Sales not a priority.

Robert Burns Centre
[Pa][Ph] ✔ [H] ♿ [Wc]

Visitor centre, regional film theatre and gallery run by Nithsdale District Council providing a variety of visual artwork for visitors.
Mill Road, Dumfries DG2 7BE, tel: 01387 264808
Contact: Kenneth Eggo, Film Theatre

Officer, Dumfries Museum, The Observatory, Dumfries, DG2 7SW, tel: 01387 253374
Open: (Apr-Sept) Mon-Sat 10-8, Sun 2-5; (Oct-Mar) Tue-Sat 10-1, 2-5, 6.30-7.30
Space: 2 galleries with 60 lin m hanging space
Exhibitions: 5 a year of which 1 originated, 4 on a hire basis
Details: The centre tells the story of Robert Burns. Temporary exhibitions of 2D work held on walls of ground floor corridor and first floor café area, usually of local artists' work. Where exhibition space is 'hired out' this is not on a hire-fee basis. Audio-visual theatre and shop also in centre. Sale of work not venue's primary concern.

Dundee
TAYSIDE

Barrack Street Museum

`Pa` `Ph` `Pr` `Cr` `Sc` ✓ ♨ ⊘

Municipal museum housing natural history collections of Dundee Art Galleries and Museums with temporary exhibitions on art and nature theme.
Barrack Street, Dundee, tel: 01382 432067
Contact: Anna Robertson, Assistant Keeper of Art, McManus Galleries, Albert Square, Dundee, DD1 1DA, tel: 01382 432020, fax: 01382 432052
Open: Mon 11-5; Tues-Sat 10-5
Space: 1 gallery with 43 lin m hanging space plus 29 lin m on screens and 127 sq m floor space
Exhibitions: 6 a year all touring
Details: Barrack Street Museum houses the Art and Nature Gallery. Aims to show works by (mainly) contemporary artists – painters, sculptors and photographers – whose work relates to theme of the Natural World. Education Officers are available to work with artists on schools workshops. Interpretation may be required to make exhibitions accessible to a wide audience, including families. Sales not a priority.

Bonar Hall

`Pa` `Ph` `Pr` `Cr` `Sc` `IA` ✓ ♨ ⊘

Multi-purpose hall with two foyers in which exhibitions can be held.
The University of Dundee, Park Place, Dundee DD1 4HN, tel: 01382 29450
Contact: Sheena Jack, Assistant Manager
Open: Check on application – opening times vary
Space: 2 galleries with 40 lin m hanging space plus 4 lin m on screens and 6 sq m floor space
Exhibitions: 1 a year originated
Details: Variable number of temporary exhibitions in a range of media. Most exhibitions arranged by hiring the space, although other systems can be operated.

The 'Ustinov Room' upstairs is occasionally made available. Written applications welcome with slides. Sales not a priority.

Duncan of Jordanstone College of Art

`Pa` `Ph` `Pr` `Cr` `Sc` `IA` ✓ ⊕ ♨ ♿ ⓦ

Diverse programme from undergraduate to international.
Perth Road, Dundee DD1 4HT, tel: 01382 223261, fax: 01382 227304
Contact: Deirdre MacKenna, Curator of Exhibitions
Open: (Francis Cooper Gallery) Mon-Sat 10-4; (other spaces) Mon-Fri 9-9, Sat 9-4
Space: 4 galleries with 200 lin m hanging space plus 944 lin m on screens and 514 sq m floor space
Exhibitions: 20 a year
Details: Four exhibition spaces showing work of under- and post-graduates in fine art, design, television and electronic imaging, architecture and planning, while also running an extensive programme of traditional to contemporary exhibitions. Painting, architecture and design lectures and events.

Dundee Rep Gallery *

`Pa` `Ph` `Pr` `Cr` `Sc` ✓

Policy to show a diverse range of contemporary work by artists in the Dundee area in multi-purpose space.
Tay Square, Dundee DD1 1PB, tel: 01382 27684, fax: 01382 28609
Contact: House Manager
Space: 1 gallery with 30 lin m hanging space
Exhibitions: 10 a year all originated
Details: Gallery activities funded by commission on work sold.

McManus Galleries

`Pa` `Ph` `Pr` `Cr` `Sc` ✓ ♨ ⓦ

Suite of galleries with various opportunities to show a range of exhibitions in terms of size, theme and media.
Dundee Art Galleries & Museums, Albert Square, Dundee DD1 1DA, tel: 01382 432020, fax: 01382 432052
Contact: Adam Ritchie, Curator
Open: Mon 11-5; Tues-Sat 10-5
Space: 3 galleries with 500 lin m hanging space plus 100 lin m on screens and 485 sq m floor space
Exhibitions: 10 a year of which 4 originated, 6 touring
Details: Municipal gallery and museum run by City of Dundee District Council. Permanent collection and programme of temporary exhibitions of historic themes and contemporary art with emphasis on Scottish art. Some organised on themes suggested by permanent collection of mainly C19th and C20th Scottish art. 'Art and Nature' gallery in nearby Barrack Street Natural History Museum is dedicated to

temporary art and sculpture exhibitions exploring artists' response to nature (see separate entry). Sales not a priority.

Roseangle Gallery

`Pa` `Ph` `Pr` `Cr` `Sc` ✓ ♨

Gallery for hire.
17 Roseangle, Dundee, tel: 01382 322429
Contact: Mr John Berridge, Secretary, As above, 25 Strawberry Bank, Dundee, tel: 01382 68572
Open: Daily 11-5 during exhibitions; or by arrangement
Space: 2 galleries with 56 lin m hanging space and 104 sq m floor space
Exhibitions: 9 a year of which 2 originated, 7 on a hire basis
Details: Bright gallery lit by 5 large windows and track lighting system. Exhibitions of contemporary art by individuals, groups and societies. Audience of regular visitors. Invigilation must be organised by renter (help may be available subject to advance notice). Hiring basic weekly rate + hourly rate + 30% commission.

Seagate Gallery

`Pa` `Pr` `Sc` ✓

Temporary exhibition space for a broad-based programme of contemporary visual art.
36-40 Seagate, Dundee DD1 2EJ, tel: 01382 226331
Contact: Dave Jackson
Open: Tues-Sat 10-5
Space: 2 galleries with 50 lin m hanging space and 170 sq m floor space
Exhibitions: 12 a year
Details: Varied range of exhibitions which provide a platform for contemporary artists in Dundee, Tayside and North East Fife; and promote the work of these artists on a local, national and international stage. Also shows a broad spectrum of the highest quality contemporary visual art from outside the local area.

Dunfermline
FIFE

Small Gallery

`Pa` `Ph` `Pr` `Cr` ✓ ⊘

Gallery in museum showing work by local artists alongside that of artists from outside the region who are well known.
Dunfermline District Museum, Viewfield Terrace, Dunfermline KY12 7HY, tel: 01383 721814
Contact: Lin Collis, Curator
Open: Mon-Sat 11-5; closed BH
Space: 1 gallery with 22 lin m hanging space
Exhibitions: 12 a year all touring
Details: Aim is to encourage visitors to

view wide variety of art. Some exhibitions are selling ones but that is not main purpose of gallery. Part of exhibition space can form alarmed display case. Exhibition fee occasionally paid.

Edinburgh
LOTHIAN

369 Gallery *

Monthly shows of contemporary artists living in Scotland and also shows gallery artists internationally.
233 Cowgate, Edinburgh EH1 1NQ, tel: 0131 225 3013, fax: 0131 225 6802
Contact: Andrew Brown, Director
Space: 3 galleries
Exhibitions: 22 a year of which 2 originated, 10 touring, 10 on a hire basis
Details: Three large galleries, an education room and recently renovated studios. Life-drawing and painting classes attracts a wide age group. The Gilded Balloon Theatre is also part of 369's operations and regular cabaret and performances are shown there.

Cameo Cinema

Long narrow space within the cinema bar showing mainly young artists, often on their first solo show.
38 Home Street, Tolcross, Edinburgh EH3 9LZ, tel: 0131 228 4141, fax: 0131 228 4022
Contact: Sarah Geddes
Space: 1 gallery with 40 lin m hanging space and 100 sq m floor space
Exhibitions: 5 a year all originated
Details: 12 exhibitions are planned a year. Programming is organised 3/4 months in advance. Artists not charged a hire fee or commission and frames available if necessary. Exhibitions publicised through cinema's programme and mailing list.

Carlyle's Gallery *

Commercial gallery/tearoom dealing in Scottish painting from C18th to contemporary decorative work.
North Bridge, Edinburgh EH1 1SO, tel: 0131 557 5068, fax: 0131 556 2691
Contact: A. Wilson, Exhibition Organiser
Space: 3 galleries with 150 lin m hanging space
Exhibitions: 4 a year all originated
Details: Also represents young Scottish painters.

Chessel Gallery

Large exhibition space on college of further education campus mainly used for student work but occasionally shows work by established artists .
Moray House College, Holyrood Campus, Edinburgh EH8 8AQ, tel: 0131 556 8455
Contact: Raphael Bates, Lecturer, Art Department
Space: 1 gallery with 140 sq m floor space
Exhibitions: 12 a year of which 8 originated, 4 touring
Details: Gallery with policy to help young artists and terms of hire of gallery negotiable, possibly to commission only on any sales made. Audience mainly students but public welcome. Sales encouraged by not priority. Gallery well lit and spacious; spotlights and high ceilings.

Citizens Studios *

Artists-run programme of their own work and the work of young, unestablished artists, particularly those who have not exhibited before.
17-21 Assembly Street, Leith, Edinburgh EH6 7BQ, tel: 0131 554 1649
Contact: Stuart Gillmore or Susan Woods
Space: 1 gallery with 52 lin m hanging space
Exhibitions: 9 a year all originated
Details: Gallery in the lively environment of an artists' studio complex affiliated to WASPs. As well as exhibitions programme during the Edinburgh festival plays host to an open exhibition. Space is plentiful and available on a hire basis.

City Art Centre

Six floors of exhibition space, showing a wide range of material from contemporary art to archaeological antiquities.
2 Market Street, Edinburgh EH1 1DE, tel: 0131 529 3993, fax: 0131 529 3977
Contact: Ian O'Riordan, Keeper of Fine Art
Open: (June-Sept) Mon-Sat 10-6; (Sept-May) Mon-Sat 10-5; (June-Sept) Mon-Sat 10-6
Space: 6 galleries with 190 lin m hanging space plus 219 lin m on screens and 1500 sq m floor space
Exhibitions: 3 a year of which 2 originated, 1 touring
Details: Solo, group and thematic shows of contemporary art, often of Scottish origin or connection. Houses collection of Scottish art. Run by the local authority.

Collective Gallery

Artist-run gallery dedicated to support & development of emerging contemporary artists and artforms.
22-28 Cockburn Street, Edinburgh EH1 1NY, tel: 0131 220 1260
Contact: Sarah Munro, Director
Open: Tues-Sat 11-5; hours extended in summer during festival.
Space: 2 galleries with 20 lin m hanging space and 40 sq m floor space
Exhibitions: 12 a year all originated
Details: Shows innovative contemporary visual art by emerging and less-established artists, often offering artists first professional exhibition. Varied programme of exhibitions, events and education programme as well as small retail outlet for sale of high-quality artwork at affordable prices. Operates as artist-run membership organisation (members receive newsletter/ job opportunities, etc and are eligible to apply for solo and group shows). Occasional shows by non-members ie international emerging artists, community groups, etc. Supports alternative art forms ie installation, live art. Sales not high priority.

Commonwealth Institute, Scotland *

Large gallery showing temporary exhibitions of contemporary Commonwealth art.
8 Rutland Square, Edinburgh EH1 2AS, tel: 0131 229 6688, fax: 0131 229 6041
Contact: Exhibition Organiser
Details: Used to lecture primary school children on Commonwealth.

Contact Gallery

Situated within a day centre which offers services to adults with learning disabilities, the gallery provides opportunities for artists to present integrated exhibitions.
Grindlay Court Centre, Grindlay Street Court, Edinburgh EH3 9AR, tel: 0131 229 7941, fax: 0131 221 1190
Contact: Fiona Macpherson, Arts Facilitator
Open: Mon-Thurs 10-4; Fri 10-2.30; occasional weekends
Space: 1 gallery with 34 lin m hanging space and 63 sq m floor space
Exhibitions: 12 a year of which 8 originated, 4 on a hire basis
Details: Gallery is primarily for the benefit of Grindlay Court Day Centre users (adults with learning disabilities). Most exhibitions result from workshops in centre led by artists on a voluntary basis. Artists exhibit their own work alongside the centre users' work. In addition to main gallery space also exhibition area in entrance with 8 meters of screens. Funding being sought to provide

access to wheelchair users. Artists contribute to exhibition costs. Sale of work not a priority.

Craigmillar Festival Society Arts Centre

Hanging space for 2D exhibitions within multi-purpose community arts centre.
58 Newcraighall Road, Edinburgh EH15 3HS, tel: 0131 669 8432
Contact: Michael Greenlaw, 63 Niddrie Mains Terrace, Edinburgh, tel: 0131 661 5877
Open: Mon-Fri 10-5
Space: 1 gallery with 27 lin m hanging space plus 6 lin m on screens and 75 sq m floor space
Exhibitions: 5 a year all originated
Details: Centre in converted church building. Plenty of activities around exhibition programme, including photography, music, drama and dance. Shows held in hall and usually present work of artists and makers from local area. Group and solo shows. Sales not a priority.

Danish Cultural Institute

Exhibition programme of Danish art, craft, photography, etc.
Carlsberg House, 3 Doune Terrace, Edinburgh EH3 6DY, tel: 0131 225 7189, fax: 0131 220 6162
Contact: Finn Andersen, Director
Open: Mon-Fri 10-5
Space: 1 gallery with 30 lin m hanging space and 70 sq m floor space
Exhibitions: 3 a year of which 2 originated, 1 touring

Designer Frames & Gallery La Belle Angele *

Gallery and framing shop showing work of established and young artists.
11 Hasties Close, Cowgate, Edinburgh EH1 1JD, tel: 0131 225 2774
Contact: H. Maboubi, Exhibition Organiser
Space: 2 galleries with 48 lin m hanging space plus 15 lin m on screens and 180 sq m floor space
Exhibitions: 10 a year of which 7 originated, 3 touring
Details: Mixture of group and one-person exhibitions. Talks by exhibiting artists. Also venue for live music and performing art with a fully-licensed bar, café.

Eastern General Hospital

Two hospital corridors with lighting tracks, preferably for works under glass and no bigger than 3'x4'.

Seafield Street, Edinburgh EH6 7LN, tel: 0131 554 4444
Contact: Dr John Munro, Convenor of Art Fund, East and Midlothian NHS Trust Art Fund
Open: Daily 9-8 for approx 36 weeks a year.
Space: 1 gallery
Exhibitions: 6 a year of which 5 originated, 1 touring
Details: Aims to provide exhibition space primarily for recent graduates from Scottish art colleges, but no fixed rules. Encourages patents, visitors and staff to "vote" for picture they most like. Encourage sales to public and purchase at least one work from each exhibition for hospital collection – depending on the votes cast.

Edinburgh City Libraries

Temporary exhibitions promoting local artists, special themes and organisations within Edinburgh's libraries.
George IV Bridge, Edinburgh EH1 1EG, tel: 0131 225 5584
Contact: Display & Exhibitions Officer
Open: Mon-Fri 9-6.30; Sat 9-1
Details: Several spaces within Edinburgh's Central public library and number of community libraries. Temporary exhibitions usually relate to a local theme or special book selection.

Edinburgh College of Art

Main exhibition area is versatile neoclassical sculpture court but also several spaces suitable for smaller exhibitions.
Lauriston Place, Edinburgh EH3 9DF, tel: 0131 221 6031
Contact: Diane Henderson, Exhibition Administrator
Open: Mon-Thurs 10-8; Fri 10-5; (during term-time) Sat 10-2
Space: 1 gallery with 54 lin m hanging space and 228 sq m floor space
Exhibitions: 18 a year of which 9 originated, 5 touring, 4 on a hire basis
Details: Exhibitions and live performance programme which forms a supportive role to academic programme. As well as showing work of students and staff of the College exhibits touring and initiated shows of UK and international origin and participates in Edinburgh International Festival Fringe. Sculpture Court and other exhibitions spaces all available for hire. Sale of work not a priority.

Edinburgh Gallery

Promotes younger artists, predominantly but not exclusively from Scotland, by showing wide variety of styles and subjects.
18a Dundas Street, Edinburgh EH3 6HZ, tel: 0131 557 5227

Contact: Katherine Grilli
Open: Mon-Fri 11-5; Sat 10-1
Space: 2 galleries with 25 lin m hanging space and 32 sq m floor space
Exhibitions: 10 a year all originated
Details: Figurative work attracts slightly greater emphasis. Audience drawn from local population and from many visitors to area.

Edinburgh Printmakers Workshop & Gallery

Programme designed to complement the work of the studio, featuring mainly in-house prints and work that shows the potential of printmaking.
23 Union Street, Edinburgh EH1 3LR, tel: 0131 557 2479
Contact: Paul Kirkwood, Gallery Assistant
Space: 3 galleries with 11 lin m hanging space
Exhibitions: 8 a year all originated
Details: The emphasis is on Scotland-based printmakers. More occasional shows by major C20th artists, especially during the Edinburgh Festival. Visitors are an international collection of people from all walks of life.

Edinburgh Sculpture Workshop

Small exhibition space for members' and visitors' shows.
25 Hawthornvale, Newhaven, Edinburgh EH6 4JT, tel: 0131 551 4490, fax: 0131 551 4491
Contact: Jeanette Harris, Administrator
Open: Mon-Fri 10-5
Space: 1 gallery with 558 sq m floor space
Details: Group exhibitions by members in a range of galleries. Provides 12 studios for rental to professional sculptors, and workshop with stone and metalwork machinery, ceramic kiln and forklift truck. An education area used for sculpture classes and workshops and to integrate with community needs. Sales not a priority.

ESU Gallery

Light and airy central venue available for the promotion of contemporary art.
23 Atholl Crescent, Edinburgh EH3 8HQ, tel: 0131 229 1528, fax: 0131 229 1533
Contact: Margaret Stewart, Assistant Director
Space: 1 gallery with 82 sq m floor space
Exhibitions: 6 a year of which 2 originated, 4 on a hire basis
Details: The ESU Gallery initiates some exhibitions and is also available for hire for £350 weekly or 20% commission on sales whichever is the greater. This includes heating, lighting, use of kitchen, etc.

Hanging by rods. Gallery can help with press and publicity, invigilating, opening party, insurance and catalogues but costs of these not included in hire fee. Work can also be hung in entrance to main gallery. Sales a priority.

Firth Gallery

Small commercial gallery specialising in contemporary paintings.
35 William Street, Edinburgh EH3 7LW, tel: 0131 225 2196
Contact: Jamie Alexander, Director
Open: Tues-Fri 11-6; Sat 12-4
Space: 1 gallery with 21 lin m hanging space and 30 sq m floor space
Exhibitions: 8 a year
Details: Exhibitions, mostly one person, of contemporary paintings by artists of any age or nationality, with occasional accompanying exhibitions of smaller sculpture and/or original jewellery. Gallery, consisting of two small but well-lit rooms, situated on popular west end cobbled street. Any styles considered but sale of work is a priority.

French Institute

Small but attractive exhibition space particularly suitable for installation/multimedia work and projects based on Franco-Scottish or Franco-British exchanges.
13 Randolph Crescent, Edinburgh EH3 7TT, tel: 0131 225 5366, fax: 0131 220 0648
Contact: Martine Beugnet, Arts Officer
Open: Mon-Fri 9.30-6; Sat 10-1
Space: 1 gallery with 40 lin m hanging space and 11 sq m floor space
Exhibitions: 10 a year of which 4 originated, 4 touring, 2 on a hire basis
Details: Attractive gallery space in Georgian building overlooking the Dean Valley. Exhibitions with a French connection. In addition to gallery space, Institute's café can be used – about 25m hanging space. Open to all artists. Fees can be paid when new work is created. One exhibition specially commissioned every year. Selling work is not gallery's primary function.

Fruitmarket Gallery

Exhibitions of international contemporary art shown.
29 Market Street, Edinburgh EH1 1DF, tel: 0131 225 2383, fax: 0131 220 3130
Contact: Graeme Murray
Space: 4 galleries with 170 lin m hanging space and 474 sq m floor space
Exhibitions: 7 a year
Details: Reopened after complete refurbishment, 1993. Continues to show the kind of international contemporary art

that earned its reputation for quality and innovation.

Galerie Mirages *

Commercial gallery specialising in ethnic art.
46a Raeburn Place, Stockbridge, Edinburgh EH4 1HL, tel: 0131 315 2603
Contact: Sheila Dharinal Wal
Details: Runs temporary thematic exhibitions of folk/ethnic art. Rugs, pottery, puppets, costume etc from around the world (India, Japan, Middle East) are the main interest, though work of local and British makers is included when it integrates with main theme. The gallery building is an old bakery with high ceilings and space for each show must be discussed individually. Exhibitions last 6/8 weeks, almost exclusively gallery originated.

Hanover Fine Arts

Exhibits and sells 'accessible' contemporary art.
22a Dundas Street, Edinburgh EH3 6JN, tel: 0131 556 2181
Contact: Richard Ireland, Proprietor
Space: 2 galleries with 30 lin m hanging space and 40 sq m floor space
Exhibitions: 13 a year all originated
Details: Temporary exhibitions change every 3 to 4 weeks. Two or three mixed exhibitions per year (usually Spring, Festival & Christmas) with 50 artists showing small works. Other shows feature individual artists or small groups. Promotes Scottish-based artists within affordable price range, £50-£1000. Foreign artists not excluded.

Inverleith House/Royal Botanic Garden Edinburgh *

Major centre for the interpretation of nature through art.
Arboretum Place/Inverleith Row, Edinburgh EH3 5LR, tel: 0131 552 7171, fax: 0131 552 0382
Contact: Paul Nesbitt, Director of Exhibitions, Royal Botanic Garden Edinburgh, Inverleith Row, Edinburgh, EH3 5LR, tel: 0131 552 7171, fax: 0131 552 0382
Space: 9 galleries with 200 lin m hanging space and 330 sq m floor space
Exhibitions: 12 a year of which 2 originated, 10 touring
Details: Formerly home of the Scottish National Gallery of Modern Art, set in 75 acres of planted grounds. Attracts 1 million visitors per year. Recent exhibitions by Peter Randall-Page, Andy Goldsworthy, Chris Drury, Sjoerd Buisman, Herman de Vries.

Kingfisher Gallery

Small commercial gallery showing work by well-established British and International artists.
5 Northumberland Street Lane N.W., Edinburgh EH3 6JL, tel: 0131 557 5454
Contact: Lena & Ronnie McGregor, Directors
Open: Tues-Sat 11-4.30
Space: 1 gallery with 20 lin m hanging space and 30 sq m floor space
Exhibitions: 10 a year all originated
Details: Mews gallery in Edinburgh's new town with monthly changing exhibitions of contemporary paintings, sculpture, ceramics and jewellery.

Malcolm Innes Gallery

Specialists in natural history, sporting, military and Scottish painting, prints and sculpture (historic and contemporary).
67 George Street, Edinburgh EH2 2JG, tel: 0131 226 4151
Contact: Anthony Woodd, Exhibition Organiser
Space: 1 gallery with 260 lin m hanging space and 270 sq m floor space
Exhibitions: 3 a year all originated
Details: Normally has seven exhibitions a year and a changing display of work for sale. Takes part in activities in London and abroad and undertakes framing and restoration.

Leith Gallery

93 Giles Street, Leith, Edinburgh EH6 6BZ, tel: 0131 553 5255, fax: 0131 553 5655

Matthew Architecture Gallery

Small gallery within University's Department of Architecture specialising in architecture and related arts.
University of Edinburgh, Department of Architecture, 20 Chambers Street, Edinburgh EH1 1JZ, tel: 0131 6502306, fax: 0131 650 8019
Contact: Fiona McLachlan, Director
Open: (University term-time) Mon-Fri 10-8; Sat & Sun 10.30-2.30; (vacations) Mon-Fri 10-4
Space: 1 gallery with 34 lin m hanging space and 90 sq m floor space
Exhibitions: 8 a year
Details: Through exhibition programme gallery aims to promote excellence in architectural design to the general public and the architectural community. Mostly touring exhibitions shown. Sales of work not primary role of gallery.

National Library of Scotland

Pa Ph Sc ✪ ❶ ❷ Wc

Collections of books, manuscripts and maps assembled over 3 centuries and exhibitions aimed at providing an insight into these; but also takes exhibitions originated elsewhere, particularly those with relevance to the book arts.
George IV Bridge, Edinburgh EH1 1EW, tel: 0131 226 4531, fax: 0131 220 6662
Contact: Dr Kenneth Gibson, Exhibitions Officer
Open: Mon-Sat 10-5; Sun 2-5; (Festival) Mon-Fri 10-8.30, Sat 10-5, Sun 2-5
Space: 1 gallery with 67 lin m hanging space and 1741 sq m floor space
Exhibitions: 2 a year of which 1 touring, 1 on a hire basis
Details: Most exhibitions mounted round a historic theme or personality and include books, manuscripts, photographs and artifacts. Sale of work is not the gallery's concern.

Netherbow Art Centre

Pa Ph Pr Cr A ✪ ❶ Wc

Gallery and café in Church of Scotland arts centre showing wide-ranging exhibitions.
43-45 High Street, Edinburgh EH1 1SR, tel: 0131 556 9579
Contact: Ellis Mckechnie, Assistant Director
Details: Centre has well-equipped small theatre which holds performances all year. Gallery is upstairs and is not accessible to wheelchair users. However rest of the building is, including theatre and café. Main space for the Scottish Puppet Festival. Exhibitions organised with the general public in mind. Activities organised for schools and community arts groups.

Open Eye Gallery

Pa Ph Pr Cr Sc ✪

Main purpose is to mount series of exhibitions covering the many aspects of contemporary arts from young emerging artists to the established school.
75-79 Cumberland Street, Edinburgh EH3 6RD, tel: 0131 557 1020, fax: 0131 557 5219
Contact: Thomas Wilson, Managing Director
Open. Mon-Fri 10-6; Sat 10-4
Space: 1 gallery with 80 lin m hanging space and 50 sq m floor space
Exhibitions: 16 a year all originated
Details: Gallery aims to promote contemporary fine art, sculpture, ceramics and crafts to as wide a range of people as possible. Selling work not gallery's primary function.

Out of the Blue Artspace

Pa Ph Pr Sc A ✪ ❶ ❷

Gallery exhibiting innovative artwork in open and informal atmosphere.
25 Blackfriars Street, Edinburgh EH1 1NB, tel: 0131 556 5204
Contact: Trudi Gibson and Anne-Marie Culhane, Co-ordinators
Open: Tues-Sat 11-5
Space: 1 gallery with 70 sq m floor space
Exhibitions: 10 a year of which 8 originated, 2 on a hire basis
Details: Gallery opened 1994 aims to increase accessibility to contemporary artwork for wide audience. Education programme; workshops organised through working closely with exhibiting artists. Sales not primary function of gallery.

Portfolio Gallery

Ph ✪ ❷ ❷

Specialist photography gallery, widely recognised as Scotland's leading gallery in the field of independent, creative photography.
43 Candlemaker Row, Edinburgh EH1 2QB, tel: 0131 220 1911
Contact: Gloria Chalmers, Director
Open: Tues-Sat 12-5.30
Space: 2 galleries with 40 lin m hanging space and 56 sq m floor space
Exhibitions: 9 a year of which 6 originated, 3 touring
Details: Promotes the work of new photographic artists and to create debate and discussion in the field of contemporary photographic practice. Tours exhibitions. Produces biannual publication, Portfolio - The Catalogue of Contemporary British Photography. Selling work is not gallery's primary function.

Queen's Hall

Pa Ph Pr ✪ ❷ Wc 4

Concert hall with exhibition space in busy restaurant and bar on two levels.
Clerk Street, Edinburgh EH8 9JG, tel: 0131 668 3456, fax: 0131 668 2656
Contact: Simon Crookall, General Manager
Open: Mon-Sat 10-5; and during performances
Space: 2 galleries with 50 lin m hanging space and 106 sq m floor space
Exhibitions: 12 a year
Details: Exhibition area in restaurant and bar is primarily hung with aim of selling work. 2D work shown is by artists based locally and outside area and includes figurative and abstract work.

RIAS Gallery *

Pa Ph ✪ ❶

Gallery shows exhibitions related to Scottish architecture and architects as artists, and contemporary art.

15 Rutland Square, off West End Princes Street, Edinburgh EH1 2BE, tel: 0131 229 7545, fax: 0131 228 2188
Contact: Liz Work, Exhibitions Coordinator
Space: 1 gallery with 16 lin m hanging space plus 30 lin m on screens and 35 sq m floor space
Exhibitions: 4 a year all on a hire basis
Details: Head office of the Royal Incorporation of Architects. Extensive bookshop. Audience for exhibitions: general public and architects.

Royal Scottish Academy

Pa Ph Pr ❷ Wc

Exhibitions mainly of work by academicians and associates.
The Mound, Edinburgh EH2 2EL, tel: 0131 225 6671, fax: 0131 225 2349
Contact: Margaret A Wilson, Assistant Administrative Secretary
Open: Mon-Sat 10-5 ; Sun 2-5; during exhibitions
Exhibitions: 5 a year all originated
Details: Mainly group exhibitions. Throughout year, gallery shows work by academicians and associates in fields of painting, sculpture, architecture and printmaking. Scottish students' work is shown every spring. Annual exhibition open to non-members every summer. This is only exhibition for which applications welcome. Sales not a priority.

Scottish Gallery

Pa Pr Cr ✪ ❷

Largest commercial fine and applied art gallery in Scotland showing contemporary and 20th Century Scottish painting and British crafts.
16 Dundas Street, Edinburgh EH3 6HZ, tel: 0131 5581200, fax: 0131 558 3900
Contact: Guy Peploe (Paintings), Amanda Game (Crafts)
Open: Mon-Fri 10-6; Sat 10-4
Space: 4 galleries with 114 lin m hanging space and 686 sq m floor space
Exhibitions: 34 a year all originated
Details: Founded in 1842. Varied monthly solo exhibition programme shows well-established and young artists. Craft department has solo exhibitions of ceramics, wood, metal, jewellery and textiles. Exhibitions by invitation only, but submissions from artists always welcome.

Scottish National Gallery of Modern Art

Pa Pr Sc

Home of Scottish national collection of modern art.
Belford Road, Edinburgh EH4 3DR, tel: 0131 556 8921, fax: 0131 343 2802
Contact: Richard Calvocoressi, Keeper
Details: Georgian converted school. Showing the permanent collection (begun

in 1960) of C20th painting, sculpture and graphic art and at least one major exhibition a year, usually to coincide with the Edinburgh Festival. Smaller exhibitions surrounding work in the collection also organised by the gallery.

Scottish National Portrait Gallery

Gallery's main purpose is to display portraits of men and women who have made a distinctive contribution to Scottish history.
1 Queen Street, Edinburgh EH2 1JD, tel: 0131 556 8921, fax: 0131 558 3691
Contact: Dr Duncan Thomson, Keeper
Open: Mon-Sat 10-5; Sun 2-5
Exhibitions: 2 a year of which 1 originated, 1 touring
Details: Part of National Galleries of Scotland. Scotland's famous faces shown in this custom-built Victorian museum shared with the National Museums of Scotland. In recent years, has revitalised the national collection of portraits, commissioning new portraits of well-known Scots by contemporary artists. Also houses the extensive and ever-increasing national collection of photography. There is now a room specially reserved for showing selections from the collection all year round. Several exhibitions held a year, with major exhibition to coincide with the Edinburgh Festival. No sale of work.

Scottish Photographic Works *

Continuous display of photography and occasional solo shows.
14a Nelson Street, Edinburgh EH3 6LG, tel: 0131 556 4017
Contact: Kate Johnstone
Space: 1 gallery with 11 lin m hanging space and 9 sq m floor space
Details: SPW holds stock of photographic prints by photographers living and working in Scotland, and Scottish photographers working elsewhere. Also holds other work made in Scotland. Exhibitions of some foreign photographers currently being planned. Audience principally composed of collectors, other galleries and museums.

Seeds Wholefood Café

Café showing a diversity of work by local artists , mainly paintings and photography.
53 West Nicolson Street, Edinburgh EH8 9DB, tel: 0131 667 8673
Contact: Andrew Medley
Space: 1 gallery with 10 lin m hanging space
Exhibitions: 12 a year all originated
Details: About twelve exhibitions a year, all living artists, mostly solo shows.

Stills Gallery

Aims to promote and widen access to photography as an art form and creative cultural practice
23 Cockburn Street, Edinburgh EH1 1BP, tel: 0131 225 9876, fax: 0131 225 4901
Contact: Director
Open: Tues-Sat; ring gallery for opening times
Space: 2 galleries with 300 lin m hanging space
Exhibitions: 9 a year
Details: Integrated programme of exhibitions and educational activities. Self-originated and national touring exhibitions. Policy of commissioning and publishing new work, both photographic and textual. Programme emphasises a diversity of approaches to the photographic medium showing innovative Scottish, UK and international work. Print Room, reference library, darkrooms. Books, postcards, prints etc for sale in the bookshop.

Talbot Rice Gallery

Spacious modern exhibition space which is flexible for showing a range of work from photography to large-scale painting and sculpture.
University of Edinburgh, Old College, South Bridge, Edinburgh EH8 9YL, tel: 0131 650 2210/3, fax: 0131 650 2213
Contact: Val Fiddes, Administrator
Open: Tues-Sat 10-5
Space: 2 galleries with 150 lin m hanging space plus 30 lin m on screens and 360 sq m floor space
Exhibitions: 10 a year
Details: Platform for established artists to mount major solo exhibitions. Younger artists are encouraged to exhibit in group shows. The gallery also shows at least one major historical show a year. Though the bias is towards Scottish work, the gallery does attract international exhibitions. Touring exhibitions organised. Accompanying education programme with every exhibition.

Theatre Workshop

Light and airy café bar/foyer area provides showcase for local artists working in variety of media.
34 Hamilton Place, Edinburgh EH3 5AX, tel: 0131 225 7942, fax: 0131 220 0112
Contact: Adrian Harris, Director
Open: Mon-Sat 10-late
Space: 30 lin m hanging space and 110 sq m floor space
Exhibitions: 12 a year of which 1 originated, 11 on a hire basis
Details: Based in café/bar and divided into

two clear spaces. As with all TW activity aims to support artists from disadvantaged groups such as ethnic minorities, women, people with special needs, etc. Gallery space is usually hired out 4-6 months in advance. No commission on sales. Insurance responsibility of hirer. We promote exhibition through print publicity and media. Selling work not gallery's main aim.

Torrance Gallery

Commercial gallery showing exhibitions of accessible contemporary work mainly by Scottish artists.
29b Dundas Street, Edinburgh EH3 6QQ, tel: 0131 556 6366
Contact: Florence Torrance, Director
Open: Mon-Fri 11-6; Sat 10.30-4
Space: 2 galleries with 274 sq m floor space
Exhibitions: 12 a year all originated
Details: Commercial gallery in a basement. Exhibitions change regularly. Often group shows of two or three artists in several media (eg jewellery and ceramics shown with paintings).

Traverse Theatre

Exhibition space in theatre bar/café.
Cambridge Street, Edinburgh EH1 2ED, tel: 0131 228 3223, fax: 0131 229 8443
Contact: Helen Wylie, Executive Director/ Theatre Manager
Open: 10-late, as bar opening times
Space: 1 gallery
Exhibitions: 12 a year
Details: Hopes to encourage artists who have never exhibited before, as well as more seasoned and established professionals. Artists who wish to apply may do so in writing with slides of their work. Programme planned to include both mixed and solo shows. Commission charged on sales.

Ware on Earth *

Gallery in shop specialising in ceramics with temporary exhibitions highlighting work of one artist, shown every two months.
15 Howe Street, Edinburgh EH3 6TF, tel: 0131 558 1276
Contact: Robert Murray Brown, Owner
Details: British and European makers shown.

WASPS Studios Gallery

Gallery within artists' studio complex available primarily for the use of resident artists but outside artists are welcome to fill empty slots in the programme.
Patriothall, off Hamilton Place, Stockbridge, Edinburgh EH3 5AY, tel: 0131 225 1289

Contact: Angus Richardson, Resident
Administrator
Space: 1 gallery with 78 sq m floor space
Exhibitions: 12 a year all originated
Details: Gallery created from the entrance
space of a warehouse building now housing
studios.

Elgin
GRAMPIAN

Elgin Museum

Pa Pr Cr Sc ● ⊕ & Wc

*To promote the literary, scientific, natural
and cultural awareness of Moray.*
**1 High Street, Elgin IV30 1EQ, tel:
01343 543675**
Contact: Jim Inglis, Curator
Open: (Main Museum) Mon-Fri 10-5; Sat
11-4; Sun 2-5; (Gallery) can be open as
many hours as required and staffed by
exhibitor.
Space: 2 galleries with 60 lin m hanging
space plus 44 lin m on screens and 120 sq
m floor space
Exhibitions: 13 a year of which 9
originated, 4 on a hire basis
Details: Museum and exhibition hall
owned and run by the Moray Society, a
group with charitable status. Exhibition
hall used for solo and group shows.
Temporary exhibition gallery in museum
'up for grabs'. Used for variety of exhibits
ranging over the entire spectrum of scale
and media.

Ellon
GRAMPIAN

Tolquhon Gallery

Pa Pr Cr Sc ●

*Shows painting, original print, sculpture
and studio craft by mainly Scottish artists –
established and emerging.*
**Tolquhon, Tarves, Ellon AB41 0LP, tel:
01651 842343**
Contact: Joan Ross, Director
Open: Mon-Wed, Fri-Sat 11-5; Sun 2-5
Space: 3 galleries with 49 lin m hanging
space and 51 sq m floor space
Exhibitions: 10 a year all originated
Details: Changing programme of solo,
group and large mixed exhibitions. Wide
audience – all ages, tastes and incomes –
mainly from Aberdeen and surrounding
area. Exhibition is by invitation but we
invite artists to complete application forms
(available from the gallery) and submit
them with slides/examples of work.
Gardens suitable for outdoor exhibition of
sculpture.

Forfar
TAYSIDE

Meffan Museum & Art Gallery

Pa Ph Pr Cr Sc ●

*Temporary exhibition programme with
one-person and mixed shows from artists
and makers from throughout the UK.*
**20 West High Street, Forfar DD8 1DD,
tel: 01307 468813**
Contact: Jake Stewart, Exhibitions Officer
Space: 2 galleries with 67 lin m hanging
space
Exhibitions: 19 a year of which 15
originated

Galashiels
BORDERS

Christopher Boyd Gallery

Pa Ph Pr Cr Sc ● & Wc

*Municipal gallery showing contemporary
work in all media.*
**Old Gala House, Scot Crescent,
Galashiels TD1 3JS**
Contact: Jackie Smith, Exhibitions Officer,
Ettrick & Lauderdale Museums, Municipal
Buildings, High Street, Selkirk, TD7 4JX,
tel: 01750 720096, fax: 01750 723282
Open: Mon-Sat 10-4; (April-Oct) Sun 2-4
Space: 1 gallery with 40 lin m hanging
space and 575 sq m floor space
Exhibitions: 8 a year of which 6
originated, 2 touring
Details: Plans to show local and national
visual art exhibitions in order to encourage
interest from local community. Workshop
and lecture programme. Sales not a
priority.

Girvan
STRATHCLYDE

McKechnie Institute

Pa Ph Pr Cr Sc ●

*Municipal art centre with a diverse
selection of temporary exhibitions.*
**Dalrymple Street, Girvan KA26 9AE, tel:
01465 713643**
Contact: Margaret McCance, Hon Curator
Space: 3 galleries with 75 lin m hanging
space and 224 sq m floor space
Exhibitions: 8 a year
Details: Managed by Girvan Community
Council in association with Kyle and
Carrick District Council. Exhibitions
include work by local artists and craft
workers and small touring exhibitions.
Interest in the gallery is fostered in the
community and schools and art classes are
held regularly.

Glasgow
STRATHCLYDE

Barclay Lennie Fine Art

Pa Cr Sc ● ⊗

*Commercial gallery specialising in Scottish
art with contemporary exhibitions and
gallery stock comprising contemporary art
and C19-20th paintings, sculpture and
decorative art.*
**203 Bath Street, Glasgow G2 4HZ, tel:
0141 226 5413**
Contact: Barclay Lennie
Open: Mon-Fri 10-5; Sat 10-1
Space: 2 galleries with 60 lin m hanging
space and 120 sq m floor space
Exhibitions: 6 a year all originated
Details: Usual layout in gallery is one area
for 'older' work and one area for
contemporary. Uses total space for large
contemporary exhibitions. Sculpture and
ceramics normally shown and decorative
arts from early C20th a feature. Client base
fairly broad, both private and institutions.

Centre for Contemporary Arts

Pa Ph Sc LA £ & Wc

*Policy is to present new developments in the
visual arts.*
**350 Sauchiehall Street, Glasgow G2 3JD,
tel: 0141 332 7521, fax: 0141 332 3226**
Contact: Nicola White, Exhibitions
Director
Space: 2 galleries with 55 lin m hanging
space
Details: Aims to present an innovative and
challenging programme of work which
explores new developments in the visual
and performing arts and which offers
opportunities to artists and audiences in a
local, national and international context.
Supports artists in making possible the
creation of new work and aims to increase
accessibility and strengthen understanding
of contemporary arts by providing range of
activities in which artists and audiences can
participate. Artists exhibit by invitation
from the programmers.

Centre for Developmental Arts Gallery

Pa Cr Sc ● Wc 4

*Gallery's main purpose is to exhibit
developmental work that is not ordinarily
seen within a gallery context.*
**18 Albion Street, Glasgow G1 1LH, tel:
0141 552 2822**
Contact: Elisabeth Gibson, Projects
Director
Open: Mon-Fri 10-5; closed BH
Space: 1 gallery with 35 lin m hanging
space plus 2 lin m on screens and 104 sq m
floor space
Exhibitions: 9 a year all originated
Details: Artists are invited to exhibit who

do not ordinarily have access to gallery exhibition space. Sale of work not gallery's primary role.

Collins Gallery

Educational gallery showing contemporary art and craft by both new and established artists with all work offered for sale.
University of Strathclyde, 22 Richmond Street, Glasgow G1 1XQ, tel: 0141 553 4145, fax: 0141 552 4053
Contact: Laura Hamilton, Curator
Open: Mon-Fri 10-5; Sat 12-4
Space: 3 galleries with 100 lin m hanging space plus 75 lin m on screens and 280 sq m floor space
Exhibitions: 14 a year of which 9 originated, 5 touring
Details: Draws visitors from both local community and further afield. Programme covers all contemporary art forms with an emphasis on live art and also historical design/art/architecture exhibitions. Most are complemented by practical workshops, talks, films, drama or music as well as an educational programme. Sales desk for catalogues, postcards and other exhibition merchandise. Sale of work is not gallery's primary role.

Compass Gallery *

Exhibitions of Scottish and international artists, both well-known and emerging.
178 West Regent Street, Glasgow G2 4RL, tel: 0141 221 6370, fax: 0141 248 1322
Contact: Cyril or Jill Gerber, Directors
Space: 3 galleries with 62 lin m hanging space and 70 sq m floor space
Exhibitions: 12 a year all originated
Details: A non-profit making gallery registered as a charity. Has been showing contemporary art in Glasgow for 23 years. Holds student exhibition every year after the Scottish art college degree shows. Permanent stock of paintings and prints always available for viewing.

Cyril Gerber Fine Art *

Commercial gallery with exhibitions of important British artists, mainly derived from changing stock.
148 West Regent Street, Glasgow G2 2RQ, tel: 0141 221 3095/041 204 0276, fax: 0141 248 1322
Contact: Cyril Gerber, Director
Exhibitions: 5 a year all originated
Details: Deals principally in late C19th to mid C20th British paintings. Changing stock which includes original prints and art objects.

Eastwood House

Available for hire for exhibitions of paintings, prints or photography.
Eastwood Park, Giffnock, Glasgow G46 6UG, tel: 0141 638 1101, fax: 0141 620 0884
Contact: Mrs A.J. Shaw, Halls Manager, Eastwood District Council, Rouken Glen Road, Giffnock, Glasgow, G46 6UG, tel: 0141 638 1101
Exhibitions: 3 a year of which 1 originated, 2 on a hire basis
Details: Temporary exhibitions and annual exhibition in October by local residents. Multi-purpose building. Whole house may be hired or one or two suites. Capelrig House Gallery designed as art gallery, available for hire for variety of functions. Mrs A J Shaw also contact for exhibition space at Capelrig House, Newton Mearns, available for hire for exhibitions of paintings, prints or photography.

Ewan Mundy Fine Art

A city centre gallery with regularly changing exhibitions showing Scottish, English and French artists' work.
211 West George Street, Glasgow G2 2LW, tel: 0141 248 9755
Contact: Ewan Mundy
Space: 1 gallery with 47 sq m floor space
Details: Drawing, painting and engravings. Emphasis on Scottish art from 1850 to contemporary work. The programme mixes younger with more recognised artists, sometimes single shows, sometimes mixed. Occasional catalogues produced of exhibitions. Gallery has loyal clientele who come from Scotland and further afield. Commission charged on sales.

Gatehouse Gallery

Commercial gallery providing quality contemporary art for the market place.
Rouken Glen Road, Giffnock, Glasgow G46 7UG, tel: 0141 620 0235
Contact: Anne Mendelow, Proprietor
Open: Wed-Mon 1.30-5.30
Space: 1 gallery with 28 lin m hanging space
Exhibitions: 11 a year all originated
Details: Regular selling exhibitions by well-established contemporary artists and recent graduates. Aims to encourage public to buy original work in preference to reproductions. Permanent stock of paintings by owner Anne Mendelow, and offers a framing service. Commission 33.5% + VAT.

Glasgow Museums

Glasgow Museums operates exhibition galleries in most of its main museums.
Art Gallery and Museum , Kelvingrove, Glasgow G3 8AG, tel: 0141 221 9600, fax: 0141 305 2690
Contact: Resource Co-ordinator
Open: Mon-Fri 10-5; Sun 11-5
Exhibitions: 31 a year of which 15 originated, 15 touring, 1 on a hire basis
Details: Including: Art Gallery and Museum, Kelvingrove; Burrell Collection; People's Palace; Museum of Transport. Programming varies according to the specialisations of the different museums. Contemporary art is an important part of these programmes. Artists are welcome to submit proposals to the Exhibitions Dept.

Glasgow Print Studio

Gallery space within print workshop.
22 King Street, Glasgow G1 5QP, tel: 0141 552 0704, fax: 0141 552 2919
Contact: John Mackechnie, Director
Open: Mon-Sat 10-5.30
Space: 2 galleries with 64 lin m hanging space
Exhibitions: 10 a year of which 9 originated, 1 touring
Details: Room to exhibit up to 50 average sized pictures. Predominantly print exhibitions but also paintings, drawings and sculptures. Mainly local audience and visitors to Glasgow. Also comprises a print workshop and a retail outlet, "The Original Print Shop" with solo print shows 6 times a year.

Glasgow School of Art

Exhibitions reflect the activities of the art school as well as the work of organisations and artists nationally and internationally.
167 Renfrew Street, Glasgow G3 6RQ, tel: 0141 353 4500, fax: 0141 353 4746
Contact: Kathy Chambers, Exhibitions Coordinator
Space: 2 galleries with 61 lin m hanging space
Exhibitions: 22 a year of which 16 originated, 6 touring
Details: The Mackintosh Gallery is within the main building designed by Charles Rennie Mackintosh. The Newbery Gallery is larger and can cater for 3D and time-based work. Disabled access by arrangement.

Haggs Castle Museum *

Permanent collection and temporary exhibitions related to children and their interests.

100 St Andrews Drive, Pollokshields, Glasgow G41 4RB, tel: 0141 427 2725
Contact: Assistant Keeper
Exhibitions: 1 a year touring

Hillhead Underground Gallery *

[Pa][Ph][Pr] ✓ [H]

A private gallery in a large café setting.
2 Creswell Lane, Glasgow G12 8AA, tel: 0141 339 0968
Contact: James B Neilson, Director
Space: 1 gallery
Exhibitions: 12 a year all on a hire basis
Details: Exhibitions of fine and applied art by contemporary and amateur Scottish artists.

Hunterian Art Gallery

[Pa][Ph][Pr][Sc] ♿ [WC]

Gallery run by University of Glasgow houses collections of work by C R Mackintosh plus exhibitions drawn largely from its collections of artists' prints, drawings and watercolours.
The University, Hillhead Street, Glasgow G12 8QQ, tel: 0141 330 5431, fax: 0141 307 8017
Contact: Pamela Robertson, Curator
Open: Mon-Sat 9.30-12.30, 1.30-5
Space: 1 gallery with 27 lin m hanging space and 50 sq m floor space
Exhibitions: 1 a year originated
Details: 4-5 exhibitions a year; most of which are drawn from the University's collection of artists' prints which dates from C15th to present. An exhibition each year is drawn respectively from collections of work by J M Whistler and C R Mackintosh. Supporting educational activities. Occasional loan and contemporary shows. Sales not gallery's primary concern.

Interdec Gallery *

[Pa][Ph][Cr][Sc] ✓ [H]

Shows Scottish contemporary art, Third World work and work by young Glasgow artists.
Maryhill Burgh Hall, 24 Gairbraid Road, Glasgow G20 8YE, tel: 0141 946 5912
Contact: Ali Abubakar, Owner
Space: 3 galleries with 24 lin m hanging space and 161 sq m floor space
Exhibitions: 9 a year of which 8 originated, 1 on a hire basis
Details: Commission on sales.

Intermedia Gallery

[Pa][Ph][Pr][Cr][Sc] ✓ ♿

Temporary gallery project in vacant shop unit offering Glasgow based artists opportunities to stage exhibitions at minimal cost.
65 Virginia Street, Glasgow, tel: 0141 337 3252
Contact: Clare Simpson, Glasgow District Council, Finance Office, 285 George Street, Glasgow, G2 1DU, tel: 0141 227 4068, fax: 0141 227 5889
Open: Tues-Sat 12-6
Space: 1 gallery with 56 lin m hanging space
Exhibitions: 10 a year all originated
Details: Submissions invited from local artists twice yearly. Exhibitors chosen by selection panel. Exhibitors required to plan, stage and invigilate own shows.

Kelly Gallery

[Pa] ✓ [H] ♿

Commercial gallery hiring space to artists for one person or group shows.
118 Douglas Street, Glasgow G2 4ET, tel: 0141 248 6386, fax: 0141 221 0417
Contact: Mr R C Liddle, Secretary, Royal Glasgow Institute of the Fine Arts, 5 Oswald Street, Glasgow, G1 4QR, tel: 0141 248 7411, fax: 0141 221 0417
Open: (During exhibitions) Mon-Fri 10.30-5; Sat 10-12.30
Space: 1 gallery with 26 lin m hanging space plus 6 lin m on screens and 72 sq m floor space
Details: Exhibitions last for minimum of 2 weeks. Artists charged rental and commission on sales. This includes services of staff during opening hours. Three days for hanging and two for dismantling are allowed at no extra cost. Sale of work is a priority.

Lillie Art Gallery

[Pa][Ph][Pr][Cr][Sc] ✓ ♿ [4]

Local authority art gallery with permanent collection of Scottish C20th art and temporary exhibitions of contemporary art and craft.
Station Road, Milngavie, Glasgow G62 8BZ, tel: 0141 943 3247, fax: 0141 943 0200
Contact: Elizabeth M. Dent, Curator
Open: Mon-Fri 10-5; Sat & Sun 2-5
Space: 3 galleries with 137 lin m hanging space plus 24 lin m on screens and 204 sq m floor space
Exhibitions: 10 a year
Details: Temporary exhibition programme of mainly contemporary art and craft and occasional exhibitions of historical art and other subjects. Sales not a priority.

McLennan Gallery

[Pa][Ph][Pr][Cr][Sc][LA] ✓ [£] ♿ [WC] [4]

Purpose-built exhibition galleries built in 1854 and refurbished in 1990 to house temporary exhibitions of work from around the world.
270 Sauchiehall Street, Glasgow G2 3EH, tel: 0141 331 1854, fax: 0141 332 9957
Contact: Stefan van Raay, Senior Curator of Art, Glasgow Museums, The Burrell Collection, Pollock Country Park, Glasgow, G43 1AT, tel: 0141 649 7151, fax: 0141 636 0086
Open: Mon-Sat 10-5; Sun 11-5
Space: 7 galleries with 305 lin m hanging space and 1158 sq m floor space
Exhibitions: 5 a year all originated
Details: Aims to bring the best of contemporary art from around the world to Glasgow, both to enhance the enjoyment of the City's public and also the establish Glasgow's artistic credentials on a world stage. Normally pays exhibition fee to artists. Sales not a priority.

Michael Main Gallery *

[Pa][Sc] ✓

Specialists in contemporary Scottish painting, also work from Europe and America.
34 Gibson Street, Kelvinbridge, Glasgow G12 8NX, tel: 0141 334 8858, fax: 0141 334 1055
Contact: Michael Main, Studio Gallery, 16 Gibson Street, Glasgow, G12 8NX
Space: 1 gallery with 16 lin m hanging space and 64 sq m floor space
Exhibitions: 3 a year all originated
Details: Open-plan space converted from an ornate Victorian chemist shop which the Daily Telegraph described as 'chic and welcoming'. More intimate space also available in the Studio Gallery, 16 Gibson St. 4-6 solo shows are scheduled each year, presenting a range of new and established artists. Also on-going exhibition of work selected from the gallery's stock.

Mitchell Library

[Pa][Ph][Pr][Cr][Sc] ✓ ♿ [WC]

Former reading room where exhibitions are mounted on temporary panels or housed in showcases.
North Street, Glasgow G3 7DN, tel: 0141 305 2803, fax: 0141 305 2815
Contact: Mrs Fionna MacPherson, Head of Reference Services
Open: Mon-Fri 9am-9pm; Sat 9-5
Space: 1 gallery with 240 sq m floor space
Exhibitions: 4 a year
Details: Glass walls, so hanging onto panels. Library has own panel system & showcases which are available to exhibitors. Audience: general public/users of library. Five other small foyer areas which can accommodate certain types of displays, depending on size, subject matter, etc.

Pearce Institute

[Pa][Pr][Cr][Sc][LA] ✓ ♿ [WC] [4]

Voluntary organisation providing social, educational and leisure facilities with three exhibition areas available.
840 Govan Road, Glasgow G51 3UT, tel: 0141 445 1941
Contact: Alan Davidson, Development Officer

Open: Daily 8am-10pm
Space: 3 galleries with 117 lin m hanging space and 421 sq m floor space
Exhibitions: 4 a year all originated
Details: Café area and small gallery area with large hall occasionally available. Wide variety of exhibitions by local groups and professional artists. Selling work is not seen as a priority.

Roger Billcliffe Fine Art

 ✓

Gallery dealing in contemporary Scottish painting and the applied arts with a stock of earlier C20th work.
134 Blythswood Street, Glasgow G2 4EL, tel: 0141 332 4027, fax: 0141 332 6573
Contact: Roger Billcliffe
Open: Mon-Fri 9.30-5.30; Sat 10-1
Space: 3 galleries with 171 sq m floor space
Exhibitions: 6 a year all originated
Details: Formerly the Fine Art Society. Shows last a month and combine known names and younger artists. Mixed and single person exhibitions. Gallery itself situated in the centre of Glasgow just off main shopping area. Attracts broad cross-section of the community, from art students to corporate collectors.

Rowan Gallery

Gallery in back area of shop in country village.
36 Main Street, Drymen, Glasgow G63 0BG, tel: 01360 660996, fax: 01360 770993
Contact: Angus MacLean, Partner
Open: Daily 10-5
Space: 1 gallery with 20 lin m hanging space and 40 sq m floor space
Exhibitions: 6 a year all originated
Details: Small, friendly gallery near Loch Lomond specialising in Scottish scenes by Scottish-based artists. Holds mixed exhibitions featuring various artists every two months. Permanent stock of paintings available all year round. Buys paintings from artists and does not sell on commission.

Royal Scottish Academy of Music and Drama

Foyer space used for limited number of exhibitions, initiated mainly by in-house or visiting performing arts groups.
100 Renfrew Street, Glasgow G2 3DB, tel: 0141 332 4101, fax: 0141 332 8401
Contact: Anna Fenge, Marketing & Public Relations Manager
Space: 1 gallery with 24 lin m hanging space plus 20 lin m on screens and 78 sq m floor space
Exhibitions: 4 a year
Details: Touring exhibitions welcome. No charges.

Springburn Museum

Independent community museum with changing exhibition programme for all ages.
Atlas Square, Ayr Street, Springburn, Glasgow G21 4BW, tel: 0141 557 1405
Contact: Curator
Open: Mon-Fri 10.30-5; Sat 10-4.30; Sun & BH 2-5
Space: 2 galleries with plus 35 lin m on screens and 200 sq m floor space
Details: Social and Industrial History Museum of the Year 1989. Changing exhibitions on the community of Springburn, once the largest centre of steam locomotive manufacture in Europe.

Strathclyde Arts Centre *

Gallery in arts education centre with mixed programme of touring and commissioned exhibitions of work by established and younger artists.
12 Washington Street, Glasgow G12 8PD, tel: 0141 221 4526, fax: 0141 204 3368
Contact: George Cherrie, Head of the Centre
Exhibitions: 4 a year
Details: Members of the centre use the gallery most frequently but exhibitions also attract the general public. At least 12 exhibitions a year, almost all showing living artists. At the time of going to press the gallery is in the process of moving and re-structuring.

Street Level Photography Gallery and Workshop

Comprehensive photography centre.
26 King Street, Glasgow G1 5QP, tel: 0141 552 2151
Contact: Exhibitions Co-ordinator
Open: Mon-Sat 10-5.30
Space: 2 galleries with 52 lin m hanging space
Exhibitions: 14 a year of which 7 originated, 7 touring
Details: Facilities include two galleries, darkroom/workshop and photographic bookshop. Exhibitions include historical and contemporary photography by local, national and international photographers. Promotes young and emerging Scottish photographers. Aims to increase understanding of photography as art and as popular culture.

t.Garner Gallery

Only Scottish gallery specialising exclusively in contemporary ceramic art.
4 Parnie Street, Glasgow G1 5RJ, tel: 0141 353 0218
Contact: Todd Garner, Director

Space: 1 gallery with 47 sq m floor space
Exhibitions: 10 a year all originated
Details: Aims to give greater exposure to ceramic artists, both functional and sculptural.

T & R Annan & Sons

Commercial gallery selling contemporary art mostly executed in a traditional way, organising 1-2 exhibitions a year of work by artists regularly featured in continuous displays.
164 Woodlands Road, Glasgow G3 6LL, tel: 0141 332 0028
Contact: Douglas Annan
Open: Mon-Fri 10-5; Sat 10-12.30
Space: 1 gallery with 26 lin m hanging space
Exhibitions: 2 a year both originated
Details: Gallery and framemaker sells original paintings and collection of old photographs. Does not welcome applications from artists for exhibitions generally but happy to look at work with a view to displaying one or two examples if they are considered suitable for gallery and clients.

Tramway

Artist-run visual art and performance space often commissioning new work from established and younger artists.
25 Albert Drive, Glasgow G41 2PE, tel: 0141 422 2023, fax: 0141 422 2021
Contact: Charles Esche or Katrina Brown, Visual Arts
Open: Wed-Sun 12-6
Space: 2 galleries with 30 lin m hanging space and 1564 sq m floor space
Exhibitions: 6 a year of which 5 originated, 1 touring
Details: Unique multi-media venue dealing with innovative work across all media. Specialises in bringing new international work to Scotland and in presenting installation-based work specially commissioned for its large-scale spaces. Main exhibition space is a vast, industrial size area, not suitable for many conventional or small-scale exhibitions. Project room space can show smaller scale exhibitions. Sales not a priority.

Transmission Gallery

Artist-run space for the exhibition and promotion of the work of local artists and their national and international contemporaries.
28 King Street, Trongate, Glasgow G1 5QP, tel: 0141 552 4813
Contact: The Committee
Open: Tues-Sat 11-5
Space: 2 galleries
Exhibitions: 11 a year

Details: Programme curated and administered by a committee of artists, supported by a membership of over 200. Aims to provide a self-determined platform for the promotion of work by local, national and international artists, stimulating long-term debate on contemporary art and ideas. Particularly interested in artists with new and unusual ideas who might not otherwise have opportunity to exhibit. Two exhibition spaces: ground floor and basement (comprising cellar, cinema and storage area) but only former has disabled access. Sale of work not a main aim.

William Hardie Gallery

Programme of modern and contemporary Scottish painting, occasional shows of European art.
141 West Regent Street, Glasgow G2 2SG, tel: 0141 221 5780, fax: 0141 248 6237
Contact: Fiona Robertson
Space: 2 galleries with 95 sq m floor space
Exhibitions: 6 a year all originated
Details: Both mixed and solo shows. Audience mixed but predominantly Scottish.

Glenrothes
FIFE

Corridor Gallery

Corridor space in a busy sports centre that aims to break down barriers by bringing regular exhibition programme to people.
The Fife Institute of Physical & Recreational Education, Viewfield Road, Glenrothes KY6 2RA, tel: 01592 771700, fax: 01592 630717
Contact: Mr A Neil, Assistant Arts Officer, Arts in Fife, Tower Block, ASDARC, Woodend Road, Cardenden, KY5 0NE, tel: 01592 414714
Open: Mon-Sun 9-11
Space: 1 gallery with 28 lin m hanging space
Exhibitions: 12 a year of which 8 originated, 4 touring
Details: Run by Arts in Fife. Aims to show new work by Scottish artists, to bridge the gap between amateur and professional practitioners and to bring contemporary work to the general public. International exhibitions shown occasionally.

Rothes Halls

A modern multi-purpose venue with theatre and conference rooms and exhibitions in reception areas.
Kingdom Centre, Glenrothes KY7 5NX, tel: 01592 612121, fax: 01592 612220

Contact: Brian Horsburgh, Halls Manager
Open: Daily 10-7 (later if there is a performance)
Space: 3 galleries with 60 lin m hanging space plus 20 lin m on screens and 440 sq m floor space
Exhibitions: 8 a year of which 5 originated, 3 touring
Details: Venue, opened in 1993, with exhibitions held in main reception area, upper foyer, long corridor and small hall. Readily accessible to a wide variety of audiences.

Greenock
STRATHCLYDE

Greenock Arts Guild

Gallery in foyer space of arts centre serving both amateur and professional groups and promoting the arts generally.
Campbell Street, Greenock PA16 8AP, tel: 01475 723038
Open: Mon-Sat 10-10
Space: 1 gallery with 24 lin m hanging space and 28 sq m floor space
Exhibitions: 6 a year all originated
Details: Exhibition space in arts centre that has 2 theatres, rehearsal/meeting room, and cafe. Promotes work by up and coming professional artists as well as by established artists. Sales not a priority.

McLean Museum & Art Gallery

Permanent collection of C19th and C20th European art and temporary exhibition programme.
Greenock PA16 8JH, tel: 01475 23741
Contact: Val Boa, Curator
Details: Museum and Art Gallery being totally refurbished 1994/95 including temporary exhibition galleries.

Gullane
LOTHIAN

Norrie Toch Studios

Open-plan space used for exhibitions, performances, conferences and seminars.
St Peters, Main Street, Gullane EH31 2AA, tel: 01620 842039
Contact: Vasile Toch/Susan Norrie, Directors
Open: Wed-Sun 10-6
Space: 1 gallery with 89 lin m hanging space plus 58 lin m on screens and 182 sq m floor space
Exhibitions: 7 a year all originated
Details: Gallery with white walls, pine floors and high ceiling (12 m). Exhibits contemporary British and international art. Encourages international exchanges and

fusion of arts including architecture. Conferences and seminars held on arts, architecture and history. Arts and architecture, dance and puppetry workshops. Sales not a priority.

Haddington
LOTHIAN

Peter Potter Gallery Trust

Small commercial gallery showing visual arts and crafts.
10 The Sands, Haddington EH41 3EY, tel: 0162 082 2080
Contact: Alison Dunlop, Administrator
Open: Mon-Wed, Fri & Sat 10-4.30; Thurs 10-1.30
Space: 3 galleries
Exhibitions: 12 a year all originated
Details: The gallery is run by a Trust and incorporates café and craft display area as well as 3 exhibition spaces. Trust aims to encourage young artists and to stimulate artistic activity and appreciation through its exhibitions, workshops, awards, etc.

Hawick
BORDERS

Scott Art Gallery

A modern purpose-built art gallery, set within a Georgian listed building, with a mix of contemporary and historical exhibitions.
Hawick Museum, Wilton Lodge Park, Hawick TD9 7JL, tel: 01450 373457, fax: 01450 378526
Contact: Fiona Colton, District Museums Curator
Space: 3 galleries with 49 lin m hanging space plus 24 lin m on screens and 153 sq m floor space
Exhibitions: 13 a year of which 9 originated, 1 touring, 3 on a hire basis
Details: Programme relies heavily on locally-based professionals and amateurs as well as integrating the Museum's own collection of C19th and C20th Scottish paintings. Audiences tend to be local or Lowland Scottish, but theatre is expanding that client base.

Inverness
HIGHLAND

Culloden Library Mini Gallery

Pa Ph Pr Cr Sc LA ✓

Regularly changing exhibitions of work by local artists working in all media and styles.
Culloden Library, Keppoch Road, Culloden, Inverness IV1 2LL, tel: 01463 792531, fax: 01463 793162
Contact: Angela Donald, Branch Librarian
Space: 30 galleries
Exhibitions: 15 a year of which 5 originated, 10 touring
Details: Programme enhances environment of the library. Talks and workshops occasionally organised in conjunction with exhibitions.

Eden Court

Pa Ph Pr Sc ✓ ⊘

Theatre foyer space for changing exhibitions of national and local artists.
Eden Court Theatre, Bishops Road, Inverness IV3 5SA, tel: 01463 239 841, fax: 01463 713 810
Contact: Val Falcon, Front of House Manager
Open: Mon-Sat 10.30 – end of performance (5pm on non-performance days)
Space: 1 gallery with 46 lin m hanging space
Exhibitions: 12 a year all originated
Details: Principal arts venue of the Highlands and Islands. The exhibition year commences in April on a four week cycle. Many visitors over and above theatre audiences. Sales not a priority.

Highland Printmakers Workshop & Gallery

Pa Ph Pr Cr Sc ✓ H ⊘

Gallery promoting the visual arts in the Highlands.
20 Bank Street, Inverness IV1 1QE, tel: 01463 712240
Contact: Adam Sutherland, Director
Open: Tues-Sat 10-5
Space: 2 galleries with 30 lin m hanging space and 34 sq m floor space
Exhibitions: 24 a year of which 19 originated, 5 touring
Details: Main gallery has open-plan staircase used for exhibiting smaller works and first time exhibitors. Shows a balanced programme of local, national and international artists. Audience is made up of tourists, visitors, local people and members.

Inverness Museum & Art Gallery

Pa Ph Pr Cr Sc ✓ H &4

Municiple museum with collections of highland archaeology, history and natural history as well as fine and applied art, which runs a varied programme of temporary exhibitions and events.
Castle Wynd, Inverness IV2 3ED, tel: 01463 237114, fax: 01463 233813
Contact: Catharine Niven, Curator
Open: Mon-Sat 10-5
Space: 2 galleries with 70 lin m hanging space and 125 sq m floor space
Exhibitions: 16 a year of which 4 originated, 8 touring, 4 on a hire basis
Details: Galleries used for museum-type displays as well as for art – contemporary or otherwise. In a major tourist town, so in summer most visitors are from outside the local area. In winter, most visitors local. Run by Inverness District Council. Sales not a priority.

Irvine
STRATHCLYDE

Harbour Arts Centre

Pa Ph Pr Cr Sc LA ✓ &

Small gallery featuring exhibitions of work from both professional and amateur artists.
Irvine Harbour Side, 114-116 Harbour Street, Irvine KA13 6RQ, tel: 01294 274059 & 01294 271419
Contact: Laura Brown, Centre Manager
Open: Sun & Mon 12-4; Tues-Sat 10-4
Space: 1 gallery with 62 lin m hanging space and 100 sq m floor space
Exhibitions: 12 a year all originated
Details: Shows a variety of work from abstract paintings to silk scarves by local, national, amateur and professional artists. Facilities open to general public. Holds lectures, a summer school and art classes. Sales not a priority.

Isle of Skye
HIGHLAND

ArtiZania

Pa Pr Cr Sc ✓ &

Aims to demonstrate versatility of modern textile art and craft and provide venue and sales point.
Captains House, Stein, Waternish, Isle of Skye IV55 8GA, tel & fax: 01470 592361
Contact: Miss MA Bolger, Proprietor
Space: 1 gallery with 15 lin m hanging space plus 2 lin m on screens and 14 sq m floor space
Exhibitions: 2 a year both originated
Details: Small room displaying modern textiles art and craft. Student and recent graduates work emphasised.

Orbost Gallery

Pa Pr ✓

Exhibits works by living artists with preference given to images of the western highlands and islands.
Dunvegan, Isle of Skye IV55 8ZB, tel: 01470 251207
Contact: Dr David Roberts
Space: 50 lin m hanging space plus 6 lin m on screens and 500 sq m floor space
Details: Exhibitors are invited to send photographs of their works in the first instance to see whether they fit in with our 'image'. SAE for return. Arrangements to exhibit up to three works may then be made for one year.

Tuireann Arts Centre (An)

Pa Ph Pr Cr Sc LA ✓ & &4

Gallery acts principally as a showcase for new local artists, interspersed with contemporary Scottish art.
Struan Road, Portree, Isle of Skye IV51 9ES, tel: 01478 613306, fax: 01478 613176
Contact: Susan Nicolson, Adminstrator
Open: Mon-Sat 10-5; evenings for performances and openings
Space: 1 gallery with 28 lin m hanging space and 30 sq m floor space
Exhibitions: 10 a year of which 4 originated, 6 touring
Details: Old, cruciform fever hospital, fully converted into high, open planned gallery. Filled with natural light. Shares building with a number of other projects and events, creating a lively centre popular with the whole community. Work on show by artists from the island and mainland, often exploring Scottish themes or connections. Sales not a priority.

Kilmarnock
STRATHCLYDE

Dean Castle

Pa Ph Cr Sc ⊘

Municipal museum with some temporary exhibitions, mainly historical and craft.
Dean Road, Kilmarnock KA3, tel: 01563 26401/ 34580
Contact: James Hunter, Curator, Kilmarnock & Loudoun District Museums, Dick Institute, Kilmarnock, KA1 3BU
Open: Mon-Sun 12-5
Space: 2 galleries with plus 25 lin m on screens and 40 sq m floor space
Exhibitions: 3 a year all originated
Details: Municipal museum run by Kilmarnock and Loudoun District Museums. The permanent collection includes mediaeval tapestries, armour and early musical instruments. Temporary exhibitions are varied and sometimes include work by living artists. Sales not a priority.

Dick Institute (The)

[Pa][Ph][Pr][Cr][Sc][LA] ✔ [H] ♿ [wc]

Public art gallery and museum showing both contemporary and historical exhibitions, alongside an impressive permanent collection of fine and applied art, geology, natural & social history, and ethnography.

Elmbank Avenue, Kilmarnock KA1 3BU, tel: 01563 526401, fax: 01563 529661

Contact: Lorraine Grant, Visual Arts Assistant, Kilmarnock & Loudoun District Council

Open: Mon, Tues, Thurs, Fri 10-8; Wed ,Sat 10-5

Space: 2 galleries with 70 lin m hanging space plus 20 lin m on screens and 160 sq m floor space

Exhibitions: 12 a year of which 8 originated, 3 touring, 1 on a hire basis

Details: Exhibitions feature contemporary work in a variety of media by local and national artists. Non-gallery based projects and residencies also a feature. Educational activities accompany some exhibitions; workshops, events and lectures. Selling work is not gallery's primary role.

Kingussie

HIGHLAND

Iona Gallery

[Pa][Ph][Pr][Cr][Sc] ✔ [£] [H] ♿

Promotes mainly Highland and Scottish art in series of solo and group shows in variety of media.

Duke Street, Kingussie

Contact: Cathy Shankland, Exhibitions Officer, Libraries and Leisure Services, Kinmylies Building, Leachkin Road, Inverness, IV3 6NN, tel: 01463 703511, fax: 01463 711177

Open: Mon, Wed & Fri 10-12, 3-5; Tues & Thurs 10-12, 7-9; Sat 10-1

Space: 1 gallery with 50 lin m hanging space plus 20 lin m on screens and 140 sq m floor space

Exhibitions: 9 a year of which 2 originated, 5 touring, 2 on a hire basis

Details: Tours contemporary art at a professional level. Programme complemented by British and international shows and some local exhibitions. No natural light; plinths and display cases if required. Visitors include high level of tourists. All originated shows are available to tour outside Highland Region. Sales not a priority. See also Swanson Gallery, Thurso and St Fergus Gallery, Wick.

Kirkcaldy

FIFE

Kirkcaldy Museum & Art Gallery

[Pa][Ph][Pr][Cr][Sc][LA] ✔

Municipal gallery with exhibitions of art, craft, photography, installation work.

War Memorial Gardens, Kirkcaldy KY1 1YG, tel: 01592 260732

Contact: Vicki White & Ellen McCance, Exhibition Officers (Job Share)

Open: Mon-Sat 10.30-5; Sun 2-5

Space: 4 galleries with 114 lin m hanging space and 248 sq m floor space

Exhibitions: 21 a year of which 13 originated, 8 touring

Details: Group shows preferred. Historical Scottish art collection upstairs. Exhibition proposals by slide and CV encouraged.

Kirkcudbright

DUMFRIES & GALLOWAY

Tolbooth Art Centre

[Pa][Ph][Pr][Cr] ✔ [H] ♿ [wc]

Demonstrates continuity of artistic and craft tradition in locality with Kirkcudbright artists' colony flourishing from 1880s.

High Street, Kirkcudbright DG6 4JG, tel: 01557 331556

Contact: David Devereux, Museums Curator, Stewartry District Council Dept of Env. Health & Leisure Services, Cannonwalls,, High Street, Kirkcudbright, DG6 4JG, tel: 01557 331643, fax: 01557

Open: (Mar-Oct) Mon-Sat 11-4; (Nov-Feb) Sat 11-4

Space: 2 galleries with 19 lin m hanging space plus 14 lin m on screens and 76 sq m floor space

Exhibitions: 20 a year of which 2 touring, 18 on a hire basis

Details: Operated as a branch of the Stewartry Museum, Kirkcudbright. Galleries designed as working studios. Artists and craftspeople encouraged to work as well as exhibit there. This aids primary objective of centre; to present historic and contemporary importance of art and crafts in the locality. Also increases sales though these not main function of gallery. 10% commission taken & £10 per week service charge. Artists from UK/Europe may apply for space.

Kirkintilloch

STRATHCLYDE

Auld Kirk Museum

[Pa][Ph][Pr][Cr] ✔ [H] ♿ [4]

Exhibition space within museum for changing displays.

Cowgate, Kirkintilloch G66 1AB, tel: 0141 775 1185

Contact: Susan Selwyn, Curator

Open: Tues-Wed & Fri 10-12, 2-5; Thurs 10-5; Sat 10-1, 2-5

Space: 1 gallery with plus 30 lin m on screens and 75 sq m floor space

Exhibitions: 10 a year of which 2 originated, 6 touring, 2 on a hire basis

Details: Housed in a C17th church in main street. Exhibition programme covers wide range of subjects including contemporary and historic art, crafts, local history, photography, archaeology and natural sciences. A commission of 20% charged on sales but sales not primary role of gallery. Ramp being installed 1994/95.

Kirkwall

ORKNEY

Tankerness House Museum

[Pa][Ph][Pr][Cr][Sc] ✔ [H]

Archaeology and local history collections enhanced by special exhibitions.

Broad Street, Kirkwall KW15 1DH, tel: 01856 3191

Contact: Curator

Space: 1 gallery with 15 lin m hanging space plus 16 lin m on screens and 500 sq m floor space

Exhibitions: 1 a year on a hire basis

Details: Displays on island's history.

Lerwick

SHETLAND

Shetland Museum

[Pa][Ph][Cr][Sc] ✔ [H] ♿ [wc]

Gallery provides high-quality exhibition space, displaying year-long series of temporary exhibitions by local artists.

Lower Hillhead, Lerwick ZE1 0EL, tel: 01595 695057, fax: 01595 696729

Contact: Tommy Watt, Curator

Open: Mon, Wed, Fri, 10-7; Tues, Thurs, Sat 10-5

Space: 1 gallery with 20 lin m hanging space plus 7 lin m on screens and 20 sq m floor space

Exhibitions: 20 a year of which 2 originated, 18 on a hire basis

Details: Small gallery mainly dealing with contemporary work of a local nature. Selling work not primary role of gallery. 10% commission taken on sales made.

Leven
FIFE

Loomshop Gallery
Pa ✓

126 Main Street, Lower Largo, Leven KY8 6BP, tel: 01333 320330
Contact: Exhibition Organiser, 82 Main Street, Lower Largo, Leven, KY8 6BS, tel: 01333 329550
Space: 24 lin m hanging space
Exhibitions: 11 a year all originated

Livingston
LOTHIAN

Inveralmond Community Education Centre *
Pa Pr Sc

A varied programme of exhibitions of fine art.
Community High School, Willowbank, Ladywell, Livingston EH54 6HN, tel: 01506 38093
Contact: Hugh Tuckermann, Exhibitions Organiser

Lochgelly
FIFE

Lochgelly Centre Gallery *
Pa Ph Pr Sc ✓

Centre with a sports hall, theatre, art and craft areas and an exhibition area.
Bank Street, Lochgelly KY5 9QU, tel: 01592 780971, fax: 01592 780732
Contact: Anne Campbell, Exhibition Organiser
Space: 1 gallery with 43 lin m hanging space and 153 sq m floor space
Exhibitions: 12 a year all originated
Details: Exhibitions are held monthly. Work by young contemporary local (Fife) artists particularly welcomed.

Macduff
GRAMPIAN

Macduff Arts Centre
Pa Ph Pr Cr Sc IA ✓ & H & Wc

Occasional exhibitions integrated within arts centre programme which ranges across the arts.
Clergy Street, Macduff AB44 1UR, tel: 01261 813384/833819, fax: 01261 833646
Contact: Iain MacAulay, Arts Development Officer, Banff & Buchan District Council, 1 Church Street, Macduff, AB44 1UR, tel: 01261 813384, fax: 01261 833646
Open: varies
Space: 2 galleries with 25 lin m hanging

space plus 25 lin m on screens and 250 sq m floor space
Details: Opened May 1994. Supports local arts scene; creating opportunities for arts groups in the community to exhibit their work. Also to spark an interest in wider arts movements with inspirational touring exhibitions.

Montrose
TAYSIDE

Montrose Library Art Gallery
Pa Ph Pr Cr Sc ✓

Temporary exhibition programme with one-person and mixed exhibitions from local and non-local artists and makers.
Public Library, High Street, Montrose, tel: 01674 673256
Contact: Jake Stewart, Exhibitions Officer, The Meffan Museum & Art Gallery, 20 West High Street, Forfar, DD8 1BB, tel: 01307 468813
Open: Library hours
Space: 1 gallery with 15 lin m hanging space
Exhibitions: 10 a year all originated

Musselburgh
LOTHIAN

Brunton Theatre
Pa Ph Pr Cr Sc ✓ & Wc

Exhibition space within theatre showing range of visual arts and crafts.
Ladywell Way, Musselburgh EH21 6AA, tel: 0131 665 9900, fax: 0131 665 7495
Contact: Michael Durnan, Exhibitions Co-ordinator
Open: Mon-Sat 10-6; 7-10 for theatre audiences
Space: 1 gallery with 36 lin m hanging space
Exhibitions: 7 a year all originated
Details: Gallery aims to show exhibitions of wide range of work selected for quality and innovation.

North Uist
WESTERN ISLES SAC

Taigh Chearsabhagh
Lochmaddy, North Uist HS6 5AA, tel: 01876 500293
Contact: Norman MacLeod, Manager
Details: Changing exhibitions of work by local and mainland artists.

Paisley
STRATHCLYDE

Paisley Arts Centre *
Pa Ph Pr Cr IA ✓ H

Arts centre showing work by local artists in foyer space.
New Street, Paisley PA1 1EZ, tel: 0141 887 1010, fax: 0141 887 6300
Contact: Paul Hogan, Exhibition Organiser
Space: 1 gallery with 25 lin m hanging space
Exhibitions: 26 a year all on a hire basis

Paisley Museum & Art Galleries
Pa Pr Sc & Wc

Municipal museum with temporary exhibition programme ranging from local art societies to adventurous contemporary work.
High Street, Paisley PA1 2BA, tel: 0141 889 3151, fax: 0141 889 9240
Contact: Andrea Kerr, Principal Museums Officer
Open: Mon-Sat 10-5
Space: 1 gallery with 31 lin m hanging space
Exhibitions: 6 a year of which 5 originated, 1 touring
Details: Established last century. Famous collection of Paisley shawls and textiles, displays on the weaving industry, natural history, ceramics and Scottish painting. One main gallery for temporary exhibitions with 4 further galleries which can be made available for exhibitions. Events programme. Sales not a priority.

Peebles
BORDERS

Tweeddale Museum & Art Gallery
Pa Ph Pr Cr Sc ✓ & H

Municipal gallery showing a lively programme of contemporary art and craft.
Chambers Institute, High Street, Peebles EH45 8AP, tel: 01721 720123
Contact: Rachel Hunter, Exhibitions Officer
Open: (Nov-Easter) Mon-Fri 10-1 & 2-5; (Easter-Oct) Mon-Fri 10-1 & 2-5, Sat & Sun 2-5
Space: 1 gallery with 45 lin m hanging space and 112 sq m floor space
Exhibitions: 8 a year of which 2 originated, 1 touring, 5 on a hire basis
Details: Gallery aims to present lively and diverse exhibition programme in order to attract new audiences and shows range of artforms. Education and interpretation activities used as a way of involving audiences and encouraging personal

development of creativity in order to enhance understanding and appreciation of exhibition programme and beyond. Where gallery is 'hired out' there is no fee charged. Sale of work not considered gallery's primary role. Gallery three flights of stairs (lift available only part of the way).

Perth
TAYSIDE

Perth Theatre Gallery

Busy and lively space surrounding the coffee bar in the main entrance.
Perth Theatre, 185 High Street, Perth PH1 5UW, tel: 01738 638123, fax: 01738 624576
Contact: Elizabeth Nicoll, Assistant House Manager
Open: Mon-Sat 10-10
Space: 1 gallery with 25 lin m hanging space
Exhibitions: 15 a year of which 14 originated, 1 on a hire basis
Details: Monthly exhibitions attract attention from daytime custom and a 500-strong audience each night. Clientele tends to be older and is therefore fairly conservative in its taste.

Peterhead
GRAMPIAN

Arbuthnot Museum

Gallery leading off from Maritime Museum showing historical and contemporary exhibitions.
St Peter Street, Peterhead AB42 6QD, tel: 01779 47778
Contact: Mrs Ann Bowes, Design & Exhibitions Officer
Open: Mon & Tues, Fri & Sat 10.30-1.30, 2.30-5; Wed 10.30-1; and by request
Space: 1 gallery with 28 lin m hanging space plus 12 lin m on screens and 65 sq m floor space
Exhibitions: 7 a year of which 5 originated, 2 touring
Details: Museum encourages all sections of community to visit and participate. Wide variety of showcase exhibitions toured around schools etc. Also videos, talks and 'hands on'. Schools are encouraged to visit and draw in gallery/museum and take part in exhibitions; competitions; etc. Sales not a priority.

St Andrews
FIFE

Byre Theatre

Coffee bar area in theatre.
Abbey Street, St Andrews KY16 9LA, tel: 01334 476288, fax: 01334 475370
Contact: Tom Gardner, General Manager
Open: Mon-Sat 10am-10pm (5 if no performance)
Space: 1 gallery
Exhibitions: 9 a year all originated
Details: Exhibitions of work for sale, primarily but not exclusively by local artists. Policy of accepting a wide variety of work.

Crawford Arts Centre

Independent organisation comprising one purpose-built large gallery, three smaller galleries in converted house, studio theatre, artist's studio and sculpture court.
93 North Street, St Andrews KY16 9AL, tel: 01334 474610
Contact: Diana A. Sykes, Director
Open: Mon-Sat 10-5; Sun 2-5
Space: 4 galleries with 78 lin m hanging space and 215 sq m floor space
Exhibitions: 28 a year of which 23 originated, 5 touring
Details: Hanging by direct fixing, showcases and plinths available. Varied programme in media and styles. Wide audience. Expanding craft shop with 20% commission. Exhibition commission 30%. Artist's residency organised for studio. Programme of workshops/classes for children and adults. Sale of work not gallery's primary concern.

Selkirk
BORDERS

Robson Gallery

Small but well-lit and appointed gallery space showing a varied programme of contemporary art and craftwork.
Halliwells House Museum, Market Place, Selkirk TD7 4BC, tel: 01750 720096, fax: 01750 723282
Contact: Jackie Smith, Exhibitions officer, Ettrich & Lauderdale Museums, Municipal Buildings, High Street, Selkirk, TD7 4JX01750 720096
Open: Mon-Sat 10-5; Sun 2-4
Space: 1 gallery with 12 lin m hanging space and 50 sq m floor space
Exhibitions: 8 a year of which 7 originated, 1 touring
Details: Shows work of professional artists and makers. About 80% solo shows by living artists and at least one unrelated to

art. Lectures occasionally held. Workshop programme relates to exhibitions. Sales not gallery's primary role.

Stirling
CENTRAL

Cowane Gallery

Gallery in busy community centre with varied programme of national and international fine art, photography and Scottish art.
Cowane Centre, Cowane Street, Stirling, tel: 01786 462367
Contact: Caroline Leverton, Arts Officer, Stirling District Council, Beechwood House, St Ninians Road, Stirling, FK8 2AD, tel: 01786 432356**
Open: Mon-Sat 10-7
Space: 1 gallery with 25 lin m hanging space
Exhibitions: 10 a year of which 4 originated, 6 touring
Details: Exhibiting artists make some contribution to exhibition costs. Sales not a priority.

MacRobert Arts Centre Gallery *

Part of University of Stirling arts centre.
University of Stirling, Stirling FK9 4LA, tel: 01786 67155, fax: 01786 51369
Contact: Elizabeth Moran, Director
Space: 2 galleries with 59 lin m hanging space plus 6 lin m on screens and 50 sq m floor space
Exhibitions: 8 a year of which 2 originated, 4 touring, 2 on a hire basis
Details: Offers a year-round programme of varied events to suit all tastes. Large student audience plus many members of the public. Programme planned well in advance and particularly welcomes contemporary arts. Policy review – hopes to extend opening hours and public use.

Smith Art Gallery & Museum

Independent museum and art gallery housing collections of fine and applied arts, social and natural history, and showing temporary exhibitions with an emphasis on contemporary art and craft.
Dumbarton Road, Stirling FK8 2RQ, tel: 01786 471917, fax: 01786 449523
Contact: Elspeth King, Director
Open: (Summer) Tues-Sat 10.30-5, Sun 2-5; (Winter) Tues-Fri 12-5, Sat 10.30-5, Sun 2-5
Space: 3 galleries with 140 lin m hanging space and 520 sq m floor space
Exhibitions: 11 a year of which 6 originated, 5 touring

Details: Aims to show a wide range of subjects and media through the temporary exhibitions programme, with an emphasis on contemporary art or aspects of art relating to the Stirling area. The Permanent collections are strong in Scottish Victorian art. The Smith is funded jointly by Stirling District Council and Central Regional Council. Where possible educational events are organised. Sales not a priority.

Stonehaven
GRAMPIAN

Riverside Gallery
Pa Ph Pr Cr Sc ✓

Commercial gallery promoting young as well as more established artists.
30a David Street, Stonehaven AB3 2AL, tel: 01569 63931
Contact: Denis Leiper, Owner
Space: 2 galleries with 37 lin m hanging space and 75 sq m floor space
Exhibitions: 8 a year all originated
Details: Gallery founded in 1982. All work shown is by living artists. Aims to build up regular buyers.

Stornoway
WESTERN ISLES

Lanntair (An)
Pa Ph Pr Cr Sc LA ✓ ♿

Situated on the first floor of Stornoway Town Hall the gallery provides access to the arts for people of the Western Isles.
Town Hall, South Beach, Stornoway PA87 2BX, tel: 01851 703307
Contact: Roddy Murray, Director
Open: Mon-Sat 10-5.30
Space: 2 galleries with 34 lin m hanging space plus 42 lin m on screens and 64 sq m floor space
Exhibitions: 12 a year of which 5 originated, 7 touring
Details: Operates a balanced monthly programme across all artistic disciplines. Its policy, where possible, is to show local or locally relevant work in the summer and import work from the national and international circuit the rest of the year. An Lanntair is the only public art gallery in the Western Isles and caters to a mixed audience. It therefore exhibits both challenging and populist shows. Sales not a high priority.

Stranraer
DUMFRIES & GALLOWAY

Stranraer Museum
Pa Ph Pr Cr Sc ✓ ⊕ Ⓗ ❸ ⓦ

Museum showing art, photography, natural history, social, local history and community groups' exhibitions.
55 George Street, Stranraer DG9 7JP, tel: 01776 705088
Contact: John Pickin, Curator
Open: Mon-Sat 10-5
Space: 1 gallery with plus 100 lin m on screens and 80 sq m floor space
Exhibitions: 7 a year of which 3 originated, 2 touring, 2 on a hire basis
Details: Exhibitions scheduled up to 18 months ahead. Audience local all year, tourists in season, children encouraged by quiz sheets and activities. Building alarmed and security TVs in place. Windows have U/V filter but not possible to achieve low lux levels. Selling work not gallery's main function.

Stromness
ORKNEY

Pier Arts Centre
Pa Ph Pr Cr Sc ✓ ❸④

Dedicated contemporary visual arts space showing wide range of exhibitions; local, national and international.
Victoria Street, Stromness KW16 3AA, tel: 01856 850209
Contact: Neil Firth, Director
Open: Tues-Sat 10.30-12.30,1.30-5.00
Space: 3 galleries with 61 lin m hanging space and 55 sq m floor space
Exhibitions: 11 a year
Details: Focus of gallery is permanent collection of works by Nicholson, Hepworth, Gabo, Frost, Heron (among others). Presents year round programme of exhibitions covering all aspects of contemporary visual arts. Most shows originated; occasional touring shows. Sales not a priority.

Thurso
HIGHLAND

Swanson Gallery
Pa Ph Pr Cr Sc ✓⊕Ⓗ ♿

Gallery promotes mainly Highland and Scottish art in series of solo and group shows in variety of media.
Davidson's Lane, Thurso KW14 7BJ, tel: 01847 66357
Contact: Cathy Shankland, Exhibitions Officer, Libraries and Leisure Services, Kinmylies Building, Leachkin Road, Inverness, IV3 6NN, tel: 01463 703511, fax: 01463 711177

Open: Mon, Tues, Wed 1-5; Fri 1-8; Sat 10-1
Space: 1 gallery with 50 lin m hanging space plus 12 lin m on screens and 120 sq m floor space
Exhibitions: 15 a year of which 8 originated, 5 touring, 2 on a hire basis
Details: Tours contemporary art at a professional level. Programme complemented by British and International shows, and some local exhibitions. Sales important but not primary role of gallery. No natural light, some plinths and display cases. All originated shows are available to tour outside Highland region. See also Iona Gallery,Kingussie and St Fergus Gallery, Wick.

Weisdale
SHETLAND

Bonhoga Gallery
Pa Ph Pr Cr Sc LA ✓ ❸ⓦ④

Gallery showing art and craft by artists living locally and throughout UK.
Weisdale Mill, Weisdale ZE2 9LW, tel: 01595 72400, **fax:** 01595 72444
Contact: Mary Smith, Visual Arts Co-Ordinator
Open: (Sept-Apr) Wed-Sat 10.30-4.30, Sun 12-4.30; (May-Aug) Tues-Sun 10.30-4.30, Fri 10.30-9
Space: 2 galleries with 30 lin m hanging space and 28 sq m floor space
Exhibitions: 4 a year of which 1 originated, 3 touring
Details: Gallery opened April 1994. 12 exhibitions a year to be held in each gallery. Upper-floor gallery concentrates on 2D wall hung work and cased applied art displays in ground-floor gallery. Education programme and student work displayed. Gallery also programmes exhibition space at Sumburgh Airport with work by local artists or with local connection. Sales not a priority.

Wick
HIGHLAND

Lyth Arts Centre
Pa Ph Pr Cr Sc LA ✓ ❸

Arts centre with annual summer season with up to 10 assorted exhibitions of contemporary fine art.
Wick KW1 4UD, tel: 01955 84270/031 226 6424
Contact: William Wilson, Director
Open: (Jul-Aug) Mon-Sun 10-6
Space: 72 lin m hanging space plus 20 lin m on screens and 160 sq m floor space
Exhibitions: 9 a year of which 7 originated, 2 touring

St Fergus Gallery

Pa Ph Pr Gr Sc ● £ ● ⊗

Exhibitions promote mainly current Highland and Scottish art in series of solo and group shows in variety of media.

Carnegie Public Library, Sinclair Terrace, Wick, tel: 01955 3498
Contact: Cathy Shankland, Exhibitions Officer, Libraries and Leisure Services, Kinmylies Building, Leachkin Road, Inverness, IV3 6NN, tel: 01463 703511, fax: 01463 711177
Open: Mon-Tues & Thurs 1-6; Wed 10-12.30; Fri 1-8; Sat 10.30-1
Space: 1 gallery with 50 lin m hanging space plus 13 lin m on screens and 100 sq m floor space
Exhibitions: 15 a year of which 8 originated, 5 touring, 2 on a hire basis
Details: Majority of exhibitions are organised by Highland Regional Council's arts team. Programme of Highland and Scottish art complemented by other British and international shows. Natural light; some plinths and display cases. Blackout facilities. All originated shows available to tour outside Highland region. Sales important but not main aim. (See also Iona Gallery, Kingussie and Swanson Gallery, Thurso.)

Wales

Oriel Mostyn, Llandudno, Wales
Exhibition of work by **Elizabeth Frink**.
Photo: Noel Brown.

Aberdare
MID GLAMORGAN

Aberdare Central Library
Pa Ph Cr Sc ✓

Small exhibition areas within library and in adjacent Victoria Hall.
**Green Street, Aberdare CF44 7AG, tel:
01685 885318, fax: 01685 881181**
Contact: Lynne Bryn Jones, Assistant
Borough Librarian, Cynon Valley Libraries,
Green Street, Aberdare, CF44 7AG, tel:
01685 885296
Open: Mon & Fri 9-7; Tues & Wed 9-6;
Thurs 9-5; Sat 9-1
Space: 3 galleries with 30 lin m hanging
space plus 4 lin m on screens and 60 sq m
floor space
Exhibitions: 12 a year
Details: Exhibition space for work by local
artists in Victoria Hall – 1960s building
adjacent to the library and in library itself.
Access to Victoria Hall impossible for
wheelchair users. Two exhibition areas in
library; wall space in reference section
(access for wheelchair users with assistance)
and floor space and screens in foyer
(independent access).

Dare Valley Country Park (Visitor Centre)
Pa Ph Pr Cr ✓ H

*Exhibitions of work compatible with
countryside environment held within
Visitor Centre.*
**Dare Valley Country Park, Aberdare
CF44 7RG, tel: 01685 874672, fax:
01685 882919**
Contact: Dave Protheroe, Countryside
Officer
Space: 1 gallery with 16 lin m hanging
space plus 12 lin m on screens and 50 sq m
floor space
Exhibitions: 8 a year of which 7
originated, 1 on a hire basis
Details: Visitor Centre (open during
summer months only) run by Cynon Valley
Borough Council. Attracts 64,000 visitors
annually. Work shown predominantly art
and crafts, including solo exhibitions.
Related slide shows, talks, and school visits
also organised.

Abergavenny
GWENT

Abergavenny Museum
Pa Ph Cr ✓ & wc

*Varied exhibitions appropriate for local
history museum sought.*
**The Castle, Castle Street, Abergavenny
NP7 5EE, tel: 01783 854282**
Contact: Frank Olding, Curator
Space: 1 gallery with 3 lin m hanging space
Details: Collection of local history,
archaeology and rural life, and temporary
exhibitions of contemporary painting and
rural craft of educational value to schools,
for which talks and workshops are
organised.

Abergele
CLWYD

Abergele Library *
Pa Ph Pr Cr ✓ H

*Library exhibition space aims to show good
quality art by local amateur and
professional artists.*
**Market Street, Abergele, tel: 01745
832638**
Contact: Elizabeth Davis
Space: 1 gallery with 4 lin m hanging space
and 19 sq m floor space
Exhibitions: 12 a year of which 6
originated, 6 on a hire basis
Details: Programme presents a variety of
media, usually in single person shows, more
occasionally group shows. Insurance
provided free by the County. Commission
charged on sales.

Aberystwyth
DYFED

Aberystwyth Arts Centre
Pa Ph Pr Cr SC LA ✓ £ & wc 4

*Multi-purpose arts centre showing
contemporary art and craft.*
**University of Wales, Penglais,
Aberystwyth SY23 3DE, tel: 01970
622887, fax: 01970 622883**
Contact: Eve Ropek/Stephen West,
Exhibition Organisers
Open: Mon-Sat 10-5; also evening
performances in Theatre & Concert Hall
Space: 4 galleries with 125 lin m hanging
space plus 25 lin m on screens and 350 sq
m floor space
Exhibitions: 40 a year of which 28
originated, 12 touring
Details: As well as four main exhibition
areas, the arts centre also comprises a
concert hall, theatre space, café, bookshop
and craftshop. Extensive education
programme including residential courses,
talks, seminars, workshops and
demonstrations, artists residencies and
outreach work. Gallery covers all exhibition
costs.

Ceredigion Museum
Pa Ph Pr Cr SC ✓ £ & wc

*Temporary exhibition galleries aiming to
encourage younger emerging artists,
particularly those whose work relates to
Ceredigion.*
**Coliseum, Terrace Road, Aberystwyth
SY23 2AQ, tel: 01970 634212/3**
Contact: Gwenllian Ashley, Assistant
Curator
Open: Mon-Sat 10-5; Suns during school
holidays
Space: 3 galleries with 40 lin m hanging
space plus 22 lin m on screens and 100 sq
m floor space
Exhibitions: 7 a year of which 6
originated, 1 touring
Details: 3 gallery spaces; large gallery
overlooking the sea and space in
auditorium of Museum (which was
originally Edwardian music hall). Aims to
provide an opportunity to those who would
find it difficult to exhibit in a commercial
gallery. Established artists also welcome.
Exhibitions mainly of those living and
working in Wales. Exhibition payment for
some shows. Exhibitions last approx 2
months. Booked 2 years in advance. Sales
not a priority.

National Library of Wales *
Pa Pr ✓

*Exhibition areas showing modern and
historical exhibitions devoted to Welsh life
and landscape.*
**Penglais, Aberystwyth SY23 3BU, tel:
01970 623816, fax: 01970 615709**
Contact: D. Michael Francis, Assistant
Keeper, Pictures & Maps
Space: 2 galleries with 50 lin m hanging
space plus 125 lin m on screens and 300 sq
m floor space
Exhibitions: 5 a year of which 3
originated, 2 touring
Details: Two main exhibitions areas: the
Gregynog Gallery and the Central Hall plus
permanent exhibition 'A Nation's
Heritage'. Retrospective and selling
exhibitions are shown. Close links with
University College which has a visual arts
department.

Bala
GWYNEDD

Bala Heritage Centre *
Pa Ph Pr Cr SC LA ✓

*Old restored chapel with plenty of natural
light and space for wide variety of
exhibitions and events.*
**Ffridd Isa, Llidiardau, Bala LL23 7SG,
tel: 01678 521233**
Contact: Andrew Roberts
Space: 1 gallery
Exhibitions: 18 a year of which 16
originated, 2 touring

Bangor
GWYNEDD

Bangor Museum & Art Gallery

Two temporary exhibition galleries to display wide range of exhibitions throughout the year.
Ffordd Gwynedd, Bangor LL57 1DT, tel: 01248 353368, fax: 01248 370149
Contact: David Huntington, Exhibitions Officer
Open: Tues-Fri 12.30-4.30; Sat 10.30-4.30; Group visits 10-12.30 by arrangement
Space: 2 galleries with 37 lin m hanging space and 83 sq m floor space
Exhibitions: 7 a year of which 4 originated, 3 touring
Details: Within museum displaying collection of items relating to North Wales' history, gallery provides mixed programme of temporary art and museum exhibitions including touring shows. Educational workshops held to tie in with particular exhibitions. Exhibition fee sometimes paid. Selling work is one of gallery's primary roles.

Theatr Gwynedd

A theatre run by the County Council that offers wall space in its bar/foyer area to mainly local artists.
Ffordd Deiniol, Bangor, tel: 01248 351707
Contact: John Webster or the Theatre Manager
Space: 1 gallery
Exhibitions: 10 a year

Barry
SOUTH GLAMORGAN

Living Archive Centre

Exhibitions on the themes of history, heritage etc in all media (including video).
Memorial Hall, Gladstone Road, Barry, tel: 01446 722166/742289, fax: 01446 738461
Contact: Phil Cope, Exhibition Coordinator, Valley and Vale, Holm View Centre, Skomer Road, Gibbonsdown, Barry, CF6 3DA, tel: 01446 742289, fax: 01446 738461
Open: (Oct-Mar) Tues-Fri 10-4, Sat 10-6, Wed am schools only; (Apr-Sept) Tues-Fri 10-4, Sat 10-6, Sun 12-6, Wed am schools only
Space: 2 galleries with 30 lin m hanging space plus 30 lin m on screens and 200 sq m floor space
Details: Opening 1995. Facility for local

people to understand and contribute to their history and view works from other community groups/artists. Exhibiting space, video screening area, performance area, workshops programme. Sales of work a main aim.

Beaumaris
GWYNEDD

David Hughes Community Centre

Provides exhibition space for visiting artists and organisations.
Community Centre, Beaumaris
Contact: K B Williams, Hon Secretary, Ffordd Deg Wen, Llaniestyn, Anglesey, LL58 8TN
Open: Daily 10-5
Space: 1 gallery with 48 lin m and100 sq m floor space
Exhibitions: 5 a year all on a hire basis
Details: Centre in C17th building adjacent to Beaumaris Castle, showing art exhibitions by local groups and individual artists during summer. Sales not a priority.

Blackwood
GWENT

Holmlands Studio Gallery

Provides facility for displaying art in area lacking in exhibition space and encourages development of art practice locally.
Bodwellty, Blackwood NP2 0BD, tel: 01443 835828
Contact: John Goods
Open: Tues-Sat 2-6; Sun 2:30-5:30
Space: 1 gallery with 99 sq m floor space
Exhibitions: 7 a year all originated
Details: Gallery open 9 months of year. Sales not of primary importance. Exhibitions often have local connections but approaches welcomed from artists outside area. Natural daylight.

Blaenau Ffestiniog
GWYNEDD

Blaenau Ffestiniog Library

Exhibition space within library with hanging space and showcase for exhibitions by Gwynedd Culture and Leisure.
Meirion Terrace, Blaenau Ffestiniog LL41 3UA, tel: 01766 830415, fax: 01766 830545
Contact: S W Jones, Community Librarian
Open: Mon & Fri 10-1, 2-7; Tues & Wed 10-1, 2-5.30; Sat 10-1
Space: 1 gallery with 24 lin m hanging space and 63 sq m floor space

Exhibitions: 12 a year
Details: Varied programme showing work by individual artists or groups, originated and touring shows. Showcase used to exhibit local craftwork.

Oriel y Ddraig

Aims to stimulate awareness of the visual arts, and give artists an opportunity to show their work with the freedom to experiment.
Church Street, Blaenau Ffestiniog LL41, tel: 01766 831777
Contact: Pat Clarke
Open: Tues-Sat 9.30-5
Space: 1 gallery with 18 lin m hanging space plus 7 lin m on screens and 29 sq m floor space
Exhibitions: 5 a year all originated
Details: Shows contemporary work in wide range of media and styles, deliberately uninfluenced by commercial pressure, encouraging both younger artists and those more established. Choice of exhibitions reflects interests of the gallery with five solo or group exhibitions annually (one by gallery owner Pat Clarke). Receives no grant aid so exhibition programme subsidised by a shop selling good range of art materials, and framing service.

Blaenavon
GWENT

Big Pit Museum Trust

Temporary exhibition space for exhibitions related to mining or locality, bringing art to visitors who are largely non-visitors to conventional galleries.
Blaenavon NP4 9XP, tel: 01495 790311, fax: 01495 792618
Contact: Claire Hamer, Marketing/Development Officer
Open: (Mar-Nov) Mon-Sun 9.30-5; (Dec-Mar) phone for details
Space: 1 gallery with 60 lin m hanging space and 200 sq m floor space
Exhibitions: 2 a year of which 1 originated, 1 touring
Details: Exhibition programme has recently been re-launche d, although the time spent on organising exhibitions is very limited. Preference towards exhibitions relating to coal mining industry and/or South Wales industrial history. Commission on sales and ability to pay exhibition fees and other costs are variable and dependent on grant funding. Sales not a priority.

Blaengarw
MID GLAMORGAN

Blaengarw Workmens Hall

Pa Ph Pr SC ⬤ 🅰️ Wc ④

Multi-media community arts centre with wide range of self-generated and touring exhibitions prioritising those exploring community, international and arts issues.
Valley & Vale, Blaengarw Workmen's Hall, Blaengarw CF32 8AW, tel: 01656 871911, fax: 01656 870507
Contact: Phil Cope, Coordinator
Open: Mon-Sat 9-5.30; some evenings & weekends
Space: 2 galleries with 30 lin m hanging space plus 30 lin m on screens and 200 sq m floor space
Exhibitions: 6 a year of which 5 originated, 1 touring
Details: Blaengarw Workmen's Hall has 300 seat auditorium/cinema, fully-equipped darkroom, hi-band edit suite, dance studio, community design area and series of community/education workshops for people of all ages and abilities. Selling work from exhibitions not a priority.

Brecon
POWYS

Beacons Fine Art Gallery

Pa Ph Pr Cr SC ⬤ 🅰️

Selling gallery specialising in contemporary ceramics by resident potters and landscape paintings and prints by artists working in Wales.
The Old School House, Defynnog, Brecon LD3 8SL, tel: 01874 638919
Contact: Colin Horsman, Director, Crincae, Llanddeusant, SA19 9YB, tel: 01550 4619
Open: (March-Christmas) Tues-Sun & BH 10-5
Space: 2 galleries with 30 lin m hanging space and 85 sq m floor space
Exhibitions: 7 a year all originated
Details: Converted school building c1590, in Brecon Beacons National Park. Two floors: pottery downstairs, showing work by resident artists; painting and prints upstairs, by artists from all over S Wales. Some artists regularly on show but new artists make an entry from time to time. All exhibitions are well publicised in local press. Ceramics workshop facilities where work can be seen in progress.

Brecknock Museum

Pa Ph Pr SC LA ⬤ 🅰️

Regional exhibition spaces for south Powys; historical and art exhibitions.
Captain's Walk, Brecon LD3 7DW, tel: 01874 624121
Contact: David Moore, Curator

Open: Mon-Fri 10-5; Sat 10-1, 2-5; (Apr-Sept) Sun 10-1, 2-5
Space: 2 galleries with 58 lin m hanging space plus 16 lin m on screens and 104 sq m floor space
Exhibitions: 8 a year
Details: Regional museum run by local authority, with temporary exhibition spaces. C19th courtroom. Temporary exhibitions of art and crafts, as well as historical exhibitions. Disabled access at the rear of the Museum. Sales.

Brecon Library

Pa Ph Pr Cr SC ⬤ 🅷 🅰️

Exhibition room in library with broad ranging programme of exhibitions.
Ship Street, Brecon LD3 9AE, tel: 01874 623346
Contact: Mrs K Thomas
Open: Flexible as exhibition room has independent access.
Space: 1 gallery with 67 sq m floor space
Exhibitions: 23 a year all on a hire basis
Details: Exhibition room accessible from library via stairs and separate level entrance from street. Room is hired out for wide variety of exhibitions; to community groups, art societies, individual artists, charitable organisations, etc. No commission taken. Hirers make own arrangements, responsible for supervising space etc.

Sable & Hogg Gallery

Pa Ph Pr Cr SC 🅰️

Small commercial gallery in listed building.
2 Castle Street, Brecon LD3 9DD, tel: 01874 625901
Contact: Mike Egbers
Open: Mon, Tues, Thurs, Fri 10-5; Sat 10-5
Space: 1 gallery with 15 lin m hanging space plus 7 lin m on screens
Exhibitions: 3 a year all originated
Details: Small ground-floor gallery with basement which doubles as photo studio. Three established local artists and seven new artists in permanent exhibition – landscapes of the local area, oils, watercolours, etchings and limited edition prints. Tries to be flexible and cater for the artists and requests from the public. Street level window available. Sales important.

Bridgend
MID GLAMORGAN

Berwyn Centre *

Pa Ph Pr Cr LA ⬤

Community theatre and cultural centre for former mining area of Ogwr, with exhibitions of work by mainly local artists.
Nant-y-moel, Bridgend, tel: 01656 870 886, fax: 01656 870 056
Contact: David Brown, Administrator

Space: 1 gallery with 20 lin m hanging space plus 20 lin m on screens and 40 sq m floor space
Exhibitions: 4 a year of which 2 originated, 2 touring
Details: Also takes touring photographic exhibitions. Commission is charged and visual documentation is required with written applications.

Mid Glamorgan County Libraries

Pa Ph Pr Cr SC ⬤

Library service coordinating exhibitions in about 20 libraries throughout area.
Coed Parc, Park Street, Bridgend CF31 4BA, tel: 01656 767451
Contact: Mr John Woods, County Librarian
Open: varies according to venue.
Details: Organises small craft showcase exhibitions, some in conjunction with Arts Council of Wales, to tour to Pontypridd, Maesteg and Bargoed libraries and exhibitions of two dimensional work to other libraries in the county. Public lectures, arts presentations also organised. Access, facilities and space varies according to venue.

Nolton Gallery

Pa ⬤ 🅰️

Private commercial gallery showing work by local artists both professional and amateur.
66 Nolton Street, Bridgend, tel: 01656 63278
Contact: Mrs A Courtney
Open: Mon-Fri 9.30-5.15; Sat 9.30-5
Space: 1 gallery with 15 lin m hanging space and 19 sq m floor space
Exhibitions: 2 a year both originated
Details: Gallery holding a mixed display of oils, watercolours and prints. Artists' materials also sold and framing service available. 25% commission on sales.

Builth Wells
POWYS

Builth Wells Library

Pa Ph Pr Cr SC ⬤ 🅷

First floor gallery within library.
20 High Street, Builth Wells LD2 3DN, tel: 01982 552722, fax: 01982 551083
Contact: Mrs Sue Jones, Branch Librarian
Open: Mon, Tues, Wed 11-1, 2-5; Fri 11-1, 2-4:30, 5-7; Sat 10-12:30; closed Thurs and Sun
Space: 1 gallery with 44 sq m floor space
Exhibitions: 12 a year of which 2 originated, 10 on a hire basis
Details: Branch library situated in the middle of the shopping area of the town. Large, well-used exhibition area adjacent to the reference library on the upper floor.

Walls have mounts and board coverings.
Floor space. Spotlit.

Wyeside Gallery

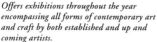 ● ⊕ ⓗ ⓖ ⓦ

*Offers exhibitions throughout the year
encompassing all forms of contemporary art
and craft by both established and up and
coming artists.*
**Wyeside Arts Centre, Castle Street,
Builth Wells LD2 3BN, tel: 01982
553668, fax: 01982 552515**
Contact: Jonathon Morgan, Director
Open: Mon, Tues, Wed-Sat 10.30-4.30
Space: 1 gallery with 32 lin m hanging
space and 54 sq m floor space
Exhibitions: 10 a year
Details: Small gallery in rural setting
presenting a wide variety of exhibitions
throughout the year. Mixture of self-
originated and touring exhibitions.
Workshops often organised in conjunction
with exhibitions. Arts Council of Wales
Collectorplan scheme offered.

Caergwrle
CLWYD

Caegwrle Library

Pa Ph Pr Cr Sc ●

*Exhibits the work of amateur artists in a
long narrow room just off the main library.*
**Derby Road, Caergwrle, tel: 01978
760093**
Contact: Mrs Marsh
Space: 1 gallery
Details: 30% commission on sales.

Caernarfon
GWYNEDD

Arfon Gallery *

Pa Pr Cr ●

*Commercial gallery showing paintings and
limited edition prints.*
**Palace Street, Caernarfon, tel: 01286
2602, fax: 01286 76728**
Contact: Eric & Glenys Gray-Thomas
Space: 1 gallery
Details: A craft shop is attached to the
gallery.

Caernarfon Library

**Pavillion Road, Caernarfon, tel: 01286
5944**
Contact: Helen Francis, Librarian
Open: Mon, Tues, Thurs, Fri 10-7; Wed
10-1; Sat 9-1
Space: 1 gallery with 79 sq m floor space
Details: Library exhibition room located
on street level. The space is available for
individual artists or groups to stage
exhibitions.

Gwynedd County Libraries

Pa Ph Cr

*Administers five libraries with special
exhibition facilities as well as museum,
gallery and sculpture park.*
**Department of Culture and Leisure,
Gynedd County Council, Caernarfon,
tel: 01286 679458**
Contact: Ann Rhydderch, Arts
Development Officer
Details: Five libraries (Holyhead, Blaenau
Ffestiniog, Caernarfon, Llangefni and
Llandudno) plus Bangor Museum & Art
Gallery, Oriel Pendeitsh and a sculpture
park at Glynllifon. Temporary exhibitions
by individual artists, local art societies,
camera clubs and craftspeople plus touring
exhibitions.

Oriel Pendeitsh

Pr Cr ● ⓖ

*Gallery opposite entrance to Caernarfon
Castle where programme strongly reflects
the work of local artists and craftspeople.*
**Castle Ditch, Caernarfon LL55 2AY, tel:
01286 679458, fax: 01286 679564**
Contact: Ann Rhydderch/Delyth Gordon,
Department of Culture & Leisure,
Gwynedd County Council, County
Offices, Carnarfon, LL55 1SH, tel: 01286
679461, fax: 01286 673520
Open: Daily; closed Wed in Winter
Space: 2 galleries
Exhibitions: 6 a year
Details: Aims to exhibit quality craft and
design in the present area of Gwynedd.
Independent access for wheelchair users to
ground floor only.

Caerphilly
MID GLAMORGAN

Coach House Gallery *

Pa Ph Cr Sc ●

*Shows work by artists and makers living
and working in Wales.*
**Mountain Road, Caerphilly CF8 1HQ,
tel: 01222 863500**
Contact: Linda Nottingham, Exhibition
Organiser
Space: 1 gallery with 40 lin m hanging
space and 60 sq m floor space
Exhibitions: 6 a year all originated
Details: Three exhibitions a year;
Christmas, Easter and Summer. Is then
open Tues-Sat. Rest of year variety of
watercolours, pastels, textiles and prints
(lino, etching etc) available.

Caldicot
GWENT

Tower Gallery *

Pa Ph Pr Cr Sc ● ⊕ ⓗ

*Part of a C14th tower administered by
Monmouth Museums Service providing
venue for local artists and from further
afield.*
**Caldicot Castle, Caldicot NP6 4HU, tel:
01291 420241**
Contact: Anne Rainsbury, Curator
Space: 3 galleries
Exhibitions: 4 a year all on a hire basis
Details: Flexible programme exhibitions
during the 8 months the castle is open.
Regular local following as well as tourist
visitors.

Cardiff
SOUTH GLAMORGAN

Albany Gallery

Pa Pr

*Specialises in work by contemporary Welsh
artists.*
**74b Albany Road, Cardiff CF2 3RS, tel:
01222 487158**
Contact: Mary Yapp & Joan Hughes,
Exhibition Organiser
Space: 3 galleries
Exhibitions: 12 a year all originated
Details: Regular solo and mixed temporary
exhibitions in two rooms on first floor, plus
changing display of work in stock.

Art Education Gallery

Pa Pr Cr Sc LA ● ⊕ ⓗ ⓖ ⓦ

*Aims to make artistic practice and processes
accessible.*
**Cardiff Institute of Higher Education,
Cynoed Road, Cardiff CF2 6XD, tel:
01222 551111 ext 6509, fax: 01222
506589**
Contact: John McNorton, Senior Lecturer
Open: Mon-Fri 9-9; Sat & Sun 10-5
Space: 2 galleries with 61 lin m hanging
space plus 73 lin m on screens
Exhibitions: 9 a year of which 4
originated, 3 touring, 2 on a hire basis
Details: Open exhibition policy. Intention
is to extend curriculum thinking for
primary, secondary, further and higher
education. Four glass display cabinets
available. Sales not a priority.

Canton Library

Pa Ph Pr Cr Sc ● ⓖ

*Exhibition room within library for
exhibitions of mainly individual artists'
work.*
**Library Street, Canton, Cardiff CF5
1QD, tel: 01222 229935**
Contact: Mr J McLennan, Librarian
Open: Library opening times; Closed Sun

Space: 1 gallery
Exhibitions: 20 a year
Details: Exhibitions of work by local artists. Also schools and groups. Fluorescent lighting and daylight. High ceilings. Paintings to be hung on hessian boards on walls. Extra display boards available. Tables for craft/sculpture displays. No booking fee but library takes 10% of sales. Previews possible to be arranged and paid for by artists.

Cardiff Central Library

Pa Ph Gr Sc ✔ 🅰 ⓦ

Seeks to promote the arts within a local framework.
St Davids Link, Frederick Street, Cardiff CF1 4DT, tel: 01222 382116
Contact: Bruna Merola, Arts Librarian
Open: Mon, Tues, Fri 9-6; Wed 9-8; Sat 9-5:30
Space: 1 gallery with 42 sq m floor space
Exhibitions: 16 a year
Details: Small display area used to show work by artists and craftspeople, photographers, local societies, etc. Hanging is on panels. Exhibitions change every three weeks. Notice boards and display case also available for exhibiting work. The Ballinger Room, on the top floor, is available for hire for group activities or exhibitions, etc. Selling work not gallery's main aim.

Chapter *

Pa Ph Pr Sc LA ✔ ⓔ 🅰 ⓦ

Three large spaces accommodating a wide range of exhibitions with large-scale sculptural/installation, media and 'time-based' work a major part of the programme.
Market Road, Canton, Cardiff CF5 1QE, tel: 01222 396061, fax: 01222 225901
Contact: Stuart Cameron, Visual Arts Programmer
Space: 3 galleries with 96 lin m hanging space plus 36 lin m on screens and 300 sq m floor space
Exhibitions: 8 a year of which 5 originated, 3 touring
Details: Selects work by artists of regional, national and international significance.

Ely Branch Library *

Pa Pr ✔

Space inside one of South Glamorgan's newest branch libraries.
Grand Avenue, Ely, Cardiff CF5 4BL, tel: 01222 562064
Contact: Richard Cox
Space: 1 gallery with 14 lin m hanging space and 21 sq m floor space
Exhibitions: 12 a year of which 4 originated, 8 touring
Details: Generally exhibitions last for one month and are organised through South East Wales Arts or by approaching the librarian direct. Local artists encouraged.

Artists provide their own insurance and publicity. South Glamorgan take 10% of sales.

Ffotogallery

Ph ✔ ⓔ 🅰

Photographicexhibitions and educational events concentrating on contemporary practice in Wales and vanguard British and European photographic art.
31 Charles Street, Cardiff CF1 4EA, tel: 01222 341 667, fax: 01222 341 672
Contact: Christopher Coppock, Director
Open: Tues-Sat 10-5:30
Space: 3 galleries with 50 lin m hanging space and 350 sq m floor space
Exhibitions: 10 a year of which 8 originated, 2 touring
Details: Aims to increase public understanding and awareness of photography, and to extend audiences for photography as a visual artform. Recently expanded to incorporate ground-floor specialist photographic bookshop.

Gallery (The)

Pa Ph Pr ✔ 🅰

Purpose-designed exhibition space with "gallery" in middle as major feature of interior design consultancy business and showroom.
Richard Beere Interiors, 111 - 117 Woodville Road, Cardiff CF2 4DY, tel: 01222 220144, fax: 01222 394148
Contact: Tisch Beere, Gallery Director
Open: Mon-Fri 9-5
Space: 100 sq m floor space
Exhibitions: 4 a year all originated
Details: Main exhibition space occupies large area on the first floor, although the display of pictures extends beyond this main space into the offices and showrooms on both the first and second floors. The gallery has a core of about 20 artists whose work is kept in stock and exhibited regularly. Sales a priority.

Llanover Hall Oriel Llanover

Pa Ph Pr Gr Sc ⓔ

Exhibition area with small monthly exhibitions run by South Glamorgan County Council Educational Authority.
Romilly Road, Canton, Cardiff CF5 1FH, tel: 01222 342022
Contact: Tony Goble, Gallery Director
Space: 1 gallery with 74 lin m hanging space and 16 sq m floor space
Exhibitions: 10 a year all originated
Details: Additional exhibition space available on adjacent main staircase. Exhibitions often feature work by young professional artists from Cardiff area. Offers classes and workshops for all ages.

Makers Gallery

A Pa Ph Pr Gr Sc ✔ 🅗 🅰

Small gallery and craftshop run by local makers stocking large selection of crafts and separate upstairs gallery.
37 Penylan Road, Roath Park, Cardiff CF2 5HL, tel: 01222 472595
Contact: Helen Lush, Exhibitions Organiser
Open: Tues-Sat 10-5.30
Space: 1 gallery with 16 lin m hanging space
Exhibitions: 11 a year all on a hire basis
Details: Contemporary one-person and group shows mainly by local artists. Sales considered primary role of gallery but no commission taken on sales.

Manor House Fine Arts

Pa Pr Sc ✔ 🅗 🅰

Private gallery specialising in C19th & C20th paintings and prints.
73 Pontcanna Street, Cardiff CF1 9HS, tel: 01222 227787
Contact: Steven Hill, Exhibition Organiser
Space: 1 gallery with 120 lin m hanging space and 100 sq m floor space
Exhibitions: 4 a year all originated
Details: 40% of hanging space devoted to contemporary work. Aims to make available sensibly priced oil paintings, watercolours and prints. Credit Sale Scheme available for contemporary work through Arts Council of Wales.

Martin Tinney Gallery

Pa Pr Sc ✔ 🅰

Commercial gallery specialising in 20th and contemporary Welsh art.
6 Windsor Place, Cardiff CF1 3BX, tel: 01222 641411
Contact: Martin Tinney
Open: Mon-Sat 10-6
Space: 4 galleries with 75 lin m hanging space and 95 sq m floor space
Exhibitions: 8 a year all originated
Details: Showing modern and contemporary painting, print and sculpture by young and established artists. Shows last approximately one month and present mixed and solo exhibitions. Gallery takes part in the Welsh Arts Council Purchase Scheme which offers 10 months interest-free credit.

National Museum of Wales (Department of Art)

Pa Pr Gr Sc

Regular programme of temporary exhibitions alongside permanent display of its art collection.
Cathays Park, Cardiff CF1 3NP, tel: 01222 397951, fax: 01222 373219
Contact: David Alston, Keeper of Art
Space: 2 galleries with 53 lin m hanging space and 112 sq m floor space

Exhibitions: 5 a year of which 2 originated, 3 touring
Details: Exhibitions of contemporary art also at Turner House, Penarth (see separate entry).

Norwegian Church Centre

Pa Pr Cr ⊙ Ⓗ Ⓧ Ⓦ

Gallery for hire on first floor overlooking main hall within cultural centre.
Waterfront Park, Harbour Drive, Cardiff CF1 5PA, tel: 01222 454899
Contact: David Griffiths, Administrator
Open: Daily 10-4.30
Space: 1 gallery with 20 lin m hanging space plus 10 lin m on screens and 80 sq m floor space
Exhibitions: 10 a year of which 2 originated, 8 on a hire basis
Details: Norwegian Church Centre has first floor gallery and ground floor main hall available for hire. Wide variety of exhibitions, music events held in cultural centre retaining peaceful atmosphere of its days as religious meeting place. Sales not primary role of gallery. Main hall, which can be used for exhibitions, is accessible to wheelchair users but not gallery.

Old Library

Pa Ph Cr Sc ⊙ Ⓔ Ⓗ Ⓑ

Exhibitions to encourage as many people as possible to come into the building and experience visual arts.
Trinity Street, Cardiff CF1 2BH, tel: 01222 342015, fax: 01222 383726
Contact: Ron Adam, Manager
Open: Mon-Sat 10-5
Space: 2 galleries with 77 lin m hanging space plus 27 lin m on screens and 329 sq m floor space
Exhibitions: 12 a year of which 8 originated, 1 touring, 3 on a hire basis
Details: Venue for temporary exhibitions, a museum of kinetic sculpture and craft centre. Varied programme of fine art, educational, historical and documentary exhibitions attracts a wide audience. Artists' studios on the premises. Due to temporary nature of the project programming of gallery only continues until end of August 1995. Sales not a priority. Exhibition fee to exhibitors sometimes paid.

Oriel

 Pr Cr Sc La ⊙ Ⓔ Ⓑ

Arts Council of Wales' own gallery with exhibitions of contemporary fine and applied arts, featuring Welsh and international artists and designer makers.
The Friary, Cardiff CF1 4AA, tel: 01222 395548, fax: 01222 221 447
Contact: Jenni Spencer-Davies, Head of Gallery
Open: Mon-Sat 9-5.30
Space: 1 gallery with 36 lin m hanging

space plus 16 lin m on screens and 144 sq m floor space
Exhibitions: 9 a year of which 6 originated, 3 touring
Details: Also promotes sale of contemporary crafts throughout the year. Commissions taken for individually designed objects through Craft Design Service, free facility for private and corporate use. Interested in working on collaborative basis with other galleries. Monthly exhibitions emphasising work of living practitioners. School workshops organised. Specialist bookshop and craft shop. Sale of work not primary role of gallery.

St David's Hall

Pa Ph Cr Sc ⊙ Ⓔ Ⓑ Ⓦ

Exhibition space in large concert hall brings the visual arts to the attention of more than 10,000 people a week.
The Hayes, Cardiff CF1 2SH, tel: 01222 342611, fax: 01222 383726
Contact: Gaynor Hill, Exhibition Officer
Open: Mon-Sat 10-4.30; and to concert goers before evening performances.
Space: 2 galleries with 232 lin m hanging space and 240 sq m floor space
Exhibitions: 29 a year of which 27 originated, 2 touring
Details: Foyers of 1965-seat concert hall where exhibitions show work by living artists. Additional space for photography and craft showcases. Promotes Welsh artists, established and new. Exhibitions also mounted to complement events in the auditorium. Venue for 6 showcases programmed by the Welsh Arts Council Craft Showcase Network.

Welsh Industrial & Maritime Museum

Pa Ph Cr ⊙ Ⓔ Ⓑ Ⓦ

Branch of National Museum of Wales covering industrial and maritime history of Wales, particularly through temporary exhibitions.
Bute Street, Cardiff CF1 6AN, tel: 01222 481919, fax: 01222 487252
Contact: Dr E S Owen-Jones
Open: Tues-Sat 10-5; Sun 2.30-5
Space: 1 gallery with 20 lin m hanging space plus 120 lin m on screens and 400 sq m floor space
Exhibitions: 10 a year of which 3 originated, 7 touring
Details: Exhibitions themes are mainly historical, industrial, transport and maritime although current issues of de-industrialisation and land reclamation are also treated. Exhibitions mainly hired in from artists and agencies. Craft demonstrations, educational displays and children's activities also held. Sales not a priority.

Cardigan
DYFED

Chelini

Pa Pr

Commercial gallery shares building with a café and a jeweller's shop.
33-34 The High Street, Cardigan SA43 1HJ, tel: 01239 614608
Contact: Helen Lloyd/Bob Morgan
Open: Mon-Sat 9.30-5; Closed half day Wednesday
Space: 2 galleries
Details: No temporary programme as such but an on-going exhibition of over 300 pieces of work by various artists including Cardigan's Aneurin M Jones.

Frame by Frame Gallery & Workshop

Pa Ph Sc ⊙ Ⓧ

Gallery on three levels promoting work of local artists, and providing framing and conservation service.
11 Black Lion Mews, Cardigan SA43 3UU, tel: 01239 615398, fax: 01239 615121
Contact: Graham Holdsworth & Roxanna, Owner
Open: Mon, Tues, Thurs-Sat 10-5
Space: 1 gallery with 60 sq m floor space
Exhibitions: 3 a year all originated
Details: Gallery shows work by local artists and is available for one-person exhibitions. Framing service for exhibitors also available. Art supplies and antiquarian prints. Sales not a priority. Applications for exhibitions welcomed from local artists only.

Theatr Mwldan

Pa Ph Pr Cr Sc ⊙ Ⓗ Ⓑ Ⓦ

The spacious foyer gallery forms part of vigorously growing independent arts centre.
Cardigan SA43 1JY, tel: 01239 612687
Contact: Anthony Stevens, Administrator
Open: Mon-Sat 9-5; (Summer) Sun 10-5
Space: 1 gallery with 25 lin m hanging space plus 10 lin m on screens and 75 sq m floor space
Exhibitions: 20 a year of which 16 originated, 2 touring, 2 on a hire basis
Details: Foyer houses coffee shop and tourist information centre facilities in addition to gallery space. Gallery aims to showcase the most interesting range of work available, with particular reference to visual arts relevant to the area. Sale of work is not gallery's primary function.

Carmarthen
DYFED

Carmarthen Library

Pa Ph Pr Cr Sc ✓ Ⓗ ⓖ

Large well-lit space aiming to show a very wide range of arts practice.
St Peters Street, Carmarthen SA31 1LN, tel: 01267 230873
Contact: Phillip Alder, County Arts Officer
Open: Mon-Fri 10-7; Sat 10-1pm
Space: 2 galleries with 74 lin m hanging space and 112 sq m floor space
Exhibitions: 8 a year of which 3 originated, 3 touring, 2 on a hire basis
Details: Large multi-purpose hall converted into an exhibition space from time to time. Access remains fairly open to artists, mainly in the form of group shows. 20% commission on sales. Aims to link the theme or background of each show with what is happening in the area at large. Used as originating venue for touring exhibitions organised by County's Arts and Exhibitions Service. Sales not a priority.

Henry Thomas Gallery

Pa Ph Pr Cr Sc ✓ⓕ ⓖ ⓦ

Public art gallery within an educational setting with broad programme of exhibitions.
Carmarthenshire College of Technology & Art, Faculty of Art and technology, Job's Well Road, Carmarthen SA31 3HY
Contact: Susan Hayward, Gallery Assistant
Space: 1 gallery with 48 lin m hanging space and 104 sq m floor space
Details: Exhibitions normally last two weeks. Programme evenly balanced between fine art, sculpture, photography, crafts and design. Gallery used for the college's final shows.

Oriel Myrddin Gallery

Pa Ph Pr Cr Sc ⓖⓦ

Craft Council listed contemporary craft centre and art gallery run by local authority.
Old School of Art, Church Lane, Carmarthen SA31 1LH, tel: 01267 222775
Contact: Sian Griffiths, Craft Development Officer
Open: Mon-Sat 10.30-4.45
Space: 2 galleries with 75 sq m floor space
Exhibitions: 15 a year of which 8 originated, 7 touring
Details: Changing displays of designer crafts produced locally, regionally and nationally alongside monthly exhibitions of contemporary crafts/design, applied and fine art. Exhibitions originated by gallery usually mixed shows, sometimes thematic. Complementary workshops and talks. Artists and craftspeople encouraged to participate. Sales of work and education both important. Craft Officer interested in seeing new work but artists/craftspeople should realise this doesn't often lead to an exhibition.

Chepstow
GWENT

Art Approach

Pa Ph Pr Sc ✓

Commercial gallery specialising in equestrian art.
The Station Building, Station Road, Chepstow NP6 5PF, tel: 01291 621854
Contact: David Dent, Exhibition Manager
Space: 1 gallery with 29 lin m hanging space and 50 sq m floor space
Exhibitions: 2 a year both originated
Details: Located in old Brunel railway station. Rarely interested in purely abstract work. 40% commission on sales (under review). Also publishes limited edition prints and interested in seeing work by artists looking for publisher or having prints marketed (all subjects).

Chepstow Museum *

Pa Ph Pr Cr ✓

Exhibition space within museum dealing predominantly with local history and run by Monmouth Borough Council.
Gwy House, Bridge Street, Chepstow NP6 5EZ, tel: 01291 625981
Contact: Anne Rainsbury, Curator
Space: 1 gallery with 23 lin m hanging space
Exhibitions: 1 a year originated
Details: Usually 5 exhibitions during the 8 month opening period, each normally shown for 6 weeks. Exhibitions explore contemporary and historical local themes in depth, also subjects such as technology and science, natural history and ethnology, art and craft. Particularly interested in professional artists and makers working in the area on local subjects and related themes.

Workshop Gallery

Pa Pr Cr Sc ✓ ⓧ

Craftsman-owned, well-lit, white gallery mounting exhibitions of contemporary ceramics in association with textiles, prints, etc.
13 Lower Church Street, Chepstow NP6 5HJ, tel: 01291 624836
Contact: Ned Heywood
Open: Mon-Sat 10-1, 2-6; Sun 2-6
Space: 2 galleries with 21 lin m hanging space and 35 sq m floor space
Exhibitions: 6 a year all originated
Details: Programme of thematic and group exhibitions in which ceramics always form the majority element. Clay works are matched with complementary craftwork, textiles, prints, wood, etc to create displays aimed at both casual visitors and knowledgeable collectors. Exhibitions last around two months. Gallery covers exhibition costs apart from transport to and from venue. Sale of work is gallery's primary role.

Colwyn Bay
CLWYD

Colwyn Bay Library

Pa Ph Pr Cr Sc ✓ ⓖⓦ④

Gallery within library showing touring exhibitions and work by regional artists.
Woodland Road West, Colwyn Bay LL29 7DH, tel: 01492 532358, fax: 01492 534474
Contact: Lynne Jones, Assistant Librarian
Open: Mon-Tues & Thurs 10-7; Wed & Fri 10-5.30; Sat 9.30-12.30
Space: 1 gallery with 19 lin m hanging space plus 10 lin m on screens and 64 sq m floor space
Exhibitions: 12 a year of which 6 originated, 6 touring
Details: Touring exhibitions and shows of regional artists' work; annual educational exhibition arranged for schools by Clwyd Library and Information Service. Children's Art Workshop. Sales not a priority.

Conwy
GWYNEDD

Royal Cambrian Academy of Art

Pa Pr Sc ⓖ ⓦ

Exhibitions held of work by academy members.
Crown Lane, Conwy LL32 8BH, tel: 01492 593413
Contact: Vicky Macdonald
Open: Tues-Sun 11-5
Space: 2 galleries with 188 sq m floor space
Exhibitions: 7 a year of which 6 originated, 1 touring
Details: Academy was established in 1882. As well as exhibitions and events held throughout the year also runs classes October-April. Annual summer exhibition. The Academy also has a Friends of the Royal Cambrian Academy Association. Sales important.

Cowbridge
SOUTH GLAMORGAN

Cowbridge Old Hall Gallery

Pa Ph Pr Cr Sc ✓ⓕ ⓖ

Showing work by groups and individuals, particularly by recently graduated local young professional artists.

Cowbridge Community Adult Education Centre, High Street, Cowbridge CF7 7JR, tel: 01446 33831
Contact: Keith James, Cowbridge Arts Group
Open: During college term-time hours vary
Space: 1 gallery with 45 lin m hanging space
Exhibitions: 10 a year all originated
Details: Work sold by not primary role of gallery. 10% commission taken.

John Owen Gallery *

Pa Pr Sc

Commercial gallery showing mainly C18th and C19th paintings with contemporary work by mainly Welsh artists.
Cowbridge Antiques, 55 Eastgate, Cowbridge CF7 7EL, tel: 01446 774774
Contact: John Owen, Exhibition Organiser
Space: 5 galleries with 19 lin m hanging space and 84 sq m floor space
Exhibitions: 4 a year all originated
Details: Applications from all regions are welcome. A commission fee is charged.

Cwmbran
GWENT

Llantarnam Grange Arts Centre

Pa Ph Pr Cr ✓ ⓔ ⒣ ⓖ ⓦ

Arts centre showing a varied programme of exhibitions and running many events.
St Davids Road, Cwmbran NP44 1PD, tel: 01633 483321
Contact: Hywel Pontin, Director
Open: Mon-Sat 10-4
Space: 3 galleries with 97 lin m hanging space and 172 sq m floor space
Exhibitions: 19 a year of which 15 originated, 2 touring, 2 on a hire basis
Details: Situated in centre of Cwmbran. Mediaeval farm house with landscaped gardens to front. Exhibition programme has slight emphasis on craft but aims to show as wide a range of media as possible. Sales encouraged. Also houses a coffee shop and craft shop. Practical involvement with artists/makers encouraged through a strong educational programme.

Moving Pictures

Pa Ph Cr Sc ✓ ⓔ ⒣

Moving Pictures organises small and medium scale exhibitions to be shown in mostly non-gallery venues
Arts Council of Wales, South East Wales Office, Victoria Street, Cwmbran NP44 3YT, tel: 01633 875075, fax: 01633 875389
Contact: Richard Cox, Arts Officer
Open: Varies according to venue.
Exhibitions: 50 a year of which 48 originated, 2 on a hire basis
Details: Non-gallery venues in which

Moving Pictures places exhibitions includes libraries, community centres, hospitals, schools, etc. These exhibitions mostly laminated. Generally show paintings, photography, drawings by young emerging artists but opportunity open to artists at all stages of their careers. Crafts work can be shown only where facilities permit. Artists can take advantage of this scheme to set up shows in new spaces. Sale of work possible but not primary role. Levels of access and facilities will vary according to venue.

Denbigh
CLWYD

Denbigh Library Museum and Gallery

Pa Ph Pr Cr Sc ✓ ⓔ ⒣ ⓖ ⓦ ④

The gallery aims to display work by regional artists as well as offering the experience of national touring exhibitions.
Hall Square, Denbigh LL16 3NU, tel: 01745 816313
Contact: Community Librarian
Open: Mon, Wed, Fri 9.30-7; Tues & Thurs 9.30-5.30; Sat 9.30-4
Space: 1 gallery with 14 lin m hanging space plus 18 lin m on screens and 52 sq m floor space
Exhibitions: 9 a year of which 4 originated, 4 touring, 1 on a hire basis
Details: Exhibitions and related events covering range of contemporary visual arts. Aims at a balanced programme between local, national and occasional international level. Audience from the market town and surrounding rural communities. Educational projects held during school holidays. Craft case display with the exhibition programme. Sales not a priority.

Dolgellau
GWYNEDD

Library Art Gallery

Pa Pr Cr Sc ✓

Gallery in a hotel with changing display, and occasional exhibitions, of work by Welsh artists or of Welsh subjects.
Borthwnog Hall, Bontddu, Dolgellau LL40 2TT, tel: 01341 430271
Contact: V.L. Hawes, Exhibition Organiser
Details: Former library of Georgian mansion, now a hotel. Constantly changing display of work for sale, interspersed with two or three solo or two-person exhibitions lasting three to six weeks. Shows some sculpture, ceramics and embroidery as well as paintings. Target audience visitors to hotel and restaurant (predominantly business and professional) and local residents.

Fishguard
DYFED

Fishguard Branch Library

Pa Ph Pr Cr Sc LA ✓ ⓖ

Small area used mainly by local artists and organisations who would otherwise have little chance of exhibiting their work.
High Street, Fishguard SA65 9AR, tel: 01348 872694
Contact: Miss Rhian M Evans, Branch Librarian
Open: Mon, Thurs 10.30-1, 2-6.30; Tues, Fri 10.30-1, 2-6; Wed 10.30-1, 2-5; Sat 10.30-12.30
Space: 1 gallery with 21 lin m hanging space and 37 sq m floor space
Exhibitions: 9 a year of which 8 originated, 1 touring
Details: Small exhibition space in library foyer. Programme of locally generated exhibitions and community use exhibitions. Part of circuit touring exhibitions to the region's libraries. Major exhibition held each July in conjunction with musical festival. Sales not a priority.

West Wales Arts Centre

Pa Pr Cr Sc ✓

Gallery run as an arts centre with specialist lectures and music recitals.
Castle Hill, 16 West Street, Fishguard SA65 9AE, tel: 01348 873867
Contact: Myles Pepper, Director
Open: Mon-Sat 9-5.30; Sun by appointment
Space: 3 galleries with 70 lin m hanging space and 150 sq m floor space
Exhibitions: 6 a year all originated
Details: Work exhibited by new artists and nationally established ones alike. Crafts Council selected for quality. Exhibitions feature fine art and ceramics. Sculpture facility currently being developed. A gallery with a fast-growing national reputation for our commitment to the arts and making them accessible to all.

Harlech
GWYNEDD

Theatr Ardudwy

Pa Ph Pr Cr Sc ✓ ⓖ ⓦ

Theatre foyer space with exhibitions changed every two months.
Coleg Harlech, Harlech LL46 2PU, tel: 01766 780667, fax: 01766 780169
Contact: Valerie Wynne-Williams, Exhibition Organiser
Open: Daily 9.30-5.30; during performances
Space: 1 gallery with 32 lin m hanging space
Exhibitions: 6 a year of which 5 originated, 1 touring

White Room Gallery at Harlech Pottery

Pa Ph Pt Cr Sc ✓ ⬤

Gallery established 1994 above pottery, specialising in pottery, ceramics and printmaking.
Pentre Efail, Harlech LL46 2YG, tel: 01766 780501
Contact: Mrs L Gayden, Owner
Open: (Apr-Oct) Mon-Sat 10-5; (Nov-March) ring first.
Space: 2 galleries with 21 lin m hanging space and 35 sq m floor space
Exhibitions: 3 a year all originated
Details: Gallery aims to promote excellence in craft and design, whether traditional or innovative. Wide spectrum of ceramic techniques displayed. Most work is for sale at reasonable prices. Access for wheelchair users with assistance to ground floor only.

Haverfordwest
DYFED

Graham Sutherland Gallery

Pa Ph Pr ✓ ⓢ ⬤ ⓥ

Small seasonal exhibition space next to Gallery's main entrance for single/mixed artists' exhibitions, and displays from main collection of National Museum of Wales.
Picton Castle, The Rhos, Haverfordwest SA62 4AS, tel: 01437 751296, fax: 01437 751322
Contact: Mr Tim Egan, Officer in Charge
Open: (26 Mar – 1 Oct) Tues-Sun 10.30-5; open B/H Mon
Space: 1 gallery with 26 lin m hanging space and 47 sq m floor space
Exhibitions: 4 a year of which 1 originated, 3 touring
Details: Branch of the National Museum of Wales administered by the new Museums Development Division. Large permanent collection of Sutherland's work and programme of temporary exhibitions. Lecture theatre, small shop.

Haverfordwest Library

Pa Ph ✓ ⬤

Circular hall in library used for exhibitions and meetings/lectures.
Dew Street, Haverfordwest SA61 1SU, tel: 01437 762070
Contact: Clive Richards, Senior Librarian
Open: Mon, Wed, Thurs 9.30-5; Tues & Fri 9.30-7; Sat 9.30-1
Space: 1 gallery with 25 lin m hanging space plus 6 lin m on screens and 126 sq m floor space
Exhibitions: 10 a year of which 8 originated, 2 touring
Details: Policy to develop an interest in art within the area. Circular hall fitted with movable hanging rods used for temporary

shows, meetings and lectures. Foyer adjacent to hall also fitted with movable rods.

Hawarden
CLWYD

Hawarden Library

Pa Ph Cr ✓

Small corridor space promotes awareness of the arts through as varied a programme as possible.
The Old Rectory, Rectory Lane, Hawarden CH5 3NN, tel: 01224 532926
Contact: Kathleen Morris, Librarian
Space: 8 lin m hanging space and 10 sq m floor space
Exhibitions: 3 a year
Details: Corridor exhibition area. Part of Clwyd Library service. Works of local artists and schools shown. Also touring exhibitions, artists in residencies. Makes available to the public work that is interesting, educational and entertaining.

Hay on Wye
POWYS

Kilvert Gallery

Pa Pr Cr Sc ⊘

Commercial gallery promoting best of the work of recent graduates.
Ashbrook House, Clyro, Hay on Wye HR3 5RZ, tel: 01497 820831
Contact: Elizabeth Organ, Owner/Director
Open: (Easter-end Sept) Tues-Sun 10-5
Space: 7 galleries with 50 lin m hanging space
Exhibitions: 6 a year all originated
Details: Owners have converted two floors of their house where they present art and craft work in a sense of 'room creating', combining paintings and objects in a domestic setting rather than a gallery context. Policy to select and promote a number of artists. A link with the Redfern Gallery, Cork Street, means there is always work by other C20th artists. Organises painting courses and lectures. Sale of work is gallery's primary role.

Meridian Contemporary Arts

Pa Cr Sc ✓ ⬤

Independent commercial gallery specialising in figurative work and studio ceramics.
13 High Town, Hay on Wye HR3 5AE, tel: 01497 821633
Contact: Tony and Anthea Britnell, Owners
Open: Wed-Sat 10-5; Sun 1-5
Space: 1 gallery with 13 lin m hanging space and 42 sq m floor space
Details: Exhibitions of contemporary fine and applied art, particularly figurative

work. Work by nationally known artists. Sales a priority.

Rogues Gallery

Pa Pr Cr Sc ✓ ⬤

Open-plan 'shop floor' exhibition space for local artists and craftspeople.
2 Broad Street, Hay on Wye HR3 5DB, tel: 01497 821677
Contact: Chris Armstrong, Co-ordinator
Open: Mon-Sat 11-5.30
Space: 1 gallery with 23 lin m hanging space and 46 sq m floor space
Details: Gallery and studio space for local artists and craftworkers. Part of growing network of arts & crafts outlets in and around Hay. Wants to develop exhibitions about Hay on Wye and surrounding area by outside artists. Space for large and small pieces.

Holyhead
GWYNEDD

Ucheldre Centre

Pa Ph Pr Cr Sc LA ✓ ⬤ ⓥ

Arts, conference and community centre that exhibits local artists and a programme of touring shows.
Millbank, Holyhead, Anglesey LL65 1TE, tel: 01407 763361, fax: 01407 769728
Contact: Mike Gould, General Manager
Open: Mon-Sat 10-5; Sun 2-5; open BH
Space: 1 gallery with 61 lin m hanging space and 74 sq m floor space
Exhibitions: 5 a year of which 3 originated, 2 touring
Details: Purpose-built exhibition room and two walls in former convent chapel (now concert hall) showing a wide selection of work mixing local with national/ international. Possible for freestanding work to be exhibited in main hall as well as gallery. Hopes to develop craft work and will be expanding shop.

Holywell
CLWYD

Holywell Library

Pa ✓

Clwyd Exhibition Service exhibitions and shows of local artists.
North Road, Holywell CH8 7TQ, tel: 01352 713157
Contact: Mrs Pennie Corbett, Librarian
Open: Mon-Fri 10-7; Sat 9.30-12.30
Space: 1 gallery with 600 lin m hanging space
Exhibitions: 30 a year of which 28 originated, 2 touring
Details: An open plan library with exhibiting space on two walls, a hanging rail and floor space adaptable for screens.

Knighton
POWYS

Knighton Library

Library exhibition space well used by local artists/groups to display work.
West Street, Knighton LD7 1DN, tel: 01547 528776
Contact: Mrs D M Price, Librarian
Open: Mon closed; Tues 10-12:30, 2-5, 6-7; Wed 10-12:30, 2-5; Sat 10-1:30
Details: Branch library with separate exhibition area in the foyer. Heavily used by local community for displays of artwork, crafts etc. Display boards and wall space available

Old School Gallery

Run by Bleddfa Trust the gallery (formerly village school) shows wide variety of art and craftwork by local and nationally-known artists.
Bleddfa, Knighton LD7 1PA, tel: 01547 550220
Contact: John Cupper, Administrator/Gallery Director, The Bleddfa Trust, The Tank House, Weston, Pembridge, Leominster, HR6 9JE, tel: 01544 388540
Open: (Mar-Dec) Wed-Sun 1-5.30
Space: 1 gallery with 25 lin m hanging space plus 45 lin m on screens and 50 sq m floor space
Exhibitions: 6 a year all originated
Details: Exhibitions run 4-6 weeks between March and December. The gallery runs a series of exhibitions on a theme every second year – these have included 'The Tree, 'The Garden' and 'The Family'. Sales considered important but not always essential.

Lampeter
DYFED

Galeri (Y)

Small commercial gallery showing work by artists mainly living in Wales.
2 Bridge Street, Lampeter, tel: 01570 423 317
Contact: Jacky Pique & Steve Dundas, Directors
Open: Mon, Tues, Thurs-Sat 9.30-5; Wed 9-1
Space: 1 gallery with 12 lin m hanging space plus 5 lin m on screens and 20 sq m floor space
Exhibitions: 6 a year all originated
Details: A gallery with a changing programme showing the work of mainly local artists. Plinths available. Also stocks cards, posters, prints, pottery, jewellery, etc.

and runs a framing service. Gallery upstairs and not accessible to wheelchair users.

St David's University College
College Street, Lampeter SA48 7ED

Theatr Felinfach *

Rural theatre and cultural centre, with space for art exhibitions.
Felinfach, Lampeter SA48 8AF, tel: 01570 470 697, fax: 01570 471 030
Contact: Exhibition Organiser
Space: 2 galleries
Exhibitions: 4 a year of which 2 touring, 2 on a hire basis

Laugharne
DYFED

Three Market Street Gallery
3 Market Street, Laugharne SA33 4SA

Llandeilo
DYFED

Country Fine Arts

Occupies the first floor of award winning barn conversion in Trapp Arts and Craft Centre.
'The Gallery at Trapp', Trapp Arts and Craft Centre, Trapp, Llandeilo SA19 6TT, tel: 01550 740649
Contact: Andrew G.L. Goolding, Proprietor, Country Fine Arts, Llanddeusant, Llangadog, SA19 9SS, tel: 01550 740649
Space: 1 gallery with 70 lin m hanging space
Exhibitions: 10 a year all originated
Details: Exposed beams and picture windows provide an excellent setting for paintings by professional artists working or linked with Wales. Mixed and solo exhibitions. Run by fine art agent Andrew Goolding as part of Country Fine Arts.

Fountain Fine Art

Commercial gallery with two windows on to main street plus rear gallery.
Rhosmaen Street, Llandeilo SA19 6EN, tel: 01558 823328
Contact: Peter Durisch and Gillian Still, Partners
Open: Tues-Fri 10-1, 2.30-5.30; Sat 10-4.30
Space: 2 galleries with 141 sq m floor space
Exhibitions: 4 a year all originated
Details: Offering varied range of sculpture, painting and print by professional artists

from all over the country. Exhibitions usually pair a sculptor with a painter. Emphasis on making work as accessible as possible. Gallery is member of Arts Council of Wales' 'Collectorplan'. Gallery keen to see new work by established professional sculptors and painters.

Llandough
SOUTH GLAMORGAN

Llandough Exhibition Space

Main hospital corridor spaces providing varied programme of two-dimensional work for public using hospital.
Llandough Hospital, Penlan Road, Llandough CF64 2XX, tel: 01222 711711
Contact: Heather Parnell, Artist in Residence
Open: Daily 9-8
Space: 2 galleries with 22 lin m hanging space
Exhibitions: 10 a year of which 5 originated, 5 touring
Details: Run with support from Arts Council of Wales. Programme aims to highlight approaches to art & design in non-gallery venue and (some slots) to highlight roles of artists in contemporary Britain. Sales not a priority but 20% commission goes to patient endowment funds.

Llandrindod Wells
POWYS

Porticus

Versatile purpose built exhibition room within commercial gallery/shop showing art and craftwork selected nationally.
1 Middleton Street, Llandrindod Wells LD1 5ET, tel: 01597 823989
Contact: Rosemary Studman, Proprietor
Open: Mon-Sat 10-5; Wed 10-1
Space: 1 gallery with 12 lin m hanging space and 12 sq m floor space
Exhibitions: 4 a year all originated
Details: Four versatile sales areas, including a special exhibition room. Stocks a continuous selection of work by designer makers. Main exhibition room downstairs. Large window display area fully accessible.

Llandudno
GWYNEDD

Fulmar Gallery

Commercial gallery specialises in wildlife paintings and limited edition prints.

44 Madoc Street, Llandudno LL30 2TW, tel: 01492 879880
Contact: M.J. Edwards, Exhibition Organiser
Space: 1 gallery with 7 lin m hanging space
Exhibitions: 2 a year both originated
Details: Changing displays of paintings and watercolours, plus six solo exhibitions annually. Framing service and public talks on framing and conservation.

Oriel Mostyn

Po Ph Pr Cr Sc ✅ ⓔ 🅰 ♿ 4

Victorian purpose-built gallery with exhibitions of international importance and those that refer to Welsh culture.
12 Vaughan Street, Llandudno LL30 1AB, tel: 01492 879201, fax: 01492 878869
Contact: Susan Daniel/ Mary Heathcote, Director/Administrator
Open: Mon-Sat 10.30-5
Space: 3 galleries with 68 lin m hanging space plus 14 lin m on screens and 194 sq m floor space
Exhibitions: 6 a year of which 4 originated, 2 touring
Details: Galleries have wonderful sense of space and light-gathering properties. Temporary exhibitions of contemporary arts and crafts with particular reference to Welsh culture; shows of international importance (contemporary) and historical exhibitions. Focus exhibitions of applied arts and crafts in craft shop area. Selling work not a priority.

Llandysul
DYFED

Museum of Welsh Woolen Industry

Cr 🅰 ♿

Museum with permanent exhibition of woollen textiles and exhibitions of contemporary textiles, photographs and other items related to the textile industry.
Dre-Fach, Felindre, Llandysul SA44 5UP, tel: 01559 370929
Contact: John Jones, Museum Officer
Open: (Apr-Sept) Mon-Sat 10-5; (Oct-Mar) Mon-Fri 10-5
Space: 1 gallery with 27 lin m hanging space plus 3 lin m on screens and 85 sq m floor space
Exhibitions: 3 a year of which 2 originated, 1 touring
Details: Exhibition and education policy in museum is based on the interpretation of the history of the textile industry. Temporary and permanent exhibitions are planned to reflect this through display, demonstrations and practical involvement of pupils, students, researchers, specialist textiles groups and community groups. Sales not gallery's primary function.

Llanelli
DYFED

Llanelli Borough Library *

Po Ph Pr Cr Sc ✅ ⓔ 🅷

Library gallery
Vaughan Street, Llanelli SA15 3AS, tel: 01554 773538, fax: 01554 750125
Contact: D.F. Griffiths, Borough Librarian
Space: 3 galleries
Exhibitions: 42 a year of which 26 originated, 4 touring, 12 on a hire basis
Details: Town centre gallery near shopping centre. Good natural lighting. Llanelli Library Service operates from here and organises exhibitions at Mansion House, Park Howard, Llanelli (see separate entry).

Mansion House *

Po Ph Pr Cr Sc LA

Small permanent regional museum and art collection run by Llanelli Library Service, with three rooms used for programme of temporary exhibitions from March to October.
Parc Howard, Felinfoel Road, Llanelli SA15 3LS, tel: 01554 772029
Contact: D F Griffiths, Borough Librarian
Space: 3 galleries

Park Howard Mansion

Po Ph Pr ✅ Ⓢ

Three exhibition rooms in mansion also housing museum and fine art collection.
Felinfoel Road, Llanelli SA15 3AS, tel: 01554 772029, fax: 01554 750125
Contact: Mr D Griffiths, Borough Librarian & Curator, Llllanelli Borough Library, Vaughan Street, Llanelli, SA15 3AS, tel: 01554 773535, fax: 01554 750125
Open: (Apr-Sept) daily 10-6; (Oct-Mar) daily 10-4
Space: 3 galleries
Exhibitions: 12 a year of which 4 originated, 6 touring
Details: Exhibitions organised by Llanelli Library Service. The house contains a small museum collection and collection or works of art. Sales of work not priority.

Llanfihangel GM
CLWYD

Mariers Pictures

Po Ph Pr ✅

Stock of paintings and limited edition prints by local artists, and programme of solo and mixed shows.
Bryn y Gwrgi, Llanfihangel GM LL21 9UW, tel: 01490 82462
Contact: Marie Wilcox
Space: 2 galleries with 5 lin m hanging space
Exhibitions: 2 a year both originated

Details: Welsh long barn looking over Clocgenog Forest and Snowdonia hills. Provides a framing service. No commission on sales. Situated off the B5105 Ruthin-Cerrigydrudion Road – turn right off this and the gallery is one mile from the road.

Llangefni
GWYNEDD

Nant yr Odin *

Po ✅

Hotel in C18th building used for painting holidays with exhibition space displaying work by local artists.
Nant yr Odyn Hotel & Restaurant, Turnpike Nant, Llangefni WLL7 7YE, tel: 01248 723354
Contact: Mr & Mrs Roberts, Exhibition Organisers
Space: 1 gallery with 3 lin m hanging space and 49 sq m floor space
Exhibitions: 3 a year all originated
Details: Encourages artists' groups to exhibit and use the studio. Does not have space to accommodate sculpture and live art.

Oriel Ynys Mon

Po Pr Cr ⓔ ♿ 4

Large flexible exhibition space with ability to control both lighting and humidity for exhibitions requiring high standards of conservation and security.
Rhosmeirch, Llangefni LL77 7TQ, tel: 01248 724444, fax: 01248 750282
Contact: Denise Morris, Principal Heritage Officer
Open: Tues-Sun10.30-5; open BH
Space: 2 galleries with 64 lin m hanging space and 299 sq m floor space
Exhibitions: 9 year all originated
Details: Contemporary programme offers mixture of single and group shows, work by local artists and craftspeople. Small stage in corner of gallery (can be moved). Admission free. Audience includes visits by outside organisations, schools and colleges. Major exhibitions originated by gallery itself, eg major retrospective of Welsh artist's work. Sales not a priority.

Llangollen
CLWYD

ECTARC

Po Ph Pr Cr Sc ✅ ⓔ ♿

Gallery's primary function is to provide a venue for local artists to exhibit their work.
Parade Street, Llangollen LL20 8RB, tel: 01978 861514, fax: 01978 861804
Contact: Sharon Thomas, Arts & Exhibitions Officer, ECTARC.
Open: Mon-Fri 9-5; weekend opening to suit exhibitors who invigilate

Space: 31 lin m hanging space and 46 sq m floor space
Details: The European Centre for Traditional and Regional Cultures – a multi-purpose centre used for the yearly international Eisteddfod events, for conferences and sport events. Exhibition policy stipulates that exhibition programme should be in keeping with ECTARC's objectives to promote and protect regional cultures. Sales not a priority.

Llangollen Library

Pa Ph Pr Cr ✔

Part of Clwyd Library Service holding many independent exhibitions of craft, photography, general interest, and a limited amount of fine art.
Parade Street, Llangollen LL20, tel: 01978 860720
Contact: A Y Jones, Temporary Community Librarian
Space: 1 gallery with 20 lin m hanging space plus 6 lin m on screens and 26 sq m floor space
Exhibitions: 3 a year all originated
Details: Wall space for temporary exhibitions. Regular very mixed programme of art and craft exhibitions, mainly from local sources but other art and craft exhibitions and contemporary art work welcome.

Llanidloes
POWYS

Studio 13

Pa Ph Pr Cr SC LA ✔

Aims to promote and provide access to all types of arts, crafts and cultural and social activities for the benefit of the Llanidloes area.
12 Greak Oak Street, Llanidloes SY18 6BU, tel: 01686 413933
Contact: Martin HIll, Secretary
Space: 1 gallery with 9 lin m hanging space and 42 sq m floor space
Exhibitions: 6 a year all originated
Details: Run by Comptons Yard Charitable Trust. Provides meeting and workshop space for educational and development activities for all ages. Open to approaches from artists/craftspeople wishing to exhibit work. Aims to provide assistance and encouragement to young/new artists.

Llantrisant
MID GLAMORGAN

Butchers Arms Gallery

Pa Cr ✔ H ✗

Occasional exhibitions form part of gallery shop and coffee shop.
Common Road, Llantrisant CF7 8BR, tel: 01443 229285

Contact: Gill Garnham, Exhibition Organiser
Open: Wed-Sun 10-5
Space: 1 gallery with 11 lin m hanging space
Exhibitions: 5 a year of which 1 originated, 4 on a hire basis
Details: Commercial gallery with local original paintings (mainly watercolours). Occasional solo exhibitions. Gallery is the first step towards bringing art, crafts and visual culture to what has been a decaying but historic town, creating a new market among local people and attracting others from much further afield. Also sells local crafts and pine furniture. Coffee shop. Sales not primary role of gallery.

Model House Craft & Design Centre

Cr ✔ H ✗ Wc

Crafts Council selected gallery.
Bull Ring, Llantrisant CF7 8EB, tel: 01443 237758, fax: 01443 229242
Contact: Jenny Rolfe, General Manager
Open: (1 May – 22 Dec) Tues-Sun 10-5; (2 Jan – 30 Apr) Wed-Sun 12-5
Space: 2 galleries with 25 lin m hanging space plus 5 lin m on screens and 192 sq m floor space
Exhibitions: 12 a year of which 11 originated, 1 on a hire basis
Details: All exhibitions show contemporary work by craftspeople and designers via its main exhibition programme and Profile programme which highlights work of one maker. All exhibitions are selling shows. Member of Arts Council of Wales Collectorplan. Crafts related workshop programme for adults and children and workshops for schools. Takes pupils and college students on work placement.

Llantwit Major
SOUTH GLAMORGAN

St Donat's Arts Centre

Pr Cr ✔ H

Varied programme of live performances and regular art and craft exhibitions.
St Donat's Castle, Llantwit Major CF6 0WF, tel: 01446 792151, fax: 01446 794163
Contact: David Ambrose, Artistic Director
Space: 1 gallery with 20 lin m hanging space and 20 sq m floor space
Exhibitions: 10 a year of which 8 touring, 2 on a hire basis
Details: In the grounds of St Donat's Castle and Atlantic College. Exhibitions/events include major annual Crafts in Action weekend.

Machynlleth
POWYS

Museum of Modern Art Wales

Pa Pr SC ✔ ☺ ✗ Wc 4

Main purpose is to strengthen Welsh art by placing it in a dynamic international context.
Heol Penrallt, Machynlleth SY20 8AJ, tel: 01654 703355
Contact: Michael Fraser, Exhibition Organiser
Open: Mon-Sat 10-4
Space: 6 galleries
Exhibitions: 11 a year of which 9 originated, 2 touring

Spectrum Gallery

Pa Ph Pr Cr ✔ ☺

Independent gallery specialising in ceramics and fine art, with an artist's approach to presentation and originality.
Maengwyn Street, Machynlleth SY20 8EB, tel: 01654 702877
Contact: Paul Martinez-Frias/Pam Taylor, Exhibition Organiser
Open: Mon-Sat 10-5
Space: 5 galleries with 20 lin m hanging space and 45 sq m floor space
Exhibitions: 6 a year all originated
Details: Mainly shows ceramics. Permanent selling exhibition of old Spanish rural pots plus changing display of paintings and one-off clocks by Paul Martinez-Frias. Promotes new talent in ceramics by solo exhibitions and by purchase of selected pieces for saleroom display, against a background of support for established studio potters. Sales a priority.

Maesteg
MID GLAMORGAN

Oriel Plasnewydd Gallery

Pa Ph Pr Cr SC ✔ ☺

Gallery and workshop space serving junior school and local community with mainly professional exhibitions of art and craft in school term time.
Plasnewydd Junior School, Castle Street, Maesteg CF34 9UN, tel: 01656 732109, fax: 01656 730274
Contact: Mrs C Brown, Headteacher
Open: Term-time, school hours or by appointment.
Space: 1 gallery with 21 lin m hanging space plus 20 lin m on screens and 92 sq m floor space
Exhibitions: 6 a year of which 5 originated, 1 touring
Details: Professional art gallery and workshop venue. The gallery is tied in with educational and community activities. The gallery area, which is also suitable for

drama/dance workshops, is in the basement of the school and has its own entrance. A full programme of exhibitions, residencies and workshops is planned for the future. Sales not a priority.

Mancot
CLWYD

Mancot Library

[Pa] [Ph] [Pr] [Sc] ✔

Exhibition space in public library for displaying local work.
Mancot Lane, Mancot CH5 2AH, tel: 01244 532430
Contact: Librarian
Open: Mon-Fri 10-1 and 2-7; Tues & Wed 2-5; Sat 9.30-12.30
Space: 1 gallery with 4 lin m hanging space
Exhibitions: 2 a year of which 1 originated, 1 touring
Details: Area in corner of library with two large wall-mounted boards and additional display screens on which local groups and artists show work to public. Programme covers range of craft, photography and painting.

Menai Bridge
GWYNEDD

Tegfryn Art Gallery

[Pa] (&)

Private art gallery in family home showing a permanent display of contemporary work, with occasional special exhibitions.
Cadnant Road, Menai Bridge, Anglesey LL59 5EW, tel: 01248 712437
Contact: Gwyn Brown
Space: 1 gallery
Exhibitions: 3 a year all originated

Merthyr Tydfil
MID GLAMORGAN

Cefn Community Centre *

[Pa] [Ph] [Pr] [Cr] [Sc] [LA] ✔

Exhibition space in large hall and conference centre.
Old Drill Hall Road, Cefn Coed, Merthyr Tydfil CF48 2NA, tel: 01685 389717
Contact: Nell Morgan
Details: Opportunity to exhibit work amid busy life of Centre's sport, education and workshop facilities. Encourages less-established artists who perhaps have not exhibited before.

Cyfarthfa Castle Museum & Art Gallery *

[Pa] [Ph] [Pr] [Sc] ✔

Work by Welsh artists, or by artists living or responding in a significant way to the country, its people, customs and history.
Brecon Road, Merthyr Tydfil CF47 8RE, tel: 01685 723112
Contact: Stephen Done, Curator
Space: 1 gallery with 50 lin m hanging space plus 12 lin m on screens
Exhibitions: 4 a year of which 3 originated, 1 touring
Details: Particularly interested in photography, oil, watercolour and print, but welcomes sculpture. Work by artists no longer living or of historical content are welcomed. Space is light and airy, with a rather dim corridor beside. Cannot house very large works.

Milford Haven
DYFED

Torch Theatre

[Pa] [Ph] [Pr] ✔ (&)(w)

Theatre foyer space for work by community groups and local artists.
St Peter's Road, Milford Haven SA73 2BU, tel: 01646 694192
Contact: Sarah Lewis, Gallery Supervisor
Open: Mon-Sat 10-3.30, 5-8; some Sun 6.30-9.30
Space: 1 gallery with 194 lin m hanging space
Exhibitions: 12 a year
Details: Exhibition space in top foyer of major regional repertory theatre. Regular monthly exhibitions throughout the year, mainly local artists plus schools exhibitions, seen by theatre audiences and other interested people. Variety of work exhibited in order to provide ever changing background for theatre patrons. Selling work not primary aim of exhibiting work.

Mold
CLWYD

Daniel Owen Centre, Exhibition Room

[Pa] [Ph] [Pr] [Cr] [Sc] ✔ (&)(w)

Temporary exhibitions gallery, small museum display relating to Daniel Owen and new Heritage Centre situated above public library run by Clwyd Library and Information Service.
Daniel Owen Centre, Earl Road, Mold CH7 1AP, tel: 01352 754791
Contact: Nia Wyn Jones, Community Librarian
Open: Mon-Tues & Thurs-Fri 9.30-7; Wed 9.30-5.30; (Oct-Apr) Sat 9.30-12.30; (May-Sept) Sat 9.30-4.30
Space: 1 gallery with 23 lin m hanging

space plus 14 lin m on screens and 95 sq m floor space
Exhibitions: 10 a year of which 7 originated, 3 touring
Details: Regular monthly exhibitions throughout the year, equally divided between touring shows, local and other artists, local community art and craft exhibitions. Target is the local community. Encourage local people to become more involved with the gallery through workshops and other events run by artists. Aims to exhibit a higher standard of work and be able to accustom the public to more 'difficult' work. Sale of work not a priority.

Oriel Theatr Clwyd

[Pa] [Ph] [Pr] [Cr] [Sc] ✔(£) (&)(w)

A dedicated temporary exhibition area showing all aspects of contemporary visual arts in a multi-media centre.
Theatr Clwyd, Mold CH7 1YA, tel: 01352 756331, fax: 01352 758323
Contact: Jonathan Le Vay, Assistant Exhibitions Officer
Open: Mon-Sat 10am-10pm; Sun 7pm-10pm
Space: 2 galleries with 100 lin m hanging space plus 20 lin m on screens and 250 sq m floor space
Exhibitions: 10 a year of which 6 originated, 4 touring
Details: Emphasis on exhibiting the work of new artists in solo or group exhibitions, but work by established artists also shown. The galleries are part of a major regional multi-media arts centre with annual visitor turnover of 350,000. Some height restrictions. Alongside the exhibition programme there is an energetic educational programme with workshops and artists' residencies.

Wern Mill Gallery

[Pa] [Ph] [Cr] ✔ (&)

Ground-floor gallery in old corn mill with artists' materials, spinning, weaving and dyeing materials and workshop upstairs.
Nannerth, Mold CH7 5RH, tel: 01352 741318
Contact: Alex Campbell, Gallery Owner
Open: Tues-Sun 10-5
Space: 1 gallery with 183 lin m hanging space
Details: Continuous changing display of work selected by gallery; mainly modern landscapes. Arts and crafts atmosphere. Spinning and dyeing workshops (half-day classes) upstairs. 25% commission taken on sales. Sales considered primary role of gallery. Collectorplan.

Monmouth
GWENT

Art Centre (Monmouth) *

Pa Pr Cr Sc ● ❶

Varied programme of temporary exhibitions.
Monk Street, Monmouth NP5 3NZ, tel: 01600 716868/ 713905
Contact: Brian Banfield, Exhibition Organiser
Exhibitions: 6 a year all on a hire basis
Details: Victorian house containing exhibition space, an art materials shop and a framing service.

Pat Yallup Studio Gallery

Pa Pr Sc

Gallery showing mainly work by artist owner but also occasionally exhibits work by other artists.
Llandogo, Monmouth NP5 4TJ, tel: 01594 530940, fax: 01594 530658
Contact: Pat Yallup, Exhibition Organiser
Open: Tues, Thurs, Fri 9.30-6; Sat, Sun 10.30-6
Space: 2 galleries with 38 lin m hanging space plus 12 lin m on screens and 60 sq m floor space
Exhibitions: 5 a year all originated
Details: Commercial gallery and Pat Yallup's open studio. Monthly solo contemporary art exhibitions throughout the year, with changing mixed display, mainly landscape, abstract, contemporary, portraiture, sculpture. Possible space for poetry and musical evenings. Seating can be hired.

Montgomery
POWYS

Country Works

Pa Cr Sc ● ⑥

Work displayed in domestic setting within 5 rooms of listed 17th town house.
Broad Street, Montgomery SY15 6PH, tel: 01686 668866
Contact: Richard and Clare Halstead
Open: (Easter-Christmas) Tues-Sat 10-5.30 & Sun 2-5.30; (mid Jan-Easter) Wed-Sat 10-5.30
Space: 2 galleries with 22 lin m hanging space and 24 sq m floor space
Exhibitions: 7 a year all originated
Details: Gallery selected exhibition work which shows commitment to craftsmanship and integrity of idea. In addition to wall space also 6 lin m of display shelving. Sales considered primary role of gallery and commission taken.

Narberth
DYFED

Gallery at Colby

Pa Pr Cr Sc Wc

A private gallery situated in a converted hay loft on National Trust property.
Colby Woodland Garden, Stepaside, Narberth SA67 8PP, tel: 01834 814164
Contact: Mrs M Knox
Space: 2 galleries with 60 lin m hanging space and 124 sq m floor space
Details: hanging space for 100 paintings, all mediums. Also miniatures and sculptures in wood, glass, bronze and porcelain. calligraphy, turned-wood bowls, marquetry, hand-painted china plates, carved and engraved glass and a wide selection of prints. Exhibitions and courses run in Little Gallery which adjoins the main gallery.

Neath
WEST GLAMORGAN

Cefn Coed Colliery Museum

Pa Ph Sc ● ⓣ ⓖ Wc

Temporary exhibition space within mining history museum showing work relevant to cultural history of area or on theme related to mining industry.
Blaenant Colliery, Crynant, Neath SA10 8SN, tel: 01639 750556
Contact: Mr Merrill
Open: (Apr-Sept) daily 10.30-6; (Oct-Mar) daily 10.30-4; closed Christmas/ New Year
Space: 1 gallery with 120 sq m floor space
Exhibitions: 3 a year of which 1 originated
Details: Local authority museum. Sales on informal basis; no commission taken. Exhibitions included in guided tour around museum for groups/school children, etc.

Newport
GWENT

Brynglas Adult Education Centre

Pa Ph Pr Cr Sc LA ● ❶

High-walled passage on ground floor plus a staircase where mainly 2D work is shown more often by amateur than professional artists.
Brynglas Hill, Newport NP9 5QU, tel: 01633 821657, fax: 01633 858225
Contact: Roger Fynn
Space: 2 galleries
Exhibitions: 8 a year of which 4 originated, 4 on a hire basis
Details: Adult education centre housed in old Victorian building. 2000 regular users.

Produces publicity to draw in a wider audience.

Newport Museum & Art Gallery

Pa Ph Pr Cr Sc ● ⓣ ⓖ Wc

Aims to exhibit best of Welsh art & design and to bring in a comprehensive range of the best work from outside Wales.
John Frost Square, Newport NP9 1PA, tel: 01633 840064
Contact: Sandra Jackaman, Exhibitions Officer
Open: Mon-Thurs 9.30-5; Fri 9.30-4.30; Sat 9.30-4
Space: 1 gallery with 92 lin m hanging space and 237 sq m floor space
Exhibitions: 15 a year of which 7 originated, 8 touring
Details: Run by Newport Leisure Services Department. Provides exhibitions and events for the benefit of Newport and visitors to the town. Work by artists/ makers, prominent locally, nationally and internationally. Exhibitions include graphic design, at least one mixed crafts exhibition, and one exhibition relating to local history. Permanent collections include C18th-20th British paintings, contemporary prints, studio ceramics. Sales not a priority.

Pauline Harries Gallery

Pa Cr ●

Mixed display of artist owner's work alongside paintings and ceramics by other artists and makers and occasional group and one-person shows.
Ty Clyd, Long Street, Newport SA42 0TL, tel: 01239 820404
Contact: Pauline Harries, Exhibition Organiser
Space: 2 galleries
Exhibitions: 2 a year both originated
Details: Run by artist Pauline Harries. Occupies two rooms of a house. Selected group of artists from Wales show representational paintings including detailed realism. Emphasis on landscape and interiors in range of painting and drawing media.

Sessions House *

Pa Ph Pr Sc ●

Gallery on first floor of framing business, showing solo exhibitions by artists based in the Pembrokeshire area.
East Street, Newport SA42 0SY, tel: 01239 820853
Contact: Richard Willson
Exhibitions: 8 a year all originated

Newtown
POWYS

Gwasg Gregynog Gallery

Small gallery displaying limited edition books printed at Gregynog Press including fine bookbindings and original signed prints.
Gregynog , Tregynon, Newtown SY16 3PW, tel: 01686 650625, fax: 01686 650656
Contact: David Esslemont, Controller
Open: Weekdays 9-5; occasional weekends
Space: 1 gallery with 7 lin m hanging space and 18 sq m floor space
Exhibitions: 2 a year both originated
Details: Gallery exhibits Gregynog books, special bindings, original signed prints from Gregynog books, original material relating to the design of particular books, smaller publications and ephemera. Occasional exhibitions of work of artists associated with the Press and of processes and techniques particular to this field. Sales not gallery's primary role.

Oriel 31

Gallery purpose-built in 1967 showing exhibitions of local, national and international significance covering whole range of visual arts.
Davies Memorial Gallery, The Park, Newtown SY16 2NZ, tel: 01686 625041, fax: 01686 623633
Contact: Elaine Marshall, Exhibitions Organiser
Open: Mon-Sat 10-5
Space: 1 gallery with 47 lin m hanging space
Exhibitions: 8 a year of which 7 originated, 1 touring
Details: Gallery purpose-built through support from public funds. As well as exhibitions holds wide range of prints, cards, books. Extensive Education Programme including talks, workshops and seminars for schools and adults. Also Craft Gallery at Oriel 31, Welshpool (see separate entry). Sale of work not gallery's primary function.

Phoenix Gallery

Library gallery showing exhibitions of work by local artists and craftspeople.
Newtown Library, Park Lane, Newtown SY16 1EJ, tel: 01686 626934, fax: 01686 625157
Contact: Mrs J Rimmer, Branch Librarian
Open: Mon, Wed, Thurs 9.30-5.30; Tues and Fri 9.30-7.30; Sat 9.30-12.30
Space: 1 gallery with 13 lin m hanging space and 60 sq m floor space

Exhibitions: 22 a year of which 16 originated, 6 on a hire basis
Details: Exhibiting area is in the foyer of the library, all visitors passing through this space into the library. Areas consist of wall space, free standing boards and glass display cases. Library service aims to encourage and promote keener participation in and enjoyment of the arts. Sales not a priority.

Pembroke Dock
DYFED

Pembroke Dock Library

Exhibitions by amateur and professional artists in library exhibition space.
Water Street, Pembroke Dock, tel: 01646 686356
Contact: Linda Holloway, Librarian
Space: 1 gallery with 8 lin m hanging space
Exhibitions: 15 a year of which 12 originated, 3 touring
Details: Clad walls and 15 movable screens arranged to artist's preference. Caters best for small to medium work and can accommodate 40-50 paintings, often more with groups exhibitions. 2-3 shows a year on touring circuit from Carmarthen Library and organised by Arts Officer. Three craft showcases filled partly by application to Librarian and partly by Arts Officer. 20% commission on sales.

Penarth
SOUTH GLAMORGAN

Turner House

Temporary exhibition space run by Department of Art of the National Museum of Wales.
Plymouth Road, Penarth CF6 2DH, tel: 01222 708870
Contact: Mark L Evans, Assistant Keeper (Fine Art), Department of Art, National Museum of Wales, Cathays Park, Cardiff, CF1 3NP, tel: 01222 397951, fax: 01222 373219
Open: Tues-Sat 11-1, 2-5; Sun 2-5; Mon closed
Space: 2 galleries with 55 lin m hanging space and 140 sq m floor space
Exhibitions: 7 a year of which 5 originated, 2 touring
Details: Branch gallery of National Museum of Wales. Shows temporary exhibitions from Museum's own collection and from elsewhere. An upstairs and a downstairs gallery but only the latter affords disabled access. Recent exhibitions include retrospectives of Terry Setch and Peter Prendergast. Sales not a priority. (See also entry for National Museum of Wales, Cardiff.)

Penglais
DYFED

Catherine Lewis Gallery

Exhibitions normally derived from university's Graphic Art collection but include student exhibitions and exhibitions of graphic art from outside college.
Hugh Owen Library, University College of Wales, Aberystwyth, Penglais SY23 1HB, tel: 01970 622460, fax: 01970 622461
Contact: Alistair Crawford, Head of School of Art, University of Wales, Buarth Mawr, Aberystwyth, SY23 1NE
Space: 1 gallery with 34 lin m hanging space and 22 sq m floor space
Exhibitions: 5 a year
Details: Houses Aberystwyth University's graphic art collection and located within the library. Exhibitions normally last 3 months. Audience is the college community though the gallery is open to the public. School visits are organised.

Pontardawe
WEST GLAMORGAN

Cross Gallery

Small gallery with hanging and free standing space integrated into busy community centre where art is considered part of the 'whole person'.
The Cross Community & Educational Resource Centre, 1 High Street, Pontardawe SA8 4HU, tel: 01792 863955
Contact: Helen Matthews, Centre Coordinator
Open: Mon-Fri 10-4; weekends by arrangment
Space: 1 gallery with 15 lin m hanging space plus 6 lin m on screens and 38 sq m floor space
Exhibitions: 4 a year all originated
Details: Exhibition room within community education resource centre funded by the LEA, offering adult education classes, workshops, advice sessions and room hire for many organisations. Making art accessible both to the people of the Swansea Valley and whole of West Glamorgan. Diverse programme of solo and group exhibitions by living artists/ makers, promoting local artists as well as artists from further afield. Related workshops when possible. Continuing education policy. Sales not a priority.

Pontypool
GWENT

Valley Inheritance Museum

Pa Ph Pr Cr SC LA ✓H ●✦

Independent local history museum with regularly used temporary exhibition room.
Park Buildings, Pontypool NP4 6JH, tel: 01495 752036
Contact: Martin Buckridge, Director
Open: Mon-Sat 10-5; Sun 2-5
Space: 1 gallery with 20 lin m hanging space and 30 sq m floor space
Exhibitions: 6 a year of which 4 originated, 1 touring, 1 on a hire basis
Details: Local history museum situated in Georgian stable block, with regularly changing temporary exhibitions and events. Coffee shop and gift shop. Special events can be organised in the large cobbled courtyard, or first-floor lecture theatre. Mainly local audience. Temporary exhibition room is rectangular with reduced natural light, track lighting, facilities for mounting/screwing pictures on walls. Sales not a priority.

Pontypridd
MID GLAMORGAN

Circle Gallery

Pa Ph Pr Cr SC LA ✓ ●✦

Primarily a gallery for Welsh artists, especially new artists, community groups and schools.
The Muni Arts Centre, Gelliwastad Road, Pontypridd CF37 2DP, tel: 01443 485934, fax: 01443 401832
Contact: Rachel Thomas, Assistant Manager
Open: Mon-Sat 10-5
Space: 1 gallery with 36 lin m hanging space plus 9 lin m on screens and 91 sq m floor space
Exhibitions: 12 a year of which 10 originated, 2 touring
Details: Gallery in complex with cinema, theatre and café. Emphasis on art involving the local community, with monthly thematic and open exhibitions. Funded by Welsh Arts Council and Taff-ely Borough Council. Welcomes applications from outside the area. Sales not a priority.

Oriel y Bont

Pa Ph Pr SC ✓£ ●✦

University campus gallery that enables students and local community to see contemporary visual arts practice.
University of Glamorgan, Pontypridd CF37 1DL, tel: 01443 480480
Contact: Alan Salisbury, Field Leader Arts & Media
Open: Term-time Mon-Fri 9-5

Space: 1 gallery with 32 lin m hanging space plus 3 lin m on screens
Exhibitions: 6 a year all originated
Details: Gallery in foyer of large building at front of the university campus. Space is roughly octagonal in shape with hanging surfaces 28' in length and 8' in height. Walls provide additional space of approx 20' x 8' also display cases. Sales not a priority. Intention is to provide arena for contemporary visual arts that will inform and extend students' visual and cultural awareness, acting as 'shop window' for institution establishing links with local community. Exhibitors usually give lectures/run workshops relating to exhibition.

Pontypridd Heritage Centre

Pa Ph Cr ✓H

Ground-floor and basement exhibition areas showing historical and contemporary exhibitions.
Bridge Street, Pontypridd CF37 4PE, tel: 01443 402077
Contact: Brian Davies, Curator
Space: 2 galleries with 25 lin m hanging space plus 40 lin m on screens and 200 sq m floor space
Exhibitions: 8 a year
Details: Converted Welsh Baptist Chapel housing permanent exhibition on the history of Pontypridd as well as two temporary exhibition spaces. Audience for exhibitions is mainly from Mid Glamorgan valleys, population c.150,000.

Port Talbot
WEST GLAMORGAN

Margam Orangery

SC ✓

Margam Park, Margam, Port Talbot SA13 2TJ, tel: 01639 881635, fax: 01639 895897
Contact: Claire Roach, Administrator
Open: (Apr-Sept) Daily 10-5; (Oct-Mar) Wed Sun 10-4
Space: 2 galleries
Exhibitions: 3 a year all originated
Details: C18th orangery in country park run by West Glamorgan County Council. Indoor gallery and an outdoor area run by Sculpture at Margam. Sculpture featured in mainly solo shows. Also a sculpture exhibition throughout the summer and a separate, permanent display in Margam Park. Plans underway to build sculpture trail which will be fully accessible to the disabled. Applications to exhibit or hire space must be in writing with CV and slides.

Porthmadog
GWYNEDD

Flour Shed Gallery

Pa Ph Cr SC ✓ ●

Gallery in large craft centre specialising in craft showcase items, some made on the premises.
Snowdon Mill, Snowdon Street, Porthmadog LL49 9DF, tel: 01766 512137 or 01766 512777
Contact: Bill Hildyard, Director
Open: Mon-Fri 9.30-5; (July & Aug) weekends; some winter opening
Space: 1 gallery with 46 lin m hanging space and 140 sq m floor space
Details: Centre owned by local co-operative used for displaying members' showcase items. Also work from guest artists and craftspeople. Frequently changing exhibitions planned. Courses on craft techniques run. Sales not primary role of gallery.

Porthmadog Community Centre *

Pa Ph Pr Cr SC LA

Exhibition space for all kinds of exhibitions, professional shows and trade fairs.
Oakley Wharf, Porthmadog LL49 9LU, tel: 01766 513372
Contact: Gwynfor Hughes, Exhibition Organiser

Stiwdio Garreg Wen *

Pa Pr Cr

Commercial artist-run gallery in centre of busy coastal resort showing work by other artists as well as the owner's work.
Snowdon Street, Porthmadog LL49 9BT, tel: 01766 513833/ 512450
Contact: Rob Piercy, Exhibition Organiser, 20 Maes Gerddi, Porthmadog, LL49 9LE
Space: 3 galleries
Exhibitions: 2 a year both originated
Details: Continuous hanging display for sale, mostly watercolour landscapes by Welsh artists, and occasional solo exhibitions lasting one month.

Prestatyn
CLWYD

Prestatyn Library

Pa Ph Cr ✓ ●

Exhibition area in library foyer showing occasional touring exhibitions plus work by local artists and makers.
Nant Hall Road, Prestatyn LL19 9LH, tel: 01745 854841
Contact: J. Beagan, Community Librarian
Open: Mon, Thurs & Fri 9.30-7; Tues & Wed 9.30-5.30; Sat 9.30-12.30

Space: 1 gallery with plus 6 lin m on screens and 26 sq m floor space
Exhibitions: 12 a year
Details: Community gallery for mirror-plated paintings and framed photographs and craft showcase as wall cabinet. Run by Clwyd Library and Information Service. Sales not a priority.

Presteigne
POWYS

MBCA Gallery (Mid Border Community Arts)

Pa Ph Pr Cr Sc ● ⊕

Voluntary non-profit making body, aims to bring more arts-based activity to area.
Shire Hall, Broad Street, Presteigne LD8 2AD, tel: 01544 260116
Contact: John Hubley, Exhibition Organiser
Open: Mon-Sat 10-5 during exhibitions
Space: 3 galleries
Exhibitions: 8 a year of which 6 originated, 2 touring
Details: Run by Mid-Border Community Arts. Programmes about six varied temporary exhibitions annually, encouraging young artists as well as presenting major touring exhibitions in all media. Space also for exhibitions by local artists. School visits and talks by exhibiting artists.

Pwllheli
GWYNEDD

Bodvel Hall Craft Centre *

Pa Ph Pr Cr Sc ●

A changing display of craftwork with some prints and paintings for sale
Pwllheli LL53, tel: 01758 613386
Contact: G Morris, Exhibition Organiser
Space: 1 gallery with 30 lin m hanging space plus 30 lin m on screens and 150 sq m floor space
Exhibitions: 4 a year all originated
Details: Currently only holds exhibitions from Easter to September, but is hoped that the programme will extend to fill the year. A resident picture framer works for the public as well as exhibitors. Applications from outside the area are welcome.

Plas Glyn-y-Weddw Gallery *

Pa Ph Pr Sc ●

Rooms in mansion (owners' home) devoted to special monthly exhibitions.
Plas Glyn-y-Weddw, Llanbedrog, Pwllheli LL53 7TT, tel: 01758 740763
Contact: Gwyneth & Dafydd ap Tomos
Space: 11 galleries with 312 lin m hanging space plus 92 lin m on screens and 493 sq m floor space

Exhibitions: 15 a year of which 13 originated, 2 touring
Details: 1856 Gothic-style mansion first used as a private art gallery at the turn of the century. Major part of the building devoted to changing mixed displays of paintings, sculpture and ceramics by contemporary artists with monthly exhibitions in some rooms. Audience of 40,000 a year includes holidaymakers, and visitors on art and sketching holidays at the gallery.

Rhayader
POWYS

Elan Valley Visitor Centre

Pa Ph Pr Cr ●

Exhibitions generally relate to natural history, etc.
Elan Village, Rhayader LD6 5HP, tel: 01597 810880, fax: 01597 811276
Contact: Mr Peter Jennings, Head Ranger
Space: 1 gallery with 20 lin m hanging space plus 18 lin m on screens and 10 sq m floor space
Exhibitions: 8 a year all originated
Details: A permanent display depicting the history of the area with regular exhibitions from local artists plus others. The audience is c.100,000 pa. People come to enjoy the peace and quiet, the scenery, the wildlife of the area. There are café facilities, toilets, etc.

Rhayader Library

Pa Cr Sc ● ⊕ &

Exhibition space available in foyer of library.
West Street, Rhayader LD6 5AB, tel: 01597 810548
Contact: Mrs Addison, Branch Librarian
Open: Mon 2-5, 6-7 ; Tues & Thurs 2-5; Wed 10-1, 2-5; Fri 10-1, 2-5, 6-7; Sat 10-12
Space: 1 gallery with plus 6 lin m on screens and 12 sq m floor space
Exhibitions: 6 a year all on a hire basis
Details: Exhibitions of cultural, educational and charitable nature may be shown free of charge. Selling work is not primary role of exhibition space.

Rhondda
MID GLAMORGAN

Rhondda Community Arts

Pa Ph Sc ● & 4

Promotes local arts initiatives as well as bringing in work of professional artists, organising shows in several venues.
c/o Parc & Dare Theatre, Station Road, Treorchy, Rhondda CF42 6NL, tel: 01443 776 090

Contact: Martin Lynch, Visual Art Development Worker
Open: To suit exhibition
Space: 2 galleries with 49 lin m hanging space and 72 sq m floor space
Exhibitions: 2 a year
Details: Community projects – art, photography, workshops, exhibitions etc. Rhondda Community Arts has national reputation for its work with children, the unemployed, women, people with disabilities and adults in the community who would not normally take part in arts workshops/classes. Selling work not main role of organisation.

Rhuddlan
CLWYD

Rhuddlan Library *

Pa Ph Pr ●

Space for temporary exhibitions usually by local artists but applications from outside the area are welcome.
Vicarage Lane, Rhuddlan LL18 2SF, tel: 01745 590719
Contact: Yvonne Davies, Branch Librarian
Space: 1 gallery
Exhibitions: 12 a year all originated
Details: Display cabinets available by arrangement.

Rhyl
CLWYD

Rhyl Library, Museum and Arts Centre

Pa Ph Pr Cr Sc LA ● £ ⊕ & ⓦ

Aims to present best in regional art, and to give the local community a good selection of national touring exhibitions.
Church Street, Rhyl LL18 3AA, tel: 01745 353814, fax: 01745 331438
Contact: Exhibitions Officer
Open: Mon-Fri 10-5; Sat 10- 4
Space: 2 galleries with 55 lin m hanging space plus 15 lin m on screens and 110 sq m floor space
Exhibitions: 10 a year of which 5 originated, 4 touring, 1 on a hire basis
Details: Represents all arts disciplines and provides a balance of the regional, national and international in contemporary art. Audience is extremely varied and quite vocal in its opinions. Workshops and weekly art classes covering adults and children. Sales not a priority.

Ruthin
CLWYD

Ruffin Craft Centre Gallery

Crafts Council selected gallery exhibiting contemporary applied art from all over the UK, and Studio 8 Gallery which shows mainly wall-mounted applied art, photography and print.
Park Road, Ruthin LL15 1BB, tel: 01824 704774
Contact: Philip Hughes, Exhibition Organiser
Open: (Summer) Mon-Sun 10-5.30; (Winter) Mon-Sat 10-5, Sun 12-5
Space: 2 galleries with 18 lin m hanging space and 100 sq m floor space
Exhibitions: 18 a year of which 14 originated, 4 touring
Details: Aims to show a constantly changing selection of top artists'/ craftspeoples' work from throughout the UK; to promote and present new and exciting work of high quality in sympathetic surroundings, therefore creating a centre of excellence for the applied arts. Sales are considered the gallery's primary concern.

St Asaph
CLWYD

St Asaph Library *

Temporary exhibitions hung on picture rail throughout library.
The Roe, St Asaph LL17 0LU, tel: 01745 582253
Contact: Yvonne Davies, Branch Librarian
Space: 50 lin m hanging space

Swansea
WEST GLAMORGAN

Attic Gallery

Wales' longest established commercial gallery showing contemporary art with four connected gallery rooms.
61 Wind Street, Swansea SA1 1EG, tel: 01792 653387
Contact: Brenda Bloxam, Director
Open: Mon-Fri 10-5; Sat 10-4
Space: 4 galleries with 45 lin m hanging space and 65 sq m floor space
Exhibitions: 6 a year all originated
Details: Changing display of contemporary paintings, original prints and small sculpture, interspersed with a regular programme of exhibitions of work from invited artists. Originally provided venue for artists working in Wales, now regularly exhibits work from outside region. Policy to maintain wide cross-section of good quality work and to promote artists who provide that work. Full framing service.

Ceri Richards Gallery

A lively gallery selling fine art, crafts, cards, etc.
Taliesin Arts Centre, University of Wales, Singleton Park, Swansea SA2 8PZ, tel: 01792 295526
Contact: Sybil Crouch, Manager
Open: Mon 11-5; Tues-Fri 11-6; Sat 12-6
Space: 2 galleries with 28 lin m hanging space plus 6 lin m on screens and 193 sq m floor space
Exhibitions: 10 a year of which 9 originated, 1 touring
Details: Modern gallery within purpose-built arts centre (1984). Fibre-board screens and display facilities for 3D work. Programme concentrates on commercial exhibitions and work by local/Wales-based artists. Sales a priority.

Craftsman Gallery

Framing business with four galleries showing work by Welsh artists.
58 St Helens Road, Swansea SA1 4BE, tel: 01792 642043
Contact: Jeff Bowden
Open: Mon-Sat 7.15-5
Space: 4 galleries with 180 sq m floor space
Exhibitions: 5 a year all originated
Details: Four galleries on premises; 1 large downstairs gallery and 3 upstairs. Exhibitions are of work by Welsh artists liked by proprietor. Framing is main business but sales of work encouraged and commission taken. Galleries lit by windows (no spots). Applications to exhibit welcomed from Welsh artists/craftspeople. Independent access for wheelchair users to ground floor-gallery only.

Glynn Vivian Art Gallery

Municipal gallery showing contemporary and historical shows of fine art, crafts and photography.
Alexandra Road, Swansea SA1 5DZ, tel: 01792 655006/ 651738, fax: 01792 651713
Contact: Alison C. Lloyd, Exhibitions Officer
Open: Tues-Sun 10.30-5; BH
Space: 4 galleries with 154 lin m hanging space and 473 sq m floor space
Exhibitions: 15 a year of which 7 originated, 8 touring
Details: Exhibitions of local and international significance, solo shows of emerging/mid-career artists, and exhibitions drawn from permanent collections of mainly C19th & C20th fine and applied art. Outdoor sculpture court. Caters for wide audience, serving both Swansea residents and wider arts audience. Sale of work not gallery's primary concern.

Gorseinon Institute

Gallery showing work by amateur and professional regional artists.
44 Lime Street, Gorseinon, Swansea SA4 2EE, tel: 01792 899221
Contact: Sian Mainwaring, Community Recreation Officer, Civic Centre, Penllergaer, Swansea, SA4 1GH, tel: 0792 893081 ext 2321
Open: Mon-Fri 10-8; variable Sat-Sun
Space: 1 gallery with 16 lin m hanging space and 38 sq m floor space
Exhibitions: 10 a year of which 6 originated, 4 touring
Details: Space is hire and commission free to selected artists. Institute is currently applying for Arts Council of Wales funding and depending on the outcome may offer EPR on some shows. Artists' applications welcome Oct-Dec of each year for exhibition programme from April onwards of following year. Selection takes place in Dec.

Mumbles Gallery

Mixed and solo exhibitions of work by local artists.
618 Mumbles Road, Swansea SA3 4EA, tel: 01792 367102
Contact: Ian & Janet Campbell, Exhibition Organiser
Space: 1 gallery with 20 lin m hanging space and 30 sq m floor space
Exhibitions: 1 a year originated
Details: Run by architect Ian Campbell and lacemaker/weaver Janet Campbell.

New Gallery

Gallery showing work by professional artists from all over UK.
59 Newton Road, Mumbles, Swansea SA3 4BL, tel: 01792 367910
Contact: Dr David Williams
Open: Mon & Tues, Thurs-Sat 10-1, 2-5
Space: 1 gallery with 66 lin m hanging space and 50 sq m floor space
Exhibitions: 8 a year all originated
Details: Gallery draws an audience from a wide radius, though not a tourist's gallery. Selling work is primary role.

Ocean Gallery *

Features responses to local environment by local artists.
1 Ocean Crescent, Swansea Marina Seafront, Swansea SA1 1YZ, tel: 01792 648180

Contact: Ann John-Upton, Owner
Space: 3 galleries with 38 lin m hanging space and 70 sq m floor space
Exhibitions: 8 a year all originated
Details: A panoramic view of Swansea Bay from 2 fully-glazed galleries. Local scenes of the Gower and South West Wales by local artists. Traditional land & seascapes, flower paintings, fabric pictures and work by local potters. Monthly exhibitions. Space aplenty on promenade for artists painting in residence (inside in inclement weather). Commissions accepted. Collector plan. Sponsored by Arts Council of Wales.

Swansea Arts Workshop Gallery

A **Pa** **Ph** **Pr** **Cr** **A** **O** **H** **S**

Artist-run gallery with a changing exhibition programme of contemporary painting, sculpture, installation, crafts and performance.
Gloucester Place, Swansea SA1 1TY, tel: 01792 652016
Contact: Jane Phillips, Gallery Co-ordinator
Open: Tues-Sun 11-5; BH
Space: 1 gallery with 34 lin m hanging space plus 5 lin m on screens and 43 sq m floor space
Exhibitions: 10 a year of which 7 originated, 2 touring, 1 on a hire basis
Details: Gallery aims to show high-quality work from Wales, UK and abroad and to be a forerunner in contemporary art. Sale of work not gallery's primary concern.

Swansea Maritime & Industrial Museum

Pa **Ph** **Cr** **O** **S** **Wc**

Exhibitions mainly chosen to reflect collections and relevance to locality.
Museum Square, Maritime Quarter, Swansea SA1 1SN, tel: 01792 650351
Contact: Mike Lewis, Curator
Open: Tues-Sun 10.30-5.15; BH
Space: 1 gallery with 15 lin m hanging space and 28 sq m floor space
Exhibitions: 10 a year of which 2 originated, 8 touring
Details: Museum occupies one of only two original dock buildings that remain in Maritime Quarter. Originated exhibitions reflect the theme of Museum. Also show touring exhibitions of art, craft and photography.

Swansea Museum

Pa **Ph** **Pr** **Cr** **Sc** **A** **O** **t** **H** **S**

Social history museum where temporary exhibitions usually themed to form the basis for a larger exhibition with objects displayed from the collection.
Victoria Road, Swansea SA1 1SN, tel: 01792 653763, fax: 01792 652589
Contact: Rosalyn Gee/Jenny Sabine, Curator/Assistant Curator

Open: Tues-Sun 10.30-5.10
Space: 3 galleries with 34 lin m hanging space
Exhibitions: 1 a year originated
Details: In the past, exhibitions have been subsidiary part of activities, but now hopes to develop this side of programme. As museum of social history unlikely to encompass anything too contemporary in style. Emphasis more upon topographical art and art connected with local history. Selling exhibitions staged to allow greater access to contemporary art and craft for visitors and workshops often available to support exhibitions. However sales are not seen as primary role.

Tenby
CLWYD

Boathouse Gallery

Sergeants Lane, St Julian Street, Tenby SA70 7AS, tel: 01834 845584

Tenby Museum & Art Gallery

Pa **Ph** **Pr**

Museum with occasional contemporary art exhibitions.
Castle Hill, Tenby SA70 7BP, tel: 01834 842809
Contact: Marianne Hutton, Art Director
Open: (Summer) Daily 10-6; (Winter) Mon-Fri 10-4
Space: 1 gallery
Details: Recent extension houses new gallery devoted to changing exhibitions of contemporary work by artists with a Pembrokeshire connection. Gallery proposes to hold 2 exhibitions a year.

Trehafod
MID GLAMORGAN

Rhondda Heritage Park Centre Gallery

Pa **Ph** **Pr** **Cr** **Sc** **O** **t** **S** **Wc**

Gallery hosts diverse programme of events including work by local, regional and national artists.
Lewis Merthyr, Coed Cae Road, Trehafod CF37 7NP, tel: 01443 682036, fax: 01443 687420
Contact: Nicole Dobbin, Marketing Assistant
Open: (Easter-Sept) Mon-Sun 10-5, last admission 4.30; (Oct-Easter) Tues-Sun 10-5
Space: 1 gallery with 34 lin m hanging space plus 11 lin m on screens and 9 sq m floor space
Exhibitions: 5 a year of which 4 originated, 1 touring
Details: Shows work that celebrates the landscape, heritage and culture of the

Rhonnda valleys. Spacious gallery adjoins centre's café Artists featured in programme are mostly from Wales or linked to it by theme. Centre draws very wide audience including regular school groups and is becoming fast growing tourist attraction. Selling work not gallery's primary role.

Treorchy
MID GLAMORGAN

Parc & Dare Theatre

Pa

Theatre and concert hall with function room available for exhibitions.
Station Road, Rhondda, Treorchy CF42, tel: 01443 775654, fax: 01443 776922
Contact: Mr Derek Ward, Arts & Events Manager

Welshpool
POWYS

Oriel 31

Pa **Ph** **Cr** **O** **S**

Temporary exhibition gallery concentrating on promoting and exhibiting quality work by contemporary designer makers.
7 High Street, Welshpool SY21 7JP, tel: 01938 552990
Contact: Helen Lawson, Exhibition Officer
Open: Mon-Sat 10-5
Space: 1 gallery with 20 lin m hanging space and 24 sq m floor space
Exhibitions: 9 a year of which 8 originated, 1 touring
Details: Run by a charity promoting the visual arts in Mid Wales. Based in a rural area and catering for widely differing tastes. Exhibitions of contemporary art and craft/applied art in wide range of media encouraging work of new and established artists/makers plus changing display of small craft/applied art items for sale. Sales a priority. (See also Oriel 31, Newtown.)

Welshpool Library

Pa **Ph** **Sc** **O** **H** **S** **Wc**

Exhibition space in public library, mainly suitable for two-dimensional work.
Brook Street, Welshpool SY21 7PH, tel: 01938 553001
Contact: Mr Roger Foulkes, Librarian
Open: Tues & Wed 10-5.30; Mon & Fri 10-7; Thurs & Sat 10-12.30
Space: 1 gallery with 6 lin m hanging space
Exhibitions: 13 a year all on a hire basis
Details: Branch library situated in the town centre with exhibition space adjacent to the library area. Its purpose is to promote the arts to the public. Exhibitions usually last 2 weeks showing work by local artists/groups. Sales not primary role.

Whitland
DYFED

Studio in the Church

Selling gallery showing contemporary mostly
Welsh crafts and fine arts in converted nave
and sanctuary of ancient country church.
**Login, Whitland SA34 0XA, tel: 01437
563676**
Contact: Alan Hemmings & Jane
Hemmings, Directors
Open: Mon-Fri 10-5; Winter opening
times may vary
Space: 2 galleries with plus 26 lin m on
screens and 156 sq m floor space
Exhibitions: 5 a year all originated
Details: Gallery space of Alan Hemmings
Associates – designers and makers of
handwoven clothes and accessories.
Exhibitions mainly during summer months.
24 lin m display areas in addition to space
given above.

Wrexham
CLWYD

Bersham Heritage Centre

Industrial museum incorporating
exhibition gallery for temporary displays
with historical/contemporary themes.
**Bersham, Wrexham LL14 4HT, tel:
01978 261529**
Contact: Hilary Williams, Administrator
Open: (Easter-Sept) Mon-Fri 10-5, Sat-
Sun 12-5; (Oct-Easter) Mon-Fri 10-4, Sat-
Sun 12-4
Space: 1 gallery with 27 lin m hanging
space plus 12 lin m on screens and 49 sq m
floor space
Exhibitions: 3 a year all originated
Details: The temporary exhibition gallery
displays work of an industrial/historical
nature. The programme includes
photography, fine art and artifact displays.
Lighting in the gallery is variable.
Exhibitions are mirror plated or free
standing. Sale of work not a priority.

Cefn Mawr

Temporary exhibitions of work by mainly
local artists; group or one person shows.
**Plas Kynaston, Cefn Mawr, Wrexham
LL14 3AT, tel: 01978 820938**
Contact: Ann Hughes
Open: Mon, Fri 10-7; Tues 10-5.30; Wed
2-5.30
Space: 1 gallery
Details: Area with display screens on which
local artists can exhibit work to public.
Number of exhibitions per year varies.

Clwyd County Art &
Exhibition Division

Centralised service organising one-off and
touring exhibitions of all sizes and media
for network of Council's venues within
Clwyd.
**Wrexham Library Arts Centre, Rhosddu
Road, Wrexham LL11 1AU, tel: 01978
261932, fax: 01978 361876**
Contact: Steve Brake, County Arts &
Exhibitions Officer
Details: See separate entries for major
council venues: Wrexham Library Arts
Centre; Denbigh Library, Museum & Art
Gallery; Rhyl Library, Museum & Arts
Centre; Oriel Theatr Clwyd, Mold;
Bersham Industrial Heritage Centre;
Ruthin Craft Centre. National and
international shows, significant proportion
of which tour throughout Britain and
abroad. A variety of other exhibition areas
attached to libraries throughout the county
are also programmed to both initiate and
receive professional exhibitions. Selling
work not a priority. Facilities and access
vary according to venue.

Rhosllanerchrugog Library

Local branch library with area for showing
work by local artists, craftspeople, etc.
**Princes Road, Rhosllanerchrugog,
Wrexham LL14 1AB, tel: 01978 840328**
Contact: Ann Hughes, Community
Librarian
Open: Mon, Fri 10-7; Tues-Wed 10-5.30;
Closed Thurs, Sat
Space: 1 gallery with 10 sq m floor space
Exhibitions: 10 a year
Details: Area for exhibition screens.
Display cabinet available. Exhibitions
arranged by library, plus Clwyd Library
Service touring exhibitions. Selling work is
not main function of space.

Wrexham Library Arts
Centre

Local authority run gallery showing
important exhibitions of contemporary art
within a busy arts centre environment.
**Rhosddu Road, Wrexham LL11 1AU, tel:
01978 261932, fax: 01978 361876**
Contact: Martin Barlow, Arts &
Exhibitions Officer – Wrexham
Open: Mon-Fri 9.30-6.45; Sat 9.30-5.00
Space: 2 galleries with 60 lin m hanging
space plus 15 lin m on screens and 150 sq
m floor space
Exhibitions: 27 a year of which 22
originated, 5 touring
Details: Main gallery has programme of 8-
9 exhibitions per year of contemporary art
in all media, by artists of regional, national
and international importance. Major

exhibitions offered for tour. Education
programme includes talks, workshops and
projects. Gallery 2 has programme of
exhibitions by local artists and groups.
Craft display cases; some performance; art,
dance and drama classes; room hire;
occasional artists' residencies; popular
coffee shop.

Channel Islands

St Helier
JERSEY

Studio 18

Pa Ph Pr Sc ✔ ⊗

Well lit airy selling gallery at first-floor level.
23a Beresford Street, St Helier JE2 4WN, tel: 01534 34920
Contact: Tony Watton, Exhibition Organiser
Open: Mon-Sat 8.30-5.30
Space: 1 gallery with 40 lin m hanging space and 64 sq m floor space
Exhibitions: 8 a year all originated
Details: Commercial gallery showing contemporary work. Specialises in painting of the Channel Islands and work by local and European artists. Also British pop artists 1960 to the present. In addition to 8 one person shows a year also mixed seasonal shows.

St Martins
GUERNSEY

Studio Renoir

Pa Pr Cr ✔ ⊛

Barn style gallery, with beams and maple strip floor, above studio pottery in rural area to show, promote and sell artists' work.
Rue Moulin Huet, St Martins GY4 6EJ, tel: 01481 37201, fax: 01481 37703
Contact: Rex Opie, Proprietor
Open: Mon-Sat 9-5; Sun 10-4
Space: 1 gallery with 85 lin m hanging space and 105 sq m floor space
Exhibitions: 4 a year all originated
Details: Gallery aims to have monthly exhibitions to promote local artists but also welcomes artists from outside the Island. Gallery takes a third of income from sales as commission.

St Peter Port
GUERNSEY

Guernsey Museum & Art Gallery *

Pa Ph Pr Cr ✔

Permanent collection on the people and history of Guernsey plus art gallery showing temporary exhibitions.
Candie Gardens, St Peter Port, tel: 01481 726518, fax: 01481 715177
Contact: Rona Cole, Director
Space: 1 gallery with 21 lin m hanging space plus 32 lin m on screens and 92 sq m floor space
Exhibitions: 2 a year of which 1 originated, 1 touring
Details: Shows primarily museum's collection of C19th and early C20th paintings of Guernsey. Special exhibitions held six to seven times a year including Renoir, Miro, Picasso, Mervyn Peake. Various touring shows.

St Peters
GUERNSEY

Coach House Gallery

Pa Ph Pr Cr ✔ ⊗

Gallery policy is to show fine quality original work by living artists in its two spacious exhibition areas.
Les Islets, St Peters GY7 9ES, tel: 01481 65339
Contact: Mrs Lintell, Director
Open: Daily 11-5; winter hours may be restricted & closed Jan.
Space: 1 gallery with 29 lin m hanging space and 98 sq m floor space
Exhibitions: 11 a year of which 10 originated, 1 touring
Details: Converted farm building containing galleries on 2 floors, etching studio & pottery. Semi-permanent exhibition on ground floor; visiting monthly exhibitions in larger upstairs; looks for high standard of work by living artists. Framing and artists' materials in adjacent shop. Sales a priority. Ground floor only fully accessible.

About the editor

Janet Ross has twelve years experience in the visual arts. She has worked for Northern Arts Board and until 1993, was Exhibitions Officer at the Laing Art Gallery, Newcastle upon Tyne. Now a freelance arts organiser, as well as editing this directory, she's been working for the Artists' Agency and The Gallery at the University of Northumbria.

Advertisers' index

Services

Services

taking art to people

artreach aim to promote the work of new & established professional artists and encourage audiences awareness & enjoyment of the visual arts.

artreach create & tour an annual programme of small scale contemporary visual art and craft exhibitions to schools, libraries, art centres and workplaces in the North West.

Interested? Contact **artreach**
Unit B61, Brunswick Small Business Centre, Brunswick Business Park, Liverpool L3 4BD
Tel 0151-708-7620

Charity Registered No. 1001446

NORTH WEST ARTS BOARD

Support for artists, craftspeople and photographers

North West Arts Board (NWAB) offers advice, information and grant-aid to artists living and working in the North West. Its Grants for Individuals scheme can help support artists in the marketing and promotion of their work, training, attendance at craft and trade fairs, travel and production.

In addition, Slidex – a slide library and skills database of North West based visual arts, crafts and design businesses and practitioners – is run on behalf of NWAB by the Liverpool Design Initiative (Tel: 0151 709 1566) and the Castlefield Gallery, Manchester (Tel: 0161 832 8034) who can be contacted for further information.

For full details of NWAB's services for artists, contact: **The Visual Arts Department, North West Arts Board, 12 Harter Street, Manchester M1 6HY. Tel: 0161 228 3062.**
Fax: 0161 236 5361.
E-mail: nwarts- info@mcr1.poptel.org.uk.

National Artists Register
For information on contemporary visual artists

A X I S

The National Artists Register is a unique multimedia database developed by AXIS to document and promote contemporary visual artists. It provides invaluable up-to-date information for a wide range of user groups such as gallery organisers, commissioning agents, architects, journalists, researchers, teachers, curators, artists and other professionals. The Register's development is being funded by the Arts Council of England, the Scottish Arts Council, and several regional arts boards in England.

Free public access to the Register is now available *by appointment* at the Axis office in Leeds Metropolitan University. Visitors can compile their own search criteria, browse through artists images, and take away illustrated printouts of artists records.

For further details phone AXIS on **0113 2833125** between **9.30** and **12.00**, **Tuesday** to **Thursday**.

AXIS - Visual Arts Information Service, Leeds Metropolitan University, Calverley Street, Leeds LS1 3HE **Tel** : +44(0)113 283 3125 **Fax** : +44(0)113 283 3112 **E-Mail** : axis@gn.apc.org

Funding bodies

NORTHERN ARTS
VISUAL ARTS DEPARTMENT

The Visual Arts Department deals with Northern Arts' strategies for the visual arts and crafts in the region (Cleveland, Cumbria, Durham, Northumberland, Tyne & Wear).

It supports a number of organisations and individuals on an annual or project basis in order to produce and/or present work of the highest standard. The scope of its work includes exhibitions, events, commissions, fellowships, residencies and awards. In addition, it undertakes a number of strategic partnerships with local authorities and other statutory or voluntary agencies in pursuit of its objectives. A significant proportion of its current activities is towards the achievement of the Visual Arts UK 1996.

The schemes, opportunities & information services available include:

AWARDS TO ARTISTS AND CRAFTSPEOPLE

EXHIBITIONS, EVENTS AND COMMISSIONS

EXHIBITION PAYMENT RIGHT

INFORMATION SHEETS FOR ARTISTS AND CRAFTSPEOPLE

TRAVEL AND TRAINING OPPORTUNITIES

VISUAL ARTS INDEX ON AXIS DATABASE

Artists wishing to be represented on AXIS national artists', register should write to the Visual Arts Department, giving full postal details, telephone number and artform.

Details from the Visual Arts Department, Northern Arts, 9-10 Osborne Terrace, Jesmond, Newcastle upon Tyne NE2 1NZ. Tel: 0191 281 6334. Voice Mail 0191 281 2866

Yorkshire & Humberside
A R T S

Support for

Artists · Craftspeople
Photographers · Film Makers
Broadcasters · Writers

Recent restructuring at Yorkshire & Humberside Arts (YHA) has led to the formation of a combined **Visual and Media Arts Unit** headed up by Director Caroline Taylor. The Unit remains committed to the support of individual artists through a variety of financial schemes and through project funding.

For full funding details/deadlines ring the Visual & Media Arts Unit on
01924 455555

Offers financial support to those wishing to mount **visual art, crafts** and **photography** exhibitions and events in London, which create new and increased opportunities for audiences to see contemporary work.

For further information write to:
Funding Enquiries, London Arts Board, Elme House, 133 Long Acre, London WC2E 9AF or telephone the London Arts Board Help Line: 0171- 240 4578

SOUTH WEST ARTS

Support for Artists, Craftspeople and Photographers

South West Arts is committed to developing the visual arts and crafts in the South West and offers grants, information, advice and encouragement to organisations and individual practitioners resident in the region.

Grants include: Annual Awards; Training and Marketing Bursaries; Exhibition Payment Right; Exhibitions and Events.

Services include: bi-monthly Newsletter for Visual Artists, Craftspeople and Photographers; Slide Library of the work of contemporary arts practitioners living in the region; a wide range of Information Sheets.

For details of all grants and services please contact the Information Service at South West Arts, Bradninch Place, Gandy Street, Exeter EX4 3LS or telephone (01392) 218188.

THE SCOTTISH **ARTS** COUNCIL

The Visual Arts Department offers support to Organisations/ Groups from the following funds

Exhibitions and Projects

Hiring Touring Exhibitions

Infrastructure (Posts and Improvements)

Travel and Training Grants

Touring Franchise

For further details write to the Visual Arts Officer, Exhibitions at:
Scottish Arts Council, 12 Manor Place, Edinburgh EH3 7DD
Tel: 0131 226 6051   Fax: 0131 225 9833

CYNGOR
CELFYDDYDAU
CYMRU

THE ARTS
COUNCIL OF
WALES

Ceir gwybodaeth am wasanaethau CCC i artistiaid gweledol, orielau a threfnwyr arddangosfeydd yng Nghymru drwy gysylltu â'r **Adran Gelf Cyngor Celfyddydau Cymru Stryd yr Amgueddfa Caerdydd, Cymru CF1 3NX.**

For information about ACW's services to visual artists, galleries and exhibition organisers in Wales, contact: **Visual Arts Department Arts Council of Wales Museum Place, Cardiff Wales CF1 3NX.**

**Ffôn: 01222 394711
Ffacs: 01222 221447**

**Tel: 01222 394711
Fax: 01222 221447**

Funding bodies

Professional bodies

A growing series which reports on key aspects of contemporary visual arts practice. They combine analysis and commentary by visual arts experts with the thoughts and experiences of professional artists. Invaluable not only to artists, makers and photographers at all stages of their careers, art and design students, arts organisers, educationalists, careers and business advisers, but to all involved in promotion and development of the visual arts.

Art with People

Who is art for? Ever since community arts emerged in the '60s, there's been debate around this thorny question. And the arguments about process versus product, popular versus 'high' art and individual versus collective responsibility are as much aired now as they were then. *Art with People* traces the cultural and political aspirations of the early pioneers and sets them beside the environment for artists nowadays. By examining why artists choose to engage directly with people as animateurs, artists in residence and through community projects, the book shows how such working practices make the question "art for whom?" a millennium issue.

Chapters cover historical and contemporary context of community arts, artists' residencies, community initiatives, media-based projects and community education work. Writers include Sally Morgan, Felicity Allen, Esther Salamon, Suhail Khan, Sean Cubitt, and Nicholas Lowe. Artists and Groups featured include Open Hand Studios, Camerawork and Catalyst Arts, Alison Marchant and Ken Wolverton.

Ed. Malcolm Dickson, PB, A5, 136pp, illus, ISBN 0 907730 23 X, £7.25

Artists' Stories

What do visual artists do? Paint pictures, design seats, have families, run galleries, construct bridges, shoot films, make sculpture, get into debt, travel the world. A 'career' can mean doing many different things at the same time, involve radical changes of direction and be interrupted by personal circumstances. Keeping work going may often not be easy or remunerative. In *Artists' Stories* up-and-coming and well-established artists, makers and photographers describe how it's worked out for them. Aimed at art and design students, recent graduates and arts educationalists, this book also deserves to be read by all involved in the development of visual arts.

Features 24 artists including Richard La Trobe-Bateman, Lei Cox, John Darwell, Hilary Green, Jane Hamlyn, Karen Knorr, Mary O'Mahony and Janice Tchalenko, Mike Stubbs.

Anna Douglas, Nick Wegner, PB, A4, 80pp, illus, ISBN 0 9077 24 8, £7.25

Investigating Galleries

the artist's guide to exhibiting

The question of how to get work seen by more than the cat and the gasman is answered in this book. Full of information and strategies to improve an artist's chance of exhibiting and minimise the risk of rejection and discouragement, it explains why artists need to investigate their own self-image, ambitions and long-term aspirations and have a clear understanding of how the art world operates before they embark on an exhibiting career. Sound advice on approaching galleries and presenting work, on sales commission, promotion and gallery education strategies means that artists who are young or isolated will find this book invaluable, and the more experienced will discover it inspires new approaches and a sharper plan of action.

Debbie Duffin, PB, A5, 120pp, illus, ISBN 0 907730 22 1, £7.25

Organising Your Exhibition

Full of sound, practical advice on all aspects of exhibition organisation and an ideal companion to Investigating Galleries, it offers an instant solution to the agonies of organising a show. Covering everything from showing in alternative spaces to the tools needed to get a show up and from how to locate spaces and selling the work, it even tells you how to estimate the wine needed for the private view!

Debbie Duffin, PB, A5, 116pp, ISBN 0 907730 14 0, £7.25

Exhibiting & Selling Abroad

Undoubtedly one of our most successful publications, this book provides food for thought for all artists, makers and photographers who are developing an international perspective. Covering everything from exhibitions and trade fairs to residencies and studio visits, *Exhibiting & Selling Abroad* combines the inspiration which comes from reading about artists' own experiences with highly practical information on exporting, sales administration and networking.

Judith Staines, PB, A5, 120pp, illus, ISBN 0 907730 21 3, £7.25

Selling

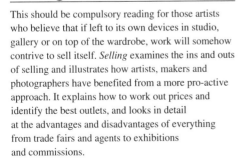

This should be compulsory reading for those artists who believe that if left to its own devices in studio, gallery or on top of the wardrobe, work will somehow contrive to sell itself. *Selling* examines the ins and outs of selling and illustrates how artists, makers and photographers have benefited from a more pro-active approach. It explains how to work out prices and identify the best outlets, and looks in detail at the advantages and disadvantages of everything from trade fairs and agents to exhibitions and commissions.

Judith Staines, PB, A5, 136pp, Illus, ISBN 0 907730 19 1, £7.25

Art in Public

what, why and how

An intelligent guide to the complex theoretical and practical issues affecting art in public, a field of work which includes both the infamous 'turd in the plaza' and the genuinely popular and imaginative initiatives which transform and revitalise public spaces. *Art in Public* provides a thought-provoking account of the values and philosophies which give rise to the range work and debates their implications for art, the artist and the public. Commissioners, agencies and artist have found this an invaluable reference, and even artists, makers and photographers with no intention of 'going public' at present will find this a stimulating introduction to debate which is set to run and run.

Ed. Susan Jones, PB, 178pp, illus, ISBN 0 907730 18 3, £9.95

Copyright

Expert advice about the applications of the 1988 Copyright, Designs & Patents Act, negotiating agreements, making sure you get the best from selling your copyright and how to deal with infringements. Contains practical examples of how artists, makers and photographers have dealt with copyright and reproduction issues.

Roland Miller, PB, A5; 125pp, illus, ISBN 0 907730 12 4, £7.25

Money Matters

the artist's financial guide

Problems with pricing? Baffled by book-keeping? Get *Money Matters* and stop the headaches. Changes in how tax is calculated for self-employed people, and introduction of self-assessment (working out your own tax bill) make it even more important for people running small businesses to have a good grasp of financial systems. This fully revised book provides expert advice on taxation and the Inland Revenue, National Insurance, VAT, pricing work, and handling customers, suppliers and banks, all backed-up with a model accounting system written just for visual arts and craft businesses.

Richard Murphy, Sarah Deeks & Sally Nolan, PB, 134pp, ISBN 0 907730 26 4, £7.25

Artist Handbooks

Live Art

Designed for all visual artists whose work involves live or temporary activities, *Live Art* combines information about the aspirations and experiences of artists with the practical considerations of putting on an event. A useful guide for artists, promoters and curators.

Ed. Robert Ayers & David Butler, PB, A5, 178pp, illus, ISBN 0 907730 13 2, £7.25

Across Europe

the artist's guide to travel and work

Looks at 24 European countries through the eyes of artists who live there and UK artists who've lived, studied or worked there and in doing so, provides valuable insights into each country's cultural character and the practicalities of exhibiting, selling, creating opportunities and making contacts. Comes with a free copy of the *Artists & the EU* Fact Pack (worth £1.85) which covers artists' rights and responsibilities, sources of information and advice, and gives profiles of EU countries.

Ed. David Butler, PB, A5, 168pp, illus, ISBN 0 907730 15 9, £9.95

Fundraising

Genuinely qualifies for the 'indispensable' tag, this book describes the range of possibilities for artists, makers and photographers to finance exhibitions, projects, travel and workspaces. Excellent sections on developing a strategy and making proposals along with revealing comments from those on the receiving-end of applications make this a recommended book not only for individual artists but for groups and small organisations involved in developing projects with artists.

Ed. Susan Jones, PB, A5, 134pp, illus, ISBN 0 907730 20 5, £7.25

Artists Newsletter

The monthly magazine providing analysis, commentary and information across contemporary visual arts practice.

ARTISTS & ARTWORK features review-based articles by curators, critics and artists commenting on what lies behind current practice. It covers exhibitions, installations, art in public, new media and issue-based projects. OUTLOOK is an illustrated round-up of new work, and WHAT'S ON is the monthly guide to temporary exhibitions and live art events around the country.

The **PRACTICAL PAGES** give comprehensive information on opportunities across the visual arts. Over 1000 are listed each year, including open exhibitions, gallery calls for applications, awards, residencies, commissions, mail-art, art and craft fairs and competitions. Features providing expert technical and business advice are run alongside the Help page, Small Ads, Sits Vac and the artists' contact page Pinboard.

In **ISSUES AND NEWS,** writers from the world of arts, education and politics map out the social, economic and political context for the arts, and in-depth articles are linked with short reports on issues.

Twelve issues a year, available from selected retail outlets at £2 a copy, or by mail-order subscription.

Individual　■ UK £22.50
　　　　　　　■ Europe £31
　　　　　　　■ Overseas £40

Institution　■ UK, Europe, Overseas £40

Prices quoted as at May 1995 are subject to alteration, please check before ordering.

Visual Arts Contracts

Introduction to Contracts

Designed to be read as the first step to making professional legal agreements, *Introduction to Contracts,* outlines the elements and terms you might find in a contract, and provides artists with the ammunition they need to negotiate, deal with disputes and find a suitable solicitor.
PB, A4, 12pp, £1.50

Residencies

Demystifies the legal arrangements for artists' residencies in any kind of settings. The ready-to-use contract form for a residency deals with having more than one partner in an agreement, and the workshop contract can be adapted for many 'one-off' activities. Also contains notes on employment and tax, copyright, moral and reproduction rights.
PB, A4, 20pp, ISBN 0 907730 25 6, £3.50

Commission Contracts

Maps out the legal arrangements necessary for all those who work with commissions and public art. By comparing public and private arrangements and describing the roles of parties in public art commissions, functions of agents and dealers and the implications of sub-contracting. Fill-in contract forms for Commissioned Design, Commission and Sale for Public Art and Private Commission Contract.
PB, A4, 20pp, £3.50

Licensing Reproductions

Make the most of your images by getting the licensing agreements right. This contract sets out how to grant or obtain permission to reproduce artwork or designs, and includes details of what licensing agreements to use, and notes on fees and royalties and negotiating and monitoring agreements.
PB, A4, 20pp, £3.50

NAA Public Exhibition Contract

The National Artists Association, commissioned this contract to cover the legal arrangements surrounding showing work in public galleries and exhibition spaces. Many artists, makers and photographers as well as galleries have found it an invaluable way to clarify responsibilities. It includes ready-to-use contract forms for a public exhibition and an exhibition tour, along with information on fees, selling, insurance and promotion.
PB, A4, 24pp, £3.50

Selling Contracts

If selling is part of your practice, then you need this contract. It deals exclusively with selling art and craft work and covers selling to private buyers, galleries and shops, and includes a contract form for selling on sale or return.
PB, A4, 14pp, £3.50

Ordering details

For mail orders add £1.50 per order for postage (UK), £2.50 per order (Europe), £4 per order (Overseas). Telephone credit card orders to 0191 514 3600 (Ref EI), or write to: AN Publications, PO Box 23, Sunderland SR4 6DG (prices quoted at May '95 are subject to change, please check before ordering).

Developed because the visual arts profession needed effective agreements to cover all aspects of contemporary visual arts prac-tice, our Visual Arts Contracts will ensure that collab-orations between artists, exhibition organisers, agents, and commission-ers are profession-al and harmonious. Written by Nicholas Sharp – a solicitor specialis-ing in contract preparation and negotiation for business and the arts – they are legally sound, and contain either ready-to-fill-in forms or a point-by-point checklist with explanatory notes. Each comes with per-mission for the purchaser to make additional copies for their own pro-fessional use.

Gallery Update Form

Please use this form (or photocopy of it) to amend an entry or for a new gallery. The *Directory of Exhibition Spaces* database is updated regularly. These updates will automatically be included in future editions of the *Directory of Exhibition Spaces*.

Name of Gallery: _____

_____

Address of Gallery: _____

_____

_____

Town: _____

County: _____

Postcode: _____

Tel: _____

Contact name: _____

Title: _____

Address for contact: (if different from gallery address)

_____

_____

Town: _____

Postcode: _____

Tel: _____

Opening hours _____

Brief description of the nature of the gallery
(see italic text in listings for reference)

_____

_____

_____

_____

What art forms does the gallery show?
☐ Painting ☐ Sculpture ☐ Installation
☐ Print ☐ Photography ☐ Craft ☐ Live art

Brief description of the space available for temporary exhibitions: (see 'Space' in listings)

_____

_____

_____

_____

_____

Number and nature of exhibitions held in a normal year: (see 'Details' in listings)

_____

_____

Details: (give other relevent information about programme, education) (see 'Details' in listings)

_____

_____

_____

_____

_____

_____

_____

_____

_____

Welcomes applications to exhibit?
☐ Yes ☐ No

Wheelchair access to the temporary exhibition galleries from outside:
☐ possible without assitance
☐ with assistance
☐ impossible
☐ toilet suitable for disabled?

DES Gallery Update, AN Publications, PO Box 23, Sunderland SR4 6DG, tel 0191 567 3589.